ADVANCED MECHANICS
OF MATERIALS

By FRED B. SEELY and JAMES O. SMITH
  Advanced Mechanics of Materials, *Second Edition*

By FRED B. SEELY
  Resistance of Materials, *Third Edition*

By FRED B. SEELY and NEWTON E. ENSIGN
  Analytical Mechanics for Engineers, *Fourth Edition*

ADVANCED MECHANICS

OF MATERIALS

Fred B. Seely, M.S.

PROFESSOR EMERITUS OF
THEORETICAL AND APPLIED MECHANICS

James O. Smith, A.M.

PROFESSOR OF THEORETICAL
AND APPLIED MECHANICS

UNIVERSITY OF ILLINOIS

Second Edition

NEW YORK · JOHN WILEY & SONS, INC.
LONDON · CHAPMAN & HALL, LIMITED

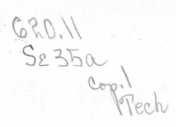

Copyright, 1932, by Fred B. Seely
Copyright, 1952
by
John Wiley & Sons, Inc.

All Rights Reserved

Library of Congress Catalog Card Number: 52–11034

PRINTED IN THE UNITED STATES OF AMERICA

PREFACE TO SECOND EDITION

Many important contributions have been made to the subject of mechanics of materials since the first edition of this book appeared twenty years ago. Likewise, more students and engineers are adequately prepared for the study of advanced topics in this field of knowledge, and a greater need exists in engineering analysis and design for an understanding of such topics. As a consequence, the treatment in the second edition of the book has been made more penetrating and comprehensive, and much new material has been added. In fact, the second edition is essentially a new book, although the main objectives are the same as in the first edition.

Although methods of analysis are given careful attention throughout the book, equal emphasis is given to the engineering evaluation and interpretation of the analyses as influenced by the assumptions made and principles used.

The book was prepared primarily for advanced undergraduate and first-year graduate students in engineering, although in selecting the topics and methods of presentation the needs of design and research engineers were kept in mind.

Where differential equations are involved in the analysis, their solutions are obtained, and the results, for a rather wide range of conditions, frequently are presented in the form of tables or curves. Numerical methods which are usually effective in the solution of differential equations for some combinations of physical conditions encountered in the analyses of this subject are not emphasized in this book.

The book consists of six parts, two new parts having been added: The Influence of Small Inelastic Strains on the Load-Carrying Capacity of Members, and Introduction to Instability—Buckling Loads. Useful material not previously published has also been presented in a number of the topics throughout the book. Likewise, two new appendixes have been added.

The purpose of the first appendix is to give the reader who is not familiar with the method employed in the theory of elasticity an opportunity to compare this method of analysis with that used in the so-called method of mechanics of materials as emphasized in this book. In treating certain topics in this edition the method of analysis and results

v

of the mathematical theory of elasticity supplement the method of mechanics of materials. And, since it is assumed that students and engineers who have not had a formal course in the theory of elasticity may wish to make use of the treatment of these topics, Appendix I should serve a useful purpose. In like manner the addition of Appendix II, The Elastic Membrane (Soap-film) Analogy for Torsion, which makes use of the method discussed in Appendix I, should be helpful to the reader who wishes to understand the mathematical basis of the analogy.

Any part of the book after Part I is essentially independent of the other parts. Likewise the chapters in Part II, Special Topics on the Strength and Stiffness of Members Subjected to Static Loads, are not dependent on each other and hence may be studied in any order. Thus the book can readily be made to fit courses of different lengths, and also of different content and objectives. The complete book was prepared with the purpose of offering sufficient material for a course covering one academic year. Selected references at the end of each chapter suggest desirable sources of information for the reader who desires to pursue the subject further.

A detailed explanation is given in Chapter I of the main steps in the general procedure or method of analysis used in mechanics of materials. This general procedure is repeatedly illustrated throughout the book, especially in the chapters of Part II.

In Part II two new chapters have been introduced. These chapters deal with beams on elastic supports and with contact stresses. In these and a number of other topics the more complex results are given in readily useful form by means of tables and graphs. It is hoped that this feature will help make the book valuable in engineering design offices. Many illustrative problems are also given which emphasize applications of theory to design.

It is the aim in Part II to give a thorough treatment of a limited number of important topics rather than a briefer consideration of a relatively large number of topics. Thus the student may be given the valuable experience of analyzing thoroughly by means of the methods and tools of mechanics of materials various types of engineering problems involving load-resisting members.

In Part III an attempt has been made to give a rational explanation of the significance of stress concentration in members of engineering machines and structures, thereby avoiding some of the confusion and difficulties which students frequently experience in the treatment of this topic.

Part IV on energy methods for determining the relationship between loads and deflections has been rewritten completely with a different approach, in order to present a more penetrating treatment. Two general methods of attack are used: work and energy and so-called complementary work and complementary energy. Emphasis is placed on the meaning, advantages, and disadvantages of these two methods of approach and on the limitations of less general but widely used procedures which are obtained from the more general methods, such as Castigliano's theorem and the dummy-load method.

The treatment in Part V of the inelastic behavior of load-resisting members contains a new, convenient approximate method of determining the load corresponding to a small specified amount of inelastic strain. The fact is emphasized in this part, as well as elsewhere in the book, that the load-carrying capacity of many members lies between two limiting values, namely: the load at which inelastic strain begins in the most-stressed fibers, and that at which a section or sections become fully plastic. The results of the method have been presented in convenient graphical form by means of interaction curves.

In Part VI a brief treatment is given of buckling of so-called thin-walled or slender members. Both elastic and inelastic (plastic) buckling are considered, primarily in relation to columns subjected to axial loads and to thin-walled cylinders subjected to uniform external pressure.

In this second edition many illustrative problems have been added as a means of introducing new methods or principles and not merely to show how to apply theories and methods previously explained.

Throughout the book there is considerable repetition of detailed statements of ideas, principles, and methods. This is done partly to make the discussion of a given topic less dependent on previously discussed topics than would otherwise be possible. The main purpose of the repetition, however, is to give emphasis to the ideas. The authors have found this procedure to be essential in the classroom and have introduced it to a limited extent in the book for the benefit of the student.

In the preparation of the second edition the authors were aided greatly by the constructive criticism of several of their colleagues who read considerable portions of the manuscript and by many students who studied various chapters in a graduate course. The authors are especially grateful to Professors Alfred M. Freudenthal and Winston E. Black for their careful examination of the manuscript and for helpful suggestions on many of the topics treated, and to Dr. C. K. Liu for contributions to the analysis of certain topics and problems and for preparing many of the drawings. Likewise, the authors are indebted to their colleagues Professors M. C. Steele and O. M. Sidebottom and to their former colleagues Professor M. C. Stippes, Dr. V. P. Jensen, and Mr. G. L.

Armstrong for valuable suggestions in the treatment of a number of the topics.

The development of the topics in various parts of the second edition reflects also the many suggestions and comments made during the past twenty years by teachers, students, and practicing engineers who used the first edition.   In addition, the authors, through oral discussions and correspondence, have obtained highly desirable information from a number of persons who were especially qualified by engineering experience to discuss recent developments in different phases of the subject; these generous contributions have been of great value to the book.

FRED B. SEELY
JAMES O. SMITH

Urbana, Illinois
October 1952

PREFACE TO FIRST EDITION

The main title of this book might well have been "A Second Course in Mechanics of Materials." The topics considered in the book lie just beyond those usually included in a first course in strength of materials as given in most engineering schools in the United States.

The book is an outgrowth of notes used by the author during the past few years in a course for advanced undergraduate students and first year graduate students. It is well adapted for a course that either precedes or accompanies the study of the mathematical theory of elasticity.

The increasing use of analytical methods, in contrast with empirical rules, in solving the engineering problems that are continually arising in engineering industry has, in recent years, created a need for further training in the analysis of stresses and strains in various members of engineering structures and machines. There is likewise a need for a better understanding of the significance of calculated stresses in relation to the usable resistance of a member subjected to different types of loading.

It is hoped that this book may be a contribution towards filling this need both for teachers and students in institutions where a second course in strength of materials is given, and for some of the younger graduate engineers who may wish to make a further study of the subject on their own initiative and direction.

It is also hoped that the material herein presented may be found helpful in engineering offices where problems involving the analysis and significance of stresses in members are of importance.

In preparing the book the following objects have been kept in mind:

1. To review and make more useful the methods and results presented in the first course in strength of materials.

2. To show the limitations of the ordinary formulas of strength of materials, to consider the conditions under which these limitations are significant, and to extend the subject to include a variety of important topics more complex than those usually considered in a first course.

3. To present a more comprehensive and useful view of the fundamental concepts and methods used in the analysis of stresses in structural and machine members.

4. To acquaint the student with various sources of information, largely through references, and thus give him an opportunity to appreciate how knowledge of this subject has grown.

5. To change the usual attitude of the student from one of dogmatic confidence in the methods employed and results obtained to one in which the methods and results are viewed as merely approximate but such that under certain conditions they become reliable and useful.

The book is divided into four parts as follows:

Part I. Preliminary considerations, consisting mainly of a discussion of the fundamental concepts involved in the subject, and a review of some of the more important methods used and results obtained in the usual first course in strength of materials.

Part II. Special topics, consisting of the analysis of stresses in a number of types of members not included, as a rule, in a first course in the subject.

Part III. Discussion of stress concentration and localized stress, in which non-mathematical methods of stress determination are emphasized.

Part IV. An introduction to the analysis of statically indeterminate stresses, in which methods involving elastic strain energy are used.

Throughout the book the engineering significance of the methods and results is strongly emphasized. Illustrative problems are frequently given, and many problems are offered for solution. References for further study are given at the end of each chapter.

In organizing the material herein presented, the results of experimental and analytical investigations from many sources have been used. The author wishes to acknowledge his indebtedness to those who have made this material available. Acknowledgment of the material used is given throughout the book where the material is presented.

FRED B. SEELY

Urbana, Illinois
August 1931

CONTENTS

PART ONE. PRELIMINARY CONSIDERATIONS

CHAPTER 1. ANALYSIS OF SUBJECT

CHAPTER 2. ELEMENTARY STRESS FORMULAS FOR STATIC LOADS

CHAPTER 3. STRESSES AND STRAINS AT A POINT. THEORIES OF FAILURE BY YIELDING

§ 1. *Relation between Stresses at a Point on Different Planes Passing through the Point*

§ 2. *Relations between Elastic Stresses and Strains at a Point*

CHAPTER 7. BEAM ON CONTINUOUS ELASTIC SUPPORT

CHAPTER 8. FLAT PLATES

§ 1. *Introduction*

§ 2. *Plates in Which Bending Action Is Dominant—Small Deflections*

§ 3. *Plates in Which Bending and Direct Tension Are Significant*
Large Deflections

CHAPTER 9. TORSIONAL RESISTANCE OF BARS HAVING
NON-CIRCULAR CROSS SECTIONS

CHAPTER 10. THICK-WALLED CYLINDERS

CHAPTER 11. CONTACT STRESSES

PART THREE. LOCALIZED STRESS—STRESS CONCENTRATION

CHAPTER 12. VALUES AND SIGNIFICANCE OF LOCALIZED STRESSES IN VARIOUS MEMBERS

§ 1. *Theoretical Stress Concentration Factors*

§ 2. *Significant Stress Concentration Factors*

PART FOUR. ENERGY METHODS

CHAPTER 13. CONSIDERATIONS OF ENERGY PRINCIPLES FOR DETER-
MINING RELATIONS BETWEEN LOADS AND DEFLECTIONS

CHAPTER 14. DEFLECTION OF MEMBERS AND SIMPLE STRUCTURES
BY CASTIGLIANO'S THEOREM

Applications of Castigliano's Theorem

CHAPTER 15. DEFLECTION OF MEMBERS AND SIMPLE STRUCTURES
BY UNIT LOAD OR DUMMY LOAD METHOD

CHAPTER 16. FORCES AND MOMENTS IN STATICALLY INDETERMINATE
MEMBERS AND STRUCTURES

Application of Dummy Load Method

PART FIVE. INFLUENCE OF SMALL INELASTIC STRAINS ON THE LOAD-CARRYING CAPACITY OF MEMBERS

CHAPTER 17. EFFECT OF SMALL INELASTIC STRAINS IN AXIALLY LOADED MEMBERS AND IN STRAIGHT BEAMS

CHAPTER 18. EFFECT OF SMALL INELASTIC STRAINS FOR COMBINED BENDING AND AXIAL LOADS

CHAPTER 19. INTRODUCTION TO ULTIMATE LOAD ANALYSIS OF STATICALLY INDETERMINATE MEMBERS

PART SIX. INTRODUCTION TO INSTABILITY—BUCKLING LOADS

CHAPTER 20. ELASTIC AND INELASTIC BUCKLING OF COLUMNS

PART ONE

Preliminary Considerations

Chapter 1

ANALYSIS OF SUBJECT

1 **Introduction.** In many structures and machines the main function of a member is to resist the external forces, called loads, that are applied to it. In resisting the loads the member must not undergo structural damage, that is, it must not fail to perform its function satisfactorily in the structure or machine. The term *structural damage* or *failure* as here used, therefore, does not necessarily mean fracture; it means any action in the member, resulting from the application of loads, which causes the member to cease to function satisfactorily in the structure or machine, such as excessive elastic deflection, inelastic deformation or yielding, and fracture.

It is sometimes convenient to restrict the term *structural* damage to mean that the loads on a member are limited by a change in the internal structure of the material such as occurs in inelastic distortion (yielding) or in fracture; whereas *functional* damage is used to indicate behavior of a member, such as excessive elastic deflection, that limits the loads because the member ceases to fulfill its function satisfactorily although the internal structure of the material is not changed by the behavior. In general, however, the term structural damage will be used in the broader sense to include any action that causes the member to fail to fulfill its purpose in the load-resisting structure or machine.

The main consideration or problem in mechanics of materials consists in obtaining the relation between the loads applied to a member and some quantity, such as tensile stress,* shearing stress, elastic strain * or deflection, strain energy, etc., which is characteristic of, or significant in, the action or phenomenon that causes the member to fail in its load-carrying function; the dimensions of the member also are involved in this relationship.

---

* *Stress* as used throughout this book means *force per unit area;* linear *strain* means change in length *per unit length*, where length denotes any linear dimension. The term stress is sometimes used in technical literature to mean the total internal force on a section, especially when this force is distributed uniformly on the section, and unit stress or intensity of stress then denotes force per unit area.

3

The first step in the solution of the problem, therefore, is to determine the nature or characteristics of the action that occurs in a given member by virtue of which the member is rendered unfit to serve its purpose in resisting further increase in the loads under the given service conditions. In other words, a decision must first be reached concerning the nature of the action in the member which causes the member to be structurally damaged (to fail), in order to determine what quantity is most significant in the failure and hence what quantity should be expressed in terms of the loads and dimensions of the member. The action that results in structural damage to a member will frequently be designated as the *mode of failure*.

The mode of failure of a member and the quantity that is most closely associated with the failure depends on such factors as nature or properties of the material, type of loading, shape of member, temperature of member, time during which the load acts, medium surrounding the member, etc. For example, the mode of failure of a member made of ductile * steel may be very different from one made of a brittle * material such as concrete; yielding (plastic deformation) may constitute structural damage in the former and fracture (separation) in the latter. The type of action that constitutes structural damage to a member subjected to repeated loads may be quite different from that in a member made of the same material but subjected to static (gradually applied) loads. Under repeated loads the member is likely to fail by progressive fracture even though the material is classed as ductile, especially if the member contains abrupt changes in section at which stress concentrations occur, whereas under static loads the mode of failure is likely to be by yielding. The action within steel which leads to its failure at elevated temperatures, such as may occur in steam turbines, may be quite different from that at room temperature, even though both actions may be classed under the heading of yielding; in general, at elevated temperatures the yielding is dependent on time whereas at ordinary temperatures it is nearly independent of time. The moisture content of the air surrounding some materials, such as plastics and timber, may affect the action which constitutes structural damage to the member and which therefore limits the maximum loads that can be applied to the member. Additional illustrations, no doubt, will occur to the reader.

* Attention should be called to the fact that both ductile behavior and brittle behavior of a material depend on the conditions to which the material is subjected (state of stress, temperature, rate of straining, type of loading, etc.) as well as on the material itself, and hence, strictly speaking, a material should not be designated as ductile or as brittle. The terms are convenient, however, to designate the relative ease with which material either yields markedly or fractures before appreciable yielding occurs, under conditions that are relatively favorable to yielding.

2 Rational procedure in design. Since a knowledge of mechanics of materials as defined in the preceding article is needed in the rational design of a load-resisting member, it will be desirable to outline the main steps involved in a rational procedure of design in order to make clear the relation of mechanics of materials to design. The term *design* as used here does not mean primarily the detailed calculations for determining the dimensions of a member, but rather the considerations that enter into the formulation of a rational code or specification for the design of a member and thus lead to an equation, formula, or method by means of which the detailed calculations can be made. In the rational procedure for the design of a member *whose main function is to resist loads*, there are, in general, four main steps, as follows.

Step 1. Determine the mode of failure of the member (of a given material under the given loading and service conditions) that would most likely take place if the loads acting on the member should become large enough to cause it to fail. Various modes of failure are discussed briefly in Art. 4. Although the choice of material is also involved in Step 1, the material used may often be controlled largely by general factors, such as availability, cost, weight limitations, ease of fabrication, etc., rather than primarily by the requirements of design for resisting loads.

Step 2. Determine a relation, usually in the form of an equation or formula, between the loads and the quantity (such as stress, deflection, etc.) which is most significant in the failure of the member and which limits the load-carrying capacity of the member; this equation or formula will, of course, also involve dimensions of the member. In many cases it is convenient to obtain first a relation between the loads and *principal stresses* (see Art. 18) because other quantities that may be considered to be most closely associated with structural damage (such as shearing stress, strain, energy per unit volume, etc.) may readily be expressed in terms of principal stresses. Step 2 constitutes the main problem considered in mechanics of materials. Our present knowledge of the actions in materials under load is not sufficient to carry out Steps 1 and 2 satisfactorily for all conditions under which members resist loads.

This fact partially explains the frequent use of empirical relationships based on tests of actual members, or of models thereof, in which the operating conditions are simulated as nearly as feasible. Moreover, residual stresses and strains are sometimes present in the member before the loads are applied which make it difficult to interpret the significance of the stresses and strains caused by the loads alone.

Step 3. By appropriate tests of the material used in the member, determine the maximum value of the quantity (stress, strain, energy, etc.)

that is considered to cause structural damage. This maximum value is the value of the quantity that exists in the material when structural damage to the member first occurs as loads are increased; it will be referred to as the *maximum utilizable value* or the *limiting resistance value* since it is the maximum or limiting value that can be used in the relationship obtained in Step 2. An appropriate or suitable test is one that will produce in the test specimen or model the same action that results in structural damage to the actual member. For many operating conditions <u>it is difficult or impossible</u> to formulate tests that are strictly suitable according to this definition, and hence the results of relatively simple tests are made to apply to the more complex conditions.

Step 4. By use of experimental observations and analysis, experience with actual structures and machines, judgment, and commercial and legal considerations, <u>select</u> for use in the equation or method established in Step 2 a working, <u>allowable or safe value</u> for the quantity which would reach the limiting resistance value if loads were increased sufficiently above the working or allowable loads. This working value is less, usually considerably less, than the limiting resistance value or maximum utilizable value.

The need for selecting a working value less than the value found in Step 3 arises mainly from uncertainties; (a) in the service conditions, especially in the loads, which are affected by a great many conditions that, as a rule, are difficult to control or to predict, (b) in the degree of uniformity of the material, and (c) in the significance or correctness of the equation or formula used in Step 2. The uncertainties under (c) may be concerned either with the quantity that is assumed to be significant in the failure, or with the equation itself, which is usually the outcome of simplifying assumptions.

Although these considerations make clear the need for applying a reduction factor (so-called factor of safety) to the test result found in Step 3, the working value of the quantity selected for use in the formula of Step 2, in almost all cases, has grown out of experience and practice which reflect many conditions and considerations that cannot be expressed quantitatively in mathematical form. For this reason, it is stated sometimes that in taking Step 4 the so-called rational method really degenerates into an empirical method, especially in the design of what might be called heavy machines and static-load structures in which excess material may even be desirable, or in any case is objectionable only to a minor degree. Such a sweeping conclusion, however, fails to give adequate importance to the rational nature of the procedure represented by the foregoing four steps of design, even though a relatively large degree of uncertainty * probably always will exist in one or more of the steps.

Caution. As noted in Art. 1, the main function of a member, as here considered, is to resist loads. Therefore, the truly rational method of introducing the so-called factor of safety is to increase the loads that are assumed to be resisted by the member by multiplying the actual design loads by the factor of safety, and then using for a working value of stress, or of deflection, etc., the value that first causes structural damage to the member, rather than to reduce the damaging value of the stress, or deflection, etc., which the actual design loads are permitted to produce. The two methods lead to the same result, *provided that the load is proportional to the quantity that first causes the structural damage to the member*. But under some conditions (such conditions will be met in subsequent chapters) the load on the member is *not* proportional to the stress, or to the deflection, etc. For example, let P be the load on a member, and let X be the quantity associated with failure. When P is directly proportional to X, a reduction in X will provide a proportionate reduction of P. However, if, for instance, the quantity X is proportional to the square of P, a reduction of X does not provide a proportionate reduction of P; in this case, if the expression relating P and X is solved for P, it is found that P is proportional to the square root of X, and hence a reduction of the quantity $\sqrt{X}$ will provide a proportionate reduction of P.

Procedure Oversimplified. It is realized that the procedure outlined in the foregoing article is oversimplified and that for many problems of design the information required in the above procedure is already available, and the various steps may be carried out without recognizing and dignifying them as isolated steps. The procedure, however, serves a very useful purpose in interpreting the general problems or topics considered in subsequent chapters, and are of special importance in dealing with new problems. It is well to recall also that considerations other than resistance to loads, such as considerations of form or appearance, may influence or even control the design of a member, structure, or machine, but such considerations are secondary in the topics treated in this book.

3 Application of design procedure. An illustration may help to make more definite the procedure outlined in the foregoing article. Let it be assumed that a simply supported beam is made of low-carbon (ductile) steel and contains abrupt changes in section as indicated in

* For a consideration of the possibility of a statistical approach to the evaluation of the rational component of the factor of safety, see reference 4 at the end of this chapter

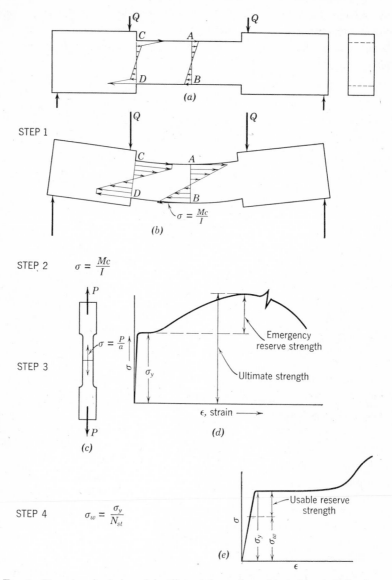

FIG. 1   Procedure in design of ductile metal member subjected to static loads.

Fig. 1a.   Let it be required to determine the section modulus I/c of the rectangular cross section of the beam under two types of loading at ordinary temperatures: (a) Let it be assumed in the first case (Figs. 1a and 1b) that the loads Q are static loads which cause a known constant bending moment M at all sections in the reduced portion of the beam.   (b) In the second case (Figs. $2a$ and $2b$) let it be assumed that the loads Q are repeatedly applied so that they cause completely reversed cycles of a bending moment whose maximum value in each cycle is M in the reduced portion of the beam.

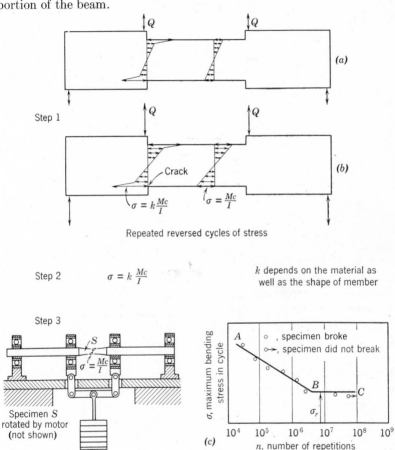

Step 1

(a)

Crack (b)

$\sigma = k\dfrac{Mc}{I}$ $\sigma = \dfrac{Mc}{I}$

Repeated reversed cycles of stress

Step 2 $\sigma = k\,\dfrac{Mc}{I}$ k depends on the material as well as the shape of member

Step 3

Specimen S rotated by motor (not shown) $\sigma = \dfrac{Mc}{I}$ S

(d)

σ, maximum bending stress in cycle

A $\circ$, specimen broke
$\circ\!\!\rightarrow$, specimen did not break

B C

σ_r

10^4 10^5 10^6 10^7 10^8 10^9

(c) n, number of repetitions or cycles to fracture

Step 4 $\sigma_w = \dfrac{\sigma_r}{N_r}$ No emergency reserve strength; therefore usually $N_r > N_{st}$

FIG. 2 Procedure in design of ductile steel member subjected to repeated loads.

The steps in the procedure for the solutions of the two cases are indicated in Figs. 1 and 2. It is assumed that the deflection of the beam is not sufficient to limit the loads that can be applied to the beam, and hence failure results from yielding (plastic deformation) or from fracture.

STATIC LOADING. *Step 1.* The member would fail by general yielding if the loads were gradually increased. By *general* yielding is meant yielding throughout a sufficient portion of the member to cause permanent distortion of the member as a whole in contrast to localized plastic deformation at a small (local) region of stress concentration.

Step 2. It will be assumed that normal (tensile) stress is the quantity most closely associated with the failure, and that the significant value of the normal stress is given by the flexure formula $\sigma = Mc/I$. The reason for this conclusion is as follows: When the loads Q are relatively small, the normal (tensile and compressive) stresses distributed on a section not close to the abrupt changes in section (such as AB, Fig. 1a) is approximately linear as assumed in the flexure formula and shown in Fig. 1a, but the stresses on sections such as AB are relatively small; whereas at section CD the abrupt change in section causes a relatively large stress concentration at C and D approximately as shown in Fig. 1a. However, as the loads are increased, the stresses at C and D soon reach the yield point of the material, and the accompanying local yielding of the material prevents the stress from exceeding this yield point stress as the loads are increased further. The redistribution of stress approaches that shown at section CD in Fig. 1b, and the local yielding which brings about this redistribution does not interfere with the function of the beam as a load-resisting member; the deflection of the beam as shown in Fig. 1b is greatly exaggerated. In other words, the local yielding near C and D does not constitute structural damage or failure of the member.

On the other hand, the stresses on section AB (and all similar sections in the reduced portion of the beam) continue to increase as the loads are increased until yielding occurs throughout the whole length of the outer fibers, and this yielding *does* constitute structural damage and failure of the member. The normal stress σ at the outer fibers before yielding occurs is given satisfactorily by $\sigma = Mc/I$, and hence this stress is the significant stress because the beam fails by yielding which starts in the outer fibers where this stress occurs. Step 2, therefore, is considered to be satisfied by the equation $\sigma = Mc/I$.

Step 3. The maximum value that σ can have without being accompanied by yielding as required by Step 2 will be considered to be the tensile yield point σ_y as found from the tension test.

Step 4. A reduction factor or factor of safety N_{st} is applied to σ_y to obtain the design or working stress σ_w. Since the material has considerable reserve strength in the nature of accident insurance as indicated in Fig. 1d, the factor of safety N_{st} may be relatively low, for, although the member will have been structurally damaged when it begins to draw on this reserve strength, nevertheless total destruction with possible damage to life and property is not likely to occur, and hence only a relatively small amount of *usable* reserve strength (see Fig. 1e) need be created, which means that a somewhat smaller factor of safety may be used compared to the factor of safety usually needed when a failure occurs by brittle fracture.

REPEATED LOADING. *Step 1.* The member (see Figs. 2a and 2b) would fail by progressive fracture, the fracture starting as a minute crack and gradually spreading, as the loads are repeated, without any visual evidence of yielding of the member as a whole; the failure is therefore frequently designated as a brittle fracture.

Step 2. The significant quantity associated with failure is considered to be the localized tensile stress (stress concentration) at the abrupt change in section where the crack started and is expressed by the equation $\sigma = k(Mc/I)$ (see Fig. 2b) where k is called a stress concentration factor.* This localized stress is considered to be the significant stress for the reason that when it reaches a certain value, and is repeated a large number of times, a crack (Fig. 2b) starts at the point of localized stress and gradually spreads until the cross section is greatly reduced and the member suddenly breaks in two.

Step 3. The maximum value that σ (as expressed in Step 2) can have without being accompanied by a progressive fracture is called the endurance limit of the material, and a suitable test or method for determining its value consists in testing, in turn, several specimens to fracture in a rotating beam machine as indicated in Fig. 2d, subjecting specimens to successively lower stresses and plotting the stress against the number of reversals n required to cause fracture, as in Fig. 2c. This curve which shows the relation between σ and n is called a stress–number of cycles diagram or briefly an S-n diagram, and the value of the stress σ corresponding to the horizontal part BC of the curve represents the maximum stress that could be repeated a very large number of times without causing progressive fracture; this value of stress then is considered to be the endurance limit of the material and is denoted by σ_r.

Step 4. The working value σ_w to be used in the equation $\sigma = k(Mc/I)$ is found by applying a factor of safety N_r to the endurance limit.† The value of N_r for some operating conditions, especially for heavy, high-speed machine parts, is relatively large because there is no emergency reserve strength in excess of σ_r since any stress which is greater than σ_r and which is repeated a large number of times leads to fracture and hence

---

* The effective or significant value for k depends on the material as well as on the shape of the member. Values of k are discussed in Part III.

† It is well to note that steel (wrought ferrous metal in general) is considered to have an endurance limit, and hence design for an indefinitely large number of repetitions of stress ("life") is justified; whereas non-ferrous metals in general do not have an endurance limit and hence design is usually based on a stress that corresponds to a finite "life" depending on the service conditions.

to total destruction of the member. A number of considerations besides reserve strength, however, are involved in selecting the value of the factor of safety; for example, in a bridge member subject to careful and frequent inspection a fatigue crack could probably be detected before complete fracture takes place, owing to the slow rate at which stress cycles occur and hence to the slow rate at which the fatigue crack progresses; this fact would tend to call for a relatively small factor of safety. In general, however, the problem of repeated loading occurs in connection with *moving parts* under conditions that are likely to require a larger factor of safety than would be considered adequate for static loading.

The fact should be emphasized also that in the design of a member to resist repeated loads the problem is often one of avoiding or reducing stress concentrations rather than that of calculating their values and designing the member to resist them.

4 General modes of failure of members. The two illustrations in the preceding article should make clear the need for an understanding of the mode of failure of a member as a *first* step in the procedure of rational design. It is desirable therefore that a brief statement of the more important types of failure be given here to serve as a background for the interpretation of the results obtained in subsequent chapters.

A member may fail, that is, may be unable to resist satisfactorily further increase in load, as a result of any one of three general actions or behaviors, namely: (*a*) elastic deflection; (*b*) inelastic or plastic deformation which will be denoted hereafter usually as yielding; and (*c*) fracture. Each of these phenomena will now be considered in greater detail. The physical action in a member leading to failure is usually a complicated phenomenon, and the phenomena pictured in the following discussion are necessarily oversimplified, but they nevertheless retain the essential features of the failures.

FAILURE BY ELASTIC DEFLECTION. The maximum load that may be applied to a member without causing it to cease to function properly may be limited by the permissible elastic strain or deflection of the member, but elastic deflection which may constitute damage to a member can occur under different conditions, namely:

(*a*) Deflection under conditions of stable equilibrium, such as the stretch of a tension member, the angle of twist of a shaft, and the deflection of a beam, particularly under gradually applied (so-called static) loads. Elastic deflections, under conditions of equilibrium, are discussed in Part IV.

(*b*) Buckling, or the rather sudden deflection associated with unstable equilibrium and often resulting in total collapse of the member, such as occurs when an axial load that is gradually applied to a very slender column exceeds slightly the Euler critical load, or when an external fluid pressure is applied to a cylindrical shell or thin-walled pipe which suddenly collapses when the pressure reaches a critical value. See Part VI.

(c) Elastic deflections which are the amplitudes of the vibration of a member sometimes are associated with structural damage of the member because of objectionable noise, shaking forces, collision of moving parts with stationary parts, etc., which result from the vibrations.

When a member fails by elastic deformation, the significant equations for design are, of course, those giving relations between loads and elastic deflection. For example, the equations for the three members mentioned under (a) are: $e = Pl/aE$, $\theta = Tl/GJ$ and $\Delta = \alpha(Wl^3/EI)$. It will be noted that these equations contain the significant property of the material involved in the elastic deflection, namely the stiffness (modulus of elasticity) of the material of which the member is made. The stresses set up by the loads are not the significant quantities; that is, the stresses do not limit the loads that can be applied to the member without causing structural damage, and hence the strength properties of the material (such as yield point, etc.) are not of primary importance. Or, to put the idea in different words, if a member of *given dimensions* will fail to perform its load-resisting function because of excessive elastic deflection, its load-carrying capacity will not be increased by merely making the member of stronger material but only by making it stiffer by using a material with a higher modulus of elasticity or by changing the shape and dimensions of the member. As a rule, the most effective method of increasing the stiffness of a *member* is by changing the shape or increasing the dimensions of its cross section, rather than by making the member of a stiffer material; moreover, if a member is made of steel its stiffness could not be increased by substituting another material since steel is the stiffest structural material available for most load-resisting members.

FAILURE BY GENERAL YIELDING. Another condition that may cause a member to fail is inelastic (plastic) deformation of a considerable portion of the member, denoted by *general* yielding to differentiate it from (localized) yielding of a very small portion of a member. General yielding of a metal member, however, may result from either one of two different conditions, depending on whether the temperature of the member while resisting the load is above or below the recrystallization temperature of the metal. Temperatures above the recrystallization temperature such as that to which steel may be subjected in steam turbines, oil-cracking apparatus, etc., are frequently referred to as *elevated* temperatures, and temperatures below the recrystallization temperature as *ordinary* temperatures. These two cases of general yielding are discussed briefly as follows:

General Yielding at Ordinary Temperature. Metals are made up of extremely large numbers of very small units called crystals or grains. The crystals have so-called slip planes on which the resistance to shearing stress is relatively small, and the yielding in any crystal is considered to be primarily the result of the slip (sliding, or shearing action) on a slip plane of one part of the crystal relative to another part. The general yielding of a metal member is the summation of these very minute shearing deformations or slips in an extremely large number of crystals. The slip planes in adjacent crystals are not likely to be parallel, but rather are oriented at random throughout the metal. Hence the yield strength of a metal is a statistical value representing the action of a large number of crystals.

After yielding has occurred in some crystals at a given load, these crystals will not yield further without an increase in load. This increased strength after yielding is thought to be mainly the result of the interference to slip caused by the disorganized sawtoothed, interlocking crystal fragments on the slip planes, and by the resistance offered by neighboring crystals which have not yielded because their slip planes are so oriented with respect to the planes of maximum shearing stress that they have greater resistance than did the crystals in which slip took place at the given load. The increased strength accompanying the yielding is called strain hardening, work hardening, cold working, or strain strengthening,* and this strain strengthening is permanent (except for time effects such as ageing, recovery, etc.) provided that the temperature at which it occurs is not above the recrystallization temperature for the metal; hence yielding does *not* continue under the same load, whereas it does continue when the temperature is above the recrystallization tem-

---

* When the yield point is reached in a tension test specimen of low-carbon steel, some yielding (2 or 3 per cent) will take place at an average stress even *less* than the average stress at which yielding started. This rather special type of yielding, exhibiting an upper and lower yield point, is encountered mainly in low-carbon steel and seems to occur largely as a discontinuous step-wise process of a series of haphazard localized slippings in thin slices or flow layers giving rise to Lüders' lines, and it seems to set up and maintain localized stresses, as it progresses, sufficient to overcome the resistance to yielding of successively stronger portions of the material until finally much of the material in the specimen yields appreciably without an increase (usually with a decrease) in the load (or average stress) at which the yielding of the weaker portions started. After this unstable heterogeneous type of yielding has spread rather generally throughout the specimen, the subsequent more homogeneous or continued yielding is apparently accompanied by less stress concentration and by strain strengthening which requires an increase in the load (or average stress) to cause an increase in yielding.

perature (discussed further under General Yielding at Elevated Temperatures).

There is considerable but not necessarily conclusive evidence, therefore, to support the assumption that when a metal member fails by general yielding *at ordinary temperatures* the significant quantity associated with the failure is shearing stress,* and hence that a satisfactory measure of the maximum utilizable strength of the material is the maximum shearing stress which accompanies yielding throughout a considerable volume of the material. This stress is the shearing yield point if the material possesses a yield point, or the shearing yield strength (stress corresponding to an arbitrary offset) if the material does not exhibit a real yield point. However, frequently the *tensile* stress is considered to be the significant quantity as was done in the preceding article, and its maximum value is taken as the *tensile* yield point. The use of the tensile stress leads to the same result as does the use of shearing stress provided that the material is subjected to normal stress in one direction only (uniaxial stress) as in a tension member and in most bending members, but its use tends to obscure the significant quantities involved in the failure.

Furthermore, when failure occurs by general yielding, stress irregularities such as those shown in Fig. 1a at section *CD* of the beam usually are *not* significant because of the interactions and accommodations that take place among the crystals at the regions of stress concentrations in the member. As the loads on the member are increased, these interactions and accommodations among the crystals cause the member as a whole to act substantially the same as would a member made of an ideal homogeneous elastic material. In other words, the slips in a few weak or poorly oriented crystals or highly stressed crystals do not limit the load-carrying capacity of the member but merely cause readjustment of stresses which permit the stronger or less stressed crystals to take higher stresses and thereby cause the stress distribution to approach more closely toward the distribution that would occur in a member free from abrupt changes in section and made of homogeneous material. Thus the member as a whole acts substantially as does an ideal homogeneous elastic member free from abrupt changes of section, until slip in a very large number of crystals occurs, resulting in failure by general yielding.

The action or behavior that leads to this type of failure is, therefore, a statistical action of a large number of the structural units (crystals) of which the member is made, as opposed to local or individual action or behavior, and the laws governing this statistical action are substantially the same as are assumed for ideal homogeneous material. All the com-

* Other criteria of failure, such as energy of distortion, will be discussed in Chapter 3.

mon elementary equations or formulas in mechanics of materials based on elastic action of homogeneous material free from residual stresses and from stress concentration, therefore, give significant values of stress, under the conditions here assumed, namely, static loads, ductile material, uniaxial state of stress, and ordinary temperature.

It is important to observe, however, that if a member that would fail by yielding, as discussed in the foregoing paragraph, is replaced by one made of a stronger material (higher yield point) so that the dimensions of the member may be reduced for resisting the same loads, the mode of failure may change completely to that of elastic deflection or buckling or by mechanical vibrations and hence the whole basis of design would then change.

General Yielding at Elevated Temperatures. Creep. If the metal member is subjected to loads at a temperature *above* the recrystallization temperature, the increase in strength (strain hardening) that accompanies the slips * in the crystals is not permanent. The recrystallization temperature is the temperature above which crystals that have slipped re-form themselves into unstrained crystals. Therefore the increase in strength accompanying slip is soon offset or neutralized by the annealing action at the elevated temperature, and hence *continuing* deformation or yielding, called creep, occurs at the same load that started the yielding.

The mechanism by means of which the strain hardening is broken down at elevated temperatures is thought to be mainly as follows: Along each slip plane in a crystal, disorganized crystal fragments are produced, and these fragments recrystallize, when the temperature is above a certain value, reorganizing themselves in harmony with the atomic structure of the parent crystal on either side of the slip plane so that the crystal assumes the same condition or state that existed before slip took place; it then undergoes further slip under the same load, etc. Sufficient creep of certain steel members at elevated temperature may occur over a period of years to cause failure at stresses that would be considered very low and safe for the material to resist at ordinary temperature.

The quantity associated with the failure of a metal by creep at elevated temperature is usually considered to be stress. However, the relation between loads and stresses (as required in Step 2 of Art. 2) in members at elevated temperatures is more complex and difficult to express mathematically than at ordinary temperatures, except perhaps in members subjected to axial tensile loads. For example, the formula

* It is here assumed that the stress is sufficiently large to cause deformation mainly by slip within the crystals. At lower stresses the creep (continuing deformation at constant load) may be the result of viscous flow of the unordered, disorganized material in the crystal boundaries.

$\sigma = Mc/I$ does not give the stress in a beam subjected to loads which cause creep at elevated temperatures because the stresses in the beam are not proportional to the corresponding strains.

The maximum utilizable strength of the material at a given elevated temperature—called the creep strength—is usually considered to be the stress corresponding to a given amount of creep in a given time, such as 1 per cent creep in 10,000 hours, depending on the service conditions.

FAILURE BY FRACTURE. Some members cease to function satisfactorily because they break (fracture) before either excessive elastic deflection or general yielding occurs. There are, however, three rather different modes or mechanisms of fracture especially in a metal member, described briefly as follows:

Sudden Fracture of Brittle Material. Some members—so-called brittle members—under static loading function satisfactorily in resisting the loads until the member breaks in two rather suddenly with little or no evidence of plastic deformation. The tensile stress in such members usually is considered to be the significant quantity associated with the failure, and the tensile static ultimate strength is the measure of the maximum utilizable strength of the material. A member made of *ductile* material and subjected to uniaxial stress (one principal stress) rarely fails by fracture under static loads because structural damage (failure) occurs by general yielding before fracture takes place. However, at regions of abrupt changes in section, at edges of defects, etc., where the distribution of stress is non-uniform and the state of stress is probably triaxial (three principal stresses) failure of the member sometimes occurs as a brittle fracture, especially when sub-zero temperatures are encountered, even though the material is classed as ductile and the member is subjected to static loads. If a member of ductile material having an abrupt change of section causing a rather high stress concentration is subjected to the combination of impact loads and sub-zero temperatures, the tendency toward brittle fracture is greatly increased.

Progressive Fracture. If a metal that would fail by general yielding under a static load is subjected to repeated cycles of completely reversed stress, it may fail by fracture without visual evidence of yielding, provided that the repeated stress is greater than a value called the endurance limit. A minute crack starts at one or more points in the member, usually at points of high localized stress such as at abrupt changes in section, and gradually spreads by continually fracturing the material at the edge of the crack where the stress is highly concentrated, until the area is greatly reduced and the member finally breaks suddenly. This mode of failure is usually called a fatigue failure, but it is better designated as failure by progressive fracture resulting from repeated loads.

The quantity that is usually considered most significant in the failure by progressive fracture is a *localized* tensile stress (although the fatigue crack sometimes occurs on the plane of maximum shearing stress), and the maximum utilizable strength of the material is considered to be the stress corresponding to a given "life" (number of repetitions of stress). If the material has an endurance limit and a design for so-called infinite life is desired, then the endurance limit is the limiting resistance value or maximum utilizable strength of the material.

Fracture with Time at Elevated Temperature. A third type of fracture of metals may occur at elevated temperature under a static load that is applied for a long period of time. The material separates with very little evidence of yielding as a result mainly of the viscous flow of the unordered material in the grain boundaries of the metal.

The foregoing discussion in this article should make it evident that the problem of carrying out Step 2 in the rational procedure in design outlined in Art. 2 becomes a definite problem only after the mode of failure of the member is known or is assumed.

5 Experimental methods. There are, in general, two methods of determining stresses and strains in a member (two methods of carrying out Step 2), namely, (*a*) by analysis, expressed mathematically, based (1) on principles of mechanics, primarily statics, (2) on reasonable assumptions concerning the geometry of the deformations of the member, and (3) on properties of the material of the body or member as found from suitable tests; and (*b*) by experimental or mechanical methods, in which either the actual member or a model of the member may be used.

The method of mathematical analysis has been responsible for much of the rapid development of rational methods of design of structures and machines; * it has limitations, however, and experimental methods are used to meet conditions for which the mathematical method is inadequate or leads to objectionable complications.

Experimental methods may be divided into two classes. One class consists of methods which supplement the analytical method by furnishing information needed in the analytical method or by solving by mechanical means an equation obtained in the mathematical analysis; the

---

* Dr. T. E. Stanton states in the Foreword to Gough's *Fatigue of Metals:* "Scientific design may be regarded as dating from the publication of Rankine's 'Applied Mechanics' in 1858. The magnitude of the advance which was then made will be realized from a comparison of the contents of this treatise with the standard work of reference at that time, Dr. Robinson's 'Mechanical Philosophy,' a work which obtained deservedly high praise from Rankine, but in which the proportioning of structural details in accordance with the stresses brought to bear on them received comparatively little attention."

determination of the distribution of strain in an irregularly shaped member by use of strain gages having short gage lengths and the elastic membrane (soap-film) analogy method for solving the equation for shearing stress in an irregularly shaped torsion member are examples of experimental methods that may be used as supplementary to the mathematical method. The other class consists of experimental methods that lead mainly to empirical results.

In one experimental method models of a member, a machine, or a structure are sometimes used in determining, often by trial and error, the maximum feasible load-carrying capacity of a member. For example, a model of a proposed member or an assembly of several members or parts is tested under conditions simulating actual service, and the load at which it failed is observed; another (supposedly improved) model is then made after observing any unfavorable action in the first model (or the first model is modified if the test does not require destruction of the model); this process is continued until the model has been improved as much as is feasible. In addition, tests of a relatively large number of members or assemblies of the type finally adopted are sometimes made in order to allow any unpredictable or fortuitous factors connected with the manufacture and fabrication of the member or assembly to exert their influence on failure and hence on the test results. Some parts of automobiles have been developed mainly by this procedure.

The design of all members of structures and machines cannot be carried out by this trial-and-error method. The method is particularly applicable (a) to some members or assemblies in machines and structures that must have maximum strength with minimum weight, that is, must have a large strength-weight ratio (by the trial-and-error method material can be added or removed in various places until the optimum strength of the member is obtained); (b) to members whose failures are dependent on unknown or unpredictable factors that may arise in the operating conditions and in the manufacturing process, such as fatigue failures connected with uncertain loading and with surface scratches, residual stress and decarburized surfaces caused by heat treatment, internal defects in steel resulting from segregation in the ingot, etc.; and (c) to members that will be made in quantity production so that the cost of many tests will be a small percentage of the total cost. Airplane and automobile parts and assemblies are the best examples of such members, machines, and structures.

Although such tests can frequently be made to contribute valuable information for use in a rational method, it is doubtful if a satisfactory rational method for some classes of members will ever completely replace empirical methods based on comprehensive tests. Both methods will no doubt continue to serve a valuable purpose, and it is important that the limitations of both methods should be appreciated.

The so-called rational or analytical method is given emphasis throughout this book, but its limitations are frequently pointed out, and results from the experimental method are used freely to supplement the rational or analytical method or to replace it when necessary. One important condition, however, is likely to modify any design whether the method has been empirical or rational; namely, the member must be designed so that it can be machined, fabricated, or built, and usually it must be built at a reasonable cost.

6   Main topics to be discussed.   The primary purpose of this book is to consider the problems involved in Step 2 of the procedure in design outlined in Art. 2, namely, to obtain relationships between the loads acting on members and the quantities that are associated with the failures of the members. The main topics to be discussed may be stated briefly as follows.

Part I. A discussion of the method employed primarily in obtaining the relation between loads and stress, and a consideration of the assumptions and limitations involved in the equations or formulas of elementary mechanics of materials; a discussion of the state of stress at a point in a stressed body involving the relations of stresses at a point on different planes passing through the point in ideal elastic material; and a discussion of the significance of the various theories of the cause of inelastic action in materials, that is, of the theories that attempt to define or specify the most significant quantity (stress, strain, energy, etc.) in a failure resulting from general yielding.

Part II. Determination of significant stresses and deflections in members subjected to *static loads* at ordinary temperatures under conditions in which the shape of the member and the loading render the elementary formulas of mechanics of materials inadequate.

Part III. Values of localized stresses or stress concentrations, and a consideration of their engineering significance.

Part IV. The use of energy methods for determining deflections of statically determinate members and for determining the internal forces in statically indeterminate members.

Part V. An analysis indicating the influence of small amounts of inelastic strains on the load-carrying capacity of members.

Part VI. Determination of buckling loads for various members, involving both elastic and inelastic buckling.

Selected References

1. Cross, Hardy, "Limitation and Application of Structural Analysis," *Engineering News-Record*, Oct. 24, 1935.
2. Fleming, Robins, "Fifty Years of Structural Engineering with Special Reference to the United States," *Engineering (London)*, Vol. CXXXII, Sept. 11 and 25, 1931.
3. Hollister, S. C., "Three Centuries of Structural Analysis," *Civil Engineering*, Vol. 8, 1938.
4. Johnston, Bruce, "Structural Significance of Stress," *Civil Engineering*, May 1939.
5. Love, A. E., *Mathematical Theory of Elasticity*, 3rd edition, Cambridge Press, 1920. The introduction to this book gives an excellent history of the development of the mathematical analysis of stresses. See also J. I. Parcel and G. A. Maney's *Statically Indeterminate Stresses*, John Wiley & Sons, 1936, Arts. 157–159, for a briefer statement.
6. Moore, H. F., "The Quest of Elasticity," *Civil Engineering*, Vol. 1, No. 3, December 1930, p. 171.
7. Moore, H. F., "On What Values Should Working Stress Be Based?" *Machine Design*, Vol. 3, February 1931, pp. 35–38.
8. Ormondroyd, Jesse, "Applied Mechanics from Aristotle to Rankine," *Mechanical Engineering*, September 1951, p. 723.
9. Rankine, W. J. M., "Harmony of Theory and Practice in Mechanics," the introduction in Rankine's *Applied Mechanics*, Chas. Griffin and Co., London, England, 1873.
10. Schuster, L. W., "Mechanical Properties versus Service Failures," *The Iron Age*, Vol. 141, Part 2, No. 26, June 30, 1938.
11. Westergaard, H. M., "One Hundred Fifty Years Advance in Structural Analysis," *Proceedings of the American Society of Civil Engineering*, Vol. 54, 1928, p. 993.

Chapter 2

ELEMENTARY STRESS FORMULAS
FOR STATIC LOADS

7 Introduction. If structural damage to a load-resisting member consists (a) of general yielding or (b) of fracture, the significant quantity (that is, the quantity most directly associated with the failure of a member) as called for in Step 2 of the rational method of design outlined in Art. 2 is usually considered to be for (a) the shearing stress and for (b) the tensile stress at a point in the member on some plane passing through the point. Moreover, if the significant quantity is considered to be strain or strain energy (as discussed in Art. 31) it will be found that these quantities may be expressed conveniently in terms of the normal and shearing stresses at the point.

The particular point in the member and the particular plane through the point to be considered in determining the desired stresses must be so selected as to give the stresses where failure of the member starts. It is recognized, however, that failure of a member may not always result from the action that occurs at a point but may involve action over a finite area or in a finite volume of the material, particularly if general yielding constitutes the failure of the member. The *stress at a point*, therefore, may not always be the significant stress. This topic is discussed further in Art. 16.

Load Stresses vs. Deformation Stresses. The stresses caused by the loads acting on a member are sometimes designated as *load stresses* to distinguish them from stresses that accompany the relative deformations of portions of the member arising from actions within the members, such as temperature gradients, shrinkage, cold working, etc. These latter stresses are sometimes called *deformation stresses*. Such stresses frequently accompany the rather violent changes in temperature in a member that occur in the operation of welding and in the heat treatment of metals, etc. They may build up to large values in the plate of a railway steel car wheel owing to the heating of the rim by brake applications and its subsequent cooling and shrinking after the brakes are released. Such stresses also may occur as a result of shrinkage of concrete in a reinforced concrete member, and also as a result of the cold working of a portion of a metal member in the process of fabrication, etc. These deformation stresses are also designated by the name *residual stresses* or *initial stresses*, and also by the term *locked-in* or *trapped* stresses.

Stresses also may be classified as micro-stresses and macro-stresses. Micro-stresses are also called textural stresses. They are produced primarily in the process of obtaining or creating the material; for example, in engineering metals they are produced in the process of solidification from the molten state and involve only minute portions of the material. They depend primarily on the previous history of the material and are essentially independent of the load stresses caused by the external forces applied to a member. Secondary textural stresses are created by the process of permanent deformation either in the fabrication process of metal parts or during actual service loading as a result of slip on planes through the crystals which breaks up the crystals into fragments referred to as crystallites.

Micro-stresses may have an influence on the inherent strength of a material even though they cannot be calculated. Thermal and mechanical treatments of materials are sometimes used to reduce the values of micro-stresses or to minimize their formation.

A macro-stress is associated with a considerable bulk of the material. It is the average stress in a relatively large number of the structural units of which the material is made, such as the crystals in metals. Macro-stresses may be either load stresses or deformation stresses.

For the present only macro-stresses will be considered, and only those macro-stresses that are caused by external loads (load stresses) are discussed, since deformation stresses are, in general, difficult to determine and their influence in limiting the loads that can be applied to the member is uncertain. Such (residual) stresses are, in general, harmful if they are of the same kind as the load stresses and hence additive to the load stresses. However, in ductile material subjected to static loads such stresses probably seldom are fully additive to the load stresses in causing structural damage. On the other hand, residual stresses are, in general, beneficial in load-resisting members if they are opposite in sign to the load stresses. An important engineering problem consists in devising methods of creating and taking advantage of residual stresses. Several methods or operations used in creating beneficial residual stresses may be mentioned as follows. Cold rolling, sand blasting, and shot peening of surfaces are used, especially where stress concentrations occur; likewise overstraining of a considerable part of a member as in the autofrettage of gun barrels; some of these methods are discussed briefly in Part III.

Elementary Formulas for Load Stresses. In the design of many simple structural and machine members, use is made of one or more of the elementary formulas given in Fig. 3, because the load stresses obtained from these formulas are frequently associated with the failure of the

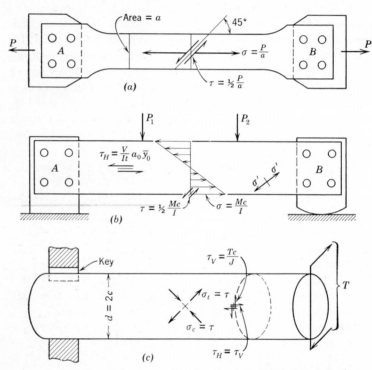

Fig. 3   Significant stresses as given by the elementary stress formulas.

member, particularly if the member is made of ductile * material and is subjected, at ordinary temperatures, to static loads (gradually applied loads that are not repeated a large number of times), so that it fails by general yielding. The three simplest types of static loading are shown in Fig. 3 and are designated as axial, bending, and torsional loading; the significant stresses for each of these types of loading are discussed in the following paragraphs.

STATIC AXIAL LOAD. *Ductile * Material.* In Fig. 3a, let it be assumed that the axial tensile load P is gradually applied to a ductile metal member through rivets at A and B. When values of P are relatively small,

* See footnote on p. 4.

the maximum stresses probably occur in the material close to the rivet holes. These stresses are localized; that is, they affect a very small portion of the material of the member. As the load P is increased, these localized stresses increase directly with the load until they reach the yield point of the material, and they then build up very slowly as the load continues to increase because the material yields at these points, thereby causing a redistribution of stress in the member. This localized yielding does not damage the member as a whole, and hence a larger load may be applied; the damaging stresses (the stresses associated with the beginning of general yielding) will finally occur in the main body of the member.* Thus the (localized) stresses that were maximum at low loads (and are difficult to calculate) become of little importance as the loads increase, whereas the stresses in the main body of the member that were relatively small under low loads are eventually the stresses that build up and become associated with the general yielding (failure) of the member, and these stresses can be calculated satisfactorily by the elementary stress formulas. In fact, from experiment and experience rules for the design of connections of members and similar regions of indefinite localized stresses have been formulated that will, in general, prevent these localized stresses from being the significant stresses. The foregoing facts are equivalent to stating that the connections are designed to permit plastic behavior whereas the members connected are designed to permit only elastic behavior.

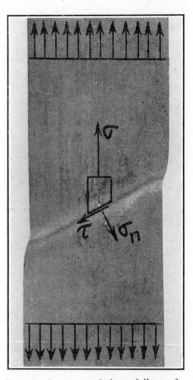

Fig. 4   One type of shear failure of a ductile steel tension member.

It is probable that in a tension member made of ductile metal the maximum shearing stress $[\tau = \frac{1}{2}(P/a)]$ as indicated in Fig. 3a is more

---

* A somewhat similar redistribution of compressive stress, resulting in a larger ultimate load for the member, is brought about by elastic buckling of thin flat plates subjected to compressive loads along two parallel edges and simple supports along the other two edges. This feature is discussed briefly in Art. 192.

closely associated with the yielding failure than is the maximum tensile stress. Figure 4 shows evidence of yielding approximately on a plane of maximum shearing stress. However, the same results in design will, of course, be obtained by the use of the maximum shearing stress $[\tau = \frac{1}{2}(P/a)]$ for the significant stress as is obtained by the use of the maximum tensile stress $(\sigma = P/a)$ provided that the maximum utilizable value for τ on which to base a working shearing stress is considered to be the *shearing* yield point *as obtained from the tensile test,* and that the corresponding value for σ is taken as the *tensile* yield point.

Brittle Material. If the member in Fig. 3a were made of a very brittle material, the localized stress near the rivet holes would continue to build up, in the absence of local yielding, until a crack would form at one or more points of localized stress and almost instantly spread completely across a section, thereby causing failure by rather sudden fracture of the whole member. Or, if the load were applied to a brittle member in such a way that local stresses were not involved, the member would fail by a sudden fracture when the tensile stress $(\sigma = P/a)$ in the main body of the member reached the ultimate strength of the material.

STATIC TRANSVERSE BENDING LOADS. *Ductile Material.* In Fig. 3b let it be assumed that the maximum bending moment occurs at the sections on which the stresses are shown. The maximum stresses σ and τ shown at this section are significant in the failure of the beam if it is

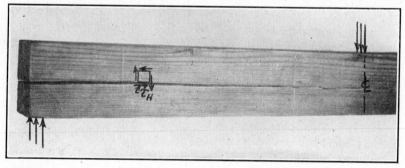

FIG. 5   Longitudinal shear failure of timber beam.

made of ductile material and is subjected to static loads; the localized stresses near the rivets and at the small areas where the loads are applied are not significant in the failure if the material is ductile, for the same reasons that were discussed previously under axial loads. In a beam made of timber, however, the stresses σ and τ at the section of maximum bending moment may not be significant because the grain of the wood may be such as to make the wood very weak in shear on a longitudinal plane, and hence the horizontal or longitudinal shearing stress τ_H (shown in Fig. 3b) may be the significant stress in the failure; a failure of a wooden beam by longitudinal shear is shown in Fig. 5.

Brittle Material. A beam made of a very brittle material would probably fail by fracture starting where the localized tensile stress is high (near the rivet holes at A in Fig. 3b, for example); such stresses as a rule cannot be calculated and are frequently "contact" stresses on small areas where one member rests or bears on another. However, many of the so-called brittle materials are able to yield slightly or strain elastically, especially if they have relatively small values of moduli of elasticity and thus adjust somewhat to localized stresses; hence the bending stress ($\sigma = Mc/I$) in Fig. 3b would probably be significant for most materials likely to be used for a structural or machine member. Furthermore, if a beam made of relatively brittle material is reinforced longitudinally to resist this bending stress as, for example, in a reinforced concrete beam, the beam would then probably fail by diagonal tension; the stress σ' (Fig. 3b) associated with this mode of failure is discussed in Art. 22.

From the above discussion it will be evident that in a beam subjected to static loads any one of five stresses (including localized stress) may be the significant stress, depending on the material of which the beam is made. Four of these stresses are shown in Fig. 3b and may be calculated satisfactorily in terms of the loads and dimensions of the member.

STATIC TORSIONAL LOADS. A *cylindrical* member made of ductile metal such as steel and subjected to a static torsional moment will, in general,

FIG. 6 Longitudinal shear failure of cylindrical timber member subjected to torsion.

fail by yielding (the localized stresses, for example, at the key in Fig. 3c would not be significant), and the transverse (circumferential) shearing stress τ_V would be primarily associated with failure; that is, the stress τ_V would limit the amount of load that could be applied to the bar, whereas a bar made of wood with a longitudinal grain might have its load-carrying capacity limited by the longitudinal shearing stress τ_H as illustrated in Fig. 6. If, however, the bar were made of brittle material, its load-carrying capacity would be limited by the diagonal tensile stress σ_t as indicated in Fig. 3c, although for a very brittle material, as previously noted, the failure (fracture) of the whole member might start where high localized stresses occur (at the key, for example, in Fig. 3c), and hence for very brittle material these localized stresses would be the significant ones rather than any of the three stresses shown in Fig. 3c.

Thus in a cylindrical member subjected to static torsion, any one of four stresses (including localized stress) may be the significant stress, depending on the material of which the member is made; three of these stresses may be calculated satisfactorily for cylindrical members in terms of the loads and dimensions of the member as indicated in Fig. 3c.

8 Procedure for deriving stress formulas. Since the normal stresses and the shearing stresses in a member subjected to loads are usually the most significant stresses, it is very important that there be a clear understanding of the widely used rational method for determining the relation between the loads on the member and each of these stresses at any point in the member on any plane passing through the point. The method will be illustrated in the next article in deriving, and in emphasizing the limitations of, one of the elementary stress formulas given in Fig. 3. The method is rather general, however, and will be used in subsequent chapters for finding the relation between loads and stresses under conditions that are less restricted than those assumed in Fig. 3. This method might be designated as the method of mechanics of materials in contrast to the method designated as the theory of elasticity which is discussed briefly in Appendix I. The main steps in the method of mechanics of materials in obtaining a relation between the loads acting on a member and the stress at some point on some plane in the member are as follows:

Step 1. The first major step is to assume the member to be in equilibrium and to apply the equations of equilibrium to the forces acting on some portion of the member so that a relation is obtained between the external forces acting on the member and the internal forces at a section through the body. In carrying out this first major step, however, attention must be given to the following two considerations:

(a) Since a body is held in equilibrium by forces (not stresses), the stress at a point is introduced into the equilibrium equations by expressing an internal force as the product of the stress at a point and a differential area of the section, including the point, over which the stress is assumed to be constant; thus a normal internal force on a differential area da is expressed as $\sigma\, da$, and a shearing force as $\tau\, da$. The internal forces at any section, therefore, will consist, in general, of a system of $\sigma\, da$ forces and a system of $\tau\, da$ forces.

(b) But the internal forces on any section must be made external forces since the equations of equilibrium apply to the forces acting on (external to) a body. This requirement is met by the common method of assuming that a section (usually a plane) is passed through the body and that the portion of the body lying on one side of this section is removed and is replaced by the forces it exerted at the cut section on the portion that remains. Thus all the forces acting on the portion that remains are external to that portion; a free-body diagram of that portion is then drawn, which will show all the original external forces that act on the portion and the forces (of the type $\sigma\, da$ and $\tau\, da$) at the cut section. And, since this system of forces holds the portion in equilibrium (as it was held in the original body), the equations of equilibrium may be applied to these forces. The section that is assumed to be passed through the body must, of course, pass through the point at which the stress is to be found and must be the plane on which the desired stress at the point acts. Furthermore, the desired stress, for design purposes, is the stress that occurs where failure of the member starts. The equations of equilibrium thus obtained, however, will contain expressions of this form $\int \sigma\, da$ and $\int \sigma y\, da$, etc., which cannot be evaluated until further information is made available by Step 2.

Step 2. The next main step is to determine the law of distribution of the stress over the area of the cut section (the relation between the stress at any point on the section and the coordinates of the point), so that when this law of stress distribution is introduced in the equations of equilibrium, as obtained in Step 1, the stress at the desired point can be found in terms of external loads and dimensions of the section by solving the resulting equations of equilibrium. This knowledge of the distribution of stress is found by carrying out the following two secondary steps.

(a) The member is thought of as being made of elements of one form or another, depending on the shape of the member and the way it is loaded, and the variation of the *strains* of these elements is observed by means of strain-measuring instruments on the member; or the distribution of strains may in some cases be assumed on the basis of certain conditions that the deformations of the body as a whole must satisfy. It should here be recalled that displacements or deformations and often strains (relative displacements) may be seen and measured (by strain gages), whereas stresses do not have this direct physical relationship with our experience, and hence the distribution of stresses must be arrived at through their relation to strain as discussed in (b).

(b) By testing, under increasing load, a specimen of the material of which the member is made in such a way that the stresses at various loads and the corresponding strains may be computed from the test results, the relation between stress and strain for the material may be found in the form of a stress-strain curve. And, if the distribution of strains in the member is determined in (a), then the distribution of stresses in the member also becomes known. Usually, when the strains are small and only one principal stress exists, the relation between stress and strain is expressed by Hooke's law, namely $\sigma = E\epsilon$, in which E is an elastic constant of the material and is called the modulus of elasticity.

Step 3. The final step consists in substituting the expression for the stress obtained in Step 2 in the equations of equilibrium as obtained in Step 1, and then solving the resulting equations for the stress in terms of the loads and dimensions of the member.

The procedure outlined in the foregoing steps will be illustrated in Art. 9 in the derivation of the elementary formula $\sigma = P/a$, which gives the maximum normal stress in an axially loaded member. The student should apply the procedure also to the derivation of the formulas $\sigma = Mc/I$ and $\tau = Tc/J$ and point out the limitations of the formulas as imposed by the various detailed steps in the procedure. The procedure will also be employed in obtaining the expressions for the stresses in load-resisting members discussed in later chapters.

9 Limitations of the direct-stress formula, $\sigma = P/a$. The procedure discussed in Art. 8 is here applied in deriving and showing

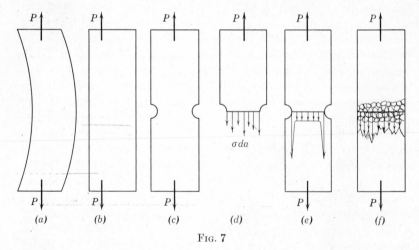

Fig. 7

the limitations of the formula $\sigma = P/a$. Let a bar of any shape be subjected to two equal opposite and collinear loads P, as indicated in Figs. 7a, 7b, and 7c. If the normal stress at any point on a plane perpendicular to the loads is to be found in any one of the members shown in Figs. 7a, 7b, and 7c, a free-body diagram is drawn in accordance with Step 1, (a) and (b), of Art. 8; the free-body diagram as applied to the situation in Fig. 7c, for example, is shown in Fig. 7d. The equilibrium equation obtained is

$$P = \int \sigma \, da \tag{1}$$

It is at once observed that if σ is constant (if σ is distributed uniformly on the area a) the above equation becomes

$$P = \sigma \int da = a\sigma \qquad \text{or} \qquad \sigma = P/a \tag{2}$$

But, in accordance with Step 2, the stresses σ at all points in the area (or the stresses acting on the areas da of all the longitudinal elements or fibers of the member) will be equal only (a) if the longitudinal strains (stretches per unit length) of these fibers at the section are equal, and (b) if the stress in each fiber is proportional to the strain of the fiber, and the proportionality factor is the same for all fibers. But, in order that the strains of the fibers shall be equal, the following conditions must be satisfied:

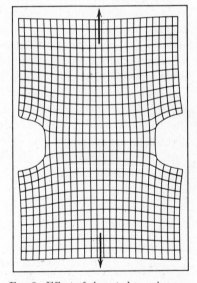

1. The portion of the member under consideration must be straight. For example, the strains of the fibers of the member in Fig. 7a would not be equal.

2. The member, if straight, must be axially and centrally loaded; thus, in the member in Fig. 7b the strains of the fibers would vary considerably.

3. The portion of the member under consideration must have a constant cross section. The abrupt change in section in Fig. 7c would

FIG. 8   Effect of abrupt change in cross section on strain distribution on section.

cause very large (localized) strains at the roots of the grooves as indicated in Fig. 7e and shown in the photograph of the rubber model in Fig. 8. The calculation of localized stresses is discussed in Chapter 12.

4. The load must be applied at a point or section well removed from the section on which the stress σ occurs. The stresses in the neighbor-

hood of the areas of contact between the loads and the members are as a rule highly localized or concentrated.

It is evident, therefore, that the stress would not be uniformly distributed and hence would not be expressed as $\sigma = P/a$ in any of the three members shown in Figs. 7a, 7b, or 7c. Furthermore, the proportionality factor between stress and strain will not be the same for all fibers unless all fibers are made of the same material; in other words:

5. The member must be a one-material member.

Moreover, if the stress is distributed on an area according to a mathematical law (here assumed to be distributed uniformly), the member must not only be a one-material member from the engineering sense, but:

6. The material must be truly homogeneous. For example, in a one-material member such as a steel bar, which is made up of a very large number of haphazardly oriented crystals or grains in which the properties vary, the stress would tend to vary in an erratic (non-mathematical) manner as suggested in Fig. 7f, particularly under low loads before the stresses at the points of high stress reach the yield point of the material when adjustments occur which tend to cause a stress distribution more nearly like that assumed for the ideal homogeneous material.

7. Since the equations of equilibrium are used to obtain the basic formula involving the desired stress, the load P must be a gradually applied (static) load and hence must not be an impact load that would accelerate the member as stresses and strain were developed.

8. The value of σ is the stress caused only by the load P, and hence it may not represent the stress in the member if the member contains initial or residual stresses, such as stresses caused by rapid cooling in welded joints, cold working of metals, etc.

When Limitations Are Significant. As discussed in previous articles, the importance or significance of the foregoing limitations depends on the mode of failure of the member. For example, if the member is made of ductile material and fails by general yielding preceded by many localized adjustments in the material, only limitations 1, 2, 5, and 7 are usually of real importance. But for very brittle material subjected to static load all limitations are likely to be significant. Likewise, for ductile material subjected to repeated reversals of loads, in which localized action (resulting in a minute crack that gradually spreads) rather than general action (yielding) in the member leads to failure, all the above limitations may be significant, as will be discussed in later chapters.

10　Limitations of the flexure formula, $\sigma = Mc/I$.　If, in applying the procedure discussed in Art. 8 to a beam, the expression $\sigma = Mc/I$ is obtained for the normal stress σ at any point on a section perpendicular to the axis of the beam, it will be found that the conditions imposed in order to obtain this expression for σ will place the following restrictions or limitations on the formula.　(In the flexure formula, c is the distance from the neutral axis to the point at which stress σ occurs, and I is the moment of inertia of the cross-sectional area of the beam about the neutral axis.)

Since the basic equation (obtained in Step 1) from which the flexure formula is developed is one of the equations that express the relations that must exist between loads and internal forces in order to satisfy the conditions of equilibrium, it follows that:

1. The loads on the beam must be static loads.　The stress in the beam due to impact loads that would accelerate the beam while the stresses and strains are being developed would therefore not be given by this formula.

2. The value of σ is the result of external forces *only* and, *hence*, if σ represents the stress in the beam, the beam must be free from initial or residual stresses due to temperature changes, heat treatment, cold working, etc.

In Step 2(*a*) of Art. 8 it is assumed that the longitudinal strains of the fibers of the beam at any transverse section are proportional to the distance of the fibers from the neutral axis of the beam.　This assumption requires that:

3. The proportions of the beam must be such that the beam acts as a unit with bending as the dominant action.　That is, the beam must fail by bending and not by twisting, lateral buckling, or local wrinkling.　For example, a rectangular beam $\frac{1}{4}$ in. wide by 12 in. deep would probably fail by twisting, and an I beam having very wide and thin flanges would probably fail by local buckling or wrinkling of the outer portions of the flanges.

4. The beam must be subjected to pure bending; the reasons are as follows:

(*a*) By pure bending is meant that the resultant of the forces that lie to one side of the transverse section on which the stress is to be found is a couple.　If this condition is not satisfied, shearing strains are developed in the beam, and hence longitudinal strains are not in general proportional to the distances from the neutral surface.　However, the shearing strains in beams that satisfy the other conditions required by the flexure formula have but small influence on the longitudinal strains, and hence this limitation as a rule is not important.

(b) The forces acting on the beam (if they do not form bending couples) must be perpendicular to the axis of the beam. Otherwise the beam is subjected to axial stress in addition to bending stress; the stress, however, may then be found by the combined use of the direct-stress formula and the flexure formula.

(c) The plane of the forces acting on the beam (if the forces do not form bending couples) must contain the longitudinal axis called the bending axis of the beam. Otherwise the beam will be subjected to a torsional moment in addition to bending, and this torsional moment may cause additional longitudinal (bending) stresses on certain sections. The bending axis is the one through which the bending loads must pass in order to prevent the beam from twisting as it bends. The intersection of the bending axis with any transverse section of the beam is called the shear center or center of twist for the section. The shear center for certain sections is discussed in Chapter 4, and the effect of the twisting of the beam on the bending stresses is discussed in Chapter 9.

5. The neutral axis of each transverse section must be perpendicular to the plane of the loads. This condition in turn requires that the plane of the loads shall contain or be parallel to an axis of symmetry (or, in general, to a principal axis of inertia) of each cross section. This topic is discussed in Chapter 5.

6. The initial curvature of the member must be relatively small (theoretically the beam must be straight). Otherwise the strains of the fibers are not proportional to the distances from the neutral surface, for, although plane sections remain plane, and hence the total deformations of the fibers are proportional to their distances from the neutral surface, the length of the fibers between two transverse plane sections of a curved beam (sections perpendicular to the curved axis of the beam) are not equal, and hence the strains (deformation per unit length) are not proportional to the distance from the neutral axis. Curved beams, that is, beams with relatively sharp initial curvatures, are discussed in Chapter 6.

7. The beam must be free from abrupt changes of section in the portion of the beam in which the stress is to be found; plane sections do not remain plane at or near such changes in sections, and hence the strains of the fibers are not proportional to their distances from the neutral surface.

8. The material must obey Hooke's law; namely, the stress is proportional to strain, and hence:

(a) The stress in the beam must not exceed the limit of proportionality of the material; and also,

(b) The proportionality factor in Hooke's law must be the same in compression as in tension; that is, the moduli of elasticity of the material in tension and compression must be equal.

These two conditions stated under (8) are satisfied approximately by most constructional load-resisting materials especially for the working stresses used in design. A two-material beam such as a reinforced concrete beam or a timber beam reinforced with steel planes on top and bottom would, of course, not satisfy the conditions directly.

9. The stress is assumed to be distributed according to a mathematical law which in turn requires that the material shall be continuous and homogeneous. A so-called one-material beam such as a steel beam is far from being homogeneous, but as discussed in Art. 3 it may be assumed to be homogeneous to obtain results that are useful in many engineering problems, particularly when statistical (rather than localized) action leads to failure, which usually occurs in ductile material subjected to static loads at ordinary temperatures.

10. The point at which the stress is to be found must not be close to the point of contact of a concentrated load; the stress distributions in the neighborhood of the points of contact of the loads and reactions are very different from that assumed in obtaining the flexure formula. (Contact stresses are discussed in Chapter 11.)

11. The bending is assumed to take place only in the plane of the loads. This assumption is known to be untrue, but the influence of the bending in the transverse plane on the bending in the longitudinal plane may be neglected without appreciable error except perhaps in very wide shallow beams. However, when the loads do not lie in a plane, as in the case of a horizontal flat plate subjected to a vertical load and supported on all edges, the bending in one vertical plane has a very large influence on the bending in other vertical planes. Flat plates are considered in Chapter 8.

11 Limitations of the torsion formula, $\tau = Tc/J$. If, in applying the procedure discussed in Art. 8 to a bar subjected to a torsional moment T, the expression $\tau_V = Tc/J$ is obtained (in which τ_V is the transverse shearing stress at a point at the distance c from the axis of the bar on a cross section perpendicular to the axis of the bar, and J is the polar moment of inertia of the cross section with respect to the axis of the bar), it will be found that the conditions imposed in order to obtain this expression for τ_V will place the following limitations on the formula:

1. Since the body is assumed to be in equilibrium, impact loads are excluded.

2. The member must be free from initial stresses if the value of τ_V given by the formula represents the stress in the member.

3. The shearing stress on any transverse cross section is assumed to vary directly as the distance from the center of the section; this requires that a plane transverse section remain plane and that a radial line in the section remain a straight line after the bar is twisted. Therefore:

(a) The transverse cross sections of the portion of the bar under consideration must be circular; otherwise a plane section will not remain plane. (Torsion of non-circular sections is discussed in Chapter 9.)

(b) The portion of the bar under consideration must have a constant diameter or at least must be free from abrupt change of section; otherwise a diameter before twisting will not be a diameter after twisting. (The shearing stress at the fillet where a cylindrical shaft is abruptly reduced in diameter is discussed in Art. 119.)

(c) The shearing stress must vary directly with the shearing strain and must, therefore, not exceed the shearing proportional limit of the material; otherwise the stress would not vary as the distance from the center of the section even though the strain did so vary.

(d) As in the cases of the two equations already discussed, the material must act substantially like a homogeneous (ideal) material, which from the practical engineering point of view means that statistical action rather than localized action in the member is significant in causing failure; otherwise the distribution of stress could not be expressed mathematically.

(e) The point at which the stress is to be found must not be near to a point of application of a load.

12 Significance of limitations of the three elementary stress formulas. Seldom if ever in engineering problems are the conditions satisfied that would make the three formulas discussed in the preceding articles strictly applicable to structural and machine members. These simple formulas, however, have a wider application and furnish more useful and reliable results than might be expected from the preceding analysis of their mathematical limitations; this fact is the result mainly of the following conditions:

1. Stresses considerably larger than the values of σ and τ given by the foregoing formulas are frequently developed in the member, particularly at abrupt changes of section, at the points of contacts of the

loads, at internal flaws, etc. If, however, the member is made of ductile material and is subjected to static loads, when these stresses reach the yield point stress, the ductility of the material permits the material to yield slightly at the regions of high stress, and thus there is brought about a redistribution of stress (particularly if the state of stress is essentially uniaxial). The stresses at the points of stress concentration do not continue to build up as the load is increased, but the increased loads are resisted by a more favorable distribution of stress. In relatively brittle material subjected to static loads or in ductile material subjected to repeated loads, the discrepancies between the actual and the assumed conditions are more serious, and hence the formulas are less reliable.

2. Working values of σ and τ (so-called working stresses) for use in the formulas are selected which, according to experiments and experience, are found to be safe; that is, the values selected are sufficiently low to make allowance for the inaccuracies or uncertainties in the conditions to which the formulas are assumed to apply. In the final analysis, therefore, the formulas become to some extent empirical.

3. With combinations of loads of two or more types (such as bending and torsion, for example) the formulas may still in most cases be used, for, by the principle of superposition as discussed in the next article, each type of load may usually be assumed to produce the same stress that it would if it were the only load acting. The stresses thus found may then be used, as discussed in the next chapter, to obtain the maximum value of σ and τ.

4. Even when the conditions are such that the values of σ and τ in the formulas cannot be considered to be the values of the significant stresses, the equations may frequently be used with a correction factor obtained from experimental data or from a more extended analysis. This method of making use of the equations will be discussed in subsequent chapters.

13 Method of superposition. In dealing with stresses, deflections, moments, etc., in elastic bodies caused by loads, it is convenient frequently to consider the loads to be composed of two (or more) systems of loads and to assume that each system produces stress, deflection, etc., independently, as though it were the only system of loads acting on the body. The actual effect is then considered to be the resultant of the effects of the two systems of loads. The method of obtaining the actual effect as a resultant effect by adding or combining independent partial effects is called the method of superposition. The method has already been used in some of the preceding articles and will be used frequently in subsequent articles. The method is applicable only if a linear relationship exists between the loads and the effect they produce.

14 Effect on the static strength of a member of removing material from the member. The meaning or interpretation of the elementary formulas discussed in the preceding articles may be emphasized further by considering the effect on the *static* strength of a member of removing material from the member under special conditions.

Let a beam having a square cross section be used under static loads so that the neutral axis is one diagonal of the square, and let it be required to determine the effect on the load-carrying capacity of the beam of removing some of the material at the top and bottom of the beam, as suggested in Fig. 9.

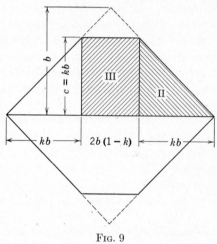

Fig. 9

It will be assumed that all the conditions required to make the flexure formula $[\sigma = M/(I/c)]$ applicable are satisfied. The stress in the beam for a given bending moment is inversely proportional to the section modulus I/c, and the stress will be a minimum when I/c is a maximum. The section modulus for the square cross section (Fig. 9) is

$$\frac{I}{c} = \frac{4 \times \frac{1}{12}b^4}{b} = \frac{1}{3}b^3 \tag{3}$$

The moment of inertia of the area in Fig. 9 is

$$I = 4I_{\text{II}} + 2I_{\text{III}} \tag{4}$$

$$= 4[\tfrac{1}{12}(kb)^4] + 2[\tfrac{1}{3}(kb)^3(1 - k)2b] \tag{5}$$

$$= \frac{k^3b^4}{3}[k + 4(1 - k) \tag{6}$$

If this expression for I is divided by c (where $c = kb$), the following expression for the section modulus is obtained.

$$I/c = \tfrac{1}{3}(4k^2b^3 - 3k^3b^3) \tag{7}$$

The value of k that will make I/c a maximum may be found by equating the first derivative to zero and solving for k. Thus

$$\frac{d(I/c)}{dk} = \frac{1}{3}(8kb^3 - 9k^2b^3) = 0 \tag{8}$$

$$k = \tfrac{8}{9} \tag{9}$$

Therefore, the section modulus of the square cross section is increased (and the bending stress for a given bending moment is proportionately decreased) by removing small triangular portions of the beam at its top and bottom; the maximum value of the section modulus is attained by removing a triangular area whose altitude is one-ninth ($\frac{1}{9}$) of the altitude of the triangle representing one-half of the square. This fact means that, if successively larger triangular areas are assumed to be removed from the area of the square (starting with very small areas), the values of both I and c of the remaining area decrease, but c decreases faster than I decreases, until the triangular area removed has an altitude $\frac{1}{9}$ that of the half-square.

Since the assumption is made in the flexure formula that the material obeys Hooke's law, it follows that, if the useful load-carrying capacity of the member having a square cross section with a diagonal as the neutral axis were limited by a stress corresponding to only a very slight deviation from Hooke's law, the useful strength of the member would be increased by the removal of the material as indicated in the preceding paragraph. If, however, the beam were made of ductile material and appreciable yielding in the top and bottom fibers of the beam were permissible, it is likely that the useful strength of the beam would not be increased by removal of the material, and the ultimate (overload) strength of the beam likewise would probably not be increased by the removal of the material. On the other hand, if the beam were made of very brittle material, it is probable that removal of the material would increase the strength of the beam. It is well to note that the removal of material from a member for the purpose of increasing the strength of the member is sometimes of considerable importance in members subjected to repeated loads and also in members that must absorb the energy of moving bodies. The problem, however, is different for each type of loading and is discussed briefly for repeated loading in Chapter 12.

Problems

(*Note.* In the following problems the material is assumed to be homogeneous and isotropic and to be free from initial stresses.)

1. State the reason why the value of σ in the equation $P = a\sigma$ would not be an accurate value of the maximum stress at the following sections:

(*a*) At sections *AB*, *CD*, and *EF* in the flat bar of Fig. 10.

(*b*) At sections *AB* and *CD* of Fig. 11.

(*c*) At section *AB* of Fig. 12.

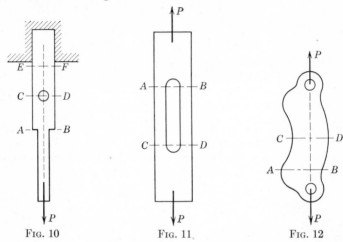

FIG. 10   FIG. 11   FIG. 12

2. State the reason why the value of σ in the flexure formula would not be an accurate value of the maximum longitudinal normal stress at the following sections:

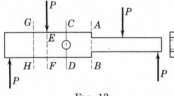

FIG. 13

(*a*) At sections *AB*, *CD*, *EF*, and *GH* of the bar in Fig. 13.

(*b*) At any section of the beam in Fig. 14.

(*c*) At any section of the channel beam in Fig. 15.

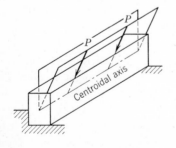

FIG. 14

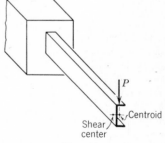

FIG. 15

3. State the reasons why the value of τ in the torsion formula would not be an accurate value of the maximum shearing stress at the following sections, the bar in each case being subjected to a twisting couple in a plane perpendicular to its axis.

(a) At sections AB and CD of the cylindrical bar in Fig. 16.

(b) At a section of a circular shaft containing a keyway.

(c) At a section of a square or rectangular bar.

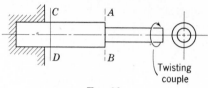

FIG. 16

4. A timber column base for a column 12 in. by 12 in. in cross section was specified to be 40 in. high and of the same cross section as the column. The contractor had no 12 in. by 12 in. column base but used a 12 in. by 16 in. base as shown in Fig. 17. Show that the maximum calculated stress in a 12 in. by 12 in. base would be 800 lb per sq in., whereas in the 12 in. by 16 in. base it is 1050 lb per sq in. The safe or working stress for the timber was specified to be 800 lb per sq in. Would the column base be safer if the excess material were sawed off along the dotted line?

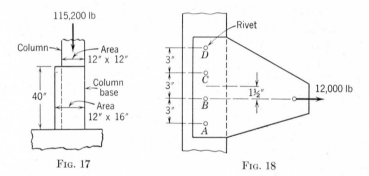

FIG. 17   FIG. 18

5. A building was constructed with a number of riveted connections like that shown in Fig. 18. The cross-sectional area of each rivet is 0.40 sq in. Show that the maximum shearing stress in the rivets of this joint (at A) is 12,000 lb per sq in. Show also that if the rivet at D is omitted the shearing stress in each of the remaining rivets is 10,000 lb per sq in. The specifications called for a working shearing stress of 10,000 lb per sq in. The contractor found it more convenient to use a larger gusset plate than was specified and added the extra rivet at D, thinking that he was making a stronger joint than was specified. Would the connection be improved by requiring the contractor to knock out the rivet at D?

6. If a beam having a square cross section is used so that the diagonal of the square is the neutral axis, how much would the elastic strength of the beam be increased if it were turned so that parallel sides of the square represented the top and bottom of the beam?

7. If a beam with a rectangular cross section 2 in. by 8 in. has its cross section increased as indicated by the cross-hatched area in Fig. 19, how much is the elastic strength of the beam increased?

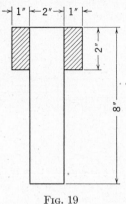

FIG. 19

15   Deflections of the three types of members. As previously noted, the elastic deflections of the members discussed in this chapter, rather than stresses, may limit the maximum loads that can be applied to the members. The deflections e, Δ, and θ of the members to which the stress equations $\sigma = P/a$, $\sigma = Mc/I$, and $\tau = Tc/J$ apply, respectively, are

$$e = Pl/aE \qquad \Delta = \alpha(Wl^3/EI) \qquad \theta = Tl/GJ$$

The energy methods for determining deflections of members, in general, are discussed in Part IV.

Chapter 3

STRESSES AND STRAINS AT A POINT
THEORIES OF FAILURE BY YIELDING

§ 1 Relation between Stresses at a Point on Different Planes Passing through the Point

16 Introduction. Many structural and machine members are subjected to loads that are combinations of those considered in the preceding chapter. The elementary formulas discussed in that chapter may be used to determine the stresses at a point in the member on certain planes passing through the point, but none of these stresses, in general, will be the maximum stress at the point. It is important, therefore, that the relations between the stresses at a point on different planes passing through the point be found. It is well to note that a stress should not be thought of apart from the area on which it acts, and hence the idea of a stress at a point, to be definite, must involve a plane passing through the point. The term "state of stress at a point" is sometimes used when the stresses on several planes passing through the point are considered.

Method of Obtaining Relations between Stresses at a Point. The method of obtaining the relation between stresses at a point in a stressed body on different planes passing through the point is essentially the same as that discussed in Art. 8 for obtaining the relations between the external forces (loads) acting on a body and the stress at any point on a section of the body.

The method consists first in considering that a small part or block of the body (including the point) is severed from the body by planes on which the stresses at the point are assumed to be given or known. This small block now constitutes a new body that is acted on by forces external to the block, and it is, of course, held in equilibrium by these forces acting on its faces; furthermore, the weight of the block may be considered to be negligible. The stress on each face of the block may be considered to be uniformly distributed since the face is very small, and hence the force on each face is equal to the product of stress on the face and the area of the face. Frequently, it is convenient to assume that the area of each face of the block is equal to unity, in which case the block is called a unit volume or unit cube, and the stress and force on any face are equal.

The stress at the point on a plane having any specified direction may now be found (in terms of the stresses at the point on the planes represented by the faces of the block) by passing a plane through the block parallel to the specified direction and applying the equations of equilibrium to the forces acting on either of the two portions of the block thus formed; the force acting on the specified (inclined) face of each of the two portions of the block will usually be considered to be composed of two components, namely, the shearing stress on the face times the area of the face, and the normal stress times the area of the face. This method is applied throughout the greater portion of this chapter and also in many of the subsequent chapters of this book.

Significance of Stress at a Point. In this chapter, the conditions required to make the mathematical analysis applicable are assumed to be fulfilled. These assumptions are discussed in the preceding chapters; one of the main assumptions is that each minute part of the material exhibits the same properties that are exhibited by the material in bulk; stated succinctly, the material is assumed to be continuous, homogeneous, and isotropic. The interpretation and significance of the *ideal* stresses thus found, for determining the maximum loads that can safely be applied to an actual member, will depend on a number of factors or conditions, including characteristics or properties of the material, type of loading, stress distribution, state of stress, temperature, etc.

The influence of these conditions, especially of stress distribution, on the significance of the stress at a point deserves further consideration. For example, if a *ductile* metal member is subjected to *static* loads at ordinary temperatures, structural damage to the member will, in general, consist of yielding of the material, but the *load* that caused the yielding that constitutes structural damage to the member depends not only on the value of the maximum stress at a point on a section of the member but also on the distribution of stress on the section. If the stress distribution on the area is non-uniform and hence not all of the area is subjected to the maximum stress, the maximum load that can be applied to the member without causing structural damage to the member by yielding, as a rule, is somewhat greater than the load that will cause the yield point of the material at the point of maximum stress; thus under such conditions the stress at a point may not be the significant stress. This condition is discussed further in Part V. On the other hand, for brittle material under static loading, and for ductile material under repeated loading, structural damage (which consists of fracture rather than yielding) is more closely related to the maximum stress at a point.

Even though the stresses *at a point* may not give, in all cases, the most significant values of stress for determining the maximum loads that a member can resist without being structurally damaged, the relations between the stresses at a point on different planes passing through the point furnish very valuable basic information that will be used in subsequent chapters of this book. Some of the more important elementary relationships are reviewed in the following articles.

17 Pure shear. If a shearing stress τ occurs on a plane at a given point in a stressed body, there must exist a shearing stress of equal

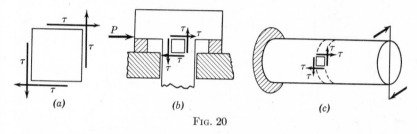

(a)   (b)   (c)

FIG. 20

magnitude at that point on a second plane at right angles to the first plane. This statement is true whether or not normal stresses also act on the planes on which the shearing stresses occur. The proof of the statement may be obtained by considering the equilibrium of a unit volume on each of whose faces a shearing and a normal stress act. Furthermore, the vectors representing these two shearing stresses lie in a third plane perpendicular to the other two planes. If shearing stresses *only* exist on two such planes, the state of stress at the point is called *pure shear*. Such a state of stress is shown acting on the unit cube in Fig. 20a, and it occurs in the bolt head subjected to shear in Fig. 20b, or in the bar subjected to torsion in Fig. 20c; it also occurs in the beam shown in Fig. 5, in which the horizontal shear was the cause of the failure of the timber beam.

18 Principal stresses defined. For any combination of stresses at a point in a stressed body three mutually perpendicular planes passing through the point can be found on which only normal stresses exist; the normal stresses on these planes on which no shearing stresses occur are called *principal stresses*. The maximum normal stress at any point is always a principal stress, and hence principal stresses are of much importance in engineering problems. The minimum normal stress at the point is also a principal stress, and the third principal stress, of course, has a value between the maximum and minimum values. In many problems, however, one of the three principal stresses is equal to zero, and frequently two of the principal stresses are equal to zero.

When only one principal stress exists at a point, the stress is frequently referred to as a uniaxial or one-dimensional stress; when two principal stresses occur, the state of stress is frequently called biaxial stress, or two-dimensional stress, or plane stress, and when all three principal stresses exist, the state of stress is designated as triaxial or three-dimensional stress. Principal stresses will be denoted by σ_1, σ_2, and σ_3.

19 Principal stresses accompanying pure shear. If at a point in a stressed body a state of pure shear exists as in Fig. 21*a*, there also

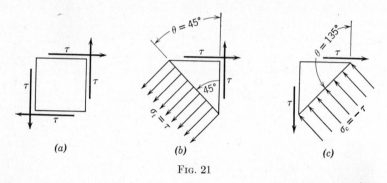

(a)   (b)   (c)

Fig. 21

exist tensile and compressive stresses on other planes through the point; the maximum and minimum normal (principal) stresses occur as shown in Figs. 21*b* and 21*c* on planes that bisect the angles between the planes on which the given shearing stresses act, and these principal stresses are equal in magnitude to the shearing stresses. The shearing stresses on these 45° (principal) planes are equal to zero. Thus, when a brittle material such as cast iron, which is relatively weak in tension, is subjected to a state of pure shear by being twisted as in Figs. 20*c* and 22*a*,

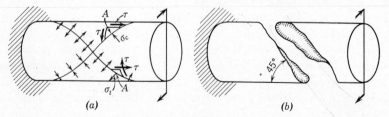

(a)   (b)

Fig. 22   Brittle material when subjected to torsion fails in tension.

the material fails on the plane of maximum tensile stress σ_t which is inclined 45° to the planes on which the maximum shearing stresses occur, as indicated in Fig. 22*b*.

Problem

8. In a beam simply supported near its ends and subjected to a concentrated load at the center, show by a sketch similar to that at A in Fig. 22a the maximum tensile and shearing stresses at any point on the neutral axis between one support and the center of the span.

20   Maximum shearing stresses in terms of principal stresses.

As pointed out in Art. 3, the failure of a member is frequently considered to be associated with the maximum shearing stresses at some point in the member. Hence, if the principal stresses at a point are known, it may be desired to determine the maximum shearing stresses at the point in terms of the principal stresses.

PROPOSITION. The maximum value of the shearing stress at a point in a stressed body is one-half of the algebraic difference of the maximum and minimum principal stresses at the point; that is,

$$\tau_{max} = \tfrac{1}{2}(\sigma_{max} - \sigma_{min}) \tag{10}$$

in which a principal stress is considered to be positive if it is a tensile stress and negative if a compressive stress. Furthermore, this maximum shearing stress occurs on each of the two planes that bisect the angles between the planes on which the maximum and minimum principal stresses occur.

Proof. The procedure outlined in Art. 16 will be used in proving the foregoing proposition. Let the block in Fig. 23a represent a small part

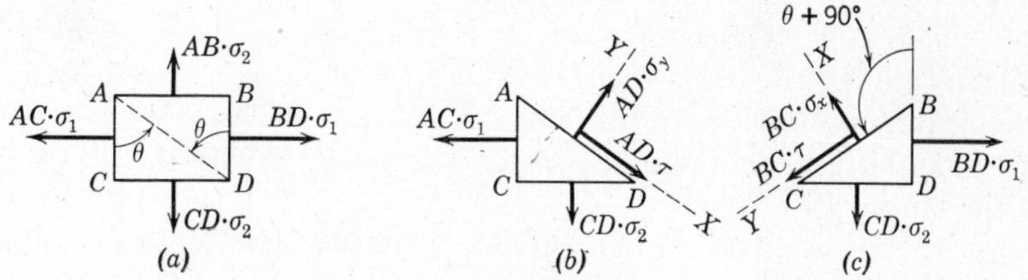

FIG. 23

of a stressed body; at this point in the body a tensile principal stress σ_1 acts on the plane AC (and BD), a tensile principal stress σ_2 on the plane AB (and CD), and a principal stress σ_3 (not shown) on the faces parallel to the plane of the paper. An oblique plane AD is passed through the block, making an angle θ with the plane on which the principal stress σ_1 acts, and one part of the block is removed; the forces holding the remaining part in equilibrium are as shown in Fig. 23b (or 23c). By applying one of the equations of equilibrium ($\Sigma F_x = 0$) to the forces in Fig. 23b, the shearing force is

$$AD\tau = AC\sigma_1 \cdot \sin \theta - CD\sigma_2 \cdot \cos \theta$$

By dividing both sides of this equation by AD, and noting that $AC/AD = \cos\theta$ and $CD/AD = \sin\theta$, the equation becomes

$$\tau = (\sigma_1 - \sigma_2)\sin\theta\cos\theta$$
$$= \tfrac{1}{2}(\sigma_1 - \sigma_2)\sin 2\theta \tag{11}$$

But $\sin 2\theta$ has a maximum value (equal to unity) when θ equals 45°, and hence one maximum shearing stress τ_{max} is

$$\tau_{max} = \tfrac{1}{2}(\sigma_1 - \sigma_2) \tag{12}$$

and acts on a plane which bisects the angle between the planes on which the stresses σ_1 and σ_2 act. Similarly another maximum shearing stress occurs on a plane which bisects the angle between the planes on which σ_1 and σ_3 act, and its value is $\tau'_{max} = \tfrac{1}{2}(\sigma_1 - \sigma_3)$; likewise $\tau''_{max} = \tfrac{1}{2}(\sigma_2 - \sigma_3)$. Thus the maximum shearing stress at the point is the largest of the three preceding values; it is given by the expression $\tau_{max} = \tfrac{1}{2}(\sigma_{max} - \sigma_{min})$ and acts on a plane bisecting the angle between the planes upon which σ_{max} and σ_{min} act.

If σ_1 and σ_2 in the foregoing equations are of like sign (both tensile stresses or both compressive stresses) and the third principal stress is zero, as is the case approximately in the shell of a cylindrical boiler, where the minimum principal stress is the internal pressure which may be considered to be negligible (equal to zero), the maximum shearing stress is $\tfrac{1}{2}\sigma_{max}$ and is on a plane that is parallel to the longitudinal axis of the boiler and that makes an angle of 45° with a plane tangent to the boiler shell at the point under consideration. If two principal stresses are zero (as in a member subjected to an axial tensile load), the maximum shearing stress is merely $\tfrac{1}{2}\sigma$, where σ is the only principal stress, and it acts on a plane making an angle of 45° with the direction of the tensile load.

Normal Stress. The normal stress σ_y (Fig. 23b) on any plane making an angle θ with the plane on which the principal stress σ_1 occurs is found by applying another equation of equilibrium ($\Sigma F_y = 0$). Thus

$$\sigma_y = \sigma_1 \cos^2\theta + \sigma_2 \sin^2\theta$$
$$= \sigma_1 \left(\frac{1 + \cos 2\theta}{2}\right) + \sigma_2 \left(\frac{1 - \cos 2\theta}{2}\right)$$
$$\sigma_y = \frac{\sigma_1 + \sigma_2}{2} + \frac{\sigma_1 - \sigma_2}{2}\cos 2\theta \tag{13}$$

This normal stress is always less than the maximum principal stress (σ_1 or σ_2) at the point.

21 Mohr's circle: principal stresses given. Mohr's circle for two-dimensional stresses furnishes a convenient graphical representation of the relation between principal stresses at a point and the shearing and normal stresses at the same point on planes inclined to the planes of principal stresses. Mohr's circle will be used first to determine the normal and shearing stresses at a point on any plane in terms of the

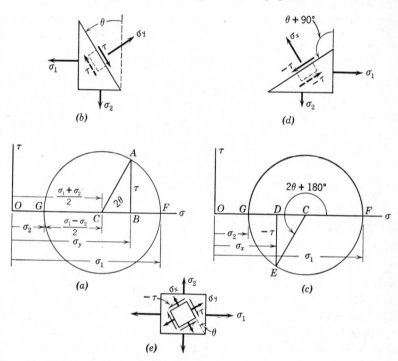

Fig. 24 Mohr's circle for obtaining stresses on any plane in terms of principal stresses.

principal stresses at the point; that is, it will be used for the solution of Eqs. 11 and 13.

In Fig. 24a let ordinates represent shearing stress, and abscissas normal stress on any plane making an angle θ with the direction of the plane on which principal stress σ_1 acts (Fig. 24b). Lay off the principal stresses σ_1 and σ_2 represented by OF and OG. It is customary to consider tensile stresses as positive and to lay them off to the right, whereas compressive stresses are considered to be negative and laid off to the left. Construct a circle having its center C on the σ axis and its diameter GF; that is, the center C is at a distance $\frac{1}{2}(\sigma_1 + \sigma_2)$ from the origin, and the circle has a radius equal to $\frac{1}{2}(\sigma_1 - \sigma_2)$.

If a radius CA is drawn, making an angle 2θ with the σ axis, the co-ordinates of the point A on the circumference represent the shearing and normal stresses existing on the plane making an angle θ (Fig. 24b) with the plane on which σ_1 acts. For, from Fig. 24a and from Eqs. 11 and 13 we obtain

$$AB = AC \sin 2\theta = \frac{\sigma_1 - \sigma_2}{2} \sin 2\theta = \tau \qquad (14)$$

$$OB = OC + CB = \frac{\sigma_1 + \sigma_2}{2} + \frac{\sigma_1 - \sigma_2}{2} \cos 2\theta = \sigma_y \qquad (15)$$

If in Fig. 24c a radius is drawn making an angle $2\theta + 180°$ with the σ axis, the coordinates of the point E on the circumference represent the normal and shearing stresses on a plane making an angle of $\theta + 90°$ with the plane on which σ_1 acts as indicated in Fig. 24d. For, from Fig. 24c and from substitution of $(\theta + 90°)$ for the angle θ in Eqs. 11 and 13, we obtain

$$DE = CE \sin (2\theta + 180°) = -\frac{\sigma_1 - \sigma_2}{2} \sin 2\theta = -\tau \qquad (16)$$

$$OD = OC - CD = \frac{\sigma_1 + \sigma_2}{2} - \frac{\sigma_1 - \sigma_2}{2} \cos 2\theta = \sigma_x \qquad (17)$$

Figure 24e shows the stresses σ_x, σ_y, and τ at the given point in the stressed body; the stresses act on two perpendicular planes through the given point making an angle θ with the planes on which the principal stresses σ_1 and σ_2 act.

Sign of τ. The direction of τ (the sign of τ) on any plane can usually be determined by inspection, and hence a sign convention for shearing stress is not, in general, of great importance; moreover, usually the magnitude of τ is the desired quantity. In Fig. 24 the angles θ and 2θ have the same sense of rotation, but the magnitude of τ will be the same regardless of the direction in which 2θ is laid off. When it is necessary to distinguish between the shearing stresses on planes at right angles to each other, τ_{xy} is used to denote the shearing stress on a plane perpendicular to the X axis acting in a direction parallel to the Y axis. Likewise, τ_{yx} denotes the shearing stress on a plane perpendicular to the Y axis acting in a direction parallel to the X axis. As shown by Eqs. 11 and 16, $\tau_{xy} = -\tau_{yx}$. One useful way of interpreting the sign of a shearing stress at a point in a stressed body on any plane passing through the point (or on the face of an elementary block which co-incides with the plane) is to consider the shearing force on the face of the block as one force of a couple (the other force of the couple acting

on the opposite face of the block) as shown in Figs. 24b and 24d and to
consider the couple to be positive or negative, depending on the positive and negative senses of rotation, which may be selected arbitrarily.
In Fig. 24e the clockwise sense of rotation is considered to be positive.

Further Study of Mohr's Circle. Special Cases. It will be seen from
Fig. 24a that the coordinates of every point on the circumference of
Mohr's circle represent the shearing and normal stresses at a point in
a body on a plane that passes through the point and that makes an
angle θ with the plane on which a principal stress acts. The center of
Mohr's circle is always on the σ axis, and therefore the circle can always
be constructed if the coordinates of two points on its circumference are
known, that is, if the normal and shearing stresses are known at the
point in the body on two planes whose inclinations are θ_1 and θ_2 with
the plane on which σ_1 or σ_2 acts. This fact will be shown in the next
article. The student should study the changes that occur in OB and
AB of Fig. 24a as the angle θ increases from zero to 360°.

The construction and interpretation of Mohr's circle for two important
states of biaxial stress deserve further attention. Figure 25a shows at a
point two principal stresses σ_1 and σ_2 (the third is zero), where $\sigma_1 = -\sigma_2$.
This combination of stresses has already been described in Art. 17 and
in Figs. 20 and 21 and has been shown to be equivalent to pure shear as
indicated in Fig. 25c. Mohr's circle for the principal stresses given in
Fig. 25a is shown in Fig. 25b; it should be noted that the coordinates of
the points D and E represent the maximum shearing stresses $\tau_{\max}$ and
that there are no normal (tensile or compressive) stresses on these planes.

Another state of biaxial stress of special interest is shown in Fig. 25d
in which σ_1 and σ_2 are equal tensions such as occur in the shell of a thin-
walled spherical pressure vessel (the third principal stress is approximately zero). Mohr's circle for these two principal stresses has a radius
of zero and is referred to as a "point circle"; it is shown by the point C
in Fig. 25e. Thus in Fig. 25b the points A, B, D, E, and all other
points on the circumference of the circle coincide with the point C in
Fig. 25e. This fact means that the normal stresses on all planes perpendicular to the plane containing the vectors representing σ_1 and σ_2 are
equal to σ_1 or σ_2, and that the shearing stresses on all these planes is
zero. Thus the state of stress in the plane of the vectors σ_1 and σ_2 in
Fig. 25d is equivalent to tensile stresses equal to σ_1 or σ_2 in all directions, as shown in Fig. 25f. It should be noted that the maximum shear-
ing stress is not zero but is equal to $\frac{1}{2}\sigma_1$ or $\frac{1}{2}\sigma_2$ since the minimum
principal stress is zero.

Furthermore, by constructing Mohr's circle as shown in Fig. 25g, a
state of stress consisting of two *unequal* principal stresses of *opposite*

sign as indicated in Fig. 25h (the third principal stress has the value zero) may be shown to be equivalent to two component states of stress in the plane of the principal stresses as illustrated in Fig. 25i, namely, a state of pure shear in which the shearing stresses are $\tau_{max} = (\sigma_1 - \sigma_2)/2$

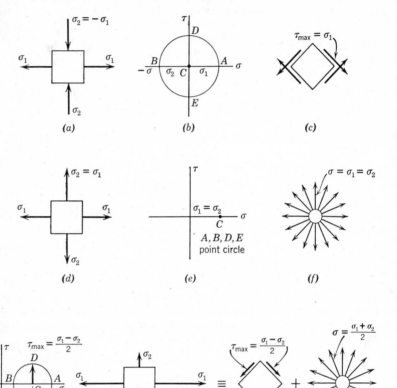

FIG. 25   Mohr's circle for special states of stress.

and a state of equal tensile stress $\sigma = (\sigma_1 + \sigma_2)/2$ in all directions in the plane.

One advantage of resolving the given state of stress into these two component states of stress is that inelastic action or yielding in a material is usually associated with a state of pure shear, whereas fracture, accompanied by little or no yielding, tends to result from a state of stress consisting of equal or nearly equal tensile stresses, especially if the stresses are triaxial tensions. However, when the equal tensile stresses are biaxial (the third principal stress is equal to zero) the material usually will yield rather than fracture, owing to the shearing stresses that develop on planes inclined 45° to the plane of the two principal stresses. Thus one disadvantage of the foregoing procedure for studying the effect of the principal stresses at a point on the type of action (yielding or brittle fracture) that is likely to take place is that only two principal stresses at a time may be considered; that is, the effects of shearing stresses on planes inclined to the plane of the two principal stresses considered are ignored. In the next article Mohr's circle for three principal stresses will be discussed and a method of finding the shearing stresses on the octahedral planes passing through the point will be given; this will make it possible to include the effect of all three principal stresses in one step.

Problems

9. Two principal stresses at a point consist of a tensile stress $\sigma_1 = 4000$ lb per sq in. and a compressive stress $\sigma_2 = 2000$ lb per sq in.; the third principal stress is zero. Determine the maximum shearing stress by using Mohr's circle, and show the planes on which it acts.

10. Construct Mohr's circle for a state of stress at a point in a body in which two principal stresses are zero and the third is a tensile stress σ_1 (a one-dimensional or uniaxial state of stress). Show by the use of the circle that the maximum shearing stress is equal in magnitude to one-half of the principal stress.

11. Show by the use of Mohr's circle that, for a state of two-dimensional stress at a point at which the two principal stresses σ_1 and σ_2 are equal tensile stresses and the third principal stress is zero, the maximum shearing stress is equal to $\frac{1}{2}\sigma_1$ or $\frac{1}{2}\sigma_2$.

12. A cylindrical boiler 6 ft in diameter is made of plates ¾ in. thick and is subjected to an internal steam pressure of 200 lb per sq in. Find by the use of Mohr's circle the maximum shearing stress in the plate and draw a sketch showing the planes on which it acts.

Ans. $\tau_{max} = 4900$ lb/in.².

13. Let it be assumed that the bending stress on any vertical section of the beam in Fig. 26 is distributed in accordance with the flexure formula as indicated. Show that the maximum tensile stress σ at a point on the top surface of the beam is $\sigma = \sigma_1/\cos^2\theta = Mc/(I\cos^2\theta)$. Thus $\sigma = 2\sigma_1$ when $\theta = 45°$.

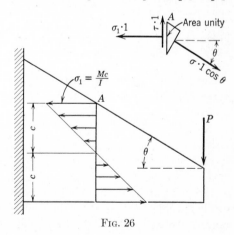

Fig. 26

14. A gun barrel or thick-walled cylinder (Fig. 27) on which hoops are shrunk (not shown in Fig. 27) is subjected to an internal pressure of 50,000 lb per sq in. by the explosion of the charge; the maximum radial compressive stress σ_r in the material on the inner surface of the gun is, then, 50,000 lb per sq in. If the maximum circumferential stress σ_t is 16,000 lb per sq in. and occurs at the same point in the cylinder as does σ_r, find by means of Mohr's circle the maximum shearing stress, and indicate the planes on which it occurs.   *Ans.* $\tau_{max} = 33,000$ lb/in.[2].

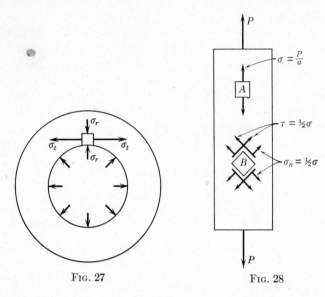

Fig. 27   Fig. 28

15. Show by use of Mohr's circle that when a bar is subjected to a central axial load P (Fig. 28) the normal stress σ_n on the 45° sections on which the maximum shearing stresses occur is $\frac{1}{2}(P/a)$, and hence σ_n is equal in magnitude to the maximum shearing stresses.

16. Show that the forces τ and σ_n acting on the faces (unit areas) of the cube B in Fig. 28 cause a stress on the horizontal diagonal plane through the cube equal to σ or P/a, and that the stress on a vertical plane through B is equal to zero.

22   Mohr's circle: shearing stress combined with two normal stresses.

At a point in a body let stresses that lie in one plane (two-dimensional stresses) consist of normal stresses and shearing stresses on two planes at right angles to each other; the shearing stresses are equal (Art. 17). This combination of stresses is illustrated by Fig. 29a where σ_x and σ_y are the normal stresses, and τ is the shearing stress. Let it be required to find the maximum and minimum normal (principal) stresses at the point and also the maximum shearing stress at the point.

This problem is solved by the use of Mohr's circle in Fig. 29b, where normal stresses are measured on the horizontal σ axis, tensile stress to the right and compressive stress to the left, and shearing stresses are measured on the vertical axis, positive shear (see Art. 21) upward and negative shear downward; the shearing stresses on the planes on which

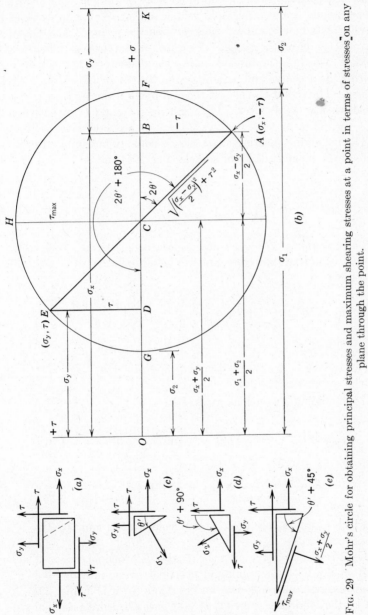

FIG. 29 Mohr's circle for obtaining principal stresses and maximum shearing stresses at a point in terms of stresses on any plane through the point.

σ_y act are positive since they form a clockwise couple. The coordinates of two points A and E on Mohr's circle are $(\sigma_x, -\tau)$ and (σ_y, τ), respectively. Mohr's circle must pass through the points A and E and also have its center on the σ axis. The center of the circle is therefore at the point C, which is the intersection of the diameter AE with the σ axis. With C as a center and a radius equal to CA or CE, Mohr's circle is drawn. The center C is also at the mid-point of the segment DB so that its abscissa is $(\sigma_x + \sigma_y)/2$. The segments CB and CD are each equal to $(\sigma_x - \sigma_y)/2$.

The maximum shearing stress $\tau_{\max}$ is equal in magnitude to the ordinate of the point H of Mohr's circle (Fig. 29b) and is

$$\tau_{\max} = CH = CA = \sqrt{\left(\frac{\sigma_x - \sigma_y}{2}\right)^2 + \tau^2} = \frac{1}{2}\sqrt{(\sigma_x - \sigma_y)^2 + 4\tau^2} \quad (18)$$

The principal stresses σ_1 and σ_2 are equal to the abscissas of the points F and G, respectively, and are found to be expressed algebraically as follows:

$$\sigma_1 = OF = OC + CF = \frac{\sigma_x + \sigma_y}{2} + \sqrt{\left(\frac{\sigma_x - \sigma_y}{2}\right)^2 + \tau^2}$$

$$= \frac{\sigma_x + \sigma_y}{2} + \frac{1}{2}\sqrt{(\sigma_x - \sigma_y)^2 + 4\tau^2} \quad (19)$$

and the minimum principal stress is

$$\sigma_2 = OG = OC - CG = \frac{\sigma_x + \sigma_y}{2} - \sqrt{\left(\frac{\sigma_x - \sigma_y}{2}\right)^2 + \tau^2}$$

$$= \frac{\sigma_x + \sigma_y}{2} - \frac{1}{2}\sqrt{(\sigma_x - \sigma_y)^2 + 4\tau^2} \quad (20)$$

in which σ_x and σ_y are positive if tensile stresses and negative if compressive stresses.

The stress σ_1 from Eq. 19 is the maximum principal stress. The stress σ_2 from Eq. 20 is the minimum principal stress, provided it is a compressive stress, but, if σ_2 is a tensile stress (as it is in Fig. 29a), it will not be the minimum principal stress, since the third principal stress is $\sigma_3 = 0$ and is the minimum principal stress in this case.

The principal stresses σ_1 and σ_2 are shown in Figs. 29c and 29d, respectively, acting on planes which make an angle of θ' and $\theta' + 90°$ with the plane upon which the normal stress σ_x acts, where the angle $\theta' = \frac{1}{2} \angle BCA$ in Fig. 29b. The angle θ' may be found from Fig. 29b by making use of the fact that

$$\tan 2\theta' = BA/CB = 2\tau/(\sigma_x - \sigma_y) \tag{21}$$

The maximum shearing stress $\tau_{\max}$ as shown by Fig. 29e acts on a plane making an angle of $\theta' + 45°$ (or $\theta' + 135°$) with the plane upon which σ_x acts, since the maximum shearing stress always acts upon planes making 45° with the planes on which the principal stress acts (see Art. 20). The sense of the angle θ' in Fig. 29 usually may be determined by inspection. The following sign convention, however, will give the sense of θ'. The angle θ' will be laid off counterclockwise or clockwise from the right face of the element, depending upon whether σ_x is a tensile or a compressive stress and whether τ acts upward or downward on this face; for example, if σ_x is a tensile stress, θ' will be measured counterclockwise for τ acting upward on the right face, and clockwise if τ acts downward on this face. If σ_x is a compressive stress, θ' will be clockwise for τ acting upward and counterclockwise for τ acting downward.

Shearing Stress Combined with One Normal Stress. Many problems involve the combination of shearing stress with only one normal stress, that is, a shearing stress τ occurs on each of two planes at right angles to each other and a normal stress σ_x (or σ) on one of the two planes, the normal stress σ_y on the other plane being zero. Mohr's circle is constructed as previously outlined. The point E in Fig. 29b will have the coordinates $(0, \tau)$, since $\sigma_y = 0$. The maximum shearing stress obtained from Eq. 18 by letting $\sigma_y = 0$ and setting $\sigma_x = \sigma$ is

$$\tau_{\max} = \sqrt{(\sigma/2)^2 + \tau^2} = \tfrac{1}{2}\sqrt{\sigma^2 + 4\tau^2} \tag{22}$$

The principal stresses are obtained in a similar manner from Eqs. 19 and 20. The maximum principal stress is

$$\sigma_1 = \sigma/2 + \sqrt{(\sigma/2)^2 + \tau^2} = \sigma/2 + \tfrac{1}{2}\sqrt{\sigma^2 + 4\tau^2} \tag{23}$$

and the minimum principal stress is

$$\sigma_2 = \sigma/2 - \sqrt{(\sigma/2)^2 + \tau^2} = \sigma/2 - \tfrac{1}{2}\sqrt{\sigma^2 + 4\tau^2} \tag{24}$$

Problem

17. Find by Mohr's circle as illustrated by Fig. 29b the magnitude of the maximum and minimum principal stresses and the direction of the plane on which each acts; also find the magnitude of the maximum shearing stress and the direction of the planes on which it acts, for each of the combinations of stresses shown in Fig. 30.

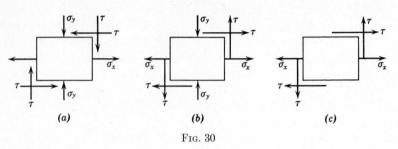

Fig. 30

Check these values by means of Eqs. 18, 19, 20, and 21. In Figs. 30a and 30b the magnitudes of the stresses are as follows: $\sigma_x = 12,000$ lb per sq in., $\sigma_y = 4000$ lb per sq in., and $\tau = 8000$ lb per sq in. In Fig. 30c σ_x and τ are the same as in Fig. 30b, and $\sigma_y = 0$.

General Problems for Review

18. When the maximum principal stress is considered to be the significant stress in a cylindrical bar subjected to combined bending and torsion, it is sometimes convenient to transform the problem to an equivalent problem in which the member is subjected to bending only. The bending moment to which the member must be subjected in order to produce a bending stress equal to the maximum normal stress (principal stress) in the actual member is called an *equivalent bending moment* and is denoted by M_e. Show that if $M_e = \frac{1}{2}(M + \sqrt{M^2 + T^2})$, where M and T are the actual bending and torsional moments, respectively, to which the member is subjected, the maximum principal stress may be computed by means of the flexure formula $\sigma_1 = M_e c/I$.

19. When the maximum shearing stress is considered to be the significant stress in a cylindrical bar subjected to combined bending and torsion, it is sometimes convenient to consider the member to be subjected to torsion only. The torsional moment to which the member must be subjected in order to produce a shearing stress equal to the maximum shearing stress in the actual member is called the *equivalent torsional moment*, denoted by T_e. Show that, if $T_e = \sqrt{M^2 + T^2}$, where T and M are the actual torsional and bending moments, respectively, to which the member is subjected, the maximum shearing stress in the shaft may be computed by the formula $\tau_{\max} = T_e c/J$.

20. The pressures on the crank pins of the main driving axle (Fig. 31) of a certain type of locomotive are 98,000 lb, and the vertical loads at A and B are 27,000 lb. The forces acting on the axles and wheels are shown in Fig. 31. Find the maximum normal and shearing stresses at any section between A and B; assume the diameter of the axle to be 10.5 in. *Note:* The bearings are assumed to fit loosely on the crank pins, and hence the pressure P of the parallel rod on the right-hand pin could temporarily be zero. Furthermore, the friction under this wheel could be very small, owing to grease or frost on the rail. Therefore, the most severe condition of stress between A and B should be assumed to be produced by the forces in Fig. 31 when F and P on the right-hand side are zero and the friction of the left-hand side is sufficient to prevent the wheels from slipping.

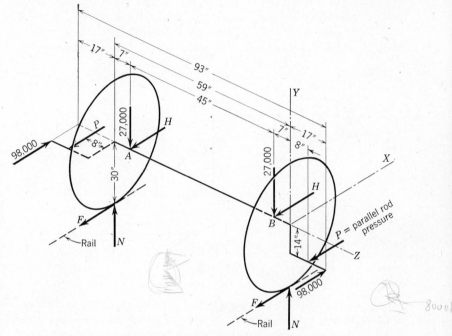

FIG. 31   Forces acting on locomotive driving wheels and axle.

21. A steel shaft 4 in. in diameter is subjected to an axial end thrust of 12 tons, and also a bending moment of 8000 lb-ft and a twisting moment of 10,000 lb-ft. Find the maximum numerical values of the normal and shearing stresses in the shaft.
$$Ans. \quad \sigma_{max} = 21,500 \text{ lb/in.}^2; \tau_{max} = 12,900 \text{ lb/in.}^2.$$

22. A shaft 5 in. in diameter resists a bending moment of 120 ton-in. and a twisting moment of 70 ton-in. Find the magnitude of the maximum normal and shearing stresses.
$$Ans. \quad \sigma_{max} = 10.5 \text{ tons/in.}^2; \tau_{max} = 5.66 \text{ tons/in.}^2.$$

23. In which of the two following shafts is the greater normal stress developed, and in which is the greater shearing stress developed? Determine the maximum stresses in each shaft. (a) A 4-in. shaft subjected to a twisting moment of 40 ton in. and a bending moment of 32 ton in. (b) A 2-in. shaft subjected to a twisting moment of 7.0 ton-in. and a bending moment of 20 ton-in.

24. In Prob. 22 let the shaft be subjected to an axial tensile load of 80 tons in addition to the bending and twisting moments. Find the magnitudes of the maximum principal stress and the maximum shearing stress.

23   Mohr's circle for three-dimensional stress. In the preceding articles a plane (biaxial or two-dimensional) state of stress was assumed to exist. In some problems, however, the stresses do not all lie in one plane, and hence the third principal stress is not zero. Such a state of stress is referred to as a triaxial or three-dimensional state of stress. When the three principal stresses are equal in magnitude and alike in sign, the triaxial state of stress is sometimes referred to as a polar-symmetric state of stress, or equiaxial state of stress. Figure 32a represents a three-dimensional state of stress at the point O in a stressed body in which the three principal stresses σ_1, σ_2, and σ_3 at the point O

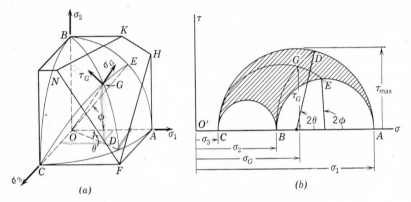

(a)   (b)

Fig. 32   Mohr's circle for three-dimensional stress.

are shown perpendicular to the faces of an elemental cube. Let σ_1 be greater than σ_2, and σ_2 greater than σ_3 (algebraically), where a tensile stress is considered to be positive and a compressive stress negative.

Let it be required to find by means of Mohr's circle, the normal and shearing stress at the point O on some plane whose direction is neither parallel nor perpendicular to either of the three principal stress axes. Such a plane is represented by $FHKN$ in Fig. 32a, the direction of which is indicated by making the plane tangent to a quadrant of a spherical surface inscribed in the elemental cube. Let OG be perpendicular to the plane $FHKN$, and let σ_G and τ_G represent the normal and shearing stresses, respectively, on the plane $FHKN$ which are to be determined. The direction of OG is determined by passing, through G, planes $OBGD$ and $OCGE$ which cut arcs of great circles BGD and CGE. The plane of arc BGD makes the angle θ with the σ_1 axis, and the plane of arc CGE makes the angle ϕ with the σ_1 axis.* The circular arcs AEB and ADC lie in the faces of the elemental cube.

* In Fig. 32a if l, m, and n are the direction cosines of the line OG, which is perpendicular to the plane on which τ_G and σ_G act, then $l = m/\tan \theta = n/\tan \phi$ will define the direction of OG with respect to the σ_1, σ_2, and σ_3 axes, respectively.

In Fig. 32*b* the principal stresses are laid off from the origin O' on the σ axis, tensile stresses to the right and compressive stresses to the left. Mohr's circles (half-circles) are drawn with AB, BC, and AC on the σ axis as diameters. For example, the τ and σ coordinates of points on the semicircles ADC and AEB in Fig. 32*b* represent the shearing and normal stresses on all planes tangent to the sphere in Fig. 32*a* along the arcs ADC and AEB, respectively; the shearing and normal stresses on the plane tangent to the sphere at D in Fig. 32*a* are given by the coordinates of D in Fig. 32*b*, and the shearing and normal stresses on the plane tangent to the sphere at E in Fig. 32*a* are given by the coordinates of E in Fig. 32*b*. Thus if Mohr's circles are constructed in Fig. 32*b* to represent stresses on planes tangent at points along arcs BGD and CGE in Fig. 32*a*, these circles should intersect in Fig. 32*b* at the point G, whose coordinates will represent τ_G and σ_G, which are the stresses required to be determined.

Since Mohr's circle may be constructed if the normal and shearing stresses on two planes through a point are known (see Art. 21), the circles for locating G may be constructed in the following manner: In Fig. 32*b* a circle is drawn through the points B and D with its center on the σ axis, and a circle is drawn through the points C and E with its center on the σ axis. These circular arcs intersect at point G, which corresponds to the point G in Fig. 32*a*. The coordinates τ_G and σ_G of the point G in Fig. 32*b* are the shearing and normal stresses, respectively, on the plane $FHKN$ in Fig. 32*a*.

It will be seen that for all possible values of the angles θ and ϕ the point G lies either inside the shaded area in Fig. 32*b* or on the circumferences of the semicircles whose diameters are AB, BC, and AC, and, if both θ and ϕ are equal to zero, the point G coincides with the point A in each diagram of Fig. 32. If $\theta = 45°$ and $\phi = 0°$, the point G is at the uppermost point of the semicircle AC and gives the maximum shearing stress $\tau_{\max}$.

24 Octahedral stresses. If in Fig. 32*a* the angles θ and ϕ are taken equal to 45°, the perpendicular OG to the plane $FHKN$ will make equal angles with the direction of the principal stresses. Such a plane is shown in Fig. 33*a* and is an *octahedral* plane; the normal and shearing stresses on this plane are called *octahedral stresses*.

Equations for the octahedral stresses may be derived by the procedure outlined in Art. 16; this is done in the next paragraph. The normal stress σ_G on an octahedral plane is found to be

$$\sigma_G = \tfrac{1}{3}(\sigma_1 + \sigma_2 + \sigma_3) \tag{25}$$

which is the average of the three principal stresses. The shearing stress

τ_G on an octahedral plane is found to be

$$\tau_G = \tfrac{1}{3}\sqrt{(\sigma_1 - \sigma_2)^2 + (\sigma_2 - \sigma_3)^2 + (\sigma_3 - \sigma_1)^2} \qquad (26)$$

The octahedral stresses may be obtained by use of Mohr's circles as shown in Fig. 33b; the construction is performed by the procedure outlined in Art. 23 by making $\theta = \phi = 45°$. The octahedral shearing stress

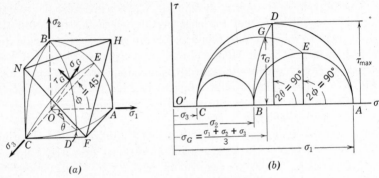

(a) (b)

FIG. 33   Mohr's circle for octahedral stresses.

for a state of uniaxial stress, as occurs in the standard tensile test, is found from Eq. 26 to be

$$\tau_G = (\sqrt{2}/3)\sigma = 0.47\sigma \qquad (27)$$

in which $\sigma = P/a$.

Proof of Expressions for Octahedral Stresses. Let Fig. 34a represent a unit volume at a point in a body at which there is one principal stress σ_1. The block is cut by the octahedral plane ABC and a free-body diagram of the tetrahedron $OABC$ is constructed as shown in Fig. 34b. The forces on the faces of the tetrahedron are $\tfrac{1}{2}\sigma_1$, $(\sqrt{3}/2)\sigma_G$, and $(\sqrt{3}/2)\tau_G$, where σ_G and τ_G are the normal and shearing stresses on the octahedral plane. The three forces lie in the plane OBG. The equations of equilibrium for this system of forces are $\Sigma F_x = 0$ and $\Sigma F_y = 0$. Thus

$$\Sigma F_x = (\sqrt{3}/2)\tau_G - (\sqrt{2}/\sqrt{3}) \cdot \tfrac{1}{2}\sigma_1 = 0 \qquad (28)$$

and therefore $\tau_G = (\sqrt{2}/3)\sigma_1 \qquad (29)$

$$\Sigma F_y = (\sqrt{3}/2)\sigma_G - (1/\sqrt{3}) \cdot \tfrac{1}{2}\sigma_1 = 0 \qquad (30)$$

and hence $\sigma_G = \tfrac{1}{3}\sigma_1 \qquad (31)$

If principal stresses σ_2 and σ_3 act on the two other faces of the unit volume in Fig. 34a, it can be shown, in a similar manner, that normal stresses σ_G having the values $\tfrac{1}{3}\sigma_2$ and $\tfrac{1}{3}\sigma_3$, respectively, will be produced on the plane ABC. Hence, the three principal stresses σ_1, σ_2, and σ_3 will produce a stress normal to the octahedral plane of

$$\sigma_G = \tfrac{1}{3}(\sigma_1 + \sigma_2 + \sigma_3) \tag{32}$$

Also, the additional principal stresses σ_2 and σ_3 will produce shearing stresses in the octahedral plane whose values are $(\sqrt{2}/3)\sigma_2$ and $(\sqrt{2}/3)\sigma_3$, respectively. These stresses will lie along the lines GA and GC. If these three octahedral shearing stresses are multiplied by the area of the octahedral plane $\sqrt{3}/2$, the three shearing forces obtained

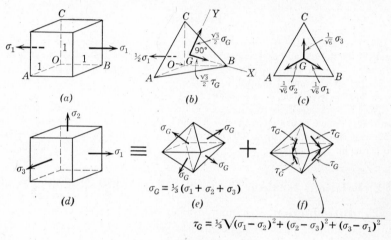

$$\sigma_G = \tfrac{1}{3}(\sigma_1 + \sigma_2 + \sigma_3)$$
$$\tau_G = \tfrac{1}{3}\sqrt{(\sigma_1 - \sigma_2)^2 + (\sigma_2 - \sigma_3)^2 + (\sigma_3 - \sigma_1)^2}$$

Fig. 34

constitute a coplanar system as shown in Fig. 34c, which may be combined into a single shearing force $(\sqrt{3}/2)\tau_G$, in which τ_G is the resultant octahedral shearing stress. Equating this expression for the resultant force to the resultant of the three forces shown in Fig. 34c gives

$$\tau_G = \tfrac{1}{3}\sqrt{(\sigma_1 - \sigma_2)^2 + (\sigma_2 - \sigma_3)^2 + (\sigma_3 - \sigma_1)^2} \tag{33}$$

Significance of Octahedral Stresses. In Art. 21 it was shown that any two principal stresses can be resolved into two component states of stress, one of which consists of the maximum shearing stresses which constitute a state of pure shear, and the other a system of equal tensions in all directions in the plane of the two principal stresses. It is now possible by using Mohr's circle for three principal stresses to resolve a system of three-dimensional stresses into two systems acting on the eight octahedral planes. One system consists of the shearing stresses τ_G, and the other system the equal normal stresses σ_G, on the octahedral planes as shown by Figs. 34d, 34e, and 34f. The normal stresses σ_G on the eight octahedral planes are equivalent to a system of equal tensile stresses σ_G in all directions, that is, normal to all possible tangent planes to a sphere inscribed in the cubical element in Fig. 34d. Such a system of equal tensile (or compressive) stresses cannot be associated with yielding or inelastic action, but may be the cause of fracture. Thus the shearing stresses τ_G on the eight octahedral planes are associated with yielding or inelastic action. The significance of the octahedral stresses are discussed more fully later in this chapter in connection with the energy of distortion theory of failure.

Problems

25. Find graphically by the use of Mohr's circle (a) the maximum shearing stress and (b) the normal and shearing stresses on the octahedral planes for the following states of stress in which all stresses are expressed in pounds per square inch. (1) Principal stresses are $\sigma_1 = 6000$, $\sigma_2 = 3000$, $\sigma_3 = 1000$. (2) Principal stresses are $\sigma_1 = 3000$, $\sigma_2 = -1000$, $\sigma_3 = -4000$.

26. Find graphically by use of Mohr's circle the normal and shearing stresses on an oblique plane such that angle $\theta = 30°$ and angle $\phi = 45°$ (see Fig. 32a) for the following state of stress: $\sigma_1 = 4000$ lb per sq in., $\sigma_2 = 1000$ lb per sq in., $\sigma_3 = -5000$ lb per sq in.

§ 2 Relations between Elastic Stresses and Strains at a Point

25 Introduction. In many structural and machine members it may be difficult or even impossible to calculate the stresses. In such cases it is sometimes possible to make measurements of the strains in the member, and, from the relationships existing between the strains and the stresses, the stresses may be calculated. The assumption that there is a definite relationship between stress and strain restricts the condition in the material mainly to that of elastic behavior which is usually characterized by a single-valued, linear relationship between stress and strain. If inelastic action occurs, the stress is dependent not on the strain alone but also on other factors such as strain rate, temperature, time, etc., as discussed in Part V.

It is the purpose of this section to present the relationships between the stresses and elastic strains at a point in a stressed body. These relationships involve certain properties of the material of which the body is made, such as Poisson's ratio, the modulus of elasticity for uniaxial stress, the shearing modulus of elasticity, and the bulk modulus of elasticity for triaxial stress.

Poisson's Ratio. If a bar is subjected to an axial tensile load, the bar is elongated in the direction of the load, that is, in the longitudinal direction, and at the same time the lateral dimension of the bar decreases.

The ratio of the lateral linear strain to the longitudinal linear strain within the elastic behavior of the material is called Poisson's ratio; it will be denoted by the symbol μ. The value for this ratio for steel is approximately $\frac{1}{4}$; values of $\frac{1}{4}$ to $\frac{1}{3}$ are frequently used. It should be recalled that linear strain means the change of dimension (deformation) *per unit length* of the dimension that is changed.

26 Elastic strains in terms of normal stresses on perpendicular planes. *Biaxial Stress.* If a rectangular elementary block of homogeneous, isotropic material is subjected to uniformly distributed stresses on two pairs of opposite faces (Fig. 35)—tensile stresses σ_1 on one pair and tensile stresses σ_2 on the other—the elastic strain in the direction of σ_1 caused by σ_1 if acting alone would be $\epsilon_1 = \sigma_1/E$; the strain ϵ_2 in the direction of σ_2 caused by σ_2 if acting alone would be $\epsilon_2 = \sigma_2/E$; and the strain ϵ'_1 in the direction of σ_1 caused by σ_2 is $\epsilon'_1 = \mu(\sigma_2/E)$, in which the modulus of elasticity E is assumed to be the same in compression as in tension. The total elastic strain in the direction of σ_1 is then assumed to be

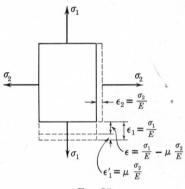

Fig. 35

$$\epsilon = (\sigma_1/E) - \mu(\sigma_2/E) \qquad (34)$$

in which a tensile stress is considered to be positive and a compressive stress negative. The strain ϵ as given by Eq. 34 will be the maximum strain at the point if σ_1 and σ_2 are, respectively, the maximum and minimum principal stresses at the point.

Shearing Stress Combined with One Normal Stress. If at a point the known or "given" stresses consist of shearing stresses on two perpendicular planes and a normal stress on one of the planes, as discussed in Art. 22, it is sometimes convenient to express the maximum strain at the point in terms of those "given" stresses. This may be done as follows: The "given" state of stress is equivalent to two principal stresses as indicated in Fig. 36 and proved in Art. 22. Thus, from Eqs. 23, 24, and 34 the elastic strain, in the direction of the principal stress σ_1, is

$$\epsilon = (1/E)[\tfrac{1}{2}\sigma + \tfrac{1}{2}\sqrt{\sigma^2 + 4\tau^2} - \mu(\tfrac{1}{2}\sigma - \tfrac{1}{2}\sqrt{\sigma^2 + 4\tau^2})] \qquad (35)$$

$$\epsilon = (1/E)[\tfrac{1}{2}(1 - \mu)\sigma + \tfrac{1}{2}(1 + \mu)\sqrt{\sigma^2 + 4\tau^2}] \qquad (36)$$

For steel the value of μ found from experimental results is 0.25 to 0.30. Thus for steel Eq. 36 becomes

$$\epsilon = (1/E)(\tfrac{3}{8}\sigma + \tfrac{5}{8}\sqrt{\sigma^2 + 4\tau^2}) \qquad \text{if } \mu = 0.25 \tag{37}$$

$$\epsilon = (1/E)(0.35\sigma + 0.65\sqrt{\sigma^2 + 4\tau^2}) \qquad \text{if } \mu = 0.30 \tag{38}$$

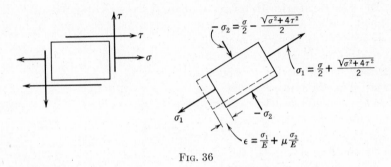

FIG. 36

Triaxial Stress. Similarly, if at a point in a stressed body three normal stresses act on mutually perpendicular planes through the point, the strains in the direction of these stresses are

$$\epsilon_1 = \frac{\sigma_1}{E} - \frac{\mu\sigma_2}{E} - \frac{\mu\sigma_3}{E}$$

$$\epsilon_2 = \frac{\sigma_2}{E} - \frac{\mu\sigma_3}{E} - \frac{\mu\sigma_1}{E} \tag{39}$$

$$\epsilon_3 = \frac{\sigma_3}{E} - \frac{\mu\sigma_1}{E} - \frac{\mu\sigma_2}{E}$$

respectively, in which tensile stresses are to be considered as positive and compressive stresses as negative. If σ_1, σ_2, and σ_3 are the principal stresses, the strain given by Eqs. 39 will be the principal strains, one of which will be the maximum strain at the point.

Experimental verification of the assumed law giving the relation between stresses and strains at a point in a material is difficult to obtain, but there are no reasons for doubting the correctness of the law for homogeneous, isotropic, elastic (ideal) material. In an actual material, however, the law should be considered to represent the stress-strain behavior in a finite portion of the material including the point rather than at the point. But, as pointed out in Chapter 1, average values of stress and strain over finite dimensions may be the significant values for many uses of materials, especially of ductile material subjected to static loads.

27   Relation between moduli of elasticity. The relation between the shearing and tensile moduli of elasticity (denoted by G and E, respectively) for ideal elastic material is

$$G = \frac{E}{2(1 + \mu)} \tag{40}$$

By definition $G = \tau/\gamma$, where γ is the elastic shearing strain accompanying the shearing stress τ, and similarly $E = \sigma/\epsilon$. Equation 40 may be derived as follows. Let an elementary block be subjected to two principal stresses of equal intensity and opposite sign ($\sigma_1 = \sigma$, and $\sigma_2 = -\sigma$) as indicated in Fig. 37. From Art. 20 it is evident that shearing stresses,

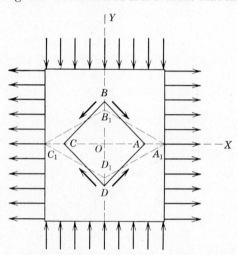

FIG. 37   Shearing strains accompanying principal stresses.

only, exist on planes making 45° with the X and Y axes. By definition the elastic shearing strain γ at any point is the change in a right angle at the point such as angle BAD, that is

$$\gamma = \text{angle } BAD - \text{angle } B_1A_1D_1 \tag{41}$$

and this shearing strain may be expressed in terms of the linear strains ϵ_x and ϵ_y in the x and y directions by the equation

$$\epsilon_x = AA_1/OA \qquad \text{and} \qquad \epsilon_y = BB_1/OB \qquad \text{angle } B_1A_1D_1 = (\pi/2) - \gamma \tag{42}$$

$$\text{Thus} \quad \tan \frac{1}{2} \angle B_1A_1D_1 = \tan\left(\frac{\pi}{4} - \frac{\gamma}{2}\right) = \frac{OB_1}{OA_1} = \frac{OB - BB_1}{OA + AA_1}$$

$$= \frac{1 + (BB_1/OB)}{1 + (AA_1/OA)} = \frac{1 - \epsilon_y}{1 + \epsilon_x} \tag{43}$$

From Eq. 34 we have

$$\epsilon_x = \frac{\sigma}{E} + \mu\frac{\sigma}{E} \quad \text{and} \quad -\epsilon_y = -\frac{\sigma}{E} - \mu\frac{\sigma}{E} \quad \text{or} \quad \epsilon_y = \frac{\sigma}{E} + \mu\frac{\sigma}{E}$$

$$(44)$$

But from trigonometry and from Eqs. 42 and 44 we obtain

$$\tan\left(\frac{\pi}{4} - \frac{\gamma}{2}\right) = \frac{1 - \tan(\gamma/2)}{1 + \tan(\gamma/2)} = \frac{1 - (\sigma/E)(1 + \mu)}{1 + (\sigma/E)(1 + \mu)} \quad (45)$$

Therefore, since for a small angle the tangent of the angle is approximately equal to the angle, we find from Eq. 45 that

$$\gamma = \frac{2(1 + \mu)\sigma}{E} \quad (46)$$

and, since $\sigma = \tau$, Eq. 46 becomes $\tau/\gamma = E/[2(1 + \mu)]$, and hence $G = E/[2(1 + \mu)]$. If μ for steel is taken to be $\frac{1}{4}$, the equation becomes $G = \frac{2}{5}E$, and thus, if $E = 30{,}000{,}000$ lb per sq in., $G = 12{,}000{,}000$ lb per sq in.

Bulk Modulus of Elasticity. The change in volume per unit of volume at any point of a body subjected to stresses is directly proportional to the algebraic sum of the three principal stresses. The ratio of the average of the principal stresses to the change of volume per unit volume is called the bulk modulus of elasticity. Let a unit volume of material be subjected to the principal stresses σ_1, σ_2, and σ_3 uniformly distributed over the faces (see Fig. 42a). All three stresses are here assumed to be tensile stresses and to be positive. The strains that accompany the stresses σ_1, σ_2, and σ_3 are ϵ_1, ϵ_2, and ϵ_3. The volume of the unit cube after it has been strained is $(1 + \epsilon_1)(1 + \epsilon_2)(1 + \epsilon_3)$, so that, if ϵ_v represents the change in volume of the unit volume due to straining, we have

$$1 + \epsilon_v = (1 + \epsilon_1)(1 + \epsilon_2)(1 + \epsilon_3) = 1 + \epsilon_1 + \epsilon_2 + \epsilon_3$$

in which the products of the strains are considered to be very small and are neglected. Hence

$$\epsilon_v = \epsilon_1 + \epsilon_2 + \epsilon_3 \quad (47)$$

Thus from Eq. 47 the change in volume per unit of volume is equal to the algebraic sum of the three principal strains.

An equation giving the relation between the volume change ϵ_v and the principal stresses can be found by substituting in Eq. 47 the sum of the three strains as found from Eq. 39; the equation thus formed is

$$\epsilon_v = \epsilon_1 + \epsilon_2 + \epsilon_3 = \frac{1 - 2\mu}{E}(\sigma_1 + \sigma_2 + \sigma_3) \quad (48)$$

From Eq. 48 the volume change is seen to be directly proportional to the algebraic sum of the principal stresses. If instead of the algebraic sum of the principal stresses we take the average value of the principal stresses as $\sigma_{avg} = \frac{1}{3}(\sigma_1 + \sigma_2 + \sigma_3)$, then Eq. 48 becomes

$$E_v = \frac{\sigma_{avg}}{\epsilon_v} = \frac{E}{3(1 - 2\mu)} = \frac{2}{3} G \frac{1 + \mu}{1 - 2\mu} \qquad (49)$$

This constant ratio E_v between the average value σ_{avg} of the three principal stresses and ϵ_v, the volume change per unit of volume, is called the *modulus of elasticity of volume* or the *bulk modulus of elasticity*. It will be used later in this chapter.

Limits of the Values of Poisson's Ratio. Equations 40 and 49 determine the minimum and maximum possible values of Poisson's ratio. In Eq. 40 it will be seen that, as the value of μ approaches the value $\mu = -1$, the value of G approaches infinity and becomes negative as μ passes the value $\mu = -1$. Hence $\mu = -1$ is the minimum value of Poisson's ratio. In a similar manner from Eq. 49 it will be seen that the maximum value of Poisson's ratio is $\mu = \frac{1}{2}$, for at this value the bulk modulus of elasticity becomes infinity, and for $\mu > \frac{1}{2}$ the bulk modulus is negative.

Problems

27. Calculate the maximum strain at a point on the surface of the shaft described in Prob. 22. Assume the shaft to be made of steel for which $E = 30 \times 10^6$, $\mu = 0.25$.

28. Calculate the maximum strain at a point in a body at which the principal stresses are as described in Prob. 25. The material is aluminum for which $E = 10 \times 10^6$ and $\mu = 0.30$.

29. Calculate the maximum strain at a point on the inside surface of the steel gun barrel described in Prob. 14 and Fig. 27. $E = 30 \times 30^6$ and $\mu = 0.25$.

§ 3 Expressions for Elastic Strain Energy

28 Total elastic strain energy. The total elastic strain (potential) energy per unit of volume at a point in a stressed member involves both the stress and the strain at the point. It will be considered later to be made up of two component parts, namely, energy accompanying change in volume, and energy accompanying change of shape; the energy involved in change of shape will be considered to be the cause of structural damage resulting from inelastic action (yielding). The *total* energy at a point, however, will first be obtained as a single quantity in terms of the stresses and strains at the point for each of several states of stress.

Uniaxial Stress. Let a unit volume (unit cube) of material be subjected to a normal stress σ in one direction only, as indicated in Fig. 38. If the stress increases gradually from zero value and causes the cube to elongate an amount ϵ, the work done is $w = \frac{1}{2}\sigma\epsilon$, and, since within the proportional limit $\epsilon = \sigma/E$, the work done per unit volume in stressing the material to any value σ less than the elastic strength or proportional limit is

$$w = \tfrac{1}{2}(\sigma^2/E) \tag{50}$$

and hence the work done per unit volume in stressing the material up to the tensile or compressive proportional limit σ_e is

$$w = \tfrac{1}{2}(\sigma_e{}^2/E) \tag{51}$$

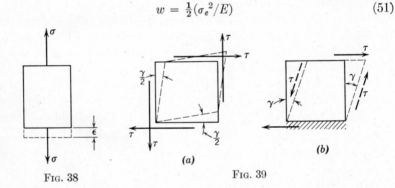

FIG. 38   (a)   (b)   FIG. 39

Pure Shear. Let a unit volume of a material be subjected to pure shear as indicated in Fig. 39a or as indicated more conveniently in Fig. 39b. The work done in gradually increasing the stress from zero to the value τ as the shearing strain increases to γ is

$$w = \tfrac{1}{2}\tau\gamma \tag{52}$$

and, if τ does not exceed the shearing proportional limit, $\gamma = \tau/G$, and hence the work done per unit volume in stressing the material in pure shear up to the shearing proportional limit τ_e is

$$w = \tfrac{1}{2}(\tau_e{}^2/G) \tag{53}$$

Shearing Stresses Combined with One Normal Stress. If a unit cube of material is stressed as indicated in Fig. 40, the work done per unit volume is the sum of the work done by the normal stress and the work done by the shearing stress, provided that the proportional limits in tension and shear are not exceeded so that the law of superposition may be applied. Hence

$$w = \tfrac{1}{2}(\sigma^2/E) + \tfrac{1}{2}(\tau^2/G) \tag{54}$$

Two Principal Stresses. If a unit volume of material is subjected to two principal stresses as shown in Fig. 41, the work done per unit volume may be found as follows. The strain in the direction of σ_1 is $\epsilon_1 = (\sigma_1/E) - \mu(\sigma_2/E)$ and the strain in the direction of σ_2 is $\epsilon_2 = (\sigma_2/E) - \mu(\sigma_1/E)$. Therefore, assuming that the stresses are applied gradually and that the law of superposition holds, the work done is

$$w = \tfrac{1}{2}\sigma_1\epsilon_1 + \tfrac{1}{2}\sigma_2\epsilon_2 \tag{55}$$

Hence $\qquad w = \tfrac{1}{2}(\sigma_1{}^2/E) + \tfrac{1}{2}(\sigma_2{}^2/E) - \mu(\sigma_1\sigma_2/E) \tag{56}$

in which a tensile stress is to be given a positive sign and a compressive stress a negative sign.

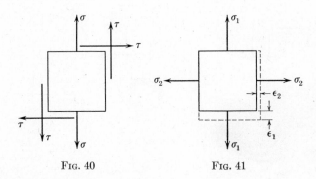

FIG. 40 FIG. 41

Three Principal Stresses. Similarly, if at a point three principal stresses σ_1, σ_2, and σ_3 exist, the work done per unit volume of material in producing these stresses is

$$w = (1/2E)(\sigma_1{}^2 + \sigma_2{}^2 + \sigma_3{}^2) - (\mu/E)(\sigma_1\sigma_2 + \sigma_1\sigma_3 + \sigma_2\sigma_3) \tag{57}$$

in which a tensile stress is to be taken as positive and a compressive stress as negative.

Problems

30. Show that Eq. 56 will reduce to Eq. 54 if the values of the principal stresses given by Eqs. 23 and 24 are substituted for σ_1 and σ_2 in Eq. 56.

31. Calculate the maximum work done per unit volume in the shaft described in Prob. 21; assume that $\mu = 0.25$.

32. Calculate the work done per unit volume at the inner surface of the gun described in Prob. 14; assume that $\mu = 0.25$. *Ans.* 52.6 in.-lb/in.^{3}.

29 Components of total elastic strain energy. The total strain energy per unit volume as given by Eq. 57 may be resolved into two component parts, one part associated with the change in volume of the unit volume and the other part associated with the (volume-constant) distortion or change in shape of the unit volume. For the purpose of resolving the total strain energy into these two parts, the three principal stresses σ_1, σ_2, and σ_3 as shown in Fig. 42a are resolved into two component states of stress as shown by Figs. 42b and 42c, such that in one of these component states the average of the three principal stresses σ_{avg} acts on each of the three faces of the element as shown by Fig. 42b, producing strains ϵ_{avg} in each direction equal to the average of the three principal strains ϵ_1, ϵ_2, and ϵ_3. The other component state as shown by Fig. 42c consists of the remainder of each of the three principal stresses (and also of each of the three principal strains). The average principal stress σ_{avg} produces the entire volume change of the unit cube; for from

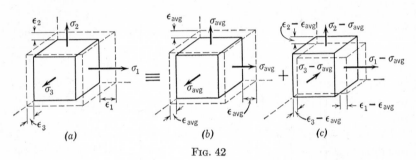

$$(a) \qquad\qquad (b) \qquad\qquad (c)$$

FIG. 42

Fig. 42b it will be seen that the sum of the three strains accompanying the average stress is $\epsilon_1 + \epsilon_2 + \epsilon_3$ which, according to Eq. 47, is equal to ϵ_v, which is the volume change per unit volume. The remaining components of the three principal stresses as shown in Fig. 42c do not produce any volume change since the sum of the three strains in Fig. 42c is equal to zero; but these three stresses do distort or change the shape of the unit cube. The sum of the strain energies produced by the two component states of stress as shown by Fig. 42b and Fig. 42c is equal to the total strain energy w as given by Eq. 57. Thus

$$w = w_v + w_d$$

where w_v is the energy of volume change per unit volume, and w_d is the energy of distortion per unit volume. The energy of volume change w_v is computed from the stresses and strains shown in Fig. 42b. The work done per unit volume to change the volume is

$$w_v = \tfrac{1}{2}\sigma_{\text{avg}}\epsilon_{\text{avg}} + \tfrac{1}{2}\sigma_{\text{avg}}\epsilon_{\text{avg}} + \tfrac{1}{2}\sigma_{\text{avg}}\epsilon_{\text{avg}} = \tfrac{1}{2}\sigma_{\text{avg}}\epsilon_v$$

Furthermore, Eq. 49 states that $\epsilon_v = \sigma_{\text{avg}}/E_v$. Therefore

$$w_v = \tfrac{1}{2}(\sigma_{\text{avg}}{}^2/E_v) \qquad\qquad (58)$$

The energy of distortion w_d may now be computed by subtracting the energy of volume change w_v in Eq. 58 from the total strain energy w as given in Eq. 57. Thus $w_d = w - w_v$.

$$w_d = \frac{1}{2E}(\sigma_1{}^2 + \sigma_2{}^2 + \sigma_3{}^2) - \frac{\mu}{E}(\sigma_1\sigma_2 + \sigma_1\sigma_3 + \sigma_2\sigma_3) - \frac{1}{2}\frac{\sigma^2{}_{\text{avg}}}{E_v} \quad (59)$$

But $\sigma_{\text{avg}} = \frac{1}{3}(\sigma_1 + \sigma_2 + \sigma_3)$ and $E_v = E/[3(1 - 2\mu)]$. Hence Eq. 59 reduces to

$$w_d = \frac{1 + \mu}{6E}[(\sigma_1 - \sigma_2)^2 + (\sigma_2 - \sigma_3)^2 + (\sigma_3 - \sigma_1)^2] \quad (60)$$

This energy of distortion as given by Eq. 60 is the elastic strain energy absorbed by the unit volume as a result of its change in shape (distortion). The strain energy of distortion has special significance in the theories of failure of material to be discussed in Art. 32. For subsequent use, expressions for w_d for three common states of stress are found as follows.

Uniaxial Stress. If a unit cube is subjected to a normal stress σ_1 in one direction only (the other two principal stresses are zero), such as in a tension specimen subjected to an axial load, Eq. 60 becomes

$$w_d = \frac{1 + \mu}{6E}(\sigma_1{}^2 + \sigma_1{}^2) = \frac{1 + \mu}{3E}\sigma_1{}^2 \quad (61)$$

This state of stress may also be treated as follows. In Fig. 43a is shown the unit cube subjected to the given state of stress; in Fig. 43b is shown

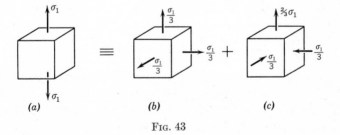

(a)   (b)   (c)

Fig. 43

a cube subjected to three equal principal stresses, each equal to the average of the given set of principal stresses; and in Fig. 43c is shown a set of principal stresses which if superimposed on those in Fig. 43b gives the state of stress in Fig. 43a. The total strain energy for the state of stress on each of the three cubes in Fig. 43 is obtained by the use of Eq. 57 as follows.

$$w = \text{Total energy (Fig. 43}a) = \tfrac{1}{2}(\sigma_1{}^2/E)$$

w_v = Energy of volume change (Fig. 43b)

$$= \frac{1}{2E}\left(\frac{3\sigma_1{}^2}{9}\right) - \frac{\mu}{E}\left(\frac{3\sigma_1{}^2}{9}\right) = \frac{(1-2\mu)\sigma_1{}^2}{6E} \tag{62}$$

w_d = Energy of distortion (Fig. 43c)

$$= \frac{1}{2E}\left(\frac{4\sigma_1{}^2}{9} + \frac{\sigma_1{}^2}{9} + \frac{\sigma_1{}^2}{9}\right) - \frac{\mu}{E}\left(-\frac{2\sigma_1{}^2}{9} - \frac{2\sigma_1{}^2}{9} + \frac{\sigma_1{}^2}{9}\right)$$

$$= \frac{(1+\mu)\sigma_1{}^2}{3E} \tag{63}$$

From the foregoing expressions it will be observed that $w = w_v + w_d$, and that Eqs. 61 and 63 are the same. For steel, $\mu = 0.25$ approximately, and hence in steel under simple tension the energy of volume change is $\frac{1}{12}(\sigma^2/E)$ per unit volume and the energy of change in shape is $\frac{5}{12}(\sigma^2/E)$ per unit volume. Thus five times as much elastic energy is absorbed in changing the shape of the unit volume as is absorbed in changing the volume when the unit volume is subjected to only one principal stress.

Pure Shear. Biaxial Principal Stresses of Equal Magnitude and of Opposite Sign. In the state of stress of pure shear (which occurs in a cylindrical bar subjected to torsion) the shearing stresses τ at the point are equal in magnitude to each of the two principal stresses σ at the point (Art. 19). Thus in Eq. 60 $\sigma_1 = \sigma$, $\sigma_2 = -\sigma$, and $\sigma_3 = 0$; furthermore, $\sigma = \tau$. Hence

$$w_d = \frac{1+\mu}{6E}\{[\sigma - (-\sigma)]^2 + (\sigma)^2 + (-\sigma)^2\} = \frac{1+\mu}{E}\sigma^2 = \frac{1+\mu}{E}\tau^2 \tag{64}$$

By comparing Eq. 64 with Eq. 61 or 63 it will be observed that the elastic energy absorbed per unit volume in changing shape in a torsion specimen at a point of maximum stress (on the surface) is three times that absorbed at any point in a tension specimen when the principal tensile stresses at the two points are equal.

It is important to note that, if yielding in a member starts because the energy of distortion reaches a critical or limiting value (which is one theory of failure to be discussed later), the maximum shearing stress τ_e at a point when yielding starts is $1/\sqrt{3}$ times the maximum tensile stress σ_e at the same point. Or, as frequently stated, the shearing yield strength of a material must be 0.577 times the tensile yield strength of the material ($\tau_e = 0.577\sigma_e$). This is proved by equating the energy of distortion in the torsion specimen to the energy of distortion in the tension specimen, when yielding starts. Thus

$$\frac{1+\mu}{E}\tau_e^2 = \frac{1}{3}\frac{1+\mu}{E}\sigma_e^2$$

$$\tau_e = \sigma_e/\sqrt{3} = 0.577\sigma_e \tag{65}$$

Shearing Stress Combined with One Normal Stress. If at a point in a body the known or "given" stresses consist of shearing stresses on two perpendicular planes and a normal stress on one of the planes, as discussed in Art. 22, it is sometimes desirable to express the strain energy of distortion per unit volume in terms of these "given" stresses rather than in terms of the principal stresses at the point. This may be done as follows.

The principal stresses at the point expressed in terms of the "given" stresses are (see Art. 22)

$$\sigma_1 = \tfrac{1}{2}\sigma + \tfrac{1}{2}\sqrt{\sigma^2 + 4\tau^2} \qquad \sigma_2 = \tfrac{1}{2}\sigma - \tfrac{1}{2}\sqrt{\sigma^2 + 4\tau^2} \qquad \sigma_3 = 0$$

If these values of the principal stresses are substituted in Eq. 60, the strain energy of distortion becomes

$$w_d = \frac{1+\mu}{3E}(\sigma^2 + 3\tau^2) \tag{66}$$

Problems

33. Calculate the elastic strain energy per unit volume absorbed (1) in changing volume and (2) in changing shape of the material at the point under the conditions stated in each of the following cases. It is assumed that the elastic strength of the material is not exceeded, and that $\mu = 0.25$.

(a) At any point in a bar made of an aluminum alloy and subjected to an axial tensile load of 16,000 lb, if the cross section of the bar is 0.75 in. by 1.5 in.; assume that $E = 10 \times 10^6$ lb per sq in.

(b) At a point on the surface of a steel shaft 4 in. in diameter subjected to twisting couples of 8000 lb-ft at its ends. *Ans.* $w_v = 0$; $w_d = 2.42$ in.-lb/in.[3].

(c) At a point on the inner surface of the gun described in Prob. 14.
Ans. $w_v = 3.22$ in.-lb/in.[3]; $w_d = 49.3$ in.-lb/in.[3].

(d) In the shaft described in Prob. 22 at a point where the stress caused by the bending moment is a maximum. Assume that the shaft is made of steel.

34. Derive Eq. 60 for strain energy of distortion by using the stresses and strains shown in Fig. 42c.

§ 4   Theories of Failure

30   Introduction. If a ductile metal bar is subjected to a gradually increasing axial tensile load causing only one principal stress on any transverse section, the material, when the load reaches a certain value, will begin to acquire inelastic (permanent) deformation.

In Art. 4 it was assumed that inelastic action after it had progressed to a small (measurable) amount constituted structural damage to the member and was designated as failure by general yielding; it was attributed primarily to slip on planes through the crystalline grains of

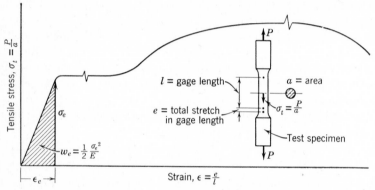

FIG. 44   Typical stress-strain diagram for ductile steel.

the metal. It was assumed also that the slip (yielding) was more closely associated with shearing stress than with any other quantity, and hence a limiting value of the shearing stress (the shearing elastic limit or yield point) was considered to be the property of the material which would limit the load-resisting capacity of a member made of ductile material. There are, however, at least five other quantities or properties of the material that have been proposed and used in design as a measure of the limiting resistance value or maximum utilizable strength of the material when the beginning of yielding is the action that destroys the load-resisting function of the member. Some of these theories are used also to explain failure by fracture, as will be discussed later.

In Fig. 44 is shown a typical tensile stress-strain curve for a specimen of ductile steel as obtained from a tension test. When the specimen starts to yield, the following six quantities are reached simultaneously:

1. The principal stress ($\sigma = P/a$) reaches the tensile elastic strength (elastic limit or yield point) σ_e of the material.

2. The maximum shearing stress [$\tau = \frac{1}{2}(P/a)$] reaches the shearing elastic limit or yield point τ_e of the material, $\tau_e = \frac{1}{2}\sigma_e$.

3. The tensile strain ϵ reaches the value ϵ_e.

4. The total strain energy w absorbed by the material per unit volume reaches the value $w_e = \frac{1}{2}(\sigma_e^2/E)$.

5. The strain energy of distortion w_d (energy accompanying change in shape) absorbed by the material per unit volume reaches a value $w_{de} = [(1 + \mu)/3E]\sigma_e^2$.

6. The octahedral shearing stress reaches the value $\tau_{Ge} = (\sqrt{2}/3)\sigma_e = 0.47\sigma_e$.

These six criteria of failure of a material are summarized in Table 1.

The six limiting values given in Table 1 occur simultaneously in a tensile specimen, in which the state of stress is uniaxial, and hence it is impossible to determine from a tension test which one of the quantities is the cause of the beginning of inelastic action. If, however, the state of stress is biaxial or triaxial, the foregoing six quantities will not occur simultaneously, and it is a matter of considerable importance in design as to which one of the quantities is assumed to limit the loads that can be applied to a member without causing inelastic action. The six limiting quantities as given in Table 1 suggest six theories of failure or six different methods for using data obtained in the tension test to predict inelastic action when the state of stress in the member is not uniaxial. These theories of failure are discussed in the next article.

Before stating the theories of failure it may be well to recall (from Chapter 1) that failure of load-resisting members, under static loading as here considered, usually consists of one of two types of action, namely, (a) inelastic deformation (yielding) or (b) brittle fracture, by which is meant separation of the material without accompanying measurable yielding. Which one of these two modes of failure occurs depends on the inherent, *internal* characteristics and structure of the material, and also on *external* conditions, such as temperature, state of stress, type of loading, rate of loading, etc.; a stress-strain diagram for a material that fails by truly brittle fracture under static loading is a straight line until the breaking or fracture stress is reached. In such a failure the elastic limit and the ultimate strength of the material are identical values. The significance of any theory of failure will depend to a considerable extent on which mode of failure occurs or is assumed to occur.

31 Statement of Theories of Failure. The six main theories of failure suggested in Table 1 for a material that is considered to fail by yielding under static loading may be stated briefly as follows:

1. The *maximum principal stress* theory, often called Rankine's theory, states that inelastic action at any point in a material at which any state of stress exists begins *only* when the maximum principal stress at the

TABLE 1

Theory of Failure	Maximum Utilizable Quantity as Obtained from Tension Test
1. Maximum Principal Stress	$\sigma_e = P/a$

2. Maximum Shearing Stress	$\tau_e = \frac{1}{2}(P/a) = \frac{1}{2}\sigma_e$

3. Maximum Strain	$\epsilon_e = \sigma_e/E$

4. Total Strain Energy	$w_e = \frac{1}{2}(\sigma_e^2/E)$

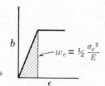

5. Strain Energy of Distortion	$w_{de} = \dfrac{1 + \mu}{3}\dfrac{\sigma_e^2}{E}$

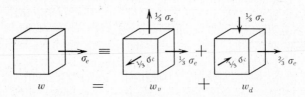

6. Octahedral Shearing Stress	$\tau_{Ge} = (\sqrt{2}/3)\sigma_e = 0.47\sigma_e$

point reaches a value equal to the tensile (or compressive) elastic limit or yield strength of the material as found in a simple tension (or compression) test, regardless of the normal or shearing stresses that occur on other planes through the point. Thus, according to this theory, if the block in Fig. 46a reaches its elastic limit when subjected to the stress σ_1, the elastic limit will still be σ_1 even if the block is subjected to the stress σ_2 (Fig. 46b) in addition to σ_1.

It will be observed that if σ_1 and σ_2 are equal and of opposite sign, shearing stresses τ equal to σ will be developed on 45° diagonal planes

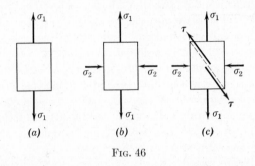

$$(a) \qquad (b) \qquad (c)$$

Fig. 46

as in Fig. 46c. A state of stress like that shown in Fig. 46c occurs in a cylindrical bar subjected to pure torsion. Thus, if this theory is true for all states of stress, the shearing elastic limit of the material must be at least equal to the tensile elastic limit. But for all ductile metals the shearing elastic limit as found from the torsion test is much less than the tensile elastic limit as found from the tension test. It is evident, therefore, that the presence of relatively large shearing stresses at a point causes limitations on the maximum principal stress theory which will be discussed further in the next article. For brittle materials which do not fail by yielding but fail by brittle fracture, the maximum principal stress theory is considered to be reasonably satisfactory, although the maximum strain theory is considered to be preferable.

2. The *maximum shearing stress* theory, sometimes called Coulomb's theory, or Guest's law, states that inelastic action at any point in a body at which any state of stress exists begins *only* when the maximum shearing stress on some plane through the point reaches a value equal to the maximum shearing stress in a tension specimen when yielding starts. This means that the shearing elastic limit must be not more than one-half the tensile elastic limit, since the maximum shearing stress in a tension specimen (on a 45° oblique plane) is one-half the maximum tensile stress in the specimen.

The maximum shearing stress theory seems to be fairly well justified for ductile material and for the states of stress encountered in most load-resisting members, that is, for states of stress in which relatively large shearing stresses are developed. However, for the state of stress of pure shear in which the maximum amount of shear is developed, as occurs in a torsion test, the shearing elastic limit of ductile metals is found to vary somewhat, but an average value is approximately 0.57 of the tensile elastic limit ($\tau_e = 0.57\sigma_e$), and hence for such a state of stress the maximum shearing stress theory errs (on the side of safety) by approximately 15 per cent.

In Art. 21 and Figs. 25g, 25h, and 25i, it is shown that maximum and minimum principal stresses may be resolved into a state of pure shear combined with equal tensions in all directions in the plane of these two principal stresses. Thus it is assumed by this theory of failure that the maximum shearing stresses alone produce inelastic action and that the equal tensile stresses have no influence in starting inelastic action. If the state of stress consists of triaxial tensile stresses of nearly equal magnitude, shearing stresses would be very small and failure would be by brittle fracture rather than by yielding, and hence the maximum shearing stress theory would not be applicable.

3. The *maximum strain* theory, often called St. Venant's theory, states that inelastic action at a point in a body at which any state of stress exists begins *only* when the maximum strain at the point reaches a value equal to that which occurs when inelastic action begins in the material under a uniaxial state of stress, as occurs in the specimen in the tension test. This value, ϵ_e, occurs simultaneously with the tensile elastic limit σ_e of the material. Thus $\epsilon_e = \sigma_e/E$.

For example, according to this theory, inelastic action in the block of Fig. 46a begins when σ_1 becomes equal to σ_e since $\epsilon_e = \sigma_e/E$, but in Fig. 41 $\epsilon = (\sigma_1/E) - \mu(\sigma_2/E)$, and hence inelastic action does not begin until σ_1 becomes greater than σ_e, since the strain in the direction of σ_1 is decreased by the amount $\mu(\sigma_2/E)$. Therefore, according to this theory of failure, σ_1 could be increased to a value somewhat higher than σ_e without causing yielding if the second normal stress σ_2 is a tensile stress, but if σ_2 is a compressive stress the maximum value of σ_1 that could be applied without causing yielding would be somewhat smaller than σ_e (Fig. 46b).

The maximum strain theory of the breakdown of elastic action is an improvement over the maximum principal stress theory, but, like the latter theory, it usually is not applicable if the failure in elastic behavior is by yielding; it is primarily applicable when the conditions are such that failure occurs by brittle fracture.

4. The *total energy* theory, proposed by Beltrami and by Haigh, states

that inelastic action at any point in a body due to any state of stress begins *only* when the energy per unit volume absorbed at the point is equal to the energy absorbed per unit volume by the material when subjected to the elastic limit under a uniaxial state of stress, as occurs in a simple tensile test. As shown by Eq. 51 and in Table 1 the value of this maximum energy per unit volume is $w_e = \frac{1}{2}(\sigma_e^2/E)$. The expressions for the total energy absorbed per unit volume for various states of stress are given in Art. 28; according to the total energy theory none of these expressions can exceed the value $\frac{1}{2}(\sigma_e^2/E)$ without causing yielding to start.

5. The *energy of distortion* theory, which grew out of the analytical work of Huber, von Mises, and Hencky and out of the results of tests by Bridgman on various materials showing that the material did *not* become inelastic under a triaxial state of stress produced by very high hydrostatic pressure, states that inelastic action at any point in a body under any combination of stresses begins *only* when the strain energy of distortion per unit volume absorbed at the point (see Art. 30) is equal to the strain energy of distortion absorbed per unit volume at any point in a bar stressed to the elastic limit under a state of uniaxial stress as occurs in a simple tension (or compression) test. As shown by Eq. 63 and in Table 1, the value of this maximum strain energy of distortion (energy absorbed in changing shape) as determined from the tension test is $w_{de} = [(1 + \mu)\sigma_e^2]/3E$.

The maximum energy of distortion theory differs from the maximum total energy theory as follows. In the maximum total energy theory it is assumed that the entire strain energy is associated with the beginning of inelastic action. However, tests of various materials under very high hydrostatic stresses show that the materials could withstand, without inelastic action taking place, strain energy values many times greater than those obtained in the simple axial load compression test. Hence, since in the hydrostatic tests the total strain energy is used in producing volume changes only, it was proposed that the energy absorbed in changing volume has no effect in causing failure by yielding, and that failure by inelastic action is associated only with energy absorbed in changing shape. It is assumed that if it were possible to make tests of materials under a negative hydrostatic pressure, which would create three *equal tensile* principal stresses, the same results as found for three equal principal compressive stresses would be obtained; that is, no yielding would take place, although fracture eventually would occur. Since change of shape involves shearing stresses, the energy of distortion theory is sometimes called (somewhat erroneously) the shear energy theory.

In a state of stress in which the maximum amount of shear exists, as in the state of pure shear shown in Fig. 46c, the energy of volume change is zero, because in Eq. 58 the average principal stress σ_{avg} is equal to zero, and therefore the total strain energy is used in distorting (changing the shape of) the unit volume. The expressions for the energy of distortion per unit volume for various states of stress are given in Art. 29, and, according to this theory, none of these expressions can exceed the value $[(1 + \mu)\sigma_e^2]/3E$ without causing the material to start to yield.

6. The *octahedral shearing stress theory* gives the same results as does the energy of distortion theory and hence may be called an *equivalent stress* theory. The octahedral shearing stress as given by Eq. 33 can be expressed in terms of the energy of distortion w_d. This is done by multiplying and dividing the right side of Eq. 33 by the quantity $\sqrt{(1 + \mu)/6E}$. Equation 33 then becomes

$$\tau_G = \frac{1}{3}\sqrt{\frac{6E}{1 + \mu}} \cdot \sqrt{\frac{1 + \mu}{6E}[(\sigma_1 - \sigma_2)^2 + (\sigma_2 - \sigma_3)^2 + (\sigma_3 - \sigma_1)^2]} \quad (67)$$

By referring to Eq. 60 it will be noted that Eq. 67 may be rewritten

$$\tau_G = \tfrac{1}{3}\sqrt{6Ew_d/(1 + \mu)} \quad (68)$$

where w_d is the energy of distortion. But the criterion of failure according to the maximum energy of distortion theory is that inelastic action begins when w_d becomes equal to $w_{de} = [(1 + \mu)\sigma_e^2]/3E$ (see Eq. 61). By substituting this value of w_{de} in Eq. 68, the octahedral shearing stress is found to be

$$\tau_G = (\sqrt{2}/3)\sigma_e = 0.47\sigma_e \quad (69)$$

It will be observed that the value of τ_G as required by the maximum energy of distortion theory in Eq. 69 is the same as the value given in Eq. 27 for the octahedral shearing stress that occurs in the standard tensile test. Thus an octahedral shearing stress theory may be stated as follows: Inelastic action at any point in a body under any combination of stresses begins *only* when the octahedral shearing stress τ_G becomes equal to $0.47\sigma_e$, where σ_e is the tensile elastic strength of the material as determined from the standard tension test. The octahedral shearing stress theory of failure makes it possible to apply the energy of distortion theory of failure by dealing only with stresses instead of dealing with energy directly; this procedure to some engineers seems desirable because stress is a more familiar quantity in engineering design than is energy.

Another way of interpreting the effect of the octahedral stresses has been given in Art. 24 and Figs. 34d, 34e, and 34f, where it was shown that any state of stress consisting of three principal stresses may be resolved into two component states of stress: one component consists of equal tensile (or compressive) stresses in all directions which does not influence the starting of inelastic action, but which may produce fracture, and the other component state of stress comprises the eight octahedral shearing stresses which are assumed by this theory to be wholly responsible for starting inelastic action.

32 Significance of the theories of failure. In Art. 2 it was pointed out that the rational procedure of design of a member requires that the general mode of failure of the member under the assumed service conditions be determined or assumed (failure usually is by yielding or by fracture) and that a quantity (stress, strain, or energy, etc.) be chosen which is considered to be associated with the failure. This means that there is a maximum or critical value of the quantity selected which limits the loads that can be applied to the member; furthermore, it was pointed out that a *suitable* test of the material must be made for determining the critical value; this value is frequently referred to as the maximum utilizable strength of the material. It is important to understand how the theories of failure fit into this picture.

For a given general mode of failure, each theory of failure, as stated in Art. 31, names the (significant) quantity which is the cause of failure when the value of the quantity reaches the critical value, and it also states that a tension test is a suitable test for determining the critical or maximum value of this significant quantity.

It is important to note that if an appropriate or suitable test could always be selected so that the material would be subjected to the same conditions of stress that it is subjected to in the actual member, there would be no need for theories of failure. For example, in Table 1 the maximum utilizable strength of a material as determined by each of the several theories of failure is obtained from a tension test, and hence in the design of any member in which the state of stress is uniaxial the member would be given the same dimensions by all the theories of failure. Similarly, if the maximum or limiting values of the various quantities that are considered to be the cause of failure were obtained from a torsion test of the material, any member of the same material subjected to a state of stress of pure shear would be given the same dimensions by all the theories of failure, since all the quantities assumed to cause failure would reach their limiting values simultaneously.

If a theory of failure were correct under all conditions in which load-resisting members are used, it would predict the nature of the quantity (stress, strain, or energy, etc.) and the limiting value thereof (as obtained from a specified test) which would limit the load that could be applied to the member without causing structural damage.

This, however, is too much to expect from a theory of failure when consideration is given to the radical difference in the modes of failure (ranging from incipient yielding to brittle fracture) and to the simplifying conditions that are necessary to impose on a suitable test. In general, we are limited, because of practical considerations, to one of two tests, namely, the tension test or the torsion test.

In interpreting the theories of failure a given general mode of failure is understood to occur. The significance of the theories will here be studied by assuming that failure occurs when inelastic strain (yielding) starts and by comparing the limiting values of the significant quantities stated in the theories, when the limiting values are obtained for each of two states of stress. The first state of stress is a uniaxial stress as exists in the tension test, and the second is a biaxial state of stress corresponding to pure shear as exists in the torsion test.

In Table 2 is shown a comparison of the limiting value (maximum utilizable strength of a material) as obtained, by each of the theories of

TABLE 2

COMPARISON OF MAXIMUM UTILIZABLE STRENGTHS OF A MATERIAL ACCORDING TO VARIOUS THEORIES OF FAILURE FOR EACH OF TWO STATES OF STRESS AS OCCUR IN THE TENSION AND TORSION TESTS

(1)	(2)	(3)	(4)
Theory of Failure	Maximum Utilizable Strength as Obtained from a Tensile Test	Maximum Utilizable Strength as Obtained from a Torsion Test	Relation between Values of σ_e and τ_e if the Theory of Failure Were Correct for Both States of Stress (col. 2 = col. 3)
Maximum normal stress theory	σ_e	τ_e	$\tau_e = \sigma_e$
Maximum strain theory: $\mu = \frac{1}{4}$	$\dfrac{\sigma_e}{E}$	$\dfrac{5}{4}\dfrac{\tau_e}{E}$	$\tau_e = 0.80\sigma_e$
Maximum shearing stress theory	$\frac{1}{2}\sigma_e$	τ_e	$\tau_e = 0.50\sigma_e$
Maximum octahedral stress theory	$\dfrac{\sqrt{2}}{3}\sigma_e$	$\dfrac{\sqrt{2}}{\sqrt{3}}\tau_e$	$\tau_e = 0.577\sigma_e$
Maximum energy of distortion	$\dfrac{1+\mu}{3}\dfrac{\sigma_e^{2}}{E}$	$(1+\mu)\dfrac{\tau_e^{2}}{E}$	$\tau_e = 0.577\sigma_e$

failure, from the tensile test (column 2) and from the torsion test (column 3). These values should be equal if all theories are correct. The relationships found by equating the two for each theory are given in column 4.

The results from tests of many ductile metals show that the shearing elastic limit (or yield strength) τ_e found from the torsion test varies from about 0.55 to 0.60 of the tensile yield strength σ_e found from the tension test, an average value being about 0.57.

The results of Table 2, therefore, indicate that the energy of distortion theory or its equivalent, the octahedral shearing stress theory, is the most satisfactory theory of failure of a ductile metal under static load for which the maximum utilizable value of the energy of distortion or of the octahedral shearing stress is found from the tension test. However, the maximum shearing stress theory, under the same conditions of stress, is also a reasonably satisfactory theory. It gives a value of the maximum utilizable strength τ_e of the material which is about 15 per cent less than that given by the energy of distortion theory. Thus, it gives values in design on the safe side. It is widely used for design of ductile metals under conditions of static loading and of ordinary temperatures in which creep is not of importance. It is also clear from Table 2 that the theories of maximum principal stress and the maximum principal strain are applicable only when the maximum principal stress in the material is very large relative to the maximum shearing stress at the same point so that the failure is by fracture rather than by yielding.

The states of stress in the tension and torsion tests represent about as wide a range of stress conditions as occurs in most engineering members that fail by yielding under static loads. In the tension test $\sigma_{max}/\tau_{max} = 2$, and in the torsion test $\sigma_{max}/\tau_{max} = 1$. For some triaxial states of stress σ_{max}/τ_{max} is greater than 2, approaching infinity when the triaxial stresses are equal and of like sign, but failure then becomes one of brittle fracture, if the stresses are tensile stresses.

For states of stress in which σ_{max}/τ_{max} lies between 2 and 1 as, for example, in a cylindrical shaft subjected to a bending moment M and a torsional moment T producing the state of stress shown in Figs. 47, 49, and 50, the results given by the various theories are shown in Fig. 47. The diameter d, which is just large enough to prevent inelastic action in the shaft, is computed by each theory of failure, and these values of d are then compared by obtaining the ratios of the various values of d to the value d_s, computed by the maximum shearing stress theory.

These ratios are obtained for combinations of T and M ranging from M acting alone ($T/M = 0$) to T acting alone. (The combination for which $T/M = \infty$, or T acting alone, is shown by the horizontal lines at the right side of the figure which are asymtotes for the curves indicated by the arrows.) It will be noted that the maximum shearing stress theory gives the largest diameter and the maximum normal stress theory the smallest diameter for all ratios of T to M, except for $T/M = 0$, where all diameters are equal.

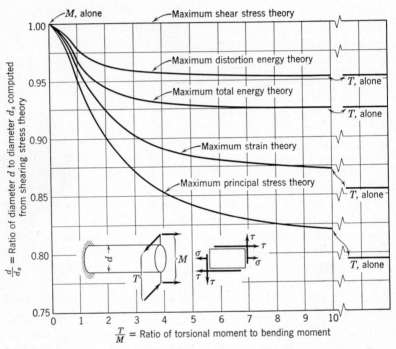

FIG. 47 Comparison of theories of failure.

Figure 48 compares in another way the two most appropriate theories of failure when the mode of failure is by yielding and when the state of stress is the same as that considered in Fig. 47, and it also covers a range in stress from $\sigma_{max}/\tau_{max} = 2$ (bending alone) to $\sigma_{max}/\tau_{max} = 1$ (torsion alone). The equations represented by these curves are found as follows: For any combination of τ and σ, yielding starts according to the maximum shearing stress theory when

$$\sqrt{(\sigma/2)^2 + \tau^2} = \sigma_e/2 \quad \text{or} \quad 4(\tau/\sigma_e)^2 + (\sigma/\sigma_e)^2 = 1 \quad (70)$$

Likewise, yielding starts according to the energy of distortion theory when

$$\frac{1+\mu}{3E}(\sigma^2 + 3\tau^2) = \frac{1+\mu}{3E}\sigma_e^2 \quad \text{or} \quad 3\left(\frac{\tau}{\sigma_e}\right)^2 + \left(\frac{\sigma}{\sigma_e}\right)^2 = 1 \quad (71)$$

Other Factors To Be Considered. The theories of failure, however, do not take account of all the conditions that the engineer must consider in the problem of failure, even of failure of ductile material subjected to static loads at ordinary temperatures. In the theories as here stated it is assumed that the failure occurs when inelastic action starts. In many

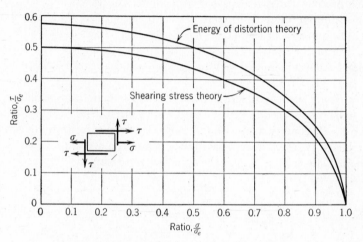

Fig. 48   Comparison of two of the theories of failure.

uses of load-resisting members some inelastic strain may occur without destroying the usefulness of the member, and these inelastic strains cause a readjustment of stresses which may permit an appreciable increase in the loads on the member. This topic is discussed in Part V.

Furthermore, if the theories are applied to a type of failure different from that assumed in the above statement of the theories, a different type of test for determining the limiting values of the quantities considered to be the cause of failure is required. For example, if the failure in a ductile material results from highly localized action in the material, such as failure caused by many (repeated) applications of the load (fatigue failure), the test of the ductile material for determining the limiting value would *not* be a *static* tensile test in which a relatively large amount of material is involved in the failure, but would be a series of repeated load (fatigue) tests in which localized action controls the failure. The value obtained from such a test usually is the endurance limit, and the limiting values required in the application of the various theories of failure would be expressed in terms of this endurance limit. This is done in Chapter 12.

33   Application of theories of failure. *Design formulas.* As stated in the preceding article, the dimensions that should be assigned to a ductile member which is to be subjected to static loads depend on the theory held concerning the cause of the breakdown of elastic action (yielding). This fact is illustrated by Fig. 47 for a cylindrical shaft which is subjected to a bending moment M and a torsional moment T, which produce the state of stress also shown in Fig. 47.

In obtaining design formulas it should be recalled from Art. 2 that the main purpose of the member considered is to resist *loads* safely and that the factor of safety N should be applied in such a way that the design *loads* are increased to N times the loads that cause inelastic action to start.

Maximum Principal Stress Theory. The maximum principal stress $\sigma_{\max}$ must not exceed the tensile elastic strength σ_e (see Table 1). Under these elastic conditions the loads are directly proportional to the stresses, and hence N can be applied to σ_e. Thus the working value of the principal stress is σ_e/N, and the equation for design is

$$\sigma_{\max} = \sigma_e/N \tag{72}$$

For the state of stress considered here as shown in Fig. 47, Eq. 72 becomes

$$\sigma_{\max} = \tfrac{1}{2}\sigma + \tfrac{1}{2}\sqrt{\sigma^2 + 4\tau^2} = \sigma_e/N \tag{73}$$

in which σ and τ may be expressed in terms of the loads (M and T) acting on the member.

Maximum Shearing Stress Theory. The maximum shearing stress $\tau_{\max}$ according to Eq. 10 is $\tau_{\max} = \tfrac{1}{2}(\sigma_{\max} - \sigma_{\min})$. The value of $\tau_{\max}$ must not exceed $\tfrac{1}{2}\sigma_e$ (see Table 1). The working value for the shearing stress is, therefore, $\tfrac{1}{2}(\sigma_e/N)$, and the design equation is

$$\tau_{\max} = \tfrac{1}{2}(\sigma_{\max} - \sigma_{\min}) = \tfrac{1}{2}(\sigma_e/N) \tag{74}$$

For the state of stress shown in Fig. 47, Eq. 74 becomes

$$\tau_{\max} = \tfrac{1}{2}\sqrt{\sigma^2 + 4\tau^2} = \tfrac{1}{2}(\sigma_e/N) \tag{75}$$

Maximum Strain Theory. The maximum strain $\epsilon_{\max}$ is given by Eq. 39

$$\epsilon_{\max} = (\sigma_1/E) - \mu(\sigma_2/E) - \mu(\sigma_3/E)$$

where σ_1, σ_2, and σ_3 are the principal stresses, σ_1 having the largest numerical value. Since $\epsilon_{\max}$ must not exceed $\epsilon_e = \sigma_e/E$ (see Table 1), its working value is ϵ_e/N, and the equation for design is

$$\epsilon_{max} = (\sigma_1/E) - \mu(\sigma_2/E) - \mu(\sigma_3/E) = (\epsilon_e/N) = (1/E)(\sigma_e/N) \quad (76)$$

In Eq. 76 the working value of strain is equal to $1/E$ times the working value of the stress, and, if the factor $1/E$ which is common to both sides of the equation is cancelled out, the design equation reduces to

$$\sigma_1 - \mu\sigma_2 - \mu\sigma_3 = \sigma_e/N \quad (77)$$

For the state of stress shown in Fig. 47 and for $\mu = \frac{1}{4}$, Eq. 77 becomes

$$\tfrac{3}{8}\sigma + \tfrac{5}{8}\sqrt{\sigma^2 + 4\tau^2} = \sigma_e/N \quad (78)$$

Maximum Total Energy Theory. According to this theory, inelastic action begins when the total energy per unit volume w has the value $w_e = \frac{1}{2}(\sigma_e^2/E)$, which is the total energy absorbed per unit volume at the elastic strength of the material in a standard tension specimen. The foregoing statement as applied to a state of triaxial stress is, from Eq. 57,

$$w = \frac{1}{2E}[\sigma_1^2 + \sigma_2^2 + \sigma_3^2 - 2\mu(\sigma_1\sigma_2 + \sigma_2\sigma_3 + \sigma_3\sigma_1)] = w_e = \frac{1}{2}\frac{\sigma_e^2}{E} \quad (79)$$

If the loads are proportional to the stresses, the energy w, as given by Eq. 79, is a function of the loads to the second power. Hence, the factor of safety N must be applied (see Art. 2) to the quantity $\sqrt{w}$ in order to limit the load to $1/N$ times the loads which will cause inelastic action to begin. Therefore, in Eq. 79 the square root of both sides of the equation is taken, and then the factor of safety N is applied. Thus

$$\sqrt{\frac{1}{2E}[\sigma_1^2 + \sigma_2^2 + \sigma_3^2 - 2\mu(\sigma_1\sigma_2 + \sigma_2\sigma_3 + \sigma_3\sigma_1)]} = \frac{\sqrt{w_e}}{N}$$

$$= \frac{\sigma_e}{N}\sqrt{\frac{1}{2E}} \quad (80)$$

If the factor $\sqrt{1/2E}$, which is common to both sides of the equation, is cancelled out, the design equation reduces to

$$\sqrt{\sigma_1^2 + \sigma_2^2 + \sigma_3^2 - 2\mu(\sigma_1\sigma_2 + \sigma_2\sigma_3 + \sigma_3\sigma_1)} = \sigma_e/N \quad (81)$$

For the state of stress as shown by Fig. 47, Eq. 81 becomes

$$\sqrt{\sigma^2 + 2(1 + \mu)\tau^2} = \sigma_e/N \quad (82)$$

Maximum Energy of Distortion Theory. In this theory inelastic action is assumed to begin when the energy of distortion per unit volume,

w_d, becomes equal to the value $w_{de} = [(1 + \mu)\sigma_e{}^2]/3E$, which is the energy of distortion per unit volume absorbed at the elastic strength of the material in a standard tensile specimen. This theory of failure is applied to a state of triaxial stress by using the expression for w_d given in Eq. 60. The design equation then may be written

$$w_d = \frac{1 + \mu}{6E}[(\sigma_1 - \sigma_2)^2 + (\sigma_2 - \sigma_3)^2 + (\sigma_3 - \sigma_1)^2]$$

$$= w_{de} = \frac{1 + \mu}{3E}\sigma_e{}^2 \qquad (83)$$

The square root of both sides of Eq. 83 is taken, and then the factor of safety is applied, for the same reason given in the foregoing treatment of the total energy. Thus

$$\sqrt{\frac{1 + \mu}{6E}[(\sigma_1 - \sigma_2)^2 + (\sigma_2 - \sigma_3)^2 + (\sigma_3 - \sigma_1)^2]} = \frac{\sqrt{w_{de}}}{N}$$

$$= \sqrt{\frac{1 + \mu}{3E}} \cdot \frac{\sigma_e}{N} \qquad (84)$$

This equation may be simplified by canceling out the common factor $(1 + \mu)/3E$ leading to the design equation

$$\sqrt{\tfrac{1}{2}[(\sigma_1 - \sigma_2)^2 + (\sigma_2 - \sigma_3)^2 + (\sigma_3 - \sigma_1)^2]} = \sigma_e/N \qquad (85)$$

For a state of stress as shown by Fig. 47, Eq. 85 reduces to

$$\sqrt{\sigma^2 + 3\tau^2} = \sigma_e/N \qquad (86)$$

Maximum Octahedral Shearing Stress Theory. In this theory of failure, inelastic action is assumed to begin when the shearing stress on the octahedral planes (planes making equal angles with the planes on which the three principal stresses act) becomes equal to the value $\tau_{Ge} = \sqrt{2}\sigma_e/3$, which is the value of the octahedral stress occurring at the elastic strength of the material in a standard tensile specimen. When there are three principal stresses, the octahedral shearing stress is given by Eq. 26. Thus the design equation is

$$\tau_{G\text{max}} = \frac{1}{3}\sqrt{(\sigma_1 - \sigma_2)^2 + (\sigma_2 - \sigma_3)^2 + (\sigma_3 - \sigma_1)^2} = \frac{\sqrt{2}}{3}\frac{\sigma_e}{N} \qquad (87)$$

For the state of stress as shown in Fig. 47, Eq. 87 reduces to

$$\tau_{G_{max}} = \frac{\sqrt{2}}{3} \sqrt{\sigma^2 + 3\tau^2} = \frac{\sqrt{2}}{3} \frac{\sigma_e}{N} \qquad (88)$$

or simply

$$\sqrt{\sigma^2 + 3\tau^2} = \sigma_e/N \qquad (89)$$

which is the same as Eq. 86.

Illustrative Problems

Problem 35. A cylindrical shaft made of steel for which the tensile elastic strength (yield strength) is $\sigma_e = 100,000$ lb per sq in. is subjected to static loads consisting of a bending moment $M = 100,000$ lb-in. and a torsional moment $T = 300,000$ lb-in. as indicated in Fig. 47. Assume that for steel $E = 30 \times 10^6$, $\mu = 0.25$. Determine the diameter d which the shaft must have for a factor of safety of 2.

Solution. The four steps in the rational procedure in design as outlined in Art. 2 (Chapter 1) will guide the solution. The failure results from yielding; therefore, in accordance with the discussion in Art. 32, the energy of distortion theory of failure, or its equivalent, the octahedral shearing stress theory, should give the most satisfactory results. The use of the shearing stress theory also can be justified, as giving conservative values. Both theories will be used.

MAXIMUM SHEARING STRESS THEORY. The design equation according to this theory of failure is (see Eq. 75)

$$\tau_{max} = \tfrac{1}{2}\sqrt{\sigma^2 + 4\tau^2} = \tau_e/N = \tfrac{1}{2}(\sigma_e/N)$$

in which $\sigma = Mc/I = 32M/\pi d^3$, and $\tau = Tc/J = 16T/\pi d^3$. Thus

$$(16/\pi d^3)\sqrt{M^2 + T^2} = \tfrac{1}{2}(\sigma_e/N)$$

$$(1,600,000/\pi d^3)\sqrt{(1)^2 + (3)^2} = \tfrac{1}{2}(100,000/2) = 25,000$$

Hence
$$d = 4.01 \text{ in.}$$

OCTAHEDRAL SHEARING STRESS THEORY. The design equation according to this theory is (see Eq. 89 or the same equation as obtained by the energy of distortion theory, Eq. 86)

$$(16/\pi d^3)\sqrt{4M^2 + 3T^2} = \sigma_e/N$$

$$(1,600,000/\pi d^3)\sqrt{4(1)^2 + 3(3)^2} = 50,000$$

Hence
$$d = 3.83 \text{ in.}$$

Thus a diameter not less than 3.83 in. would be justified for strength.

Problem 36. A cylindrical bar of cast iron is subjected to a bending moment of $M = 10,000$ lb-in. and a torsional moment of $T = 30,000$ lb-in., as shown in Fig. 47. Assume that for cast iron $\sigma_e = 30,000$ lb per sq in., $E = 15 \times 10^6$, and $\mu = 0.25$.

Determine the minimum diameter the bar should have, based on a factor of safety of 3.

Solution. The four steps in a rational design procedure as outlined in Art. 2 (Chapter 1) are involved in the solution. The bar will fail by brittle fracture. Therefore, in accordance with the discussion in Art. 31, the maximum principal stress theory and the maximum principal strain theory are the most satisfactory theories. Both theories will be used in the solution.

MAXIMUM PRINCIPAL STRESS THEORY. The design formula (Eq. 73) is

$$\sigma_{max} = \tfrac{1}{2}\sigma + \tfrac{1}{2}\sqrt{\sigma^2 + 4\tau^2} = \sigma_e/N$$

in which $\sigma = Mc/I = 32M/\pi d^3$ and $\tau = Tc/J = 16T/\pi d^3$

Thus $\tfrac{1}{2}(32M/\pi d^3) + \tfrac{1}{2}\sqrt{(32M/\pi d^3)^2 + 4(16T/\pi d^3)^2} = \sigma_e/3$

$$\tfrac{1}{2}(32/\pi d^3)(M + \sqrt{M^2 + T^2}) = 10{,}000$$

$$(160{,}000/\pi d^3)[1 + \sqrt{(1)^2 + (3)^2}] = 10{,}000$$

$$\pi d^3 = 16 \times 4.16 = 66.56$$

Hence $d = 2.77$ in.

MAXIMUM PRINCIPAL STRAIN THEORY. According to this theory of failure the design formula is (see Eq. 78)

$$\epsilon_{max} = (\sigma_1/E) - \mu(\sigma_2/E) = \epsilon_e$$

or $\tfrac{3}{8}\sigma + \tfrac{5}{8}\sqrt{\sigma^2 + 4\tau^2} = \sigma_e/N$

Hence $(32/\pi d^3)(\tfrac{3}{8}M + \tfrac{5}{8}\sqrt{M^2 + T^2}) = 30{,}000/3$

$$(320{,}000/\pi d^3)[\tfrac{3}{8} \times 1 + \tfrac{5}{8}\sqrt{(1)^2 + (3)^2}] = 10{,}000$$

$$\pi d^3 = 75.2$$

Hence $d = 2.88$ in.

Thus, if fracture occurs because the strain reaches a limiting value, the shaft should have a diameter of 2.88 in. in order to prevent the shaft from fracturing when the loads on the shaft are three times the actual loads. The maximum strain theory seems to fit the small amount of test data that are available somewhat better than does the maximum principal stress theory.

Problems

37. A pressure P of 10,000 lb on the crank pin of the crank shaft in Fig. 49 is required to turn the shaft at constant speed. The crank shaft is made of ductile steel having a tensile (and compressive) elastic limit or yield strength of 40,000 lb per sq in. as found from a tension (or compression) test. Assume that $E = 30 \times 10^6$ and $\mu = 0.25$. Calculate the diameter of the shaft based on a factor of safety of 2. In the solution make it clear how the four steps in the procedure of design outlined in Art. 2 (Chapter 1) are applied, and which theory or theories of failure are used.

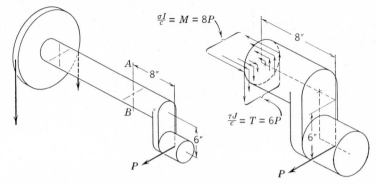

Fig. 49   Stresses in crankshaft.

38. Determine the diameter of the ductile steel bar shown in Fig. 50 if the tensile load P is 8000 lb and the torsional moment Qq is 16,000 lb-in.   Use a factor of safety $N = 1.5$, $E = 30 \times 10^6$, $\mu = 0.25$, and $\sigma_e = 30,000$ lb per sq in.   Solve by trial and error.

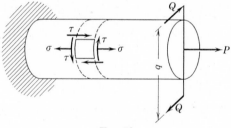

Fig. 50

39. The thick-walled hollow cylinder shown in Fig. 27 is made of an aluminum alloy whose tensile elastic limit is 30,000 lb per sq in.   The internal pressure σ_r in the cylinder is 20,000 lb per sq in.   If the material is at the point of failing by inelastic action in accordance with the maximum shearing stress theory, what is the value of σ_t?

40. A cast-iron cylindrical bar is subjected to combined bending and torsion.   The diameter of the bar is 2 in., and the bending moment M applied is 8000 lb-in.   If the bar is at the point of failure by brittle fracture in accordance with the maximum strain theory of failure, what is the value of the torsional moment T?   Assume for cast iron that the tensile elastic limit and ultimate strength are each $\sigma_e = 30,000$ lb per sq in.   Assume also that $E = 15 \times 10^6$ and $\mu = 0.25$.

41. At a point in a steel member the state of stress is the same as that shown in Fig. 48.   The tensile elastic limit or yield strength as found from a tension test is $\sigma_e = 60,000$ lb per sq in.   If the shearing stress τ at the point is 30,000 lb per sq in. when yielding starts, what is the tensile stress σ at the point (a) according to the maximum shearing stress theory and (b) according to the energy of distortion theory or the octahedral shearing stress theory?   *Ans.*   (a) zero.   (b) 30,000 lb/in.^{2}.

42. Reduce Eqs. 72, 74, 77, 81, and 85 to design equations for a cylindrical shaft of radius c subjected to a torsional moment T alone, which produces a state of stress of pure shear in which the three principal stresses are $\sigma_1 = \tau$, $\sigma_2 = -\tau$, and $\sigma_3 = 0$, where $\tau = Tc/J$.

Selected References

1. Frocht, M. M., *Photoelasticity*, Vol. I, Chap. 1, John Wiley & Sons, 1941. A summary of the mathematical relationships between stresses, between strains, and between stresses and strains is given.

2. Nadai, A., "Theories of Strength," *Journal of Applied Mechanics*, Vol. I, No. 3, July–September 1933, pp. 111–129. A summary of conditions for inelastic action.

3. Richart, F. E., A. Brandtzaeg, and R. L. Brown, "A Study of the Failure of Concrete under Combined Compressive Stresses," *Bulletin* 185, Engineering Experiment Station, University of Illinois.

4. Peterson, R. E., "Strength Theories Applied to Fatigue of Ductile Materials," *Proceedings of the Society for Experimental Stress Analysis*, Vol. I, No. 1, 1943, pp. 124–127.

5. Moore, H. F., "On What Value Should Working Stress Be Based?" *Machine Design*, Vol. 3, February 1931, pp. 35–38.

6. Soderberg, C. R., "Factor of Safety and Working Stress," *Transactions of the American Society of Mechanical Engineers*, Vol. 52, No. 11, 1930.

7. Noll, G. C., and C. Lipson, "Allowable Working Stresses," *Proceedings of the Society for Experimental Stress Analysis*, Vol. III, No. 2, 1946.

PART TWO

Special Topics on the Strength and Stiffness of Members Subjected to Static Loads

Chapter 4

SHEAR CENTER FOR A CROSS SECTION
OF A BEAM

34 Bending axis and shear center defined. The bending axis of
a beam is the longitudinal axis through which the transverse bending
loads must pass in order that the bending of the beam shall not be accompanied by twisting of the beam. The *shear center* or *center of twist* *
for any transverse section of the beam is the point of intersection of the
bending axis and the plane of the transverse section.

The bending axis and the shear center are of special importance in
beams having cross sections composed of thin parts which offer large resistance to bending but small resistance to torsion, such as I sections,
channels, angles, and various sections of beams made of thin plate material as in airplane construction.

The bending axis for a beam whose cross section has two axes of symmetry is the longitudinal *centroidal* axis of the beam, as will be shown
later, and hence the shear center for such a section is also the centroid
of the section. For sections having only one axis of symmetry, however,
the shear center is not coincident with the centroid, as is proved later
in this chapter and illustrated in Fig. 51. For example in Figs. 51a and
51c the cantilever channel and angle beams twist as they bend when the
load P is applied at the centroids C of the sections, but they bend without twisting as shown in Figs. 51b and 51d when P is applied through the
shear centers O of the sections; the location of O for an equal leg angle
is found in Art. 35, and for a channel section in Art. 36. This chapter
deals primarily with the shear centers for beams having open cross
sections composed of narrow rectangles and with only one axis of symmetry; the angle and channel sections of Fig. 51 are examples of such
sections.

It should be noted further that, if the bending loads cause the beam

* If a bar is subjected to a transverse twisting couple one point in any transverse
cross section will not be displaced; this point is also called the center of twist. It is
not necessarily the same point as the shear center.

to twist as it bends, the longitudinal stresses in the beam are no longer given by the flexure formula $\sigma = Mc/I$. The maximum longitudinal stress in the beam may be greatly in excess of that caused by loads of the same magnitude which act through the bending axis. Thus one limitation on the flexure formula is that the loads must pass through

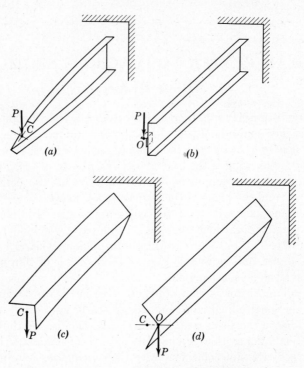

Fig. 51   Effect of applying load through shear center.

the bending axis; the increase in the longitudinal stress resulting from the twisting which accompanies the bending of a beam is discussed in Chapter 9.

Method of Locating Shear Center.   The principle involved in locating the shear center for a cross section of a beam is that the loads acting on the beam must lie in a plane which contains the resultant (resisting) shearing force on each cross section of the beam as computed from the shearing stresses produced in the beam when it is loaded so that it does not twist as it bends. For, if this condition is not satisfied, the beam at any cross section will be subjected to a twisting moment in addition to a bending moment. Thus the main problem in locating the shear center for a cross section of a beam is that of locating the *action line* of the resultant shearing force on the section; it will be observed that if the beam is subjected to a bending couple causing bending without shear (pure bending) in the beam, a resultant shearing force on any section would not exist, and hence the shear center has no meaning for pure bending. This method of locating the shear center is illustrated in the next two articles and in subsequent illustrative problems.

35 Shear center for an equal-leg angle section. Let an equal-leg angle bar be used as a beam and be subjected to transverse bending loads in a plane perpendicular to the axis of symmetry of the cross section, as shown in Fig. 52a. As noted in the preceding article,

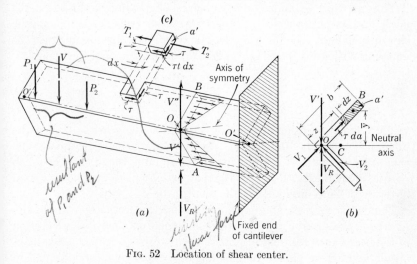

Fig. 52   Location of shear center.

the bending loads must produce shear in the beam, and the bar is assumed here to be a cantilever beam as a convenient way of satisfying this condition. In order to prevent the beam from twisting as it bends, the plane of the loads must contain the action line of the resultant resisting shearing force V_R acting on each cross section.

This fact becomes evident if the loads P_1, P_2, etc., in Fig. 52a are replaced by their resultant V, and if V is then resolved into a force V' at O in any section AB and a couple composed of the force V and V''. This is done by introducing two equal, opposite, collinear forces in the plane of the loads at O such that $V' = V'' = V$. The bending couple composed of V and V'' is held in equilibrium by a resisting moment at any transverse section of the beam in accordance with the flexure formula, the bending stress in each leg of the angle varying as shown at section AB. Likewise, the vertical shear V' at the section is held in equilibrium by a resisting shearing force V_R on the section, provided that V' is collinear with V_R; otherwise V' and V_R will form a twisting couple and the beam will twist as it bends, giving rise to a torsional shearing resisting moment on the section which must be combined with V_R to satisfy the conditions of equilibrium.

The action line of the resultant shearing force V_R in any section such as AB in Fig. 52a must pass through the point of intersection of its components V_1 and V_2, which for these thin sections lie along the center lines of the upper and lower legs, respectively, as is shown in Fig. 52b and proved in the next paragraph. Thus the point O in Fig. 52a is the shear center, and the axis OO' is the bending axis.

The fact that V_1 and V_2 act along the center line of the leg of the angle and are components of the resultant shearing force V_R may be shown as follows: The force V_1 may be determined by summing up the differential shearing forces $\tau\, da$ (Fig. 52b) over the area of the upper leg; that is,

$$V_1 = \int \tau\, da \tag{90}$$

where τ is the shearing stress at any point in the cross section of the upper leg, and da is a differential area including the point. Equation 90 cannot be solved for V_1 without first determining the manner in which τ varies along the leg of the angle so that τ at any point may be expressed in terms of the coordinate z of the point.

The shearing stress τ at any point in a *transverse* section is found by determining the shearing stress at the same point on a *longitudinal* section of the beam, for according to Art. 17 the two stresses are equal in magnitude and act on planes at right angles to each other as indicated in Fig. 52a. Furthermore, as shown in books on elementary mechanics of materials, the shearing stress at any point on a longitudinal plane section of a beam as obtained by considering the equilibrium of the longitudinal forces acting on the block in Fig. 52c, is given by the expression

$$\tau = (V/It)a'\bar{y} = VQ/It \tag{91}$$

in which V is the vertical shear for the section of the beam, a' is the area in the cross section between the point at which τ occurs and the outermost edge of the leg, $\bar{y}$ is the distance of the centroid of the area a' from the neutral axis, I is the moment of inertia of the entire cross section with respect to the neutral axis, and t is the thickness of the area a' at the longitudinal section where the stress τ is to be found; $a'\bar{y}$ is the moment of the area a' and is denoted by Q. Thus the shearing stress at any point on a *transverse* plane through the beam also is given by Eq. 91, and the direction of this shearing stress is perpendicular to the plane in which the *longitudinal* shearing stress lies. In Fig. 52c the longitudinal plane in which τ lies is perpendicular to the upper leg, and hence the stress τ in the transverse plane lies along the leg of the angle; furthermore, since the leg is assumed to be a thin rectangle, the stress may be assumed to lie along the center line of the leg.

Equation 90 may now be solved for the force V_1.

$$V_1 = \int \tau \, da = \int_0^b \frac{V}{It} a' \bar{y} \, da = \frac{V}{It} \int_0^b a' \bar{y} \, da \qquad (92)$$

But from Fig. 52b it is found that $a' = t(b - z)$, $\bar{y} = (\sqrt{2}/2) \cdot (b + z)/2$ and $da = t \, dz$, where z is measured along the leg from the point of intersection of the center line of the two legs, or from the outer corner of the legs since the sections are thin. Hence

$$V_1 = \frac{\sqrt{2}}{4} \frac{Vt}{I} \int_0^b (b^2 - z^2) \, dz = \frac{\sqrt{2}}{6} \frac{Vtb^3}{I} \qquad (93)$$

Since $I = \frac{1}{3}tb^3$, the shearing force V_1 on the area of the upper leg may be written

$$V_1 = (\sqrt{2}/2)V \qquad (94)$$

The shearing force V_2 in the lower leg is found by the foregoing procedure to be equal in magnitude to V_1 and to act along the center line of the lower leg, as shown in Fig. 52b. The forces V_1 and V_2 each have a direction that makes an angle of 45° with the vertical, and, since $V_1 = V_2 = (\sqrt{2}/2)V$, their resultant is a vertical force equal in magnitude to V. But for equilibrium of the beam $V = V'$ must be equal to V_R. Therefore V_1 and V_2 are components of the resisting shearing force V_R, and their point of intersection is a point on the action line of V_R. Thus the point O where the shearing force V_R intersects the axis of symmetry is the shear center, and the longitudinal axis OO' (Fig. 52a) is the bending axis.

Shear Flow. It is sometimes convenient to write Eq. 91 in the form $\tau t = VQ/I$ in which τt is the force per unit length along the center line of the narrow area. This force per unit length is called the shear flow at a point in the section.

As previously noted, beams whose cross sections are composed of narrow rectangles (approximately) such as I sections, angle sections, channel sections, built-up sections using thin plate, and cold-formed sections such as are used in airplane structures are designed to offer large resistance to bending in accordance with the flexure formula but are poorly designed to resist twisting. For such sections it may be of great importance to prevent twisting by insuring that the transverse bending loads pass through the bending axis of the beam.

36   Shear center for a channel section.   In Fig. 53a is shown a cantilever channel beam subjected to bending loads in a plane perpendicular to the axis of symmetry of each cross section of the beam. The problem is to locate the plane of the load so that the channel bends

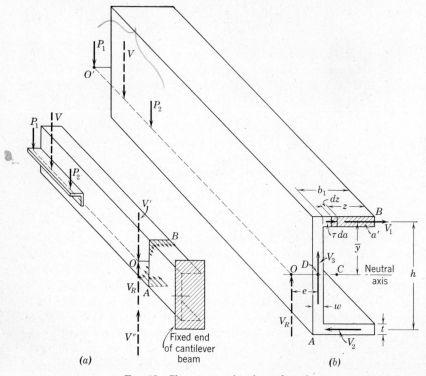

FIG. 53   Shear center for channel section.

without twisting. In other words, it is required to locate the bending axis OO' of the beam, or the shear center O of any cross section AB. This will be done by the method stated in Art. 34 for obtaining an expression for the distance e from the center line of the web to the action line of the resisting shear V_R as shown in Fig. 53b.

The loads P_1, P_2, etc., in Fig. 53a are replaced by their resultant V, and then V is transformed into a force and a couple by introducing, at the shear center O whose location is as yet unknown, two equal and opposite forces V' and V'', each equal to V. The forces V and V'' constitute the external bending couple which is held in equilibrium by the internal or resisting moment at any section AB in accordance with the flexure formula; the distribution of stress on section AB caused by the bending couple is shown in Fig. 53a. The force V' is the vertical shear at section AB, and if twisting is to be prevented V' must be collinear with the resultant resisting shearing force V_R on the section. Thus, as previously noted, the solution for the action line of the shearing force V_R in section AB will serve to establish the location of the shear center O.

Action Line of Resisting Shear Force. The action line of the resultant shearing force V_R in a transverse section of the beam is found by first computing the shearing force in each of the rectangular elements of the cross section of the channel and then obtaining the resultant of these component shearing forces. From the discussion in the preceding article it may be assumed that the shearing force that acts on each rectangular part of the cross section lies along the center line of the rectangle. These component shearing forces are V_1, V_2, and V_3 as shown at section AB of Fig. 53b. The magnitude of the force V_R is already known, from the conditions of equilibrium, to be equal to the vertical shear V. Therefore, it is necessary to compute only the forces V_1 and V_2 since, in using the principle of moments to locate the action line of V_R, the force V_3 will not appear in the equation if a moment center D is selected on the action line of V_3.

The force V_1 may be found from the equation

$$V_1 = \int \tau \, da = \int (VQ/It) \, da = (V/It) \int a'\bar{y} \, da \qquad (95)$$

in which V is the vertical shear for the section AB, I is the moment of inertia with respect to the neutral axis, and the other quantities have the same meaning as in Art. 35 (see Eqs. 90 and 91) and are shown in Fig. 53b. But from Fig. 53b it is found that $a' = tz$, $da = t \, dz$, and $\bar{y} = h/2$. Hence

$$V_1 = \frac{V}{It} \int_0^{b_1} tz \cdot \frac{h}{2} \cdot t \, dz = \frac{Vthb_1^2}{4I} \qquad (96)$$

The value of I for the cross section as expressed by use of the parallel axis theorem is

$$I = 2b_1t(h/2)^2 + \tfrac{1}{12}wh^3 = \tfrac{1}{2}b_1th^2[1 + \tfrac{1}{6}(wh/b_1t)] \qquad (97)$$

in which w is the thickness of the web, and b_1 is the distance from the web to the outer edge of the flange. Therefore, Eq. 96 may be written

$$V_1 = \frac{Vb_1}{2h[1 + \tfrac{1}{6}(wh/b_1t)]} \qquad (98)$$

In a similar manner the force V_2 may be computed, and it is found to be equal in magnitude to V_1.

Since the principle of moments states that the moment of the resultant is equal to the algebraic sum of the moments of the components of the resultant, the following equation may be written

$$V_R \cdot e = \Sigma M_D = V_1(h/2) + V_2(h/2) \qquad (99)$$

By combining Eqs. 98 and 99 we have

$$V_R \cdot e = \frac{Vb_1}{2[1 + \frac{1}{6}(wh/b_1t)]} \qquad (100)$$

And, since $V_R = V$,

$$e = \frac{\frac{1}{2}b_1}{1 + \frac{1}{6}(wh/b_1t)} = \frac{\frac{1}{2}b_1}{1 + \frac{1}{6}(a_w/a_f)} \qquad (101)$$

in which a_w is the area of the web, and a_f is the area of the outstanding flange. This expression shows that e is large when the ratio of the area

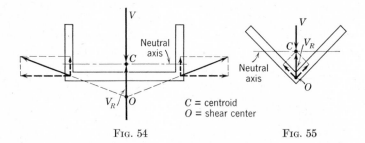

C = centroid
O = shear center

Fig. 54   Fig. 55

of the web to the area of the outstanding flange is relatively small, but the value of e is always less than one-half the width of the outstanding

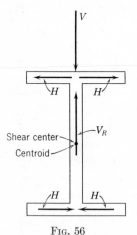

Fig. 56

flange. It should be emphasized that Eq. 101 applies to channels composed of *narrow* rectangles.

It should be noted also that the shear center for a cross section of a beam depends only upon the dimensions of the section. Moreover, the shear center has no physical meaning unless the bending loads on the beam are such that the section is subjected to shear. Thus if a beam is subjected to a bending *couple* the beam will not twist, regardless of the location of the plane of the bending couple.

Furthermore, if the plane of the loads is in a plane of symmetry as shown in Figs. 54 and 55, the resultant resisting shearing force V_R passes through the shear center and also through the centroid of the section. It should be noted also that, for a section having two axes of symmetry such as the I section shown in Fig. 56, a lateral shearing force H is developed in each outstanding flange just as in the channel section of Fig. 53b, but the shearing forces in the two parts of each flange of the I section are equal and opposite and hence the resultant shearing force passes through the centroid of the section; thus the centroid is also the shear center.

Illustrative Problems

Problem 43. A beam has the cross section composed of thin rectangles as shown in Fig. 57a. The loads on the beam lie in a plane perpendicular to the axis of

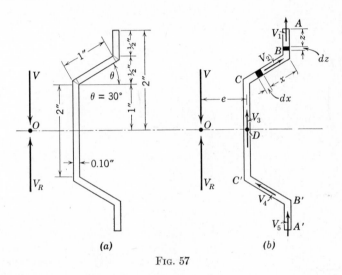

(a)   (b)

Fig. 57

symmetry of the cross section and so located that the beam does not twist; the bending loads cause for any section a vertical shear V. Determine the location of the plane of the loads; that is, locate the shear center for a cross section of the beam.

Solution. The shear center is located by determining the action line of the resultant resisting shear V_R on a cross section of the beam. First the resisting shearing forces V_1, V_2, etc., shown in Fig. 57b in the various parts AB, BC, etc., of the cross section must be found. It should be noted that the condition of symmetry gives $V_1 = V_5$ and $V_2 = V_4$.

The value of V_1 is given by the equation $V_1 = \int \tau \, da$ in which τ is the shearing stress at any point in the part AB and is found from the equation $\tau = VQ/It = (V/It)a'\bar{y}$. But from Fig. 57b it will be noted that Q, which is the statical moment of the area between the point where τ occurs and the upper free edge of the cross section, is given by the equation $Q = a'\bar{y} = tz(2 - \frac{1}{2}z)$ in which t is the thickness and z is measured from the free edge of the cross section. Hence $\tau = (V/I)z(2 - \frac{1}{2}z)$.

Thus

$$V_1 = \int_0^{\frac{1}{2}} \tau \, da = \frac{V}{I} \int_0^{\frac{1}{2}} z \left(2 - \frac{1}{2} z \right) t \, dz = 0.23 \frac{Vt}{I}$$

Similarly, $V_2 = \int \tau \, da$ in which $\tau = (V/It)a'\bar{y}$. And $a'\bar{y}$ corresponding to a point in part BC at the distance x from B is

$$a'\bar{y} = \tfrac{7}{4}(\tfrac{1}{2}t) + (\tfrac{3}{2} - \tfrac{1}{4}x)tx = t(\tfrac{7}{8} + \tfrac{3}{2}x - \tfrac{1}{4}x^2)$$

and hence the shearing stress at any point in the part BC is

$$\tau = (V/I)(\tfrac{7}{8} + \tfrac{3}{2}x - \tfrac{1}{4}x^2)$$

Thus $$V_2 = \int_0^1 \tau \, da = \frac{V}{I} \int_0^1 \left(\frac{7}{8} + \frac{3}{2} x - \frac{1}{4} x^2 \right) t \, dx = 1.54 \frac{Vt}{I}$$

But $I = \tfrac{1}{12}t(2)^3 + 2[\tfrac{1}{12}2t(\tfrac{1}{2})^3 + t(1.25)^2] + 2[\tfrac{1}{12}t(\tfrac{1}{2})^3 + \tfrac{1}{2}t(1.75)^2] = 6.92t$

Therefore $$V_1 = V_5 = 0.23Vt/6.92t = 0.033V$$

$$V_2 = V_4 = 1.54Vt/6.92t = 0.22V$$

Since the moment of the resultant V_R is equal to the algebraic sum of the moments of its components, the following equation may be written:

$$-V_R e = \Sigma M_D = (V_1 + V_5)0.866 - (V_2 + V_4)0.866 = -0.33V$$

$$e = 0.33 \text{ in., since } V_R = V$$

Further, since e is found to be positive, the assumed position of V_R shown in Fig. 57 is correct. Therefore, the shear center O is at a distance $e = 0.33$ in. to the left of D. It will be noted that by selecting D on the action line of V_3 we did not need to use the magnitude of V_3 in the solution.

Problem 44. A beam is built up of aluminum alloy sheet metal having a thickness t of 0.02 in. bent into the shape of a channel whose dimensions are shown in

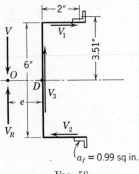

Fig. 58. The flanges of the channel are stiffened at the outer edges by riveting to the flanges two aluminum alloy angles, each having a cross-sectional area of 0.99 sq in. whose centroidal distance from the neutral axis is 3.51 in. If the beam is subjected to loads in a plane perpendicular to the axis of symmetry, determine the location of the plane so that the beam will not twist as it bends.

Solution. In computing the shearing stress in beams having cross sections built up of a thin plate with heavy stiffening flanges as in Fig. 58, it is customary to assume that the distribution of shearing stress along the thin plate on any cross section is constant. This simplifying assumption is justifiable when the area of the thin plate is small in comparison to the area of the stiffeners. This fact may be illustrated as follows: The shearing stress in the thin plate in this beam at the rivet line is $\tau = (V/It)a'\bar{y} = 3.47V/It$, where $a'\bar{y}$ is the statical moment of the area of the stiffening angle with respect to

Fig. 58

the axis of symmetry of the cross section of the beam. The shearing stress at the point D on the axis of symmetry is $\tau = (V/It)a'\bar{y} = 3.68V/It$, where $a'\bar{y}$ is the statical moment of the area of the angle plus the statical moment of the area of the thin plate section above D. Thus the shearing stress in the thin plate varies only by about 6 per cent.

The location of the shear center and hence the location of the plane of the loads is determined by finding the action line of the resultant shearing force V_R on a cross section of the beam. First, the shearing forces V_1 and V_2 must be found. In finding the forces V_1 in the upper horizontal thin web of Fig. 58, the stiffening angle is assumed to offer little or no resistance to shear. Further, from the condition of symmetry it is known that $V_1 = V_2$. Since the shearing stress is assumed to be constant in the thin web, the force V_1 may be expressed as $V_1 = \tau \times 2t$, in which $\tau = 3.47V/It$ as computed previously. Thus $V_1 = V_2 = 6.94V/I$. It is further assumed that the area of the thin web may be neglected in computing the moment of inertia. Hence $I = 2 \times (3.51)^2 a_f = 24.4$ in.^{4}. Thus $V_1 = V_2 = 0.284V$. The action line of V_R may now be found from the principle of moments. If the moment center D is selected on the action line of V_3, we may write

$$V_R \cdot e = \Sigma M_D = 3V_1 + 3V_2 = 1.7V$$

$$e = 1.7 \text{ in., since } V_R = V$$

It should be noted that the distance e from the web to the shear center is relatively large when compared to the shear center for a channel section which does not have heavy stiffening flanges. For example, if the thin-walled channel considered in this problem did not have the angles riveted to its flanges, the distance e as given by Eq. 101 would be equal to 0.67 in., and thus by adding the angle stiffeners to the beam the value of e becomes approximately $2\frac{1}{2}$ times as large as it is for the channel without the stiffeners.

Problems

45. From Eq. 101, locate the shear center for each of the sections of rolled steel channels shown in Fig. 59. The sections are: (a) a 6-in. 15.3-lb ship channel; (b) a

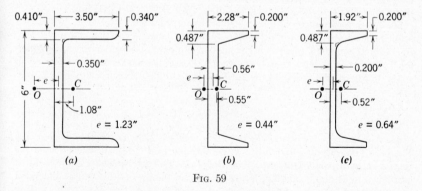

FIG. 59

6-in. 15.5-lb (heavy) structural channel; and (c) a 6-in. 8.2-lb standard structural channel. The dimensions of these channel sections are given in Fig. 59, and the answers also are given.

46. A thin-walled hollow tube has a cross section in the form of a square, each side of which has the dimension b. The tube is slit along one of the corners the whole length of the tube. The tube is used as a cantilever beam to resist a concentrated load at the free end. Derive an expression for locating the shear center. Check the result by referring to Fig. D of Table 3 and considering that $b_1 = b$.

47. Find the shear center for a thin-walled circular tube which has a thin longitudinal slit along its entire length. *Hint:* Use the expression for the circular arc section shown in Fig. E of Table 3.   *Ans. $e = 2R$.*

48. A lipped channel whose cross section has the dimensions shown in Fig. 60 is used as a cantilever beam. The plane of loading contains the bending axis of the beam and is perpendicular to the axis of symmetry of each cross section. The maximum shear in the beam is $V = 1500$ lb. Compute the shearing stress in the plane of the cross section of the beam at points A, B, C, and D. The point D is at the midpoint of the upper lip of the flange.

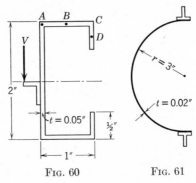

FIG. 60   FIG. 61

49. A cantilever beam has the cross section shown in Fig. E of Table 3 in which $2\theta = 180°$. A concentrated load $P = 400$ lb acts at the end of the beam in a transverse plane which contains the centroid of the section and is perpendicular to the axis of symmetry. Compute the twisting moment at any cross section of the beam if the dimensions of the section are as follows: $R = 10$ in., $t = 0.25$ in.

50. A beam is built up of a thin metal sheet of thickness $t = 0.02$ in. bent into a semicircular shape as shown in Fig. 61. Stiffening flanges consisting of 1 in. by 1 in. by $\frac{1}{8}$ in. aluminum T sections, weighing 0.323 lb per ft (see *Alcoa Structural Handbook*) are riveted to the thin web as shown. Locate the shear center for this section.

51. In Fig. D of Table 3 let the lips b_1 be horizontal and show that

$$e = \frac{b_1}{2[\frac{1}{3}(b/b_1) + 1]}$$

52. A cantilever beam is made up of two channels latticed together as shown in Fig. 62. The beam is subjected to a concentrated load P at a distance d from the centroid C of the whole cross section of the beam. Two arrangements of the channels are shown in Figs. 62a and 62b, but in each beam the over-all horizontal dimension is h. The beam at any section is subjected to a bending moment and a twisting moment. It may be assumed that the lattice bars will cause the two channels to act as one body in resisting torsion, and hence the beam has a relatively large resistance to twisting; but it is assumed that the lattice bars will allow each channel to act independently in bending in resisting the twisting moment. Under these conditions the twisting moment caused by P may be considered to be resisted primarily by the bending in the two channels; the twisting moment causes the left channel in each

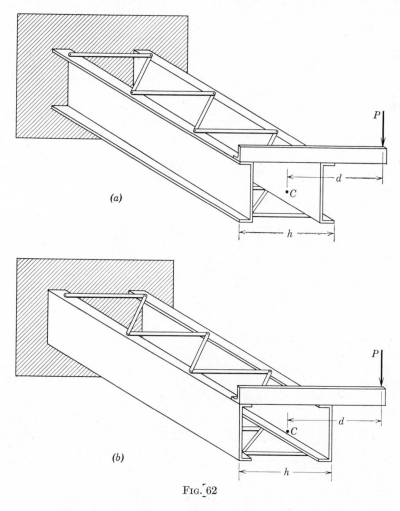

Fig. 62

arrangement to bend vertically upward and the other channel to bend vertically downward. Which arrangement would resist the load P with the lesser amount of bending of the channels? Explain.

37   Shear center for various sections composed of thin rectangular areas.   In Table 3 are given the shear centers for various types of sections made up of thin rectangles and having only one axis of symmetry. These formulas were derived by locating the action line of the

TABLE 3

LOCATIONS OF SHEAR CENTERS FOR SECTIONS HAVING ONE AXIS OF SYMMETRY

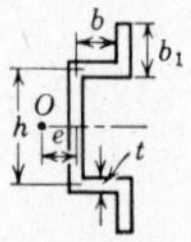

FIG. A

$$e = b \left[\frac{1 + \dfrac{1}{2}\dfrac{b}{b_1} - \dfrac{4}{3}\left(\dfrac{b_1}{h}\right)^2}{1 + \dfrac{1}{6}\dfrac{h}{b_1} + \dfrac{b}{b_1} + 2\dfrac{b_1}{h}\left(1 + \dfrac{2}{3}\dfrac{b_1}{h}\right)} \right]$$

Both of these equations reduce to Eq. 101 when $b_1 = 0$

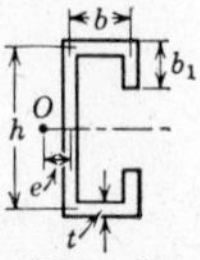

FIG. B

$$e = b \left[\frac{1 + \dfrac{1}{2}\dfrac{b}{b_1} - \dfrac{4}{3}\left(\dfrac{b_1}{h}\right)^2}{1 + \dfrac{1}{6}\dfrac{h}{b_1} + \dfrac{b}{b_1} - \dfrac{2b_1}{h}\left(1 - \dfrac{2}{3}\dfrac{b_1}{h}\right)} \right]$$

FIG. C

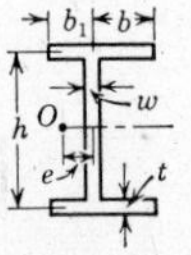

$$e = \frac{3(b^2 - b_1^2)}{(w/t)h + 6(b + b_1)}; \quad b_1 < b$$

FIG. D

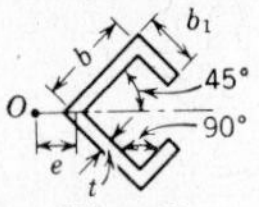

$$e = b_1 \cdot \frac{\dfrac{b}{b_1}\left(3\dfrac{b}{b_1} - 2\right)}{\sqrt{2}\left[\left(\dfrac{b}{b_1}\right)^3 + 3\left(\dfrac{b}{b_1}\right)^2 - 3\dfrac{b}{b_1} + 1\right]}$$

FIG. E

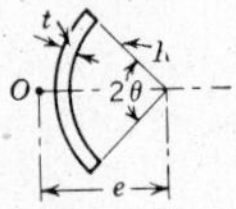

$$e = \frac{2R(\sin\theta - \theta\cos\theta)}{\theta - \sin\theta\cos\theta}$$

For semicircle, $\theta = \dfrac{\pi}{2}$ and

$$e = 4R/\pi$$

$$e = R \cdot \frac{12 + 6\pi\dfrac{b + b_1}{R} + 6\left(\dfrac{b}{R}\right)^2 + 12\dfrac{b}{R}\cdot\dfrac{b_1}{R} + 3\pi\left(\dfrac{b_1}{R}\right)^2 - 4\left(\dfrac{b_1}{R}\right)^3\dfrac{b}{R}}{3\pi + 12\dfrac{b + b_1}{R} + 4\left(\dfrac{b_1}{R}\right)^2\left(3 + \dfrac{b_1}{R}\right)}$$

For $b_1 = 0$:

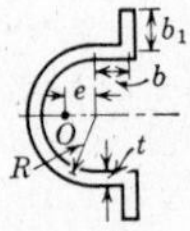

FIG. F

$$e = R \cdot \frac{4 + 2\pi\dfrac{b}{R} + 2\left(\dfrac{b}{R}\right)^2}{\pi + 4\dfrac{b}{R}}$$

For $b = 0$:

$$e = R \cdot \frac{3\left[4 + \dfrac{2b_1\pi}{R} + \pi\left(\dfrac{b_1}{R}\right)^2\right]}{3\pi + 4\left(\dfrac{b_1}{R}\right)^3 + 12\dfrac{b_1}{R} + 12\left(\dfrac{b_1}{R}\right)^2}$$

resisting shearing force V_R as was done in the preceding articles for the equal-leg angle and the channel sections and also in the preceding illustrative problems.

For a method of determining the shear center for an area which has no axis of symmetry, see Art. 46.

Selected References

1. Kuhn, P., "Elementary Principles of Shell Stress Analysis with Some Notes on the Use of the Shear Center," *Technical Note* 691, 1939, National Advisory Committee for Aeronautics. The method of determining the shear center of sections made up of thin rectangular areas is discussed.
2. Bruhn, E. F., *Airplane Structural Design*, John S. Swift Co., 1943. On pages A14.1 to A14.7 are given a number of illustrative problems in which the location of the shear center is determined.
3. Seely, F. B., W. J. Putnam, and W. L. Schwalbe, "Torsional Effect of Transverse Bending Loads on Channel Beams," *Bulletin* 211, Engineering Experiment Station, University of Illinois, 1930.

Chapter 5

UNSYMMETRICAL BENDING

38 Introduction. One of the assumptions on which the flexure formula $M = \sigma I/c$ is based is that the neutral axis for each cross section of the beam is perpendicular to the plane of the loads. But, as shown in the next article, this condition requires that the plane of the loads shall be coincident with, or parallel to, a plane containing a principal * centroidal axis of inertia of each cross section of the beam. If the cross section of the beam has an axis of symmetry, the foregoing condition required by the flexure formula will be satisfied if the plane of the loads contains the axis of symmetry of each section, for the reason that an axis of symmetry of an area is always a principal axis of inertia. Bending caused by loads that do *not* lie in (or parallel to) a plane that contains the principal centroidal axes of inertia of the cross sections is usually called unsymmetrical bending.

Some beams, such as roof purlins, are subjected to loads that lie in planes that make large angles with principal planes, as indicated in Fig. 63, whereas many beams in structures and machines are subjected

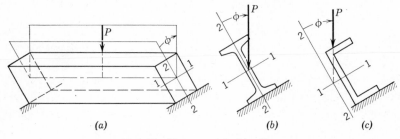

(a) (b) (c)

Fig. 63   Unsymmetrical loading.

to loads whose planes are inclined only slightly to principal planes, but these small inclinations may be of importance. The shapes of most of the rolled sections, such as I sections, channel sections, etc., that are

* Principal axes of inertia are discussed in Appendix III.

112

used for beams are designed to give large resistance to bending *on the assumption* that the stresses developed are in accordance with the flexure formula $\sigma = M/(I/c)$; in other words, the shape of cross section is made so that I/c is as large as is practicable. It will be shown in this chapter, however, that a section that is well designed to resist bending due to symmetrical loading may be poorly designed to resist bending due to unsymmetrical loading, even though the plane of the loads deviates only slightly from a plane of symmetry.

Notation. The following coordinate axes are used in this chapter:

X', Y' are perpendicular axes lying in a transverse section of the beam and passing through any arbitrarily chosen point in any arbitrarily chosen directions.

X, Y are perpendicular axes lying in a transverse section of the beam and passing through the centroid of the section, but having any arbitrarily chosen directions.

U, V are the centroidal principal axes of inertia of a transverse section of the beam.

M, N are perpendicular centroidal axes in a transverse section of the beam such that the N axis coincides with the neutral axis of the beam.

39   Stress in beam subjected to unsymmetrical bending. In the following discussion it is assumed that the beam is straight and of constant cross section. Furthermore, the loads are assumed to act through the bending axis of the beam so that the beam is not subjected to torsion in addition to bending, and to act in a direction perpendicular to the bending axis so that bending stresses are not accompanied by direct axial tensile or compressive stresses.

In Fig. 64a is shown a cantilever beam subjected to loads that lie in a plane containing the bending axis and making an angle ϕ with the vertical longitudinal plane. Let it be required to determine the normal (bending) stress σ at any point in a cross section, such as section AB, and also the position of the neutral axis NN in the section. An enlarged portion of the beam to the left of the section is shown in Figs. 64b and 64c.

In accordance with Step 1 of the procedure discussed in Art. 8, a free-body diagram is drawn of the portion of the beam to the left of section AB as indicated in Fig. 64b, and the equations of equilibrium are applied to the forces shown in the diagram. The normal force $\sigma\, da$ on only one element da of area is shown, and the shearing forces $\tau\, da$ are neglected since only normal stresses are here under consideration. In Fig. 64*b* the axes X' and Y' are any set of perpendicular axes in section AB; they are chosen as horizontal and vertical axes passing through the shear center O, although the same result would be obtained in the following analysis if these axes intersected at any other point in the section. The axes X and Y pass through the centroid C and are parallel to the axes OX' and OY'.

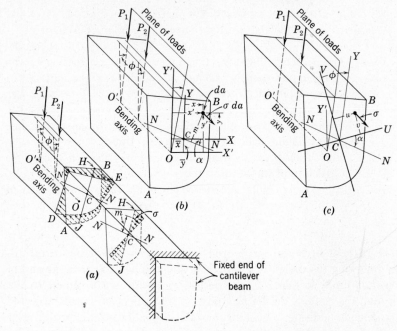

Fig. 64   Analysis of stresses in unsymmetrically loaded beam.

The application of the three equations of equilibrium to the forces in Fig. 64*b* gives

$$\int \sigma \, da = 0 \tag{102}$$

$$M_{x'} = \int y' \sigma \, da \tag{103}$$

$$M_{y'} = \int x' \sigma \, da \tag{104}$$

in which $M_{x'}$ and $M_{y'}$ are the bending moments with respect to the axes OX' and OY', respectively, or to the axes CX and CY, since the moment about all parallel lines in the section are equal. The moments $M_{x'}$ and

$M_{y'}$ are the components of the bending moment M that lie in the vertical and horizontal planes, respectively. Thus

$$M_{x'} = M \cos \phi \tag{105}$$

$$M_{y'} = M \sin \phi \tag{106}$$

In accordance with Step 2 of Art. 8, the distribution of the stress on the area must now be determined; that is, the relation between σ at any point and the coordinates x' and y' of the point must be found, for use in Eqs. 102, 103, and 104.

It is assumed that on any cross section of the beam such as AB in Fig. 64a the stress varies directly as the distance from the neutral axis NN, provided that the elastic strength of the material is not exceeded; the justification for this assumption of linear distribution of stress is the same as that for bending due to symmetrical loading. Thus in Fig. 64a, the stress σ at points on any line HJ, which is perpendicular to the neutral axis NN, is proportional to the distance m from the neutral axis. The distribution of stress on the cross section, therefore, is expressed by the equation

$$\sigma = km \tag{107}$$

where k is a constant.

Equations 102 and 107 are sufficient to prove that the neutral axis for any cross section of the beam passes through the centroid of the cross section. The proof is as follows. Equation 102 may be written

$$\int \sigma \, da = k \int m \, da = 0 \tag{108}$$

Since k is not equal to zero, $\int m \, da$ must be equal to zero. Therefore, the axis from which m is measured (the neutral axis) must pass through the centroid C of the cross-sectional area and not, in general, through the shear center O.

The direction of the neutral axis (the value for α) and the value for the stress σ at any point may be found from Eqs. 103, 104, and 107. But before substituting the value of σ from Eq. 107 in Eqs. 103 and 104 it will be convenient to express m in terms of x and y and α. From the geometry of Fig. 64b the expression for m is

$$m = (y' - \bar{y}) \cos \alpha + (x' - \bar{x}) \sin \alpha$$

$$= y \cos \alpha + x \sin \alpha \tag{109}$$

where $\bar{x}$ and $\bar{y}$ are the distances from OX' and OY', respectively, of the centroid of the section. Equation 107 may now be written

$$\sigma = km = k[(y' - \bar{y}) \cos \alpha + (x' - \bar{x}) \sin \alpha]$$

$$= k(y \cos \alpha + x \sin \alpha) \tag{110}$$

The substitution of the value of σ from Eq. 110 in Eq. 103 gives

$$M_{x'} = \int y' \sigma \, da$$

$$= k \int [(y'^2 - y'\bar{y}) \cos \alpha + (x'y' - \bar{x}y') \sin \alpha] \, da \tag{111}$$

$$= k \cos \alpha \left(\int y'^2 \, da - \bar{y} \int y' \, da \right)$$

$$+ k \sin \alpha \left(\int x'y' \, da - \bar{x} \int y' \, da \right) \tag{112}$$

$$= k \cos \alpha (I_{x'} - \bar{y} \cdot \bar{y}a) + k \sin \alpha (I_{x'y'} - \overline{xy}a) \tag{113}$$

But

$$I_{x'} - a\bar{y}^2 = I_x \qquad \text{and} \qquad I_{x'y'} - a\overline{xy} = I_{xy} \qquad \text{(see Appendix III)}$$

Therefore

$$M_{x'} = M_x = kI_x \cos \alpha + kI_{xy} \sin \alpha \tag{114}$$

in which I_x denotes the moment of inertia of the cross-sectional area with respect to a centroidal axis CX parallel to the axis OX', and I_{xy} denotes the product of inertia with respect to a set of rectangular centroidal axes CX and CY parallel to the axes OX' and OY'. It is important to note that the foregoing derivation shows that axes passing through the centroid are needed in the solution.

Since the axes CX and CY are any arbitrary set of perpendicular axes passing through the centroid of the section, they may be chosen to be principal axes of inertia designated as the U and V axes as shown in Fig. 64c. Equation 114 may then be written in the simple form

$$M_u = kI_u \cos \alpha \tag{115}$$

since I_{uv} is equal to zero for principal axes (see Appendix III).

Similarly, Eqs. 104 and 110 give

$$M_{y'} = M_y = \int x' \sigma \, da = kI_{xy} \cos \alpha + kI_y \sin \alpha \tag{116}$$

and when the principal axes are used this equation becomes

$$M_v = kI_v \sin \alpha \tag{117}$$

Direction of Neutral Axis. The angle α between the principal axis of inertia CU and the neutral axis CN in Fig. 64c is found by dividing Eq. 117 by Eq. 115 and making use of Eqs. 105 and 106 in which the principal axes U and V are used instead of X' and Y'. This gives

$$\frac{M_v}{M_u} = \tan\phi = \frac{I_v}{I_u}\tan\alpha$$

or

$$\tan\alpha = \frac{I_u}{I_v}\tan\phi \tag{118}$$

in which u and v refer to *principal* centroidal axes, and ϕ is measured from the V principal axis whereas α is measured from the U principal axis. Principal axes are frequently designated as 1 and 2, as indicated in Fig. 63. If this is done Eq. 118 could be written $\tan\alpha = (I_1/I_2)\tan\phi$. From Eq. 118 the direction of the neutral axis may be determined if ϕ and the properties of the area are known.

This equation shows that, if the loads lie in (or parallel to) one principal centroidal plane, the neutral plane is the other principal centroidal plane, since α is equal to zero when ϕ is zero. Furthermore, it should be noted that in Fig. 64c the angle ϕ is measured from one principal axis while α is measured in the same sense from the other, and hence if the plane of the loads lies in the first quadrant the neutral axis must lie in the fourth quadrant, as shown in Fig. 64c. Thus the following very convenient physical interpretation of Eq. 118 can be made.

If the plane of the loads is rotated about the bending axis of the beam through an angle ϕ from one principal centroidal plane (or a plane parallel

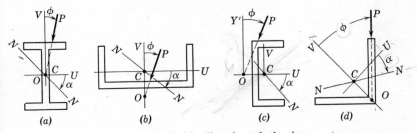

FIG. 65   Unsymmetrical loading through the shear center.

thereto), the neutral plane will rotate about the longitudinal centroidal axis of the beam in the same direction from the other principal plane through an angle α as given by Eq. 118. This condition is illustrated in Fig. 65 for beams having four different cross sections.

Stress at Any Point in Cross Section. Equation 110 gives the stress in terms of the coordinates x, y with reference to any set of centroidal axes and the angle α. If in Eq. 110 the axes of reference are chosen as the principal axes of inertia through the centroid, the equation becomes

$$\sigma = k(v \cos \alpha + u \sin \alpha) \tag{119}$$

By solving Eq. 115 for $\cos \alpha$ and Eq. 117 for $\sin \alpha$, and by substituting these values in Eq. 119, the expression for σ becomes

$$\sigma = \frac{(M \cos \phi)v}{I_u} + \frac{(M \sin \phi)u}{I_v} = \frac{M_u v}{I_u} + \frac{M_v u}{I_v} \tag{120}$$

in which u and v are coordinates of any point in the section with reference to *principal* centroidal axes as shown in Fig. 64c; M_u is the bending moment about the U principal centroidal axis (or any axis in the area parallel thereto) and is equal to $M \cos \phi$, where ϕ is measured from the V principal centroidal axis; M_v is the bending moment about the V principal centroidal axis (or any axis parallel thereto) and is equal to $M \sin \phi$.

Sign Convention. In Eq. 120 the sign of M_u (or $M \cos \phi$) is to be considered positive if it produces tensile stress (and negative if it produces compressive stress) at points that have a positive v coordinate, and similarly M_v (or $M \sin \phi$) is positive if it produces a tensile stress (and negative if it produces compressive stress) at points that have a positive u coordinate. In many problems the sign of the stress σ in Eq. 120 (whether a tensile or a compressive stress) can be determined easily from inspection, but by following the foregoing conventions of signs σ will be a tensile stress when Eq. 120 indicates that it has a positive sign, and a compressive stress when it has a negative sign.

Equation 120 shows that the stress at any point in the cross section of the beam may be found as follows: First determine the direction of the principal centroidal axes; then calculate the bending moments that lie in planes perpendicular to these principal axes; then calculate by means of the flexure formula the stress due to each of these component moments as if acting alone, and add (algebraically) the stresses thus found.

Limitation on the Flexure Formula. Equation 120 reduces to the flexure formula $\sigma = My/I$ when ϕ is equal to zero, since then $\sin \phi = 0$ and $\cos \phi = 1$. Likewise, in Eq. 118, when ϕ is equal to zero, α is also equal to zero. Therefore, the flexure formula applies only when the plane of the loads is parallel to (or coincident with) one principal centroidal plane of the beam, in which case the other principal centroidal plane is the neutral plane. In other words, since principal planes are at right angles to each other, the flexure formula is applicable only when the neutral axis is perpendicular to the plane of the loads, and this condition will be satisfied only if the plane of the loads contains, or is parallel to, a principal centroidal axis of inertia of each cross section of the beam.

Combined Bending and Axial Loads. If the beam is subjected to loads that are not perpendicular to the bending axis of the beam, the longitudinal normal (tensile or compressive) stress at any point on a cross section of the beam may usually be found, in accordance with the principal of superposition (Art. 13), by resolving the loads into components along the bending axis and perpendicular thereto, and adding (algebraically) the stress caused by the components along the bending axis and the bending stress caused by the bending moment of the components perpendicular to the bending axis. That is,

$$\sigma = (P/a) + (M_u v/I_u) + (M_v u/I_v) \tag{121}$$

Illustrative Problems

Problem 53. The rectangular beam shown in Fig. 66 is 6 in. wide and 8 in. deep; it is used as a simply supported beam on a span of 16 ft. Two loads of 800 lb each are applied to the beam, each load being 4 ft from a support; the plane of the loads makes an angle of 30° with the vertical plane of symmetry. Find the direction of the neutral axis and the bending stress at A.

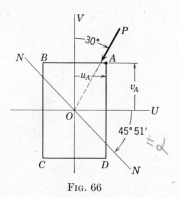

Fɪɢ. 66

Solution. The U and V axes shown are principal centroidal axes. Hence

$$\tan \alpha = (I_u/I_v) \tan \phi = (256/144) \tan 30° = (256/144) \times 0.577 = 1.028$$

since

$$I_u = \tfrac{1}{12}bh^3 = \tfrac{1}{12}6(8)^3 = 256 \text{ in.}^4$$

$$I_v = \tfrac{1}{12}hb^3 = 144 \text{ in.}^4$$

Therefore

$$\alpha = 45° 51' \quad \text{(as shown in Fig. 66)}$$

All points in the area above the neutral axis NN are subjected to compressive stresses, and all points below to tensile stresses. The stress at the corner A is

$$\sigma_A = (M_u v_A)/I_u + (M_v u_A)/I_v$$

It is evident from inspection that each component moment causes compressive stress at A, and that the numerical value of σ_A is found by adding the two parts of the right-hand member of the equation; however, the signs of u, v, M_u, and M_v will cause the equation to yield the correct results. Thus, $u_A = -3$ in.; $v_A = +4$ in.; $M_u = -(800 \times 4 \times 12 \times 0.866) = -33,300$ lb-in.; and $M_v = +(38,400 \times 0.5) = +19,200$ lb-in. Therefore

$$\sigma_A = \frac{-33,300 \times 4}{256} + \frac{19,200 \times (-3)}{144}$$

$$= -518 - 400 = -918 \text{ lb/in.}^2 \quad \text{(compression)}$$

Problem 54. An 8-in. by 8-in. by $\frac{3}{4}$-in. angle is loaded as shown in Fig. 67a, the total load P being 10,000 lb. Find the direction of the neutral axis for the section BC. Also calculate the values of the bending stresses at A, B, and C; compare these values with those found by assuming (erroneously) that the neutral axis is perpendicular to the plane of the loads and using the ordinary flexure formula. Assume that the beam is prevented from twisting by lateral supports not shown in Fig. 67a.

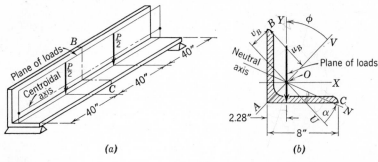

FIG. 67

Solution. The U and V axes (Fig. 67b) are the principal centroidal axes since the V axis is an axis of symmetry. The following values are obtained from a steel-maker's handbook.

$$a = 11.44 \text{ sq in.} \qquad x_0 = y_0 = 2.28 \text{ in.} \qquad \text{(see Fig. 67b)}$$

$$I_x = I_y = 69.7 \text{ in.}^4 \qquad r_u = 1.57 \text{ in.}$$

Hence $\qquad I_u = a r_u^2 = 11.44 \times (1.57)^2 = 28.2 \text{ in.}^4$

Also $\qquad I_u + I_v = I_x + I_y \qquad \text{(Appendix III)}$

Hence $\qquad I_v = 2(69.7) - 28.2 = 111.2 \text{ in.}^4$

Therefore

$$\tan \alpha = (I_u/I_v) \tan \phi = (28.2/111.2) \tan 45° = (28.2/111.2) \times 1 = 0.254$$

Therefore $\alpha = 14° 20'$ in the counterclockwise direction from the U axis as shown in Fig. 67b, since ϕ is counterclockwise from the V axis.

The central portion of the beam is subjected to a bending couple having a moment $M = 5000 \times 40 = 200{,}000$ lb-in. Furthermore, the magnitude of M_u and of M_v is $200{,}000 \times 0.707 = 141{,}400$ lb-in., but the sign of M_u is negative and that of M_v is positive.

Stresses at A, B, and C:

$$\sigma_A = \frac{M_u v_A}{I_u} + \frac{M_v u_A}{I_v} = \frac{-(141{,}400) \times (-3.22)}{28.2}$$

$$= 16{,}200 \text{ lb/in.}^2 \quad \text{(tension)}$$

$$\sigma_B = \frac{-(141{,}000) \times 2.44}{28.2} + \frac{141{,}000 \times (-5.66)}{111.2}$$

$$= -19{,}300 \text{ lb/in.}^2 \quad \text{(compression)}$$

$$\sigma_C = \frac{-(141{,}000) \times 2.44}{28.2} + \frac{141{,}000 \times 5.66}{111.2}$$

$$= -5100 \text{ lb/in.}^2 \quad \text{(compression)}$$

The values for σ at A, B, and C as found from the flexure formula, assuming (erroneously) that the X axis is the neutral axis, are

$$\sigma_A = \sigma_C = \frac{M y_A}{I_x} = \frac{200{,}000 \times 2.28}{69.7} = 6550 \text{ lb/in.}^2 \quad \text{(tension)}$$

$$\sigma_B = \frac{200{,}000 \times 5.72}{69.7} = 16{,}400 \text{ lb/in.}^2 \quad \text{(compression)}$$

If the stress at B should be considered to govern the allowable moment or load, the value of the allowable load for this angle beam as found from the flexure formula, assuming the X axis to be the neutral axis, would be about 15 per cent too large.

Problems

55. In Fig. 64b is the plane of the internal or resisting moment on section AB (the plane in which the resultant of the tensile $\sigma\, da$ forces and the resultant of the compressive $\sigma\, da$ forces lie) parallel to the plane of the bending moment M?

56. A timber beam 10 in. wide by 12 in. deep by 14 ft long is used as a simply supported beam on a span of 12 ft. It is subjected to a concentrated load of 6000 lb at the mid-section of the span. If the plane of the load makes an angle of 45° with the vertical plane of symmetry, find the direction of the neutral axis and the maximum stress in the beam.   *Ans.* $\alpha = 55° 15'$, $\sigma = 1400$ lb/in.²,

57. In Fig. 68 let $b = 2$ in., $h = 6$ in., and $l = 20$ in. If the maximum bending stress caused by P is 2000 lb per sq in., calculate the value of P.

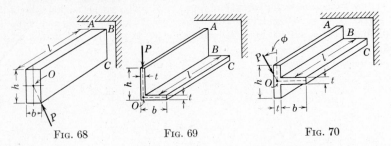

FIG. 68   FIG. 69   FIG. 70

58. In Fig. 69 let $b = 8$ in., $h = 8$ in., $t = \frac{3}{4}$ in., $l = 50$ in., and $P = 4000$ lb. Calculate the bending stresses at A and C.

59. In Fig. 70 let $b = 6$ in., $t = 2$ in., $h = 6$ in., $l = 40$ in., $P = 6000$ lb, and $\phi = 30°$. Calculate the bending stress at A, and determine the location of the neutral axis.

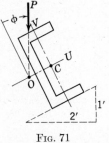

FIG. 71

60. A 6-in. 8.2-lb rolled steel channel is used as a simply supported beam as a purlin in a roof (Fig. 71). If the pitch of the roof is $\frac{1}{4}$ (that is, the roof rises $\frac{1}{2}$ ft per horizontal foot) and the span of the beam or purlin is 10 ft, find the maximum stress in the beam caused by a uniformly distributed vertical load of 100 lb per ft of span, and state the location in the section where this stress occurs; the plane of the load contains the bending axis of the beam. *Ans.* $\sigma = -16,500$ lb/in.^{2}.

61. A load P of 25,000 lb is applied to a 6-in. by 6-in. by $\frac{3}{8}$-in. angle by means of a riveted connection as shown in Fig. 72. The load P acts through O' parallel to the longitudinal centroidal axis of the angle which passes through O. Find the maximum stress at a section, such as AA, of the angle. *Hint:* Resolve the load P into the load (equal to P) at the centroid and a bending couple. *Ans.* $\phi = 8° 19'$; $\sigma_B = 12,950$ lb/in.^{2}, tension.

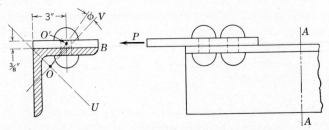

FIG. 72

62. An 8-in. 11.5-lb. channel (Fig. 71) is used for a roof purlin. The span is 12 ft, and the pitch of the roof is $\frac{1}{4}$ (see Prob. 60). The purlin is subjected to a uniformly distributed load of 100 lb per ft of span; the load is assumed to lie in a vertical plane containing the bending axis in the purlin. Find the maximum stress in the purlin.
Ans. $\sigma = -16,400$ lb/in.^{2}.

63. A 5-in. by $3\frac{1}{4}$-in. by $\frac{5}{16}$-in. Z-bar (Fig. 73) is used for a roof purlin. The span is 10 ft and the pitch of the roof is $\frac{1}{4}$ (see Prob. 60). The purlin is subjected to a uniformly distributed load of 100 lb per ft of span; the load is assumed to lie in a vertical plane containing the bending axis. (a) Find the maximum stress in the purlin. (b) If the Z-bar were placed with CD pointing upward along the roof and BA downward, what would be the maximum stress developed in the bar?

$\qquad$ *Ans.* (a) $\sigma_A = -2260$; $\sigma_B = -2670$ lb/in.^{2}.

$\qquad\qquad$ (b) $\sigma_A = +7200$; $\sigma_B = -10{,}300$ lb/in.^{2}.

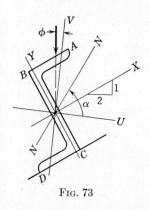

Fig. 73

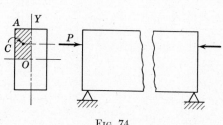

Fig. 74

64. A timber beam having a cross section 8 in. by 16 in. is subjected to an end thrust of 400 lb per sq in. over one-quarter of the area of the end as indicated in Fig. 74, the resultant thrust P of 12,800 lb acting at the centroid C of the shaded area. The beam is also subjected to a uniformly distributed load of 300 lb per ft of span in the OY plane. The span is 10 ft. Find the maximum longitudinal stress in the beam. The deflection of the beam may be neglected.

40 Change in direction of neutral axis and increase in stress in rolled sections due to a very small inclination of plane of loads to a principal plane.

Equation 118 shows that α is large even though ϕ is relatively small, provided that the cross section of the beam is of such a shape that I_u is much larger than I_v which is a condition that exists with respect to some of the commonly used sections such as I sections and channels. Thus the neutral axis of I beams, channels, etc., is steeply inclined to the horizontal axis of symmetry when the plane of the loads deviates but little from the vertical plane of symmetry, and likewise the maximum bending stress is increased considerably, as is indicated in the following problem and in Table 4 in which the plane of the loads is assumed to make an angle of only 1° with a principal plane.

Illustrative Problem

Problem 65. A 27-in. 90-lb I beam is subjected to a bending moment M in a plane making an angle ϕ of 1° with the vertical plane of symmetry (refer to Fig. 75).

Find the direction of the neutral axis and the increase in the bending stress at A due to the 1° deviation of the plane of the loads from the vertical plane of symmetry.

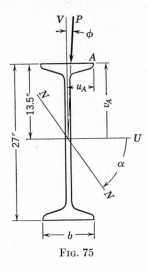

FIG. 75

Solution. $\tan \alpha = (I_u/I_v) \tan \phi$. A steel-maker's handbook gives

$$I_u = 2958 \text{ in.}^4 \qquad I_v = 75.3 \text{ in.}^4 \qquad b = 9.0 \text{ in.}$$

Hence $\qquad\qquad\qquad \tan \alpha = (2958/75.3) \times 0.0175 = 0.686$

Therefore $\qquad\qquad\qquad \alpha = 34° 20 \qquad$ (as shown in Fig. 75)

$$\sigma_A = \frac{(M \cos \phi)v_A}{I_u} + \frac{(M \sin \phi)u_A}{I_v}$$

$$\cos 1° = 1 \text{ (nearly)} \qquad \text{and} \qquad \sin 1° = \tan 1° \text{ (nearly)} = 0.0175$$

Hence $\qquad \sigma_A = M \left[-\frac{13.5}{2958} - \frac{0.0175 \times 4.5}{75.3} \right]$

$$= -M(0.00457 + 0.00105) = -0.00562M \qquad \text{compression)}$$

If the X axis were assumed to be the neutral axis, the calculated stress at A would be

$$\sigma_A = -Mv_A/I_u = -0.00457M$$

and hence the percentage increase in the elastic stress at A due to a deviation of 1° of the plane of the loads from the vertical plane of symmetry is

$$(105/457) \times 100 = 23.0 \text{ per cent}$$

Since ϕ could easily be as large as 1° without being detected, it follows that this I beam might be stressed 23 per cent more than is assumed when it supposedly subjected to symmetrical loading. But this maximum stress does not occur on all the fibers along the outer edge of the flange as is the case if a beam is symmetrically loaded; only a relatively small part of the beam is stressed to the maximum value, and hence the usable strength of the beam for most purposes is not decreased to the same extent that the maximum stress is increased, provided that the material is ductile; the small volume of highly stressed material will yield when the stress in it reaches the yield point without damaging the member as a whole, and this yielding will cause some of the understressed material to take more stress.

Excess Stress in Various Rolled Sections. The values in Table 4 are found by the method employed in the above problem. Table 4 indicates

TABLE 4

PERCENTAGE INCREASE IN FIBER STRESS AND CHANGE IN DIRECTION OF THE
NEUTRAL AXIS IN I BEAMS, CAUSED BY A ONE-DEGREE INCLINATION OF
THE PLANE OF THE LOADS WITH A PRINCIPAL PLANE

(See Fig. 76)

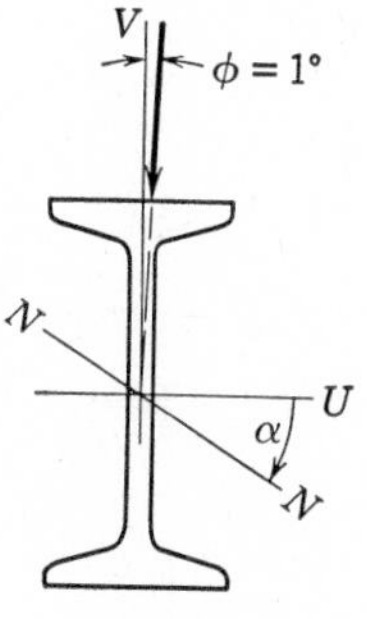

I Beam	$\dfrac{I_u}{I_v}$	Increase in Fiber Stress, %	Change in Direction, α, of Neutral Axis
27-in. 90-lb	39.3	23.0	34° 20′
20-in. 65-lb	41.8	22.8	36° 10′
18-in. 55-lb	37.5	21.8	33° 15′
15-in. 42-lb	30.2	19.3	27° 15′
12-in. $31\frac{1}{2}$-lb	22.7	16.5	21° 35′
10-in. 25-lb	17.7	14.4	17° 14′
8-in. 18-lb	15.0	13.1	14° 40′
6-in. $12\frac{1}{4}$-lb	11.8	11.5	11° 40′

FIG. 76

clearly that a section that is well proportioned to resist elastically bending due to loads in a plane of symmetry, such as I sections, may be poorly designed to resist bending due to loads in a plane that makes only a very small angle with the plane of symmetry. But, as noted in the above problem, if only a very small volume of the beam is subjected to a stress in excess of the calculated stress, the strength of the beam, when made of ductile material, is decreased somewhat less than the increase in stress would indicate. However, it is important to know that the excess stress may exist and that the margin of strength (the reserve strength) of the beam is thereby reduced to some extent, particularly if the beam is made of brittle material or is subjected to repeated stress. The table also indicates the desirability of sidewise or lateral bracing for beams of slender sections.

41 Kern of a section. If a member is subjected to combined direct compression and bending, the portion of the area of a section through which the resultant load must pass to avoid tensile stress on the section is called the *core, kernel,* or *kern* of the section.

In Fig. 77a let a short compression member of rectangular cross section be subjected to the eccentric longitudinal load P. This load may be resolved into an axial load P and a bending moment $M = Pe$, which does not lie in a principal plane.

The normal stress σ at any point in section $ABCD$ is

$$\sigma = \frac{P}{a} + \frac{M_u v}{I_u} + \frac{M_v u}{I_v} = \frac{P}{a} + \frac{Pe_v \cdot v}{I_u} + \frac{Pe_u \cdot u}{I_v} \tag{122}$$

in which u and v refer to principal centroidal axes of the area.

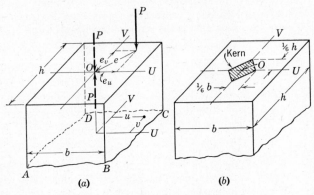

Fig. 77   Kern of cross-section.

It is evident that the least value of σ will occur at A and that its value will be given by Eq. 122 when $u = -b/2$ and $v = -h/2$; furthermore, it will be a tensile stress if the sum of the last two terms in the equation is greater than P/a. If a tensile stress on section $ABCD$ is to be avoided, therefore, the values of e_u and e_v cannot be greater than those found from the equation

$$\frac{Pe_v(h/2)}{I_u} + \frac{Pe_u(b/2)}{I_v} = \frac{P}{a} \quad \text{or} \quad \frac{e_v(h/2)}{\frac{1}{12}bh^3} + \frac{e_u(b/2)}{\frac{1}{12}hb^3} = \frac{1}{bh} \tag{123}$$

whence $\qquad \dfrac{e_v}{h} + \dfrac{e_u}{b} = \dfrac{1}{6} \quad \text{or} \quad \dfrac{e_u}{b/6} + \dfrac{e_v}{h/6} = 1 \tag{124}$

which is the equation of a straight line that intersects the axis OU at a distance $b/6$ from O, and the axis OV at a distance $h/6$ from O, as indicated in Fig. 77b. Similar lines may be drawn in the other quadrants, and hence the resultant load on the member having a rectangular cross section must pass within the shaded area of a section as shown in Fig. 77b if tensile stress on a section is to be avoided. Thus the kern of a rectangular section is a rhombus, the diagonals of which are the middle thirds of the principal axes of the section. Similarly, the kern of a circular section is the area within the circle whose diameter is the middle fourth of the diameter of the circular section.

42 Flexure modulus. In the flexure formula, $\sigma = M/(I/c)$, the quantity I/c involves only the dimensions of the section on which the stress is desired and is usually called the *section modulus*. Thus with symmetrical loading the stress may be found by dividing the bending moment by the section modulus. If Eq. 120 is written in the form

$$\sigma = \frac{M}{I_u I_v / (v I_v \cos \phi + u I_u \sin \phi)} \tag{125}$$

the denominator of the expression is a quantity having the same dimensions (cubic inches) as has the section modulus, but it involves the direction ϕ of plane of loading in addition to the properties of the section; it is often called the *flexure modulus* and is frequently denoted by S. Thus, with unsymmetrical loading the stress at any point A in a section may be found by dividing the bending moment by the flexure modulus, that is, $\sigma_A = M/S_A$. It will be observed that, if ϕ in the expression for the flexure modulus is made equal to zero, the expression reduces to that for the section modulus (assuming that v is the distance to the outermost fiber and hence is equal to c). For graphical methods making use of S polygons see references 5, 6, 7, and 8 at the end of this chapter.

43 Formulas for stress referred to any set of rectangular axes. In deriving Eqs. 114 and 116 *any* convenient set of rectangular centroidal axes (not principal axes) were used, shown as CX and CY in Fig. 64b; for such axes the product of inertia is not zero. Equations 114 and 116 may be used as follows for obtaining expressions for α and σ. Equations 114 and 116 are

$$M_x = M \cos \phi = k I_x \cos \alpha + k I_{xy} \sin \alpha \tag{126}$$

$$M_y = M \sin \phi = k I_{xy} \cos \alpha + k I_y \sin \alpha \tag{127}$$

But from Eqs. 107 and 109

$$k = \frac{\sigma}{m} = \frac{\sigma}{y \cos \alpha + x \sin \alpha} \tag{128}$$

Hence $\quad M_x = \sigma \cdot \dfrac{I_x \cos \alpha + I_{xy} \sin \alpha}{y \cos \alpha + x \sin \alpha} = \sigma \cdot \dfrac{I_x + I_{xy} \tan \alpha}{y + x \tan \alpha} \tag{129}$

Similarly $\quad M_y = \sigma \cdot \dfrac{I_{xy} \cos \alpha + I_y \sin \alpha}{y \cos \alpha + x \sin \alpha} = \sigma \cdot \dfrac{I_{xy} + I_y \tan \alpha}{y + x \tan \alpha} \tag{130}$

Since tan $\phi = M_y/M_x$, the relation between ϕ and α is obtained by dividing Eq. 130 by Eq. 129. Thus

$$\tan \phi = \frac{M_y}{M_x} = \frac{I_{xy} + I_y \tan \alpha}{I_x + I_{xy} \tan \alpha} \tag{131}$$

Solving Eq. 131 for tan α we have

$$\tan \alpha = \frac{I_{xy} - I_x \tan \phi}{I_{xy} \tan \phi - I_y} \tag{132}$$

which gives the direction of the neutral axis with reference to any set of rectangular centroidal axes.

The stress σ at any point (x, y) referred to any set of rectangular centroidal axes may be found by Eqs. 132 and 129 or 130. However, by combining Eqs. 129 and 130, tan α may be eliminated and the resulting expression for the stress at any point referred to any set of rectangular centroidal axes may be put in a form * similar to that of Eq. 120. The expression is

$$\sigma = (M_x y/I_x) + (M'_y x'/I'_y) \tag{133}$$

in which the last member is made up of quantities that are not actual physical quantities but are expressed in terms of the actual moments and actual properties of the cross-sectional area by the expressions

$$M'_y = M_y - M_x(I_{xy}/I_x) \tag{134}$$

$$x' = x - y(I_{xy}/I_x) \tag{135}$$

$$I'_y = I_y - I_{xy}(I_{xy}/I_x) \tag{136}$$

Sign Convention. In Eqs. 133 and 134 the signs of M_x and M_y are obtained in the same way as the signs of M_u and M_v in Eq. 120. In Eq. 132 the angle ϕ may be considered to be the angle from the Y axis to a line through the centroid parallel to the plane of the loads and may be clockwise or counter-clockwise, depending on the location of the plane of the loads. The sign of tan ϕ is obtained from the relation tan $\phi = M_y/M_x$ in which M_y and M_x have signs as previously described. The angle α is measured from the X axis to the neutral axis and is clockwise if the tan α has a positive value in Eq. 132, counterclockwise if tan α is negative in Eq. 132. Use of these sign conventions in Eq. 133 will give a positive stress when σ is tension, negative when compression.

---

* An alternate useful form is $\sigma = (M'_x/I'_x)y + (M'_y/I'_y)x$, in which $M'_x = M_x - M_y(I_{xy}/I_y)$; $M'_y = M_y - M_x(I_{xy}/I_x)$; $I'_x = I_x - I_{xy}(I_{xy}/I_y)$ and $I'_y = I_y - I_{xy}(I_{xy}/I_x)$.

Illustrative Problem

Problem 66. Solve Prob. 61 by use of Eq. 133, selecting axes parallel to the two legs of the angle.

Solution. From a steel-maker's handbook the following are found: $a = 4.36$ sq in., $I_x = I_y = 15.39$ in.[4]. The various dimensions needed are shown in Fig. 78. The

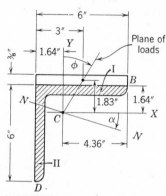

FIG. 78

value of I_{xy} may be found from the equation $I_{xy} = \bar{I}_{xy} + axy$ (see Appendix III). $\bar{I}_{xy}$ for each of the two parts I and II is zero. The values needed are given in tabular form.

Part	Area	$\bar{x}$	$\bar{y}$	I_{xy}
I	2.25	1.36	1.45	+4.43
II	2.11	−1.45	−1.55	+4.75
			$I_{xy} =$	9.18 in.[4]

Hence
$$I_{xy}/I_x = 9.18/15.39 = 0.596$$

The components of the bending couple M about the X and Y axes are

$$M_x = 25,000 \times 1.83 = 45,700 \text{ lb-in.}$$

$$M_y = 25,000 \times 1.36 = 34,000 \text{ lb-in.}$$

Thus
$$\tan \phi = M_y/M_x = 34,000/45,700 = 0.722$$

Hence Eq. 132 gives

$$\tan \alpha = \frac{9.18 - (15.39 \times 0.722)}{-15.39 + (9.18 \times 0.722)} = +0.264$$

Therefore, $\alpha = 14° 48'$ measured clockwise from the X axis as shown in Fig. 78. The maximum tensile stress is at point B and is given by the expression

$$\sigma = \frac{P}{a} + \frac{M_x y_B}{I_x} + \frac{M'_y x'_B}{I'_y}$$

in which
$$M'_y = 34,000 - (45,700 \times 0.596) = 6800 \text{ lb-in.}$$

$$x'_B = 4.36 - (1.64 \times 0.596) = 3.38 \text{ in.}$$

$$I'_y = 15.39 - (9.18 \times 0.596) = 9.91 \text{ in.}[4]$$

Hence $\sigma_B = \dfrac{25,000}{4.36} + \dfrac{45,700 \times 1.64}{15.39} + \dfrac{6800 \times 3.38}{9.91}$

$= 5730 + 4870 + 2320 = 12,920 \text{ lb/in.}^2$ (tensile stress)

Problems

67. Show from Eq. 131 that the OX axis is the neutral axis ($\alpha = 0$) if the plane of the loads makes an angle ϕ with the OY axis such that $\tan \phi = I_{xy}/I_x$. Also show that if the OX axis is the neutral axis the stress σ (Eq. 129) at any distance y from the neutral axis is found to be

$$\sigma = M_x y / I_x \qquad \text{or from Eq. 130} \qquad \sigma = M_y y / I_{xy}$$

68. Show from Eq. 132 that if the loads lie in the OY plane ($\phi = 0$), $M_y = 0$ and $M_x = M$, whence $\tan \alpha = -I_{xy}/I_y$. Similarly, if the loads lie in the OX plane ($\phi = 90°$), $M_x = 0$ and $M_y = M$, and hence $\tan \alpha = -I_x/I_{xy}$.

69. Solve Prob. 56 by use of Eq. 133.

70. Solve Prob. 60 by use of Eq. 133.

71. Solve Prob. 63 by use of Eq. 133.

72. In Prob. 54 (Fig. 67) find the angle ϕ that the plane of the bending couple must make with the vertical (Y) axis in order that the neutral axis shall be horizontal. When the neutral axis is horizontal, what is the value of the stress at B?

Ans. $\sigma_B = 14,100 \text{ lb/in.}^2$ (compression).

73. A 5-in. by 3¼-in. by ½-in. Z bar is used as a simple beam on a slope of 1 to 2 (as in Fig. 73). The span of the beam is 10 ft, and the beam is subjected to a uniformly distributed load of 100 lb per ft of span. The load lies in a vertical plane passing through the bending axis. Find, by use of Eq. 133, the maximum bending stress in the beam.   *Ans.* $\sigma_D = +1610$, $\sigma_C = +1870 \text{ lb/in.}^2$.

74. A cantilever beam of length l (Fig. 79) has a right triangular cross section and is loaded by a concentrated load P at the end. Solve for the stress at A and at C at the fixed end if $P = 1000$ lb, $h = 6$ in., $b = 3$ in., and $l = 50$ in.

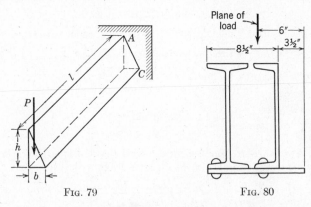

FIG. 79   FIG. 80

75. A girder which supports a brick wall is built up of a 12-in. 31.5-lb I beam, a 12-in. 20.5-lb channel, and a cover plate 12 in. wide by ⅜ in. thick riveted together as shown in Fig. 80. The girder is 18 ft long, simply supported at the ends, and the brick wall gives a uniformly distributed load of 1500 lb per ft of length of the beam;

the plane of the load passes through the bending axis of the beam. Solve for the location of the neutral axis and the values of the maximum tensile and compressive bending stresses in the girder.

44 Formulas for stress referred to rectangular axes one of which is the neutral axis.* In the beam of Fig. 81 (assumed to have a rectangular cross section for convenience only) the X and Y axes are assumed to be any convenient rectangular axes passing through the centroid of the area, but the N and M axes are rectangular axes, one of which (the N axis) is the neutral axis. The plane of the loads (or the plane of the bending moment M) makes an angle λ with the neutral axis. From equations of equilibrium we obtain

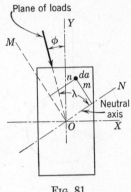

Fig. 81

$$M \cos \lambda = M_m = \int n\sigma \, da \qquad (137)$$

$$M \sin \lambda = M_n = \int m\sigma \, da \qquad (138)$$

But since the stress varies directly as the distance from the neutral axis, we may write $\sigma/m = $ constant. Therefore, Eqs. 137 and 138 may be written

$$M_m = \frac{\sigma}{m} \int mn \, da = \frac{\sigma I_{mn}}{m} \qquad (139)$$

$$M_n = \frac{\sigma}{m} \int m^2 \, da = \frac{\sigma I_n}{m} \qquad (140)$$

But $\quad M = \sqrt{M_m{}^2 + M_n{}^2} \quad$ or $\quad M = (\sigma/m)\sqrt{I_n{}^2 + I_{mn}{}^2} \quad (141)$

This may be written in a form the same as that of the flexure formula. Thus

$$\boldsymbol{M = \sigma R/m} \qquad (142)$$

in which $R = \sqrt{I_n{}^2 + I_{mn}{}^2}$ is called the *directed moment of inertia*.

The direction of the neutral axis may be found from the equation

$$\tan \lambda = M_n/M_m = I_n/I_{mn} \qquad (143)$$

which is obtained by dividing Eq. 140 by Eq. 139.

Equations 142 and 143 may be used most readily by employing a graphical method for determining λ and R. The construction for a

* See Prob. 67 for another approach to this problem.

beam loaded as in Fig. 82a is shown in Fig. 82b. OX and OY are any convenient rectangular axes through the centroid of the area for which I_x, I_y, and I_{xy} are known. Draw $OF = I_x$, $FH = I_y$, and $FC = I_{xy}$. Draw a circle having OH as its diameter. Draw OG in the direction of the plane of the loads. Draw GA through C. Now draw the diameter

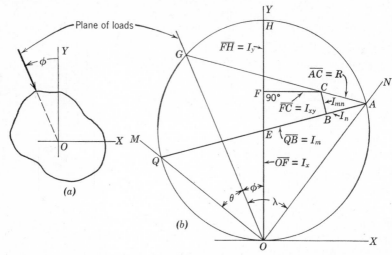

FIG. 82   Mohr-Land construction for directed moment of inertia.

AQ and drop CB perpendicular to AQ. Then, $CB = I_{mn}$, $AB = I_n$, and $AC = \sqrt{I_n{}^2 + I_{mn}{}^2} = R$. (For proof see Mohr-Land construction, in Appendix III.) Further, OA is the neutral axis. Proof:

$$\angle GOQ = \tfrac{1}{2}\,\text{arc}\,GQ = \theta \qquad \angle GOA = 90° - \theta = \angle ACB$$

$$\tan \angle ACB = AB/BC = I_n/I_{mn} = \tan \lambda \qquad \text{(Eq. 143)}$$

Therefore $\qquad\qquad\qquad\qquad \angle GOA = \lambda$

Problems

76. Solve Prob. 73 by use of Eq. 142 and the graphical construction of Fig. 82.
77. Solve Prob. 61 by use of Eq. 142 and the graphical construction of Fig. 82.

45 Deflection of beam subjected to unsymmetrical loading.
The elastic deflection of a beam subjected to unsymmetrical loading may be found by a method similar to that used in the preceding articles for determining the stress in the beam: The bending moment may be resolved into components parallel to the principal planes, and the deflections caused by these components of the moment are calculated from the

usual equations for deflections of symmetrically loaded beams; the actual deflection of the beam is the vector sum of the deflections found from the component moments (see Fig. 83). This method gives both

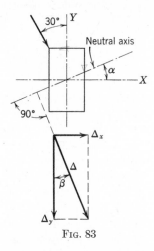

Fɪɢ. 83

the magnitude and direction of the deflection; it will be found that the direction of the deflection is always perpendicular to the neutral axis.

Illustrative Problem

Problem 78. Find the deflection Δ of a timber beam if the beam is simply supported and is subjected to a single concentrated load of 3000 lb at the center of the span in a plane that makes 30° with the vertical plane of symmetry. The beam is 6 in. wide by 8 in. deep, and the span is 10 ft. Neglect the weight of the beam; use $E = 1,200,000$ lb per sq in., and assume that the elastic strength of the material is 3000 lb per sq in.

Solution. The maximum stress in the beam is less than the elastic strength, and hence the following equations apply:

$$\Delta_y = \frac{1}{48} \frac{P \cos 30° \, l^3}{EI_x}$$

$$= \frac{1}{48} \frac{3000 \times 0.866 \times (10 \times 12)^3}{1,200,000 \times 256} = 0.305 \text{ in.}$$

$$\Delta_x = \frac{1}{48} \frac{3000 \times 0.5 \times (10 \times 12)^3}{1,200,000 \times 144} = 0.313 \text{ in.}$$

$$\Delta = \sqrt{(0.305)^2 + (0.312)^2} = 0.437 \text{ in.}$$

The value of α is found (from Eq. 118) to be 45° 45', and the deflection Δ is found to be perpendicular to the neutral axis, since β is found to be equal to α(tan β = Δ_x/Δ_y).

Problems

79. Calculate the maximum deflection of the timber beam described in Prob. 53, assuming that the deflection is the same as that which would be caused by an equal total load uniformly distributed. Show by a sketch the direction of the deflection. Assume that $E = 1,000,000$ lb per sq in.   *Ans.* $\Delta = 0.714$ in.

80. Calculate the maximum deflection of the beam described in Prob. 54, assuming that the total load (10,000 lb) is uniformly distributed. Show by a sketch the direction of the deflection.   *Ans.* $\Delta = 0.194$ in.

46 Shear center for unsymmetrical section.

In Art. 34 (Chapter 4) a method was developed for locating the shear center of open cross sections which were composed of narrow rectangles and which had one axis of symmetry. This method may be used also to find the shear center of a section composed of narrow rectangles but with no axis of symmetry, that is, an unsymmetrical section. The following procedure is used. The principal axes of inertia passing through the centroid of the section are located, and the moment of inertia about each of these axes is computed. The plane of the loads on the beam is assumed to act in a direction perpendicular to one of the principal axes, and the action line of the resisting shear is found by the method of Art. 34. Then a plane of loads is assumed to act in a direction perpendicular to the second principal axis, and the action line of the resisting shear is found as before. The intersection of the action lines of these two resisting shears determines the location of the shear center. This procedure is illustrated in the following problem.

In unsymmetrical bending, as well as in the more restricted case of bending discussed in the preceding chapter, it may be important to locate the shear center (and bending axis) in order to place the plane of the loads so that it will contain the axis of bending and hence prevent the beam from twisting as it bends.

Illustrative Problem

Problem 81. A beam has an unsymmetrical section whose shape and dimensions are as shown in Fig. 84a. Locate the point (shear center) in the plane of each cross section through which the plane of the loads on the beam must pass if the beam is to bend without twisting.

Solution. The centroid C of the section is located, and the values of I_x, I_y, and I_{xy} for the section with respect to a convenient set of centroidal axes (X, Y as shown in Fig. 84a) are computed. These values are $I_x = 0.0218$ in.^{4}, $I_y = 0.0118$ in.^{4}, and $I_{xy} = -0.0067$ in.^{4}. The principal axes of inertia U, V, and the values of I_u and I_v with respect to these axes, are computed by using the equations in Appendix III. The values are: $I_u = 0.0252$ in.^{4}, and $I_v = 0.0084$ in.^{4}.

A shearing force (load) V' is assumed to be applied to the beam in a direction perpendicular to the U axis as shown in Fig. 84b. In order to bend without twisting, the resisting shear V_R must be equal, opposite, and collinear with V'. But V_R is the resultant of the component resisting shearing forces V_1, V_2, and V_3, as shown in Fig. 84b. We need to compute only the force V_1, since the point D (through which

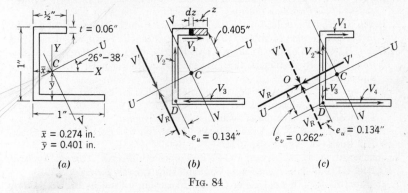

$\bar{x} = 0.274$ in.
$\bar{y} = 0.401$ in.

(a)   (b)   (c)

FIG. 84

V_2 and V_3 pass) may be used as a moment center in locating the action line of V_R by the principle of moments. V_1 is computed as follows:

$$V_1 = \int \tau \, da = \int_0^{\frac{1}{2}} \tau z t \, dz$$

in which z is the distance from the free edge of the $\frac{1}{2}$-in. flange. The stress $\tau = V'Q/I_u t$ in which $Q = zt(0.405 + \frac{1}{2}z \sin 26° 38')$ is the moment of the area about the U axis. Therefore

$$V_1 = \frac{V't}{I_u} \int_0^{\frac{1}{2}} z(0.405 + \tfrac{1}{2}z \sin 26° 38') \, dz = 0.143 V'$$

Using the principle of moments we have $\Sigma M_D = V_R e_u$, where e_u is the distance from D to the action line of V_R. But $\Sigma M_D = 0.94 V_1 = 0.134 V'$ and $V_R = V'$; and hence

$$e_u = 0.134 \text{ in.} \quad \cdot 143$$

In a similar manner a value of $e_v = 0.262$ in. is found for the distance from D to the action line of the resisting shear perpendicular to the V axis, as shown in Fig. 84c. Therefore the shear center O is the intersection of the action lines of the two resisting shears V_R as shown in Fig. 84c.

Problem

82. A steel bar used as a part of the center sill (beam) in railway cars has a cross section whose dimensions are shown in Fig. 85. Locate the point (shear center) in the cross section through which the plane of the bending loads must pass so that the beam bends without twisting.

Ans. $e_u = 2.6$ in., $e_v = 9.2$ in.

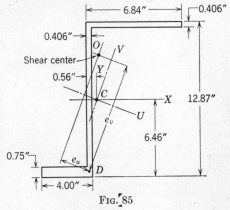

FIG. 85

Selected References

1. Batho, C. B., "The Distribution of Stress in Certain Tension Members," *Transactions of the Canadian Society of Civil Engineers*, Vol. 26, p. 224.
2. Batho, C. B., "The Effect of the End Connections on the Distribution of Stress in Certain Tension Members," *Journal of the Franklin Institute*, August 1915.
3. Cross, H., "The Column Analogy," *Bulletin* 215, Engineering Experiment Station, University of Illinois, 1930. Develops equations similar to Eq. 133 in a different form.
4. Fleming, R., "Tables Aid Selection of Steel Purlins for Sloping Roofs," *Engineering Record*, March 3, 1917.
   References 5–8 make use of flexure modulus polygons.
5. Hoole, G. A., and W. S. Kinne, *Structural Members and Connections*, McGraw-Hill Book Co., New York, 1924.
6. Johnson, J. B., C. W. Bryan, and F. E. Turneaure, *Modern Framed Structures*, Part III, 9th edition, Appendix C, John Wiley & Sons, New York, 1916.
7. Johnson, L. J., "An Analysis of General Flexure in a Straight Bar of Uniform Cross-Section," *Transactions of the American Society of Civil Engineers*, Vol. 56, 1906, p. 169.
8. Johnson, L. J., "The Determination of Unit Stresses in the General Case of Flexure," *Journal of Engineering Societies*, Vol. 28, 1902.
9. Moore, H. F., "A Brief Discussion of the General Theory of the Flexure of a Straight Bar of Uniform Cross Section, with Special Application to the Flexure of Steam Turbine Blades," *Bulletin* 183, Engineering Experiment Station, University of Illinois, 1928.
10. Saville, W. G. S., "Analyzing Non-Homogeneous Sections Subjected to Bending and Direct Stress," *Civil Engineering*, Vol. 10, No. 3, March 1940, p. 170.
11. Talbot, A. N., "Fifth Progress Report of Special Committee on Stresses in Railroad Track," *Bulletin of the American Railway Engineers Association*, Vol. 31, No. 319, September 1929, pp. 36–40.
12. Waterbury, L. A., *Stresses in Structural Steel Angles*, John Wiley & Sons, 1917.

Chapter 6

CURVED FLEXURAL MEMBERS

47 Introduction. One of the assumptions on which the flexural formula $M = \sigma I/c$ is based is that the member (beam) to which the bending moment M is applied is initially straight; this formula, therefore, will be referred to as the *straight*-beam formula.* Many members that are subjected to bending, however, are curved before a bending moment is applied to them, as, for example, crane hooks, chain links, and frames of punching machines. Such members will be called curved beams. Furthermore, some members have curved portions that are subjected to bending even though the members as a whole are not flexural members; for example, the portion in the eye of an eye bar in a bridge. It is important, therefore, to determine the effect of *initial* curvature of a beam on the stresses and deflections caused by loads applied to the beam in the plane of initial curvature.†

Essential Difference between Straight Beams and Curved Beams. In the following discussion it will be assumed that all the conditions required to make the straight-beam formula applicable are satisfied except that the beam is initially curved.

Let the curved beam DOE (Fig. 86) be subjected to the loads (and reactions) Q. The assumption is made that there is one surface in the beam in which the fibers do not change in length (this surface is called the neutral surface), and that the total deformations of the fibers between two normal sections such as AB and A_1B_1 vary directly with the distances of the fibers from the neutral surface, shortening above the neutral surface and stretching below the neutral surface; or, as fre-

---

* It will be found, however, that this straight-beam formula applies with very little error to many beams that would normally be thought of as curved; the term "curved beam," then, usually means a flexural member with a *relatively sharp* curvature.

† For a treatment of "Circular Beams Loaded Normal to the Plane of Curvature," see paper by M. B. Hogan, *Journal of Applied Mechanics*, June 1938; *Transactions of the American Society of Mechanical Engineers*, Vol. 5, p. A81; and a paper by R. B. B. Moorman, "Stresses in a Curved Beam under Loads Normal to the Plane of Its Axis," *Bulletin* 145, Engineering Experiment Station, Iowa State College, 1940.

quently stated, plane sections before bending are assumed to be plane
sections after bending. This assumption of conservation of plane sections is verified approximately by direct measurements of the deformations by means of a strain gage except for beams having sections such
as H, I, or T sections with either thin webs or wide flanges, as the discussion in the next article will show.

In Fig. 86 the two lines AB and A_1B_1 are traces of two normal sections of the beam before the loads are applied. After the beam is loaded,
the change in the length of any fiber between these two normal sections

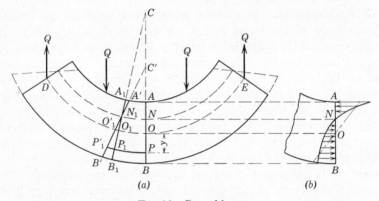

FIG. 86   Curved beam.

is represented by the distance along the fiber between the lines A_1B_1
and $A'B'$; the neutral surface is represented by NN_1, and the stretch
of fiber PP_1 is $P_1P'_1$, etc. For convenience it will be assumed that the
line AB is a line of symmetry and does not change direction.

Although the total deformations of the fibers in the curved beam are
proportional to the distances of the fibers from the neutral surface, the
strains (deformations per unit length) of the fibers are *not* proportional
to these distances because the fibers are not of equal length; whereas in
a straight beam the fibers *are* of equal length, and hence the strains in a
straight beam, as well as the total deformations, are proportional to the
distances of the fibers from the neutral axis. But for bending stresses
that do not exceed the elastic strength of the material the stress on any
fiber in the beam is proportional to the strain of the fiber, and hence the
elastic stresses in the fibers of a *curved* beam are *not* proportional to the
distances of the fibers from the neutral surface. It follows, then, that
the resisting moment in a curved beam is not given by the expression
sI/c, since this expression is obtained on the assumption that the stress
varies directly as the distance from the neutral axis. For the same

reason, the neutral axis in a curved beam does not pass through the centroid of the section. The distribution of stress over the section and the relative position of the neutral axis are shown in Fig. 86b; if the beam were straight, the stress would be zero at the centroidal axis and would vary directly with the distance from the centroidal axis as indicated by the dot-dash line in Fig. 86b. The stress on a normal section such as AB is called the circumferential stress. A quantitative expression for the circumferential stress at any point on a normal section is found in the next article.

48 Circumferential stress at any point in a curved beam. The Winkler-Bach formula. Let it be required to express the normal

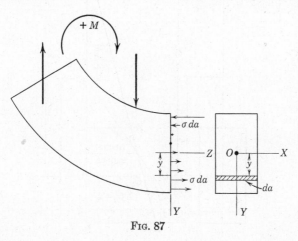

FIG. 87

stress at any point on a cross section perpendicular to the axis of the curved beam in terms of the bending moment M at the section and the dimensions of the section. In accordance with Step 1 of Art. 8, a free-body diagram is drawn of the portion of the body on one side of the section, as indicated in Fig. 87, and the equations of equilibrium are applied to the forces acting on this portion. The equations thus obtained are

$$\Sigma F_z = 0 \qquad \text{or} \qquad \int \sigma \, da = 0 \tag{144}$$

$$\Sigma M_x = 0 \qquad \text{or} \qquad M = \int y\sigma \, da \tag{145}$$

In accordance with Step 2 of Art. 8, the relation between σ and y must now be found for use in Eq. 145. Within the elastic properties of the material,

$$\sigma = E\epsilon \tag{146}$$

in which E is the modulus of elasticity in tension (and compression) and ϵ is the circumferential strain of any fiber at the distance y from the centroidal axis of the cross-sectional area. If the strain ϵ can be expressed in terms of y (and other dimensions of the beam), Eq. 146 can then be made to express σ in terms of y (and E, etc.).

It will be found convenient to express ϵ of any fiber in terms of the strain ϵ_0 of the centroidal fiber, the angle of rotation $\Delta\,d\theta$ of the section,

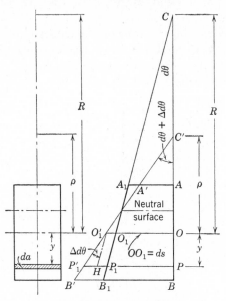

FIG. 88   Strains in curved beam.

and the distance y from the centroidal axis. Let Fig. 88 represent the part ABB_1A_1 of Fig. 86a enlarged; the angle between the two sections AB and A_1B_1 is $d\theta$. The bending moment causes the plane A_1B_1 to rotate through an angle $\Delta\,d\theta$ (Fig. 88), thereby changing the angle this plane makes with the plane BAC from $d\theta$ to $(d\theta + \Delta\,d\theta)$; the center of curvature is changed from C to C', and the distance of the centroidal axis from the center of curvature is changed from R to ρ. It should be noted that y, R, and ρ at any section are measured from the centroidal axis and not from the neutral axis.

Let ds denote the length of the centroidal fiber OO_1, and ϵ_0 the strain of this fiber; then, since the two planes AB and A_1B_1 are only a differential distance apart,

$$\epsilon_0 = O_1O'_1/OO_1 \qquad \text{or} \qquad O_1O'_1 = \epsilon_0 ds = \epsilon_0 R\,d\theta$$

and the strain at a distance y from the centroidal axis is

$$\epsilon = \frac{P_1 P'_1}{PP_1} = \frac{P_1 H + HP'_1}{PP_1} = \frac{O_1 O'_1 + HP'_1}{PP_1}$$

in which $O_1 O'_1 = \epsilon_0 R \, d\theta$; $HP'_1 = O'_1 H \cdot \Delta \, d\theta = y \, \Delta \, d\theta$ and $PP_1 = (R + y) \, d\theta$.

Therefore $\qquad \epsilon = \dfrac{\epsilon_0 R \, d\theta + y \Delta \, d\theta}{(R + y) \, d\theta} = \dfrac{R\epsilon_0 + y(\Delta \, d\theta/d\theta)}{R + y}$

For convenience let the angular strain, $(\Delta \, d\theta)/d\theta$, be denoted by ω. By adding and subtracting $\epsilon_0 y$ to the numerator, the above expression may be transformed to

$$\epsilon = \epsilon_0 + (\omega - \epsilon_0) \frac{y}{R + y} \tag{147}$$

From Eqs. 146 and 147 we obtain

$$\sigma = E\epsilon = E\left[\epsilon_0 + (\omega - \epsilon_0) \frac{y}{R + y}\right] \tag{148}$$

By substituting this expression for σ in Eqs. 144 and 145 we obtain

$$M = \int y\sigma \, da = \int Ey\left[\epsilon_0 + (\omega - \epsilon_0) \frac{y}{R + y}\right] da \tag{149}$$

and $\qquad \displaystyle\int \sigma \, da = \int E\left[\epsilon_0 + (\omega - \epsilon_0) \frac{y}{R + y}\right] da = 0 \tag{150}$

If the modulus of elasticity E has the same value for all the fibers, which is approximately the case for a one-material beam, Eqs. 149 and 150 may be written

$$M = E\left[\epsilon_0 \int y \, da + (\omega - \epsilon_0) \int \frac{y^2}{R + y} \, da\right] \tag{151}$$

and $\qquad \displaystyle\epsilon_0 \int da = -(\omega - \epsilon_0) \int \frac{y}{R + y} \, da \tag{152}$

But $\displaystyle\int da = a$, and since y is measured from the centroidal axis, $\displaystyle\int y \, da = 0$. Furthermore, in Eq. 152 for convenience let

$$\int \frac{y}{R + y} \, da = -Za \quad \text{or} \quad Z = -\frac{1}{a} \int \frac{y}{R + y} \, da \tag{153}$$

in which Z is a property of the area somewhat similar to the moment of inertia in the straight-beam formula; values of Z for various areas a are to be found later. The integral in Eq. 151 may also be expressed in terms of Z as follows: *

$$\int \frac{y^2}{R + y}\, da = \int \left(y - R\frac{y}{R + y} \right) da = -R \int \frac{y}{R + y}\, da = ZaR \quad (154)$$

Equations 151 and 152 now become

$$M = E(\omega - \epsilon_0)ZaR \quad (155)$$

$$\epsilon_0 = (\omega - \epsilon_0)Z \quad (156)$$

Hence $\quad (\omega - \epsilon_0) = \dfrac{M}{EZaR} \qquad \epsilon_0 = \dfrac{M}{EaR} \qquad \omega = \dfrac{1}{Ea}\left(\dfrac{M}{R} + \dfrac{M}{RZ} \right) \quad (157)$

Substituting these values in Eq. 148 we obtain

$$\sigma = \frac{M}{aR}\left(1 + \frac{1}{Z}\frac{y}{R + y} \right) \quad (158)$$

in which σ is the tensile or compressive (circumferential) stress at a point at the distance y from the centroidal axis of a transverse section at which the bending moment is M; R is the distance from the centroidal axis of the section to the center of curvature of the central axis of the unstressed beam; a is the area of the cross section; and Z is a property of the cross section defined by Eq. 153 or Eq. 154, the values of which for various areas are given in Appendix III. Equation 158 is frequently referred to as the Winkler-Bach formula; the distribution of stress on the section of a curved beam as given by this formula is indicated in Fig. 86b.

Signs. The bending moment M is positive when it decreases the radius of curvature, and negative when it increases the radius of curvature; y is positive when measured toward the convex side of the beam, and negative when measured toward the concave side, that is, toward the center of curvature. With these sign conventions, when σ is positive it is a tensile stress.

Limiting Case. Since a curved beam becomes a straight beam when R is infinitely large, the expression for σ in the Winkler-Bach formula

---

* Equation 154 is used for numerical integration of an area for the value of Z, particularly when the value of Z is very small. See Appendix III.

should reduce to $\sigma = My/I$ when R becomes infinitely large. The proof of this fact may be made by noting that Eq. 158 may be written

$$\sigma = \frac{M}{aR} + \frac{M}{ZaR} \cdot \frac{y}{R+y} = \frac{M}{aR} + \frac{M}{\displaystyle\int \frac{y^2}{R+y}\,da} \cdot \frac{y}{R+y}$$

$$= \frac{M}{aR} + \frac{My}{\left(1 + \dfrac{y}{R}\right)\displaystyle\int \frac{y^2\,da}{1+y/R}} \tag{159}$$

If in this last expression R is made infinitely large, the expression for the stress becomes $\sigma = My/I$.

Location of Neutral Axis. Equation 158 gives the circumferential stress σ on any fiber at the distance y from the centroidal axis, on any section where the bending moment is M. But the stress at the neutral axis is zero, and hence, if y_0 denotes the distance of the neutral axis from the centroidal axis, the value of y_0 may be found by equating to zero the expression for σ in Eq. 158. Thus,

$$1 + \frac{1}{Z}\frac{y_0}{R+y_0} = 0$$

$$y_0 = -ZR/(Z+1) \tag{160}$$

As previously explained, the negative sign means that y_0 is measured from the centroidal axis towards the center of curvature. It is important to note that Eq. 160 applies to a beam that is subjected to bending only.

Axial and Bending Loads Combined. If a curved beam is subjected to a normal load P acting through the centroid of the area of the section in addition to a bending moment, the resulting elastic stress is the algebraic sum of the stress σ_1 caused by the centroidal axial load and the stress σ_2 caused by the bending loads. It is usually assumed that the stress caused by the load passing through the centroid is P/a at each point on the area, and hence the stress at any point on the section of the curved beam becomes

$$\sigma = \sigma_1 + \sigma_2 = \frac{P}{a} + \frac{M}{aR}\left(1 + \frac{1}{Z}\frac{y}{R+y}\right) \tag{161}$$

The sign of M and y are determined the same as for Eq. 158, and the sign of P is plus when it produces tensile stress and negative when it produces compressive stress.

It should be noted, however, that the assumption that $\sigma_1 = P/a$ is probably somewhat in error, since one of the conditions required by this assumption (as brought out in Art. 9) is not satisfied; namely, the member is not straight, and σ_1 on the concave side of the beam is somewhat greater than P/a. This condition is discussed further in the next article.

Limitations on the Winkler-Bach Formula. The limitations given for the formula $\sigma = Mc/I$ as applied to straight beams in Art. 10 hold also for the Winkler-Bach formula as applied to a curved beam. To these limitations the following restrictions should be added for curved beams having H, I, T, or similar sections.

(*a*) The assumption that plane sections remain plane is only approximately true in a curved beam whose cross section consists of a web and flange or flanges, such as T or I sections. Although the section does remain approximately plane, the flanges tend to rotate about neutral axes lying near the centroid of the flange area. This additional rotation of plane sections of the flanges causes the stresses at the extreme fibers to be somewhat greater than those given by Eq. 158 or 161. These facts are discussed further in Art. 51.

(*b*) For such cross sections the flanges must not be excessively wide or thin. If the two flanges of an I section, for example, are wide and thin, the flange that is under compressive stress will buckle near the free edges (deflect away from the center of curvature), and the free edges of the flange that is under tensile stress will move toward the center of curvature; thus the stresses near the free edges of both flanges will be relieved or lowered and, therefore, the stresses in the middle of the flanges will be increased.

(*c*) If the web of an H, I, or T section is too thin, there is a tendency for the web to fail by buckling when the bending moment is positive, and to fail by stretching or by fracture in tension in the radial direction when the moment is negative. Thin-webbed beams made of brittle material and loaded by a negative bending moment have frequently failed by tensile fracture (separation) of the inner flange from the web owing to high tensile stresses in the direction of the radius, that is, radial stresses, as will be discussed in Art. 52.

Frequently, curved beams having H, I, or T sections have stiffeners riveted or welded to the flanges and web in order to reinforce the flanges and to strengthen the web to prevent the types of failure described in the foregoing paragraphs.

Illustrative Problem

Problem 83. In Fig. 89 are shown the approximate dimensions of a 10-ton crane hook. Find the circumferential stress σ_A on the inside fiber, and the circumferential stress σ_B on the outside fiber at the section AB, and compare these values of σ_A and σ_B with the values found by using the straight-beam formula.

Solution. The area of the section is $a = 9.85$ sq in., and the centroid G is found to be at the distances $c_A = 1.85$ in. and $c_B = 2.65$ in. from A and B, respectively. Hence $R = 2.5 + c_A = 2.5 + 1.85 = 4.35$ in. The moment of inertia of the cross section about the centroidal axis is found to have the value $I = 15.0$ in.[4]. The value of Z may be found by calculation from the equation in Art. 205 (Appendix III) or by graphical and numerical methods explained in Arts. 206 and 207 (Appendix III). The value is $Z = 0.085$, and hence $1/Z = 11.8$.

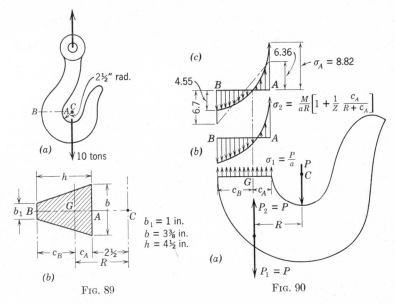

$b_1 = 1$ in.
$b = 3\frac{3}{8}$ in.
$h = 4\frac{1}{2}$ in.

FIG. 89   FIG. 90

As indicated in Fig. 90, the load P may be resolved into a load $P_1 = P$ and a bending couple whose moment M is negative and equal to PR; thus $M = -PR = -10(1.85 + 2.5) = -43.5$ ton-in. The stress σ_A is considered to be the sum of the stress σ_1 due to the axial load $P_1 = P$, and the stress σ_2 due to the bending moment M. Thus

$$\sigma_A = \sigma_1 + \sigma_2 = \frac{P}{a} + \frac{M}{aR}\left[1 + \frac{1}{Z}\frac{-c_A}{R + (-c_A)}\right]$$

$$= \frac{P}{aZ}\frac{c_A}{R - c_A}$$

The stress at B is

$$\sigma_B = \frac{P}{a} + \frac{M}{aR}\left(1 + \frac{1}{Z}\frac{c_B}{R + c_B}\right) = -\frac{P}{aZ}\frac{c_B}{R + c_B}$$

Therefore $\sigma_A = \dfrac{10 \times 11.8}{9.85} \dfrac{1.85}{4.35 - 1.85} = 8.82$ ton/in.$^2 = 17,640$ lb/in.^{2}

and $\sigma_B = \dfrac{10 \times 11.8}{9.85} \dfrac{2.66}{4.35 + 2.66} = -4.55$ ton/in.$^2 = -9100$ lb/in.^{2}

If the hook is considered to be a straight beam, the corresponding values are

$$\sigma_A = \frac{P}{a} + \frac{Mc_A}{I} = \frac{10}{9.85} + \frac{43.5 \times 1.85}{15} = 6.36 \text{ ton/in.}^2 = 12,700 \text{ lb/in.}^2$$

$$\sigma_B = \frac{P}{a} - \frac{Mc_B}{I} = \frac{10}{9.85} - \frac{43.5 \times 2.66}{15} = 6.70 \text{ ton/in.}^2 = -13,400 \text{ lb/in.}^2$$

Figure 90c shows graphically the difference in the stresses computed by the two methods. At the inner fibers the stress as found from the curved-beam formula is 28 per cent larger than that found from the straight-beam formula. Since for steel the yield points in tension and compression are approximately equal, it is evident from the foregoing stresses obtained from the straight-beam formula that the hook was designed according to the straight-beam theory. If the true cross section (similar to Fig. 94a) were used instead of the circumscribed trapezoidal area, the calculated maximum stress would have been somewhat larger than that found in the foregoing solution (see Prob. 94).

Problems

84. Check the value for Z in the solution of Prob. 83.

85. Locate the position of the neutral axis in the section AB of the hook described in Prob. 83, and show that since P passes through the center of curvature, making $M = PR$, the neutral axis coincides with the centroidal axis; the position that the neutral axis would have if the hook were subjected to bending only is indicated in Fig. 90b; the effect of the direct tensile stress may be seen by comparing Fig. 90b and 90c.

86. The load P applied to the frame shown in Fig. 91 is 400 lb. Calculate the circumferential stress at A and at B, and compare the values with those found by use of the straight-beam formula. Also locate the position of the neutral axis. Assume that the elastic strength of the material is not exceeded.

Ans. $Z = 0.097$; $\sigma_A = 15,200 \text{ lb/in.}^2$.

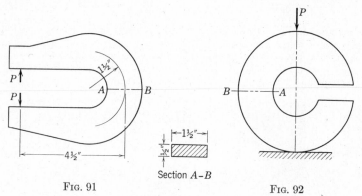

Section $A-B$

Fig. 91   Fig. 92

87. A ring (Fig. 92) is made of stock with a circular cross section 3 in. in diameter. The inside diameter of the ring is 4 in. The load P is 4000 lb. Calculate the stress at A and at B, and compare the values with those found by the straight-beam formula. Assume that the material is not stressed above its elastic strength.

Ans. $Z = 0.050$; $\sigma_A = 8500 \text{ lb/in.}^2$.

88. A load P of 3000 lb is applied to the clamp shown in Fig. 93. Calculate the maximum circumferential stress on sections AB and DE, assuming that the material is not stressed above its elastic strength. In finding the stress on DE obtain the value

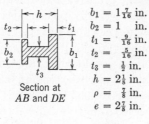

$$b_1 = 1\tfrac{7}{16} \text{ in.}$$
$$b_2 = 1 \text{ in.}$$
$$t_1 = \tfrac{9}{16} \text{ in.}$$
$$t_2 = \tfrac{5}{16} \text{ in.}$$
$$t_3 = \tfrac{1}{2} \text{ in.}$$
$$h = 2\tfrac{1}{8} \text{ in.}$$
$$\rho = \tfrac{7}{8} \text{ in.}$$
$$e = 2\tfrac{7}{8} \text{ in.}$$

Section at
AB and DE

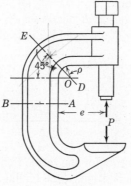

Fig. 93

of Z by the line polygon method (see Appendix III) and check the result by calculation (see table in Appendix III). *Ans.* $Z = 0.158$.

89. A wrought-iron crane hook having the section shown in Fig. 94a when tested reached its maximum elastic strength when subjected to a load of 16,000 lb. (The

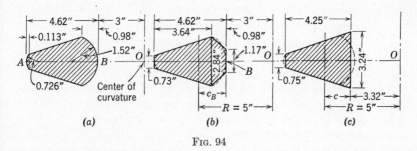

Fig. 94

section in Fig. 94a is located in the hook in a position corresponding to section AB in Fig. 89.) Calculate the maximum circumferential stress at B in Fig. 94a; obtain a value of Z graphically (see Appendix III).

49   Correction factors for use in the straight-beam formula.
The Winkler-Bach formula derived in the preceding article, although
satisfactory theoretically, is limited in its usefulness because of the
difficulty in evaluating the property Z of the area.   The expression for
this property of the cross section is too complicated for practical use for
all sections except perhaps the circle and the rectangle (see table in Appendix III).   Furthermore, graphical methods (see Appendix III) give
results that are likely to be considerably in error, particularly since the
value of Z is always small, rarely exceeding 0.8 for a relatively sharp
curvature and being less than 0.005 for a relatively large curvature.

It is desirable, therefore, to have available correction factors for use
in the straight-beam formula for a variety of sections likely to be used
in curved flexural members.   If K denotes such a correction factor, the
stress at the extreme fiber of a curved beam is given by

$$\sigma = K(Mc/I) \tag{162}$$

in which
$$K = \frac{\dfrac{M}{aR}\left(1 + \dfrac{1}{Z}\dfrac{c}{R+c}\right)}{Mc/I} \tag{163}$$

Values of correction factors for the inside fiber A and for the outside
fiber B for twelve common sections, each having ten different degrees of
curvature, as found mainly by Wilson and Quereau are given in Table 5.
Great care was used in obtaining the values of Z.   The values of Table 5
may be used in determining an approximate but reliable value of the
stress in a curved beam of practically any degree of curvature and any
shape of section.   The variation of values of K with R/c is shown graphically for several sections in Fig. 95.

It is important to note that the values of K in Table 5 should be used
in calculating the stress only in the extreme fibers of the curved beam,
but in a beam that is free from abrupt changes of section the maximum
stress occurs at an extreme fiber and is usually the stress desired; the
value of c in the ratio R/c in Table 5 is the distance from the *centroidal*
axis to the fiber nearest to the center of curvature of the section.   Furthermore, these values of K are applicable mainly to so-called solid sections, since it is shown in Art. 51 that the values of stress as found from
the Winkler-Bach formula for I, T, and similar sections are appreciably
smaller than the actual maximum stresses in the extreme fibers of the
beam.   Table 5 also gives the distance of the neutral axis from the
centroidal axis of the section when the beam is subjected to bending
only.

TABLE 5

VALUES OF K FOR DIFFERENT SECTIONS AND DIFFERENT RADII OF CURVATURE

Section	$\dfrac{R}{c}$	Factor K		y_0*
		Inside Fiber	Outside Fiber	
Fig. A K the same for circle and ellipse and independent of dimensions.	1.2	3.41	0.54	0.224R
	1.4	2.40	0.60	0.151R
	1.6	1.96	0.65	0.108R
	1.8	1.75	0.68	0.084R
	2.0	1.62	0.71	0.069R
	3.0	1.33	0.79	0.030R
	4.0	1.23	0.84	0.016R
	6.0	1.14	0.89	0.0070R
	8.0	1.10	0.91	0.0039R
	10.0	1.08	0.93	0.0025R
Fig. B K independent of section dimensions.	1.2	2.89	0.57	0.305R
	1.4	2.13	0.63	0.204R
	1.6	1.79	0.67	0.149R
	1.8	1.63	0.70	0.112R
	2.0	1.52	0.73	0.090R
	3.0	1.30	0.81	0.041R
	4.0	1.20	0.85	0.021R
	6.0	1.12	0.90	0.0093R
	8.0	1.09	0.92	0.0052R
	10.0	1.07	0.94	0.0033R
Fig. C	1.2	3.01	0.54	0.336R
	1.4	2.18	0.60	0.229R
	1.6	1.87	0.65	0.168R
	1.8	1.69	0.68	0.128R
	2.0	1.58	0.71	0.102R
	3.0	1.33	0.80	0.046R
	4.0	1.23	0.84	0.024R
	6.0	1.13	0.88	0.011R
	8.0	1.10	0.91	0.0060R
	10.0	1.08	0.93	0.0039R
Fig. D	1.2	3.09	0.56	0.336R
	1.4	2.25	0.62	0.229R
	1.6	1.91	0.66	0.168R
	1.8	1.73	0.70	0.128R
	2.0	1.61	0.73	0.102R
	3.0	1.37	0.81	0.046R
	4.0	1.26	0.86	0.024R
	6.0	1.17	0.91	0.011R
	8.0	1.13	0.94	0.0060R
	10.0	1.11	0.95	0.0039R

* y_0 is distance from centroidal axis to neutral axis, when beam is subjected to pure bending.

TABLE 5 (*Continued*)

VALUES OF K FOR DIFFERENT SECTIONS AND DIFFERENT RADII OF CURVATURE

Section	$\dfrac{R}{c}$	Factor K		y_0*
		Inside Fiber	Outside Fiber	
Fig. E	1.2	3.14	0.52	0.352R
	1.4	2.29	0.54	0.243R
	1.6	1.93	0.62	0.179R
	1.8	1.74	0.65	0.138R
	2.0	1.61	0.68	0.110R
	3.0	1.34	0.76	0.050R
	4.0	1.24	0.82	0.028R
	6.0	1.15	0.87	0.012R
	8.0	1.12	0.91	0.0060R
	10.0	1.10	0.93	0.0039R
Fig. F	1.2	3.26	0.44	0.361R
	1.4	2.39	0.50	0.251R
	1.6	1.99	0.54	0.186R
	1.8	1.78	0.57	0.144R
	2.0	1.66	0.60	0.116R
	3.0	1.37	0.70	0.052R
	4.0	1.27	0.75	0.029R
	6.0	1.16	0.82	0.013R
	8.0	1.12	0.86	0.0060R
	10.0	1.09	0.88	0.0039R
Fig. G A = 1.05b^2 I = 0.18b^4 c = 0.70b	1.2	3.65	0.53	0.269R
	1.4	2.50	0.59	0.184R
	1.6	2.08	0.63	0.136R
	1.8	1.85	0.66	0.106R
	2.0	1.69	0.69	0.085R
	2.5	1.49	0.74	0.0535R
	3.0	1.38	0.78	0.0373R
	4.0	1.27	0.83	0.0209R
	6.0	1.19	0.90	0.0091R
	8.0	1.14	0.93	0.00524R
	10.0	1.12	0.96	0.00329R
Fig. H	1.2	3.63	0.58	0.418R
	1.4	2.54	0.63	0.299R
	1.6	2.14	0.67	0.229R
	1.8	1.89	0.70	0.183R
	2.0	1.73	0.72	0.149R
	3.0	1.41	0.79	0.069R
	4.0	1.29	0.83	0.040R
	6.0	1.18	0.88	0.018R
	8.0	1.13	0.91	0.010R
	10.0	1.10	0.92	0.0065R

* y_0 is distance from centroidal axis to neutral axis, when beam is subjected to pure bending.

TABLE 5 (*Continued*)

VALUES OF K FOR DIFFERENT SECTIONS AND DIFFERENT RADII OF CURVATURE

Section	$\dfrac{R}{c}$	Factor K		$y_0{}^*$
		Inside Fiber	Outside Fiber	
Fig. I	1.2	3.55	0.67	0.409R
	1.4	2.48	0.72	0.292R
	1.6	2.07	0.76	0.224R
	1.8	1.83	0.78	0.178R
	2.0	1.69	0.80	0.144R
	3.0	1.38	0.86	0.067R
	4.0	1.26	0.89	0.038R
	6.0	1.15	0.92	0.018R
	8.0	1.10	0.94	0.010R
	10.0	1.08	0.95	0.0065R
Fig. J — For similar sections having same values of K see Table 26	1.2	2.52	0.67	0.408R
	1.4	1.90	0.71	0.285R
	1.6	1.63	0.75	0.208R
	1.8	1.50	0.77	0.160R
	2.0	1.41	0.79	0.127R
	3.0	1.23	0.86	0.058R
	4.0	1.16	0.89	0.030R
	6.0	1.10	0.92	0.013R
	8.0	1.07	0.94	0.0076R
	10.0	1.05	0.95	0.0048R
Fig. K	1.2	3.28	0.58	0.269R
	1.4	2.31	0.64	0.182R
	1.6	1.89	0.68	0.134R
	1.8	1.70	0.71	0.104R
	2.0	1.57	0.73	0.083R
	3.0	1.31	0.81	0.038R
	4.0	1.21	0.85	0.020R
	6.0	1.13	0.90	0.0087R
	8.0	1.10	0.92	0.0049R
	10.0	1.07	0.93	0.0031R
Fig. L — See also I section Table 26	1.2	2.63	0.68	0.399R
	1.4	1.97	0.73	0.280R
	1.6	1.66	0.76	0.205R
	1.8	1.51	0.78	0.159R
	2.0	1.43	0.80	0.127R
	3.0	1.23	0.86	0.058R
	4.0	1.15	0.89	0.031R
	6.0	1.09	0.92	0.014R
	8.0	1.07	0.94	0.0076R
	10.0	1.06	0.95	0.0048R

* y_0 is distance from centroidal axis to neutral axis, when beam is subjected to pure bending.

Correction Factor for Combined Axial and Bending Loads. As pointed out in Art. 48, if the curved beam is subjected to an axial load passing through the centroid of an area in addition to a bending couple, the stress caused by the centroidal axial load usually is assumed to be equal to

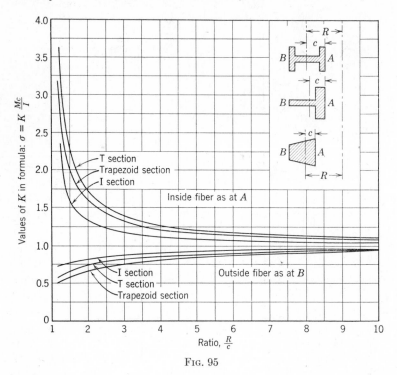

Fig. 95

P/a, and hence the stress at the outer fiber of the section of the curved beam would be given by the expression

$$\sigma = P/a + K(Mc/I) \tag{164}$$

But the stress caused by the axial load probably is somewhat greater than P/a on a fiber on the concave surface because of the shorter length of these fibers, and hence to obtain the stress on such a fiber (where the maximum bending stress occurs) a correction factor may be applied to the expression P/a as well as to the expression Mc/I. If the same correction factor is assumed to apply to both expressions, the expression for the stress at the concave outer or surface fiber becomes

$$\sigma = K[(P/a) + (Mc/I)] \tag{165}$$

This expression gives a value for the maximum stress that agrees reasonably well with the results of a photoelastic analysis by Dolan and Levine.*

In the subsequent articles of this chapter, especially those dealing with the deflection of curved beams, Eq. 164 will be employed as a matter of convenience.

Problems

90. Solve Prob. 86 by use of the straight-beam formula and a correction factor.
91. Solve Prob. 87 by use of the straight-beam formula and a correction factor.
92. Solve Prob. 88 by use of the straight-beam formula and a correction factor.
93. Solve Prob. 83 by use of the straight-beam formula and a correction factor.

50 Equivalent-area method. If a curved beam has a cross-sectional area composed of segments of circles, ellipses, or other areas having curved boundaries such as that shown in Fig. G in Table 5, the computation of the value of Z by means of equations similar to those given in Appendix III usually becomes too complex and laborious. Such an area may be replaced by an equivalent area composed of trapezoids, rectangles, etc., which approximate the boundary of the actual area. The value of Z may then be computed for the equivalent area. This procedure is used in the illustrative problem at the end of this article, in which the stresses are computed for a crane hook whose actual cross section is indicated in Fig. 94a. The equivalent cross section is shown in Fig. 94b in which the equivalent section has an area equal to that of the actual section and is obtained by replacing the segment of circles by trapezoids.

There are two principles which should be applied in the use of the equivalent-area method. First, the value of the ratio R/c for the equivalent section should be approximately the same as that for the actual section, since, as may be seen from Table 5, a relatively small change in the ratio R/c causes a rather large change in the circumferential (bending) stress, particularly for small values of R/c. Second, the area substituted for the part of the actual area which is nearest to the center of curvature of the beam should be a rather close approximation to the shape of the actual area. This condition arises from the fact that, in the expression for Z, errors in the smaller values of the denominator $R + y$ have a relatively large effect on the value of Z, as may be seen by considering Eq. 153; for the area nearest to the center of curvature the values of $R + y$ may be quite small, and an error in the value of $R + y$ may be magnified in its effect upon the value of Z. The applica-

* T. J. Dolan and R. E. Levine, "A Study of the Stresses in Curved Beams," *Proceedings of the Thirteenth Semi-Annual Eastern Photoelastic Conference*, June 1941.

tion of these principles in the use of the equivalent-area method is illustrated in the following problem.

Transformed-area Method. It is possible to transform graphically the cross-sectional area of a curved beam in accordance with the expressions in Art. 48 so that the centroidal axis of the transformed area coincides with the neutral axis of the original area of the beam. Résal showed that by using such a transformed area the only properties of the area needed in calculating the stress in the curved beam are the moment of inertia of the transformed area with respect to its centroidal axis and the distance between the centroidal axes of the original and the transformed areas. Résal's method is not used in this book; it is discussed in reference 4 at the end of this chapter.

Illustrative Problem

Problem 94. A wrought-iron crane hook having the section shown in Fig. 94a when tested reached its maximum elastic strength at a load of 16,000 lb. (The section in Fig. 94a is located in the hook in a position corresponding to section AB in Fig. 89a). Calculate the circumferential stress at the innermost fiber B by assuming that the cross-sectional area is replaced by an equivalent area in which the circular sectors are approximated by trapezoids as shown in Fig. 94b (see Appendix III for value of Z). Also, compute the stress at B by using the straight-beam formula and a correction factor K from Table 5.

Solution by Equivalent-area Method. The area of the equivalent section AB in Fig. 94b is 8.46 sq in., which is the same as the area of the actual section in Fig. 94a (see Fig. G, Table 5). The centroid G of the equivalent section is found to be at the distance $c_B = 2$ in. from B. Therefore, $R = 3 + c_B = 3 + 2.00 = 5.00$ in., and hence $R/c = 2.5$. The value of Z for the equivalent section is given by the equation (see Appendix III)

$$Z = -1 + \frac{R}{a} \left\{ \left[b_1 + \frac{b - b_1}{h_1} (R + c_1) \right] \log \frac{R + c_1}{R - c_2} \right.$$

$$\left. + \left[b_2 - \frac{b - b_2}{h_2} (R - c_3) \right] \log \frac{R - c_2}{R - c_3} + b_1 - b_2 \right\}$$

$$= -1 + \frac{5}{8.46} \left\{ \left[0.73 + \frac{2.84 - 0.73}{3.64} (5 + 2.62) \right] \log \frac{7.62}{3.98} \right.$$

$$\left. + \left[1.17 - \frac{1.67}{0.98} (5 - 2) \right] \log \frac{5 - 1.02}{5 - 2} + 0.73 - 1.17 \right\}$$

$$= 0.058$$

The stress at B is

$$\sigma_B = \frac{P}{a} + \frac{M}{aR} \left(1 + \frac{1}{Z} \frac{-c_B}{R - c_B} \right) = \frac{16,000}{8.46} + \frac{-16,000 \times 5}{8.46 \times 5} \left(1 + \frac{1}{0.058} \frac{-2}{5 - 2} \right)$$

$$= 21,750 \text{ lb/in.}^2$$

Solution by the Straight-beam Formula and a Correction Factor. The area of the actual section in Fig. 94a is 8.46 sq in., and the centroid G is found to be at the distance $c_B = 1.98$ in. from B. The moment of inertia of the cross section about the centroidal axis is found to be $I = 11.59$ in.[4]. The value of R is 4.98 in., and $R/c = 2.51$. Therefore, the stress at B is

$$\sigma_B = (P/a) + K(Mc/I)$$

in which the value of K is found in Table 5 for Fig. G to be $K = 1.49$. Therefore

$$\sigma_B = \frac{16,000}{8.46} + 1.49\,\frac{4.98 \times 16,000 \times 1.98}{11.59} = 22,200 \text{ lb/in.}^2$$

The use of the equivalent area in Fig. 94b results in an error of only about 2 per cent. If a single trapezoid such as that shown in Fig. 94c is used as the equivalent area, the stress σ_B at the innermost fiber is 18,140 lb per sq in. This value represents an error of 22 per cent resulting from the fact, previously noted, that the value of R/c has been changed too much ($R/c = 3.00$ for this equivalent area as compared to 2.5 for the actual section) and also from the fact that the trapezoid does not approximate closely the boundary of the portion of the actual section which is nearest the center of curvature.

Problems

95. Let the steel hook of Fig. 89a have a rectangular cross section at AB with rounded corners as shown in Fig. 96, and let $P = 10$ tons. The circumferential stress at the innermost fiber of the section as determined from Eq. 161 is 23,000

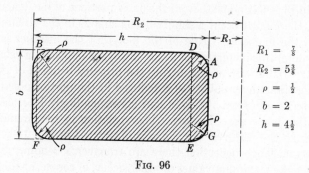

$$R_1 = \tfrac{7}{8}$$
$$R_2 = 5\tfrac{3}{8}$$
$$\rho = \tfrac{1}{2}$$
$$b = 2$$
$$h = 4\tfrac{1}{2}$$

Fig. 96

lb per sq in., using a value of $Z = 0.254$ as found by the graphical method. Compute the circumferential stress at A or G by making use of an equivalent area consisting of a rectangle and a trapezoid as indicated by the dotted lines in Fig. 96. *Note:* If an equivalent rectangular area is used to solve for the stress at point A, a value of $\sigma_A = 21,200$ lb per sq in. is obtained.   *Ans.* $Z = 0.248$; $\sigma_A = 23,600$ lb/in.².

96. In Fig. 93 let the sections of the clamp at AB and DE be as shown in Fig. 97a. Solve for the maximum circumferential stress at DE by replacing the section by an equivalent section as indicated by the dotted lines; this equivalent area is shown in Fig. 97b, in which the various parts of the equivalent area are placed together to form a trapezoid and rectangle.

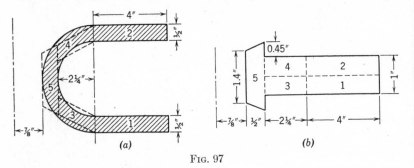

Fig. 97

51 Circumferential stress in curved beams having I, T, or similar cross sections.

As stated in Art. 48, the Winkler-Bach formula may give values of circumferential stresses which are considerably in error for curved I beams, T beams, or tubular members. This is due primarily to the fact that the circumferential stresses in the flanges of a curved I beam or T beam cause the outer portions of the flanges to deflect radially, thereby distorting the cross section of the beam, the effect of which is to decrease the stiffness of the member and to increase the maximum circumferential stresses in the beam. This fact is made evident qualitatively (analyzed quantitatively later in this article) by observing in Figs. 98 and 99 that, as the outer portions of the flanges deflect radially, there must occur a simultaneous change in the circumferential strain in the flange by virtue of the fact that the member is curved. Furthermore, this increment of strain always is opposite in sense to the circumferential strain accompanying the primary bending of the beam. Thus, the circumferential stress is reduced in the portions of the flange which are remote from the web, and correspondingly increased in the part of the flange near the web. The variation in the circumferential stress across the width of the flange is illustrated in Fig. 100. Accompanying the flange deflection there are transverse bending stresses in the flange, the maximum values of which occur, of course, at the junction of the flange with the web; these transverse stresses may be as great or even greater than the maximum circumferential stress.

It has been observed in tests * of curved I beams having very thick flanges that plane cross sections do not remain plane, but that each

---

* D. C. Broughton, M. E. Clark, and H. T. Corten, *Tests and Theory of Elastic Stresses in Curved Beams Having I- and T-Sections*, Society for Experimental Stress Analysis, Vol. VIII, No. 1, 1950, pp. 143–155.

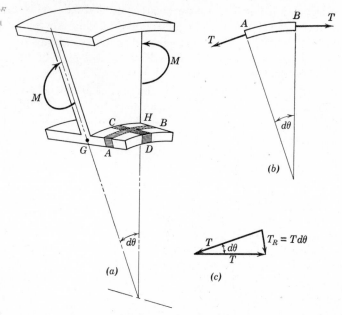

FIG. 98   Curved beam with I cross section.

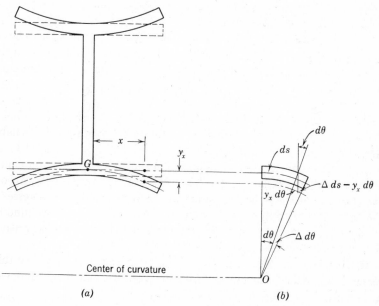

FIG. 99   Bending of flanges of I section of curved beam.

flange cross section tends to rotate about a neutral axis of its own in addition to the rotation about the neutral axis of the beam as a whole, as shown in Fig. 101. This action causes the flange stresses to be increased somewhat, although the effect is small and may be neglected except for curved beams with very thick flanges.

The maximum radial stress in a curved I or T beam occurs at the junction between the web and the inner flange, but its value is not affected significantly by the transverse bending of the flanges nor by the

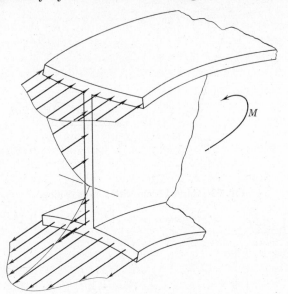

FIG. 100   Stresses in I section of curved beam.

warping of the cross section. As a result, radial stresses in curved I or T beams may be computed satisfactorily by the method developed in Art. 52 for solid-type sections.

Circumferential Stresses. In Fig. 98a is shown a segment of a curved I beam in which the flanges are thin relative to the other dimensions of the beam. Let the beam be loaded with a pure bending moment M in the central plane of the web such that the inner flange is subjected to tensile stress. A circumferential strip $\overline{AB}$ of the inner (tension) flange is acted upon by the circumferential forces T applied at its ends, as shown in Fig. 98b. Since the flange is curved, the resultant of these two forces is a radial force $Td\theta$, as shown in Fig. 98c. In the outlying (or unsupported) portions of the flange the radial forces $Td\theta$ cause the flange to bend as though each *transverse* strip CD of the flange were a cantilever beam fixed at the junction with the web.

This transverse deflection of the flange tends to reduce the circumferential stresses in the outlying portions of the flange in a manner that may be explained as follows: Let Fig. 99a represent the cross section of the curved beam illustrated in Fig. 98a. Since the thickness of the flanges is assumed to be small relative to the other dimensions of the beam, it is permissible to deal with the average circumferential bending stresses in

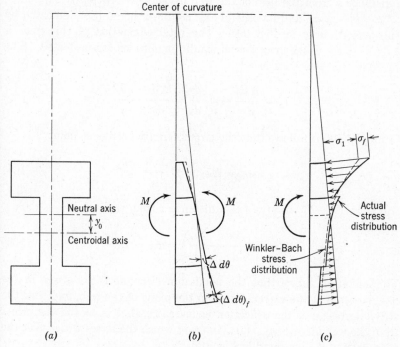

FIG. 101   Bending of thick flanges of I section of curved beam.

the flanges. The average stresses and strains in the inner flange shall be designated by $\bar{\sigma}$ and $\bar{\epsilon}$, respectively, and are assumed to occur at the mid-thickness of the flange, the radius of curvature to this location being r. At a point a distance x from the face of the web, the average circumferential stresses and strains are $\bar{\sigma}_x$ and $\bar{\epsilon}_x$, respectively; the deflection of the flange at this point is y_x.

In Fig. 99b is shown a circumferential segment of length ds of the inner flange of the unstressed curved beam. The length ds subtends the angle $d\theta$ relative to the center of curvature O, and hence $ds = r\,d\theta$. As the bending moment M (Fig. 98a) is applied to the beam, the inner flange elongates and the angle $d\theta$ increases by an amount $\Delta\,d\theta$. The central circumferential fiber GH of the flange (Figs. 98a and 99b) will increase in length by an amount $\Delta\,ds$, and hence the strain in this fiber is

$$\bar{\epsilon}_G = \frac{\Delta\,ds}{ds} \qquad (166)$$

A circumferential strip of the flange (such as AB in Fig. 98a) located at a distance x from the face of the web deflects, as previously explained, by an amount y_x, and its central axis assumes the position indicated by the dashed curve in Fig. 99b. The total elongation of this fiber is $\Delta\,ds - y_x\,d\theta$, if higher orders of small magnitudes are neglected. The strain in this fiber then is

$$\bar{\epsilon}_x = \frac{\Delta\,ds}{ds} - y_x\frac{d\theta}{ds} = \frac{\Delta\,ds}{ds} - \frac{y_x}{r} \qquad (167)$$

From Eq. 166 it follows that the circumferential stress at point G is

$$\bar{\sigma}_G = E\bar{\epsilon}_G = E\frac{\Delta\,ds}{ds} \qquad (168)$$

and from Eq. 167 the stress at a distance x from the web is

$$\bar{\sigma}_x = E\left(\frac{\Delta\,ds}{ds} - \frac{y_x}{r}\right) = \bar{\sigma}_G - E\frac{y_x}{r} \qquad (169)$$

This equation shows that the maximum circumferential stress in the flange occurs at the extreme fiber in the plane of the web, and that the stress decreases as the deflection y_x increases, that is, as the distance x from the web increases. The manner in which the stress varies over the cross section is illustrated in Fig. 100.

Although Eq. 169 is useful for interpreting the manner of variation of the circumferential stresses across the flange, it does not completely solve the problem as it merely expresses the relationship between the two variables $\bar{\sigma}_x$ and y_x. An additional relationship between these quantities is needed before a solution for the stresses can be obtained.

An approximate solution to this problem has been presented by H. Bleich,[*] in which he obtained the additional relationship needed by utilizing the elastic curve equation of a transverse strip of the flange such as CD in Fig. 98a, considered as a simple cantilever beam. From

---

[*] Navy Department, The David W. Taylor Model Basin, Translation 228, January 1950, of "Die Spannungsverteilung in den Gurtungen gekrümmter Stabe mit T- und I-formigem Querschnitt," by H. Bleich, Der Stahlbau, Beilage zur Zeitschrift, Die Bautechnik, Vol. 6, No. 1, Jan. 6, 1933, pp. 3–6.

the resulting differential equation, he obtained solutions for the circumferential stress, the transverse bending stress, and the deflection of the flange, in terms of the mean flange stress $\bar{\sigma}_G$. For purposes of practical application, the solution is reduced to a workable form by replacing the given beam cross section with a modified section having narrower flanges, in which the circumferential flange stresses may be assumed to be uniform across the entire width of the flange. The reduced flange width was determined by Bleich in such a manner that the total force in each flange remains unchanged, so that the equilibrium of the beam is not disturbed thereby. The Winkler-Bach formula may then be applied to the modified section, and a close approximation to the true maximum stress will be obtained. The reduced or effective width of the projecting part of the flange is given by

$$b' = \alpha b \tag{170}$$

in which b' = reduced or effective projecting width of flange (on each side).

b = projecting width of the actual flange (on each side).

α = a ratio obtained from Bleich's solution (see Table 6).

Transverse Bending Stress. The transverse bending stress in the flange is given by Bleich as a function of the average longitudinal flange stress $\bar{\sigma}_G$ as follows.

$$\sigma' = \beta \bar{\sigma}_G \tag{171}$$

in which σ' = maximum lateral bending stress in the flange.

$\bar{\sigma}_G$ = circumferential bending stress at a distance $t/2$ from the extreme fiber, computed by the Winkler-Bach equation, using the modified section.

β = a ratio obtained from Bleich's solution (see Table 6).

For purposes of calculation, the values of α and β are represented as functions of b^2/rt in Table 6. Here t is the flange thickness, b is the projecting width of the flange (on each side), and r is the radius of curvature to the center of the flange of the unstressed curved beam.

It will be noted from Table 6 that the resistance of a curved I section decreases rapidly as the ratio b^2/rt increases above 0.3, indicating that curved beams with wide, thin flanges are wasteful of material. A commonly used method of strengthening curved I sections with thin flanges is to weld stiffeners or gussets to both flange and web to minimize distortion of the section.

Although Bleich's analysis was developed for curved beams with relatively thin flanges, the results thus obtained agree closely with a similar solution obtained by Anderson * for I beams and box beams in which the analysis was not restricted to thin-flanged sections. Thus, the values of α and β from Table 6 may be expected to be reasonably accurate for all values of the ratio b^2/rt which are listed, even though the flanges of the beam may be relatively thick and narrow. Similar

TABLE 6

TABLE FOR CALCULATING THE EFFECTIVE WIDTH AND THE LATERAL BENDING
STRESS OF CURVED I OR T BEAMS

b^2/rt	0.2	0.3	0.4	0.5	0.6	0.7	0.8	0.9	1.0
α	0.977	0.950	0.917	0.878	0.838	0.800	0.762	0.726	0.693
β	0.580	0.836	1.056	1.238	1.382	1.495	1.577	1.636	1.677

b^2/rt	1.1	1.2	1.3	1.4	1.5	2.0	3.0	4.0	5.0
α	0.663	0.636	0.611	0.589	0.569	0.495	0.414	0.367	0.334
β	1.703	1.721	1.728	1.732	1.732	1.707	1.671	1.680	1.700

analyses of curved tubular members with circular and rectangular cross sections have been made by von Kármán † and by Timoshenko,‡ respectively.

Illustrative Problem

Problem 97. A curved beam having the dimensions shown in Figs. 102a and 102b is made of mild steel having a yield point of 35,000 lb per sq in. If it is subjected to the loads $P = 3000$ lb as shown in the figure, compute the maximum circumferential and the maximum transverse stresses on section AB.

Solution. First it is necessary to determine the dimensions of the modified section according to Bleich's method. For the inner flange, $b^2/rt = (1.5)^2/(2 \times \frac{1}{2}) = 2.25$. Entering Table 6 with this value, we find $\alpha = 0.475$. Therefore, the total width of the inner flange of the modified section is $2 \times 0.475 \times 1.5 + 0.5 = 1.92$ in. Simi-

* C. G. Anderson, *Flexural Stresses in Curved Beams of I- and Box Sections*, presented to the Institution of Mechanical Engineers, Nov. 3, 1950.

† Th. von Kármán, *Zeitschrift des Vereines deutscher Ingenieure*, Vol. 55, 1911, p. 1889.

‡ S. Timoshenko, *Transactions of the American Society of Mechanical Engineers*, Vol. 45, 1923, p. 135.

larly, for the outer flange, $b^2/rt = 0.82$, and $\alpha = 0.755$. The width of the outer flange is then $2 \times 0.755 \times 1.5 + 0.5 = 2.76$ in. The entire modified section is shown in Fig. 102c.

The centroid of the modified section must then be found; its location is 2.19 in. from B. The radius of curvature to the centroid of the modified section is R'

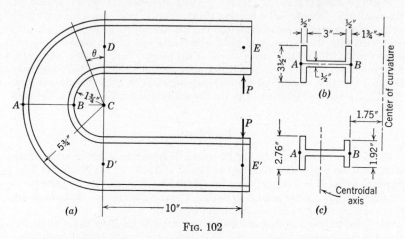

FIG. 102

$= 3.94$ in., and the area $a' = 3.84$ sq in. From Table 26 in Appendix III, the value of Z_m for the modified section may be computed.

$$Z_m = -1 + \frac{3.94}{3.84}(2.76 \log 5.75 - 2.26 \log 5.25 + 1.42 \log 2.25 - 1.92 \log 1.75)$$

$$= +0.187$$

The maximum circumferential stress is computed by the Winkler-Bach formula, using the properties of the modified section.

$$\sigma_{max} = \frac{P}{a'} + \frac{M}{a'R'}\left(1 + \frac{1}{Z_m}\frac{-c}{R'-c}\right)$$

$$= \frac{3000}{3.84} + \frac{-3000 \times 13.94}{3.84 \times 3.94}\left(1 + \frac{1}{0.187}\frac{-2.19}{1.75}\right)$$

$$= 780 - 2760(1 - 6.70)$$

$$= 780 + 15,750 = 16,530 \text{ lb/in.}^2 \quad \text{(tension)}$$

If the actual dimensions of the section were used, the maximum computed stress would have been 10,400 lb per sq in.

To find the maximum transverse stress in the inner flange, the circumferential stress at mid-thickness of the flange first must be computed.

$$\bar{\sigma}_G = 780 - 2760\left(1 + \frac{1}{0.187}\frac{-1.94}{2.00}\right)$$

$$= 780 + 11,600 = 12,380 \text{ lb/in.}^2$$

Re-entering the table with a value of $b^2/rt = 2.25$ for the inner flange, we find β = 1.698, and therefore by Eq. 171 the maximum lateral bending stress is

$$\sigma' = \beta \cdot \bar{\sigma}_G = 1.698 \times 12,380 = 21,000 \text{ lb/in.}^2 \qquad \text{(compression)}$$

It will be noted that in this problem the transverse bending stress is greater than the maximum circumferential bending stress. Furthermore, since the two stresses at the point are of opposite sense (one tension, the other compression), the stress associated with the beginning of yielding probably will be the maximum shearing stress (or the octahedral shearing stress) at the point. This, however, represents a local condition, and it is probable that a more general yielding of the flange would be the action that would limit the load-carrying capacity of the member, and such yielding is associated primarily with the circumferential bending stress in the flange.

Problems

98. Let the curved beam in Fig. 92 have a T-shaped cross section whose dimensions have the proportions described in Fig. H of Table 5. Let R and t in Fig. H have the values $R = 4$ in. and $t = 1$ in. If the load $P = 4000$ lb, compute the circumferential stress at the point A by the use of the modified section method. Assume that the elastic limit of the material is not exceeded.

99. Compute the maximum circumferential stress in the inner flange at the location DE in the curved beam in Prob. 88 by use of the modified section method.

52   Radial stresses in curved beams. In Arts. 48 through 51 are given methods of computing the normal stresses in curved beams on plane sections passing through the center of curvature perpendicular to the plane of curvature; these stresses are called circumferential stresses. A bending moment acting on a curved beam as shown in Fig. 103a also causes normal stresses on planes at right angles to the radius of curvature, called radial stresses since their direction is along the radius. The radial stress at the inside (concave) and outside (convex) surface of a curved beam are zero since there are usually no loads on these surfaces, and the radial stresses have relatively small values at points within beams having circular, rectangular, trapezoidal, or similar (so-called solid) cross sections. However, in beams having H, I, T, or similar sections the maximum radial stresses occur in the web and may have a value larger than the maximum circumferential stress in the beam; these radial stresses may be the cause of damage to the beam, particularly if the beam is made of brittle material or is subjected to repeated cycles of stress.

The radial stress at any point in a curved beam (Fig. 103a) may be found from one of the conditions of equilibrium by equating to zero the radial components of the forces acting on a small block of the beam, such as $ABDE$ in Fig. 103a, shown enlarged in the free-body diagram in Fig. 103c. The faces AE and BD, which form a very small angle $d\theta$, have the area a' as shown in Fig. 103b. The total circumferential force T (Fig. 103c) on each of these faces is given by the expression

$$T = \int_{-c}^{y} \sigma \, da \qquad (172)$$

where σ is the circumferential stress at any point given by Eq. 158. The radial force F_r on face DE is equal to the product of the radial stress σ_r and the area of the face. Thus $F_r = \sigma_r(R + y)t \, d\theta$, where t is the thickness of the beam at the distance y from the centroidal surface. The

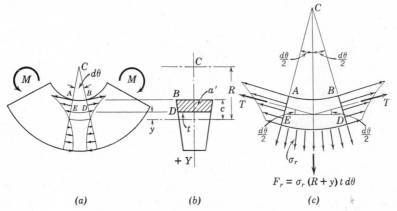

$$F_r = \sigma_r (R + y) t \, d\theta$$

(a)   (b)   (c)

Fig. 103   Radial stresses in curved beam.

equation of equilibrium applied to the radial components of the forces acting on block $ABDE$ in Fig. 103c gives

$$\sigma_r(R + y)t \, d\theta = 2T \sin (d\theta/2) = T \, d\theta$$
$$\sigma_r = T/[t(R + y)] \qquad (173)$$

To compute the radial stress from Eq. 173, the value of the force T from Eq. 172 must be found. The expression for σ from Eq. 158 is substituted in Eq. 172, which becomes

$$T = \frac{M}{aR} \int_{-c}^{y} da + \frac{M}{aRZ} \int_{-c}^{y} \frac{y \, da}{R + y} \qquad (174)$$

In Eq. 174 the first integral represents the area a' as shown in Fig. 103b, and the second integral has the same form as that which defined Z in Eq. 153. This integral is represented by Z'. Thus

$$Z' = -\frac{1}{a'} \int_{-c}^{y} \frac{y \, da}{R + y} \qquad (175)$$

where Z' is a property of the area a' analogous to the property Z of the entire cross section area a. The substitution of these symbols in Eq. 174 gives

$$T = (Ma'/Ra)[1 - (Z'/Z)]$$

Substituting this value of T in Eq. 173, we obtain

$$\sigma_r = \frac{Ma'}{Rta(R + y)}\left(1 - \frac{Z'}{Z}\right) \tag{176}$$

where σ_r is the radial stress at a point located at a distance y from the centroid of the section. The signs of M and y are determined as stated in Art. 48. Equation 176 gives nearly correct values of the radial stress in the web of an I or T section, despite the fact that in Art. 51 it is shown that the Winkler-Bach equation (Eq. 158), which is used to compute T in Eq. 174, does not give the correct circumferential stress; the value of the force T in the flange of an I or T section is changed very little by the distortion of the cross section as discussed in Art. 51. Furthermore, the addition of an axial load to a pure bending moment does not alter the radial stress.

Illustrative Problem

Problem 100. A curved beam used as a heavy clamp is shown in Fig. 104a. The dimensions of section AB are shown in Fig. 104b. The beam is made of cast

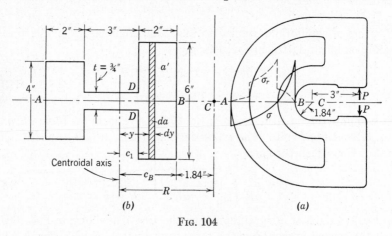

Fig. 104

iron and is subjected to a load $P = 10,000$ lb. Compute the radial stress in the beam at the section in the web where the web joins the inner flange. Assume that the material is elastic and that the elastic limit is not exceeded.

Solution. The area a of the section is 22.25 sq in., and the area a' between the inner surface and the minimum section DD where the radial stress is to be computed is 12 sq in. It is found that $c_B = 3.05$ in., $c_1 = 1.05$ in., and $R = 4.89$ in. From Eq. 175 the value of Z' is

$$Z' = -\frac{1}{a'} \int_{-c_B}^{-c_1} \frac{y\, da}{R + y} = \frac{6}{a'} \int_{-3.05}^{-1.05} \frac{y\, dy}{R + y}$$

$$= -\tfrac{6}{12}[y - R \log (R + y)]_{-3.05}^{-1.05} = 0.78$$

The value of Z as found by calculation (see Appendix III) is $Z = 0.293$. The bending moment on section AB is $M = -78{,}900$ lb-in., and hence the radial stress as found from Eq. 177 is

$$\sigma_r = \frac{Ma'}{Rta(R - c_1)} \left(1 - \frac{Z'}{Z}\right)$$

$$= \frac{-78{,}900 \times 12}{4.89 \times 0.75 \times 22.25(4.89 - 1.05)} \left(1 - \frac{0.78}{0.293}\right)$$

$$= 5000 \text{ lb/in}^2.$$

This value of σ_r is a tensile stress since it has a positive sign; it will be noted that a negative bending moment will always produce a tensile radial stress. This value of σ_r is the maximum radial stress as may be noted from the dashed curve in Fig. 104a, the ordinates to which represent the distribution of radial stress across the depth AB of the beam. The ordinates to the solid curve represent the circumferential stress σ as found from Eq. 161; the maximum value of the circumferential stress is 4940 lb per sq in. Thus the maximum normal (tensile) stress in the beam is the radial stress; this means that if the loads are increased the beam is likely to fail by fracture occurring as a separation of the inner flange from the web. This type of failure has been observed for curved beams made of brittle material.

In this problem the effect of the stress concentration at the fillet joining the flange to the web has not been considered. This stress concentration will increase the magnitude of the maximum radial stress. The increase in stress is somewhat localized and may not be significant in beams made of ductile metal and subjected to static loads. However, for beams made of brittle materials or for beams of ductile material subjected to repeated loads the localized stresses are significant. Stress concentrations at fillets are considered in Chapter 13.

Problems

101. In the frame described in Prob. 86 and in Fig. 91 compute the radial stress at a point 1 in. from the point A in section AB.

102. In Prob. 88 let it be assumed that in the curved portion of the clamp shown in Fig. 93 there is a fillet of radius $\tfrac{1}{4}$ in. joining the web and the flanges. Compute the radial stress at the juncture of the web and the fillet at the inner flange. Assume that there is no stress concentration at the fillet.

53 Deflection of curved beams having so-called solid sections.

Curved beams are frequently used in machines or structures as load-carrying members which may cease to function properly (fail) because of an excessive amount of elastic deflection. In this article a procedure is derived for determining the relation between the loads and the elastic deflection of a curved beam. If the beam has only a small initial curvature, the methods for determining the deflection of straight beams may be employed; otherwise the influence of the initial curvature of the beam must be considered. Probably the most convenient method for determining deflections is by use of Castigliano's theorem. (This theorem is discussed more fully in Chapter 15, to which the reader is referred if he is not familiar with the method; the method is used at this point in order to complete the discussion of curved beams in one chapter.) The theorem states that, if external forces act on an elastic member or structure, the displacement, in the direction of any one of the forces, of the point of application of the force is equal to the partial derivative of the total elastic strain energy U in the member with respect to the force. That is

$$\delta_P = \partial U/\partial P \tag{177}$$

Since we are dealing with elastic conditions, the strain energy in a differential element of a member is equal to the work done on the element by the forces acting on it, and the total strain energy in the member is equal to the summations of the strain energy of the differential elements. Thus an expression for U in a curved beam subjected to a load P and moment M_0 as illustrated in Fig. 105a may be obtained by summing up the work done on each differential block, such as $ABCD$, in the beam by the internal moments and forces which act on that block. The bending moment M, the shearing force V, and the normal force N acting on any section as shown in Fig. 105b may be expressed in terms of P, M_0, θ, R, and d by applying the equations of equilibrium to the forces acting on this part of the beam. The forces V and N and the moment M are shown acting on both ends of the differential block in Fig. 105d. The block has been selected such that V, N, and M are positive. Let the strain energy of the block be dU, which is equal to the work done on any such block $ABCD$ by M, N, and V. The total strain energy for the whole beam is $U = \int dU$. The strain energy dU in any block is found as the sum of the work done by each of the forces N and V and by the bending moment M in deforming the block elastically. These expressions for the strain energy are derived in the following paragraphs.

Axial Force N. Let the cross-sectional area a of the block be that shown by Fig. 105c. The force N is assumed to produce a stress $\sigma = N/a$ which is uniform over the area a. The strain energy per unit volume of the block due to N alone is $\frac{1}{2}(\sigma^2/E) = \frac{1}{2}(N^2/Ea^2)$. The volume of the block is $a \cdot ds$ where ds is the arc length of the block at its centroid.

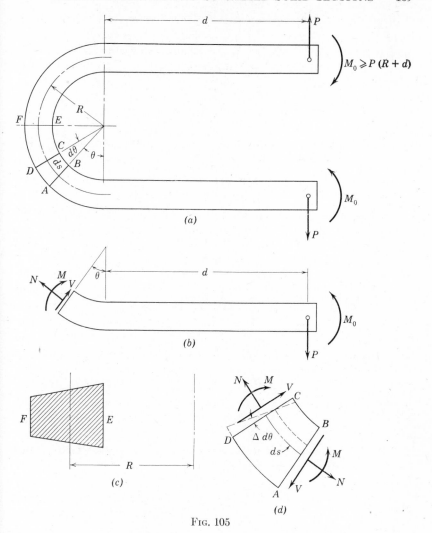

Fig. 105

Therefore, the work done on the block by the force N is equal to the strain energy due to N and is

$$dU_N = \frac{1}{2}\frac{N^2}{Ea^2}(a\,ds) = \frac{1}{2}\frac{N^2\,ds}{Ea} \tag{178}$$

The total strain energy in all the blocks (and hence on the whole beam) due to the normal forces N is

$$U_N = \int dU_N = \frac{1}{2}\int \frac{N^2\,ds}{Ea} \tag{179}$$

Shear Force V. An approximate * expression for the strain energy in the differential block due to the shearing force V is found in a manner similar to that for the force N, by using the average shearing stress $\tau = V/a$. The strain energy per unit volume is $\frac{1}{2}(\tau^2/G) = \frac{1}{2}(V^2/Ga^2)$, and for the block is

$$dU_V = \frac{1}{2}\frac{V^2}{Ga^2}(a\,ds) = \frac{1}{2}\frac{V^2\,ds}{Ga} \tag{180}$$

The total strain energy in the whole beam due to the shearing forces V is

$$U_V = \int \frac{1}{2}\frac{V^2}{Ga}\,ds \tag{181}$$

Bending Moment M. The work done on the differential block by the bending moment M is equal to the average moment $M/2$ multiplied by the angle through which plane AB rotates relative to plane CD ($\Delta\,d\theta$ in Fig. 105d), or $\frac{1}{2}M\cdot\Delta\,d\theta$. The angle $\Delta\,d\theta$ may be found from Eq. 157 in

which $\omega = \dfrac{\Delta\,d\theta}{d\theta} = \dfrac{1}{Ea}\left(\dfrac{M}{R} + \dfrac{M}{RZ}\right)$, thus:

$$\Delta\,d\theta = \frac{d\theta}{Ea}\left(\frac{M}{R} + \frac{M}{RZ}\right) = \frac{M\,d\theta}{Ea}\cdot\frac{Z+1}{ZR} \tag{182}$$

But from Eq. 160, $(Z+1)/ZR = 1/y_0$ (if the sign of y_0 is neglected); therefore

$$\Delta\,d\theta = \frac{M\,d\theta}{Eay_0} = \frac{M\,ds}{Eay_0R} \tag{183}$$

By means of this expression, the work done on the block, which is equal to the strain energy, may be stated as

$$dU_M = \frac{1}{2}M\cdot\Delta\,d\theta = \frac{1}{2}\frac{M^2\,ds}{Eay_0R} \tag{184}$$

and the total strain energy absorbed by the entire beam by virtue of the bending moments in the beam is

$$U_M = \int \frac{1}{2}\frac{M^2\,ds}{Eay_0R} \tag{185}$$

---

* A correction factor is sometimes used in Eqs. 180 and 181 to obtain a more accurate value of the energy due to shear. For example, if the cross section is rectangular, the right side of Eqs. 180 and 181 is multiplied by 1.2. Such corrections as this are unnecessary, however, unless the energy due to shear is the predominant part of the total energy U of the whole beam.

It should be remembered that the Winkler-Bach derivation neglects the radial stresses and whatever effects they might have on the circumferential stresses or displacements. These effects, however, are very small for beams with so-called solid types of cross sections, since in this type of member the radial stresses generally are very small in comparison to the circumferential stresses.

For beams in which the depth of the member is small relative to the radius of curvature, i.e., $R/c > 4$, a simpler approximation for the work done by the bending moments is justified. In such beams, the initial curvature may be neglected, and the expression for the angle change $\Delta d\theta$ becomes $(M\, ds)/EI$. The work done on the differential block by the moment M in producing the angle change $\Delta d\theta$, which is equal to dU_M, then becomes

$$dU_M = \frac{1}{2}Md\theta = \frac{1}{2}\frac{M^2\, ds}{EI} \tag{186}$$

The total strain energy due to the bending moments on all the differential blocks in the beam is

$$U_M = \int \frac{1}{2}\frac{M^2\, ds}{EI} \tag{187}$$

The approximate value of U_M given by Eq. 187 is always larger than that given by Eq. 185, but for beams with ratios of R/c greater than 4, the values given by the two expressions differ by a negligible amount. Thus, for beams in which the depth of the section is small relative to the radius of curvature, Eq. 187 may be used.

Combination of Moment and Axial Force. When a curved beam is subjected to both bending stress and direct stress simultaneously, additional internal work is done beyond that already described. Let it be considered that the normal force N is applied first, and the bending moment M second. This is permissible since the total internal work will be the same for elastic strains, irrespective of the order of application of the loads. The rotation of the faces AB and CD of the block in Fig. 105d due to the moment M causes the resultant normal force N (assumed to act through the centroid of the section) to move through a distance $\epsilon_0 \cdot ds$, resulting in the additional work or strain energy of the amount

$$dU_{MN} = N\epsilon_0\, ds \tag{188}$$

But from Eq. 157, $\epsilon_0 = M/EaR$. Therefore,

$$dU_{MN} = \frac{MN}{EaR}\, ds \tag{189}$$

The total strain energy of all the differential blocks due to the simultaneous action of bending moment and direct stress is

$$U_{MN} = \int \frac{MN}{EaR}\,ds \qquad (190)$$

In Fig. 105d both the bending moment M and the normal force N are positive, and the resulting strain energy given by Eq. 190 also is positive. For the type of loading illustrated in Figs. 91 and 93, however, M is negative whereas N is positive, and therefore the term $\int (MN/EaR)\cdot ds$ will be negative, whereas all the other work-energy expressions (Eqs. 179, 181, and 185) will be positive.

Total Deflection. The total strain energy in the beam (Fig. 105) is equal to the sum of the values of the work obtained from Eqs. 179, 181, 185, and 190 which gives

$$U = U_N + U_V + U_M + U_{MN}$$

or $$\quad U = \int \frac{1}{2}\frac{N^2}{Ea}\,ds + \int \frac{1}{2}\frac{V^2}{Ga}\,ds + \int \frac{1}{2}\frac{M^2}{Eay_0R}\,ds + \int \frac{MN}{EaR}\,ds \quad (191)$$

The deflection of the point of application of a load P in the direction of the load P is found by taking the partial derivative of Eq. 191 with respect to P. Thus

$$\delta_P = \frac{\partial U}{\partial P} = \int \frac{N}{Ea}\frac{\partial N}{\partial P}\,ds + \int \frac{V}{Ga}\frac{\partial V}{\partial P}\,ds + \int \frac{M}{Eay_0R}\frac{\partial M}{\partial P}\,ds$$

$$+ \int \frac{M}{EaR}\frac{\partial N}{\partial P}\,ds + \int \frac{N}{EaR}\frac{\partial M}{\partial P}\,ds \quad (192)$$

For beams in which the depth of the section is small relative to the radius of curvature, as in arches and similar curved frames, the initial curvature may be neglected and the last two terms in Eq. 191 are replaced by Eq. 187. The partial differentiation of this approximate equation for U with respect to P gives

$$\delta_P = \frac{\partial U}{\partial P} = \int \frac{N}{Ea}\frac{\partial N}{\partial P}\,ds + \int \frac{V}{Ga}\frac{\partial V}{\partial P}\,ds + \int \frac{M}{EI}\frac{\partial M}{\partial P}\,ds \qquad (193)$$

In many problems, it will be found that the influence of direct stress and shear upon deflections is negligible compared to the effect of the bending moments, and in such problems it is common practice to neglect the first two terms of Eq. 192 or 193.

It would appear that the deflection can be found from Eqs. 192 and 193 only at the point of application of the load P, but, if the deflection of some other point of the beam is desired, a fictitious load P' may be assumed to act at the point, and the expression for the partial derivative of U with respect to P' is found. In the final expression P' is made equal to zero. This method is illustrated by the solution of the following problem.

Illustrative Problem

Problem 103. A load P of 3000 lb is applied to a steel curved beam as shown in Fig. 106a. Compute the increase in distance between the points A and B on the beam caused by the load P where A is a distance $d = 10$ in. from P. Assume that the elastic limit is not exceeded and that $G = \frac{2}{5}E = 12,000,000$ lb per sq in.

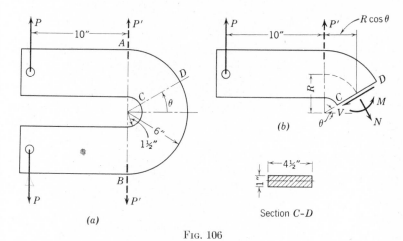

Fig. 106

Solution. Fictitious loads P' are applied at A and B as shown. The expressions for M, N, and V on any section such as CD shown in Fig. 106b are

$$M = -Pd - (P + P')R \cos \theta$$

$$N = (P + P') \cos \theta$$

$$V = (P + P') \sin \theta$$

The partial derivatives of these expressions with respect to P' are

$$\partial M/\partial P' = -R \cos \theta \qquad \partial N/\partial P' = \cos \theta \qquad \partial V/\partial P' = \sin \theta$$

Substituting these quantities into Eq. 192, putting $ds = R\,d\theta$, and making $P' = 0$, we find the deflection to be

$$\delta_{P'} = \int_{-\pi/2}^{+\pi/2} \frac{PR\cos^2\theta}{Ea}\,d\theta + \int_{-\pi/2}^{+\pi/2} \frac{PR\sin^2\theta}{Ga}\,d\theta + \int_{-\pi/2}^{+\pi/2} \frac{(Pd + PR\cos\theta)R^2\cos\theta}{Eay_0 R}\,d\theta$$

$$+ \int_{-\pi/2}^{+\pi/2} \frac{-(Pd + PR\cos\theta)R\cos\theta}{EaR}\,d\theta + \int_{-\pi/2}^{+\pi/2} \frac{P\cos\theta(-R\cos\theta)R}{EaR}\,d\theta$$

$$= \frac{PR}{Ea}\left[\frac{\theta}{2} + \frac{\sin 2\theta}{4}\right]_{-\pi/2}^{+\pi/2} + \frac{PR}{Ga}\left[\frac{\theta}{2} - \frac{\sin 2\theta}{4}\right]_{-\pi/2}^{+\pi/2}$$

$$+ \frac{PR^2}{Eay_0}\left[\frac{d}{R}\sin\theta + \frac{\theta}{2} + \frac{\sin 2\theta}{4}\right]_{-\pi/2}^{+\pi/2} - \frac{PR}{Ea}\left[\frac{d}{R}\sin\theta + \frac{\theta}{2} + \frac{\sin 2\theta}{4}\right]_{-\pi/2}^{+\pi/2}$$

$$- \frac{PR}{Ea}\left[\frac{\theta}{2} + \frac{\sin 2\theta}{4}\right]_{-\pi/2}^{+\pi/2}$$

The first and last terms cancel each other, and when we reduce the other terms we get

$$\delta_{P'} = \frac{PR}{Ea}\left(\frac{E}{G}\frac{\pi}{2} + \frac{2d}{y_0} + \frac{R}{y_0}\cdot\frac{\pi}{2} - \frac{2d}{R} - \frac{\pi}{2}\right)$$

Substitute the following values: $P = 3000$ lb, $R = 3.75$ in., $d = 10$ in., $a = 4.5$ sq in., $y_0 = 0.513$ in., $E = 30 \times 10^6$ lb per sq in., $G = \frac{2}{5}E = 12 \times 10^6$ lb per sq in.

$$\delta_{P'} = \frac{3000 \times 3.75}{30 \times 10^6 \times 4.5}(2.4 + 38.9 + 11.5 - 5.3) = 0.0040 \text{ in.}$$

Using Eq. 193, we obtain

$$\delta_{P'} = \int_{-\pi/2}^{+\pi/2} \frac{PR\cos^2\theta}{Ea}\,d\theta + \int_{-\pi/2}^{+\pi/2} \frac{PR\sin^2\theta}{Ga}\,d\theta + \int_{-\pi/2}^{+\pi/2} \frac{(Pd + PR\cos\theta)R^2\cos\theta\,d\theta}{EI}$$

$$= \frac{PR}{Ea}\left[\frac{\theta}{2} + \frac{\sin 2\theta}{4}\right]_{-\pi/2}^{+\pi/2} + \frac{PR}{Ga}\left[\frac{\theta}{2} - \frac{\sin 2\theta}{4}\right]_{-\pi/2}^{+\pi/2}$$

$$+ \frac{PR^2}{EI}\left[d\sin\theta + \frac{R\theta}{2} + \frac{R\sin 2\theta}{4}\right]_{-\pi/2}^{+\pi/2}$$

$$= \frac{PR\pi}{2Ea} + \frac{PR\pi}{2Ga} + \frac{PR^2}{EI}\left(2d + \frac{R\pi}{2}\right) = 0.0053 \text{ in.}$$

For this sharply curved member, in which the R/c ratio is 1.67, Eq. 193 gives a value of deflection about 33 per cent greater than the more exact value given by Eq. 192. When the R/c ratio is equal to or greater than 3, however, the error will not exceed about 5 per cent.

Problems

104. In Prob. 103 compute the deflection (increase in distance between points of application of the load) of the beam at the load.

105. In the ring of Prob. 87 (see Fig. 92), compute the deflection along the action line of the load P. Assume that the elastic limit is not exceeded and that $G = \frac{2}{3}E = 12,000,000$ lb per sq in. *Ans.* 0.0026 in.

106. In the U-shaped member of Fig. 105 let load $P = 2000$ lb, $M_0 = 0$, $d = 4$ in., $R = 4$ in., and the trapezoidal section be similar to Fig. D in Table 5 in which the dimension $b = 1$ in. Compute the deflection between the points of application of the load P. Assume that the elastic limit of the material is not exceeded and that $G = \frac{2}{5}E = 12,000,000$ lb per sq in.   .

54   Deflections of curved beams having I, T, or similar cross sections. The equations derived in the preceding article for the deflections of curved beams of so-called solid-type sections give values of deflection that are too small for curved I or T beams. This is due primarily to the distortion of the cross section which occurs in curved beams of this type and which was described in Art. 51. It is logical, therefore, to use Bleich's modification of the cross section for the computation of deflections as well as for stresses, since the reduction of the flange width required by this method reflects with reasonable accuracy the decrease in stiffness of the beam due to the distortion of the cross section. Other factors, however, also contribute to the increase in deflection, including the radial stresses in the web, and the tendency for each flange cross section to rotate about a neutral axis of its own in addition to the rotation of the whole cross section. In view of the several uncertain variables involved, it is appropriate to use an approximate expression for the angle change $\Delta\, d\theta$ of a beam segment of length ds, similar to that used for straight beams, except for the use of the moment of inertia of the modified section. This expression is

$$\Delta\, d\theta = \frac{M}{EI'}\, ds \tag{194}$$

in which $I' =$ moment of inertia of the modified section (see Table 6) about its centroidal axis. The strain energy due to bending of the curved I beam then becomes

$$U_M = \int \frac{1}{2}\frac{M^2\, ds}{EI'} \tag{195}$$

In expressing the strain energy due to shear in an I or a T beam, whether straight or curved, it generally is assumed (see footnote for Eq. 180 and 181) that the shear is resisted entirely by the web and that the shear stress is uniformly distributed over the area of the web. The strain energy due to shear may then be written

$$U_V = \int \frac{1}{2}\frac{V^2}{Ga_w}\, ds \tag{196}$$

in which a_w is the cross-sectional area of the web.

Utilizing the above expressions, we may write the expression for the strain energy of a curved I or T beam as follows:

$$U = \int \frac{1}{2} \frac{N^2}{Ea'} \, ds + \int \frac{1}{2} \frac{V^2}{Ga_w} \, ds + \int \frac{1}{2} \frac{M^2}{EI'} \, ds \tag{197}$$

in which a' and I' are properties of the modified section. Hence,

$$\delta_P = \frac{\partial U}{\partial P} = \int \frac{N}{Ea'} \frac{\partial N}{\partial P} \, ds + \int \frac{V}{Ga_w} \frac{\partial V}{\partial P} \, ds + \int \frac{M}{EI'} \frac{\partial M}{\partial P} \, ds \tag{198}$$

The above expression has been found to yield results in close agreement with measured deflections of test models of curved I beams of various proportions. If the depth of the member is small compared to the radius of curvature of the centerline, the effect of shear and direct stress generally will be negligible, and in such cases the first two terms of Eq. 197 and Eq. 198 may be neglected without introducing serious error. Although the discussion in this article has been limited to curved I and T beams, similar modifications of the analysis also are required for curved tubular members.

Illustrative Problem

Problem 107. Compute the deflection of point E relative to E' in the steel frame described in Prob. 97 and illustrated in Fig. 102, due to a load P of 3000 lb. Assume that the elastic limit of the material is not exceeded.

Solution. The properties of the actual section are (see Illustrative Prob. 97)

$$a = 5.00 \text{ in.}^2 \qquad I = 11.92 \text{ in.}^4 \qquad a_w = 2.00 \text{ in.}^2$$

The properties of the modified section for use with the curved portion are

$$a' = 3.84 \text{ in.}^2 \qquad I' = 8.18 \text{ in.}^4 \qquad a_w = 2.00 \text{ in.}^2 \qquad R' = 3.94 \text{ in.}$$

Let $E = 30 \times 10^6$ lb per sq in., and $G = \frac{2}{5}E$. If θ is measured as shown in Fig. 102a, the following expressions hold for the curved portion of the beam:

$$M = -P(10 + R \sin \theta) \qquad \partial M/\partial P = -(10 + R \sin \theta)$$

$$N = P \sin \theta \qquad \partial N/\partial P = \sin \theta$$

$$V = P \cos \theta \qquad \partial V/\partial P = \cos \theta$$

For the straight portion, the following expressions hold:

$$M = Px \qquad \partial M/\partial P = x$$

$$N = 0 \qquad \partial N/\partial P = 0$$

$$V = P \qquad \partial V/\partial P = 1$$

Substituting these expressions in Eq. 198, we get

$$\delta_P = \int_0^\pi \frac{PR' \sin^2 \theta}{Ea'} d\theta + \int_0^\pi \frac{PR' \cos^2 \theta}{Ga_w} d\theta + 2\int_0^{10} \frac{P}{Ga_w} dx$$

$$+ \int_0^\pi \frac{PR'(100 + 20R' \sin \theta + R'^2 \sin^2 \theta)}{EI'} d\theta + 2\int_0^{10} \frac{Px^2}{EI} dx$$

$$\delta_P = \frac{PR'}{Ea'}\frac{\pi}{2} + \frac{PR'}{Ga_w}\frac{\pi}{2} + \frac{20P}{Ga_w} + \frac{100PR'}{EI'}\pi + \frac{40PR'^2}{EI'} + \frac{PR'^3}{EI'}\frac{\pi}{2} + \frac{2000P}{3EI}$$

$$\delta_P = \frac{P}{E}(1.7 + 7.7 + 25.0 + 152 + 76.0 + 11.5 + 56.0)$$

$$= 330\frac{P}{E} = \frac{330 \times 3000}{30,000,000} = 0.033 \text{ in.}$$

Problems

108. Compute the deflection of point D relative to point D' in terms of P and E in the curved beam shown in Fig. 102. Assume that the elastic limit is not exceeded.

109. Assume that the steel curved member in Fig. 92 has the type of cross section illustrated in Fig. I of Table 5, in which $t = 1$ in. and $R = 6$ in. Compute the deflection of the member along the action line of the load P if $P = 25$ tons. Assume that that elastic limit is not exceeded and that $G = \frac{2}{5}E = 12,000,000$ lb per sq in.

55 Curved beam with restrained ends. In the preceding articles the curved beam considered was assumed to be unrestrained at one or both ends, and hence the bending moment at any section could be calculated directly from the known external forces lying to one side of the section. If, however, the curved beam has restrained ends, the moment at any section cannot be calculated directly; the moment at a restrained section must first be found. To find the moment at a restrained end the elastic behavior of the beam must be considered in much the same way as in finding the moment at the end of a fixed-ended straight beam or any other statically indeterminate beam. This problem, being statically indeterminate, is considered by one method in Part IV according to the outline in Art. 6 (Chapter 1), but it is also discussed here for convenience by a method different from that used in Part IV.

56 Closed ring subjected to a concentrated load. A closed ring (Fig. 107a) is an example of a curved beam with restrained sections or ends. Let the ring be subjected to a central load of P. From the conditions of symmetry the distribution of stress in any one quadrant is known to be the same as in another. One quadrant, then, may be considered to be the curved beam in which the bending moment at any section is to be found. Let Fig. 107b represent one quadrant of the ring;

the quadrant may be considered to be fixed at the section BB and subjected to an axial load $\frac{1}{2}P$ at section AA and also to a bending couple M_A.

The bending moment M at any section DD which makes an angle θ
with the section AA is to be found. The bending moment at section DD
is the algebraic sum of the moments of the forces that lie to one side of
the section, and hence

$$M = M_A + (P/2)(R - x)$$

$$= M_A + \tfrac{1}{2}PR(1 - \cos\theta) \tag{199}$$

in which the sign of M_A as well as its magnitude is assumed to be unknown and hence is considered in Fig. 107 to be positive although by
inspection it is known to be negative.

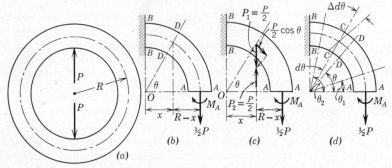

FIG. 107   Stresses in closed ring.

After finding a value of M_A as explained in the next paragraph, Eq.
199 will give a value of the bending moment M at any section, and from
this value of M the stresses at the section may be found. The tensile or
compressive stress at any point in the section DD is the algebraic sum
of the bending stress due to M and a direct stress due to a load $\frac{1}{2}P\cos\theta$.
This may be shown by resolving the force $\frac{1}{2}P$ at section AA (Fig. 107c)
into a force $\frac{1}{2}P$ and a couple whose moment is $\frac{1}{2}P(R - x)$, by introducing two equal opposite and collinear forces P_1 and P_2 each equal to $\frac{1}{2}P$.
The force $P_1 = P_2$ may be resolved further into two components, one
component being $\frac{1}{2}P\sin\theta$ which produces shearing stress, and the other
$\frac{1}{2}P\cos\theta$ which is perpendicular to the section and which is assumed to
produce a uniform tensile stress. The shearing component of the load
and the corresponding shearing stress will be neglected in this treatment.
The stress σ at any point of any section then can be found from the
equation $\sigma = \sigma_1 + \sigma_2$, where σ_1 is the direct stress due to the force
$(P/2)\cos\theta[\sigma_1 = (P\cos\theta)/2a]$ and σ_2 is the bending stress caused by

the moment M and must be found from Eq. 158 of Art. 48 or Eq. 162 of Art. 49. But before M can be found, M_A must be determined.

Value of M_A. A value of M_A may be found by considering the elastic behavior of the beam. The problem is simplified if the effect of initial curvature is neglected in determining an expression for the elastic rotation of any section in terms of the moment at the section. (The elastic rotation of any section is equivalent to the change in slope of the beam at this section due to the loads.) Although this simplification results in an approximate value for M_A, the error introduced is relatively small in most cases, as will be shown later. It is important to observe, however, that, although the initial curvature may be neglected in obtaining a satisfactory value for the moment at any section of the initially curved beam, the initial curvature cannot, in general, be neglected in expressing the stress at any point in the section in terms of the moment at the section. In other words, the curved-beam formula for stress must be used (and not the straight-beam formula) to determine the stress caused by the moment at the section. The fact that the initial curvature can have a large influence on the stress at a section and a negligible influence on the moment at the section will not appear to be contradictory if it is observed that various distributions of stress on a section could produce the same moment of the internal forces on the section, and hence a condition that may influence the moment only slightly may influence largely the maximum stress accompanying the moment.

As indicated in Fig. 107d the angle $d\theta$ between two normal sections a differential distance apart changes, when the loads are applied, by the amount $\Delta\, d\theta$; this may be written $(\Delta\, d\theta/d\theta)\cdot d\theta\ =\ \omega\, d\theta$, where ω is the change in angle per unit of angle and may be called the angular strain at the section considered. Hence the total change of angle between two sections that make the angles θ_1 and θ_2 with the section AA is given by the expression $\int_{\theta_1}^{\theta_2} \omega\, d\theta$. Since sections AA and BB remain at right angles to each other, the change in the angle between these planes is equal to zero. Hence,

$$\int_0^{\pi/2} \omega\, d\theta = 0 \tag{200}$$

In an initially straight beam the rate of change of slope of the elastic curve is $d^2y/dx^2 = M/EI$. In the initially curved beam the rate of change of slope of the elastic curve is $\Delta\, d\theta/R\, d\theta$, which is the angle change per unit of arc length. But $\Delta\, d\theta/R\, d\theta = \omega/R$. Therefore $\omega/R = M/EI$, if the initial curvature of the beam is neglected.

If $\omega = MR/EI$ is substituted in Eq. 200, the resulting equation is

$$\int_0^{\pi/2} \frac{MR}{EI}\, d\theta = 0 \tag{201}$$

But, from Eq. 199, $M = M_A + \frac{1}{2}PR(1 - \cos\theta)$. Therefore, since E, I, and R are here considered to be constant, Eq. 201 becomes

$$\int_0^{\pi/2} M_A\, d\theta + \frac{1}{2}\int_0^{\pi/2} PR\, d\theta - \frac{1}{2}\int_0^{\pi/2} PR\cos\theta\, d\theta = 0$$

Integrating, we have

$$M_A(\pi/2) + PR(\pi/4) - \frac{1}{2}PR\sin(\pi/2) = 0$$

Hence
$$M_A = \frac{1}{2}PR[(2/\pi) - 1] \tag{202}$$

Since $2/\pi$ is less than unity, M_A is negative and hence it increases the radius of curvature of the quadrant (beam). If the influence of the initial curvature of the beam is not neglected, the result is

$$M_A = \frac{1}{2}PR\left[\frac{2}{\pi(1 + Z)} - 1\right] \tag{203}$$

and since Z is small compared to unity this value of M_A differs but little from the approximate value given by Eq. 202.

Stress at Any Section of Ring. The bending moment M at any section may be found from Eqs. 199 and 202, and the stress at any point in the section, as previously noted, may be obtained as the sum of the direct stress and the bending stress. Thus the stress σ at any point is given approximately by the equation (see Eq. 161)

$$\sigma = \frac{\frac{1}{2}P\cos\theta}{a} + \frac{M}{aR}\left(1 + \frac{1}{Z}\frac{y}{R + y}\right) \tag{204}$$

or the straight-beam formula with a correction factor may be used as in Art. 49. If this is done, the stress is found by use of the equation

$$\sigma = \frac{\frac{1}{2}P\cos\theta}{a} + K\frac{Mc}{I} \tag{205}$$

Deflection of Ring. The deflection of the ring in Fig. 107a may be found by using Eq. 192 or 193. If the deflection of section AA in Fig. 107b is obtained by using either of these equations, this value will be only half the total deflection. The maximum circumferential stress in a closed ring and the deflection of the ring are found in the following illustrative problem.

Illustrative Problem

Problem 110. A ring (Fig. 108) with a mean diameter of 5 in. and with a circular cross section 2 in. in diameter is subjected to a load $2P$ that does not cause a stress greater than the elastic strength of the material. Calculate the circumferential stress on the inside fiber of the ring at A and at B. Also calculate the deflection of the ring along the diameter containing the action line of the load.

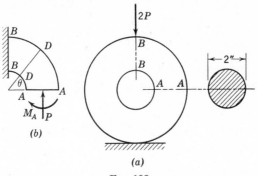

(b)

(a)

Fig. 108

Solution. CIRCUMFERENTIAL STRESS. Stress at A is (see Eq. 204)

$$\sigma_A = \frac{P}{a} + \frac{M_A}{aR}\left(1 + \frac{1}{Z}\frac{y}{R+y}\right) \qquad \text{in which } y = -1 \text{ in.} \qquad (204a)$$

$$R = 2.5 \text{ in.} \qquad c = 1 \text{ in.} \qquad c/R = \tfrac{2}{5} \qquad a = \pi c^2 = \pi \text{ sq in.}$$

$$Z = \tfrac{1}{4}(c/R)^2 + \tfrac{1}{8}(c/R)^4 + \cdots + = \tfrac{1}{4}\times\tfrac{4}{25} + \tfrac{1}{8}\times\tfrac{16}{625} \qquad \text{(see Appendix III)}$$

$$= 0.040 + 0.0032 = 0.0432 \qquad 1/Z = 23.1$$

Stress at B is (see Eq. 204)

$$\sigma_B = 0 + \frac{M_A + PR}{aR}\left(1 + \frac{1}{Z}\frac{y}{R+y}\right) \qquad \text{in which } y = -1 \text{ in.} \qquad (204b)$$

From Eq. 202 we have, noting that in Fig. 108b P is negative,

$$M_A = -PR[(2/\pi) - 1] = +0.364PR = +0.910P \qquad (202a)$$

Hence
$$\sigma_A = -\frac{P}{a} + \frac{0.364P}{a}\left(1 + 23.1\frac{-1}{2.5 - 1}\right)$$

$$= -\frac{P}{a} + \frac{0.364P}{a}(-14.4) = -6.25\frac{P}{a}$$

The stress at A, then, is a compressive stress equal to 6.25 times the direct compressive stress on the section AA.

From Eqs. 204 and 202 we have

$$\sigma_B = \frac{0.364PR + (-PR)}{aR}\left(1 + \frac{1}{Z}\frac{y}{R+y}\right)$$

$$= \frac{-0.636P}{a}(-14.4) = 9.17\frac{P}{a}$$

and hence the stress at B is a tensile stress equal to about nine times the direct compressive stress at section AA and considerably larger than the maximum compressive stress on section AA.

DEFLECTION. In Fig. 108b is shown one quadrant of the ring. For convenience we let section BB remain fixed and find the vertical deflection of the plane AA due to the forces acting on the quadrant of the ring by using Eq. 193; this gives one-half of the deflection. On any section DD in Fig. 108b the direct force N, the shearing force V, and the bending moment M are (see Art. 53)

$$N = -P\cos\theta \qquad V = -P\sin\theta$$

$$M = M_A - P(R - R\cos\theta) = -0.636PR + PR\cos\theta$$

The partial derivatives with respect to P are

$$\partial N/\partial P = -\cos\theta \qquad \partial V/\partial P = -\sin\theta \qquad \partial M/\partial P = -0.636R + R\cos\theta$$

The substitution of these values in Eq. 193 gives

$$\frac{\delta}{2} = \frac{PR}{Ea}\int_0^{\pi/2}\cos^2\theta\,d\theta + \frac{PR}{Ga}\int_0^{\pi/2}\sin^2\theta\,d\theta + \frac{PR^3}{EI}\int_0^{\pi/2}(-0.636 + \cos\theta)^2\,d\theta$$

$$\frac{\delta}{2} = \frac{PR}{Ea}\left[\frac{\theta}{2} + \frac{\sin 2\theta}{4}\right]_0^{\pi/2} + \frac{PR}{Ga}\left[\frac{\theta}{2} - \frac{\sin 2\theta}{4}\right]_0^{\pi/2}$$

$$+ \frac{PR^3}{EI}\left[0.904\theta - 1.27\sin\theta + \frac{\sin 2\theta}{4}\right]_0^{\pi/2}$$

$$\delta = \frac{PR\pi}{2Ea} + \frac{PR\pi}{2Ga} + 0.3\frac{PR^3}{EI} = 1.25\frac{P}{E} + 1.25\frac{P}{G} + 5.97\frac{P}{E}$$

If the ring is made of steel, $E = 2.5G$, and hence the value of the deflection is

$$\delta = 10.2(P/E)$$

Problems

111. Solve for σ_A and σ_B in Prob. 110 by making use of the straight-beam formula and a correction factor (Eq. 205).

112. Compute the stress at the outer fiber of section AA and at the outer fiber of section BB of the ring in Prob. 110.   *Ans.* $\sigma_A = 1.96\,P/a$

113. Locate the section in the ring of Prob. 110 for which the bending moment is zero, and compute the uniform stress over this section.

114. Compute stresses in the ring in Prob. 110 at the inner and outer fibers for the following values of θ: $0°, 30°, 45°, 60°, 90°$; plot these stresses radially on AB as a base line, and draw curves showing the variation of stress in these fibers between sections AA and BB.

115. A steel ring (Fig. 109) with a mean diameter of 6 in. and with a rectangular cross-section 3 in. in depth by 2 in. in width is subjected to a central tensile load P equal to 4800 lb. Assume that the elastic strength of the material is not exceeded. (a) Compute the maximum tensile stress in the ring by the curved-beam formula.

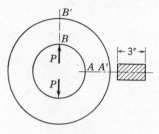

Fig. 109

(b) Check the result by use of the straight-beam formula and a correction factor. (c) Compute by use of Eq. 192 the deflection of the ring along the diameter in which the load is applied. Let $E = 10^7$ lb per sq in.

57 Closed ring subjected to uniform load. In Fig. 110a let it be assumed that a vertical load is distributed uniformly over the horizontal projection of the ring of diameter $2R$ (not $2R_o$, where R_o is the

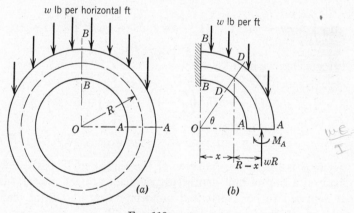

(a)   (b)

Fig. 110

outer radius of the ring). The error introduced by assuming that the load is distributed over the distance $2R$ instead of $2R_o$ will be small if the thickness of the ring is small relative to R. Let the depth of the ring be unity, and let the load per unit length parallel to a diameter be w.

The bending moment M at any section DD is the algebraic sum of the moments of the forces that lie to one side of the section, and hence (see Fig. 110b)

$$M = M_A - wR(R - x) + w(R - x)\frac{R - x}{2} \qquad (206)$$

in which $x = R \cos \theta$. Hence

$$M = M_A - wR^2(1 - \cos \theta) + (wR^2/2)(1 - \cos \theta)(1 - \cos \theta) \qquad (207)$$

The value of M_A may be found by considering the elastic behavior of the quadrant of the ring as was done in the case of a concentrated load (Art. 56), namely, by expressing the fact that sections AA and BB remain at right angles when the ring is deflected by the load.

It was pointed out in Art. 56 that relatively little error is introduced in the value of M_A by neglecting the initial curvature of the quadrant in considering the elastic behavior of the ring, and that when this is done the fact that sections AA and BB remain at right angles is expressed by the equation

$$\int_0^{\pi/2} \frac{MR}{EI}\, d\theta = 0 \qquad (208)$$

By substituting the value of M from Eq. 207 in Eq. 208 and noting that E, I, and R are constants, we obtain the equation

$$M_A \int_0^{\pi/2} d\theta - wR^2 \int_0^{\pi/2} (1 - \cos \theta)\, d\theta + \tfrac{1}{2}wR^2 \int_0^{\pi/2} (1 - \cos \theta)^2\, d\theta = 0$$

Integrating, we have

$$M_A \frac{\pi}{2} - wR^2 \left(\frac{\pi}{2} - 1\right) + \frac{wR^2}{2}\left(\frac{3\pi}{4} - 2\right) = 0$$

Thus
$$M_A = \tfrac{1}{4}wR^2 = \tfrac{1}{16}wd^2 = \tfrac{1}{16}Wd \qquad (209)$$

where d is the mean diameter of the ring, and W is the total vertical load on a ring of unit depth (perpendicular to the paper). If the load is assumed to be distributed uniformly over the outer diameter $2R_o$ instead of the mean diameter $d = 2R$, the expression for M_A is

$$M_A = \frac{wR}{4} \cdot \frac{R_o}{R}\left(2 - \frac{R_o}{R}\right). \qquad (209a)$$

The value of M_A obtained from Eq. 209 may now be substituted in Eq. 207, and the bending moment M at any section may thus be found. The bending moment at section BB is equal and opposite to that at section AA; this fact may be shown as follows.   From Eq. 207 we have

$$M_B = M_A - \tfrac{1}{2}wR^2 = \tfrac{1}{4}wR^2 - \tfrac{1}{2}wR^2 = -\tfrac{1}{4}wR^2 = -\tfrac{1}{16}Wd \quad (210)$$

Furthermore, the bending moment has its maximum value at sections AA and BB.

Stress in Ring.   The stress at any section in the ring (Fig. 110) may now be found from the curved-beam formula (Eq. 204, in which $\tfrac{1}{2}P = wR$) or from the straight-beam formula and a correction factor (Eq. 205, in which $\tfrac{1}{2}P = wR$).   If the thickness of the ring is small compared to the mean radius, that is, if the ring may be considered to be a thin elastic ring, the correction factor may be considered to be unity (see Table 5).

Deflection of Ring.   The deflection of the ring due to the distributed load is found by using Eq. 192 or 193 as illustrated in Prob. 110 for the concentrated load.

Problem

116. A cast-iron culvert pipe with an internal diameter of 48 in. and a wall thickness of 1.25 in. is subjected to a total distributed load W of 20,000 lb.   The pipe is 24 in. long.   Assume that the material obeys Hook's law, and calculate the maximum stress in the pipe.   *Ans.* $-10,100$ lb/in.^{2}.

58   Stresses in chain links.   Chain links are important curved flexural members.   The method of analysis discussed in the preceding articles has been extended, by Goodenough and Moore, to chain links, in connection with an analytical and experimental investigation of the stresses in open links and in stud links; the method and results are presented and discussed in reference 3 at the end of this chapter.   Figures 111 and 112, taken from this reference, show the distribution of stress in the links, when the maximum stress does not exceed the elastic strength of the material.   The conclusions from this investigation are:

(*a*) *The maximum tensile elastic stress in open links of usual proportions* (similar to that shown in Fig. 111) was found to be approximately four times the average stress.   That is, the maximum tensile stress in a link loaded as in Fig. 111 is

$$\sigma = 4(\tfrac{1}{2}P/a) = 2(P/a) \quad (211)$$

in which P is the total load on the link and a is the cross-sectional area of one side of the link.

(*b*) A stud-link chain (Fig. 112) having the same dimensions as an open-link chain will, within the elastic strength of the material, resist from 20 to 25 per cent more load than the open-link chain. The *ultimate* strength of the stud-link chain is, however, probably less than that

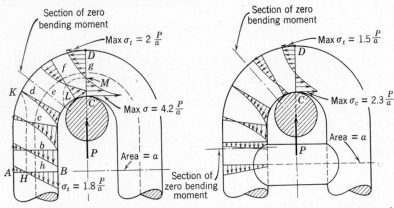

Fig. 111   Stress distribution in open chain link.

Fig. 112   Stress distribution in stud chain link.

At section h (Fig. 111), lying along the minor axis, the inner fiber (at B) is subjected to a tensile stress of $1.8(P/a)$ and the outer fiber (at A) to a compressive stress of $0.77(P/a)$. At section c, the tensile stress at the inner fiber is slightly greater due to the curvature at that section. At section e the bending moment changes sign by passing through the value zero; hence at this section the stress is distributed uniformly. From L to C the inner fiber is in compression and the maximum compressive stress σ_c reaches its maximum value of $4.2(P/a)$ at the point C. From A to K the outer fiber is in compression and from K to D it is in tension. The maximum tensile stress occurs at D and has the value [max. $\sigma_D = 2(P/a)$]. The lines HK and LM indicate points in the link at which the stress is zero.

of the open-link chain; this condition arises from the greater freedom of the open-link chain to adjust itself better to resist the load after the yield point has been passed, as is suggested in Fig. 113.

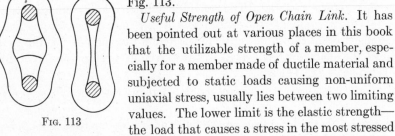

Fig. 113

Useful Strength of Open Chain Link. It has been pointed out at various places in this book that the utilizable strength of a member, especially for a member made of ductile material and subjected to static loads causing non-uniform uniaxial stress, usually lies between two limiting values. The lower limit is the elastic strength—the load that causes a stress in the most stressed fiber equal to the yield point of the material—and the upper limit is the load that causes the yield point stress to extend to all the fibers at the most-stressed section; this is called the fully plastic load and is discussed in Part V. The lower limit is the load that initiates yielding, and the upper limit is considered to be the maximum load that can be applied without causing general yielding that destroys the usefulness of the member.

The advantageous redistribution of stress in certain members, including curved beams, accompanying the inelastic strains involved in reaching the fully plastic load causes a rather wide spread between the two limiting values. This fact explains why the rated capacities (useful strengths) of wrought-steel crane hooks and open-chain links are usually much larger than the elastic strengths of the members. This condition is discussed further at the close of the solution of Prob. 328 (Chap. 19).

Selected References

1. Bach, C., *Elastizität und Festigkeit*, 8th edition, Julius Springer, Berlin, 1920.
2. Cross, H., "The Column Analogy," *Bulletin* 215, Engineering Experiment Station, University of Illinois, 1930. Discusses briefly (p. 66) a transformed-area method as suggested in Art. 51.
3. Goodenough, G. A., and L. E. Moore, "Strength of Chain Links," *Bulletin* 18, Engineering Experiment Station, University of Illinois, 1907.
4. Slocum, S. E., and E. L. Hancock, *Strength of Materials*, revised edition, Ginn and Co., 1911. Gives derivation of Résal's formula which makes use of a transformed area in accordance with the idea discussed in Art. 50.
5. Frocht, M. M., *Photoelasticity*, Vol. I, John Wiley & Sons, 1941. See p. 208, Fig. 6.36, for stresses in curved beam determined photoelastically.
6. Goodman, J., "An Experimental Investigation of the Maximum Stresses in Loaded Crane Hooks," *Minutes of Proceedings*, Institution of Civil Engineers, Vol. 167, 1906–1907, Part I, p. 296.
7. Morley, A., "Bending Stresses in Hooks and Other Curved Pieces," *Engineering* (*London*), Vol. 98, Sept. 11 and 25, 1914. Discusses the discrepancies in calculations due to errors introduced in the graphical method of determining the property of the section (see Appendix II). See also *Strength of Materials*, 5th edition, Longmans and Co., London, 1919.

Chapter 7

BEAM ON CONTINUOUS ELASTIC SUPPORT

59 Introduction. Occasionally a beam rests on a continuous foundation (support) that may be assumed, without introducing serious error, to be elastic, and the beam is subjected to a concentrated load at one or more points along the beam or to a distributed load over a portion of the length. If the stiffness of the continuous support is relatively small compared to the stiffness of the beam, the deflection of the beam, and likewise the curvature and hence the bending moment in the beam, may become relatively large, especially in the neighborhood of a concentrated load. Thus it is important to obtain the maximum bending normal stress ($\sigma = Mc/I$), the maximum shearing stress ($\tau = VQ/It$), and the elastic deflection for the beam for the reason that any one of these quantities may limit the loads that the beam can resist satisfactorily. It is important to note, however, that damage to a beam on a continuous elastic support when the beam is subjected to a repeated concentrated load, such as the pressure of railway car wheels on the rails of the track, may result from the local so-called contact stresses rather than from the bending stresses or from the deflection. Contact stresses are discussed in Chapter 11.

In some problems in which bending of the beam is the dominant action the support of the beam is not actually continuous but consists of a series of rather closely spaced reactions exerted by elastic supports; however, the assumption that such a support is continuous as well as elastic often leads to useful, though approximate, results. One such illustration is that of a steel railroad rail which rests on timber cross ties; the so-called elastic support consists of the ties, the ballast, and the subgrade.

The term "continuous" suggests also that the beam and the support are indefinitely long. It will be found that the analysis of bending stresses and deflections for an elastic beam on a continuous elastic support must be modified for application to a relatively short beam or to a long beam subjected to a concentrated load near to one end.

60 The problem defined. A beam whose length is very large compared to its depth and width will be considered first because the treatment of this case will serve as the basis for the analysis of the behavior of all beams resting on elastic supports. In choosing a beam whose length is relatively large, the ends of the beam are removed far enough from the loads to justify the assumption that the deflection, the slope, the shear and the moments at the ends are zero. In Fig. 114a is shown a portion of a long beam supported on a continuous elastic foundation and subjected to a concentrated load P; the load and the reaction of the foundation are assumed to lie in a plane of symmetry of the beam. The problem is to express the deflection, the slope, the bending moment, and the shear at any section of the beam in terms of the load, the elastic (spring) constant of the support or foundation, the elastic constant (spring constant or modulus of elasticity) of the beam material, and the dimensions of the cross section of the beam.

The solution of this problem for a single concentrated load is sufficient for the solution of problems involving various types of loading because the principle of superposition may be used to combine the effects of several concentrated loads and also of distributed loads; the latter may be treated as a series of closely spaced concentrated loads. Let the upward pressure (reaction) at any point along the beam be q (expressed as force per unit of length of the beam). The manner in which q varies along the beam is unknown and must be determined in the solution of the problem. The forces acting on the beam in Fig. 114a constitute a parallel system of forces to which two equations of equilibrium apply, namely $\Sigma F = 0$ and $\Sigma M = 0$. These two equations are not sufficient to determine the distribution of the reaction, and hence the problem is a statically indeterminate one. Therefore, as is usual in statically indeterminate beam problems, the equation of the elastic curve assumed by the beam is utilized for obtaining the necessary additional equations. Thus, before attacking the main problem, the elastic curve equation of the beam will be found.

Elastic Curve Equation. The equation of the elastic curve in the familiar form $EI(d^2y/dx^2) = -M$ is widely used in connection with statically indeterminate beams, especially when M can conveniently be expressed in terms of x. In this problem the distribution of the pressure q is not known, but since it is assumed to be proportional to the deflection y it will be desirable to modify the foregoing equation of the elastic curve as follows. By differentiating twice both sides of the equation the result found is

$$EI(d^4y/dx^4) = -d^2M/dx^2 \qquad (212)$$

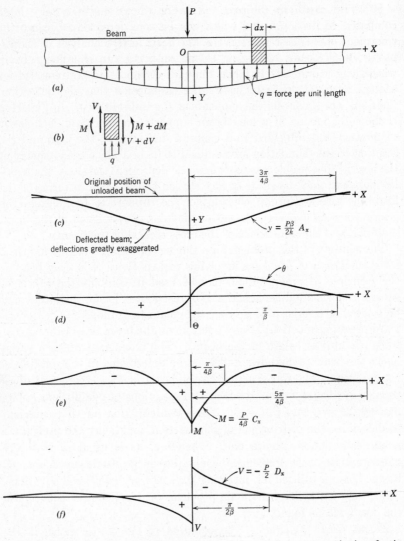

FIG. 114 Deflection, slope, bending moment and shear in beam on continuing elastic support.

But $d^2M/dx^2 = q$. This fact may be shown as follows. In Fig. 114b are shown the forces acting on a block of differential length dx cut from the beam. By applying the equilibrium equation $\Sigma F = 0$ to those forces and neglecting the product of differential terms, the following relationship is found:

$$dV/dx = q \tag{213}$$

It is important to note the sign convention; the positive sense of x is to the right, positive y is downward, the bending moment M is positive when it causes compression in the top fibers, and the shearing force is positive when it is an upward force on the *left* face of an elemental portion of the beam. But $V = dM/dx$, and hence Eq. 213 may be written $d^2M/dx^2 = q$. Therefore, Eq. 212 may be written

$$EI(d^4y/dx^4) = -q \qquad (214)$$

If q in Eq. 214 is expressed as a function of the deflection y, the equation can be integrated. This may be done as follows. Since the continuous support is elastic, the pressure q per unit length may be expressed as $q = wk_0y$, where w is the width of the bottom of the beam, and k_0 is the spring constant of the elastic support (the spring constant is the force exerted by the elastic support per unit deflection of the support). The units of k_0 are lb per in.[3], that is, pounds per square inch per inch. Finally, the value of wk_0 is set equal to k, and therefore $q = ky$, in which k will be called the spring constant per unit length of the elastic support, but it should be remembered that k includes the effect of the width of the bottom of the beam and will be numerically equal to k_0 only when the beam is one unit in width. The substitution of $q = ky$ in Eq. 214 gives

$$EI(d^4y/dx^4) = -ky \qquad (215)$$

which is the differential equation of the elastic curve of any beam on an elastic support. This is a homogeneous linear differential equation of the fourth order. The solution of Eq. 215 as given in books on differential equations has four terms, but as applied to the (long) beam under consideration two of the terms are equal to zero and the final solution is

$$y = e^{-\beta x}(c_1 \cos \beta x + c_2 \sin \beta x) \qquad (216)$$

for positive values of x only; this restriction on the solution, however, is not serious for the reason that for a very long beam as here assumed a condition of symmetry with respect to the load may be considered to exist, and the same numerical values for deflection, moment, etc., for equal distances from the load on either side of the load may be assumed to occur. In Eq. 216 $\beta = \sqrt[4]{k/4EI}$. The dimensional unit of β is L^{-1}, in which L is the dimension of length. Furthermore, x has the dimension of length, and hence the term βx is dimensionless and is usually thought of as being expressed in radians. In Eq. 216, c_1 and c_2 are constants of integration and e is the base of Naperian logarithms. Equation 216 is the algebraic equation of the elastic curve for the beam in Fig. 114 and will now be used in conjunction with the equations of equilibrium for the solution of the problem defined in this article.

61   Beam with concentrated load.   As stated in Art. 60, it is desired to obtain primarily the bending moment and the deflection at any section of the beam shown in Fig. 114a.   This will be done by use of Eq. 216 and the equations of equilibrium.   The values of constants c_1 and c_2 in Eq. 216 must be found.   For this purpose Eq. 216 is differentiated once with respect to x to obtain the expression for the slope, and a value of zero is assumed for the slope at $x = 0$.   Thus the following equation is obtained:

$$\frac{dy}{dx}\Bigg]_{x=0} = -\beta(c_1 - c_2) = 0 \tag{217}$$

This equation shows that $c_1 = c_2 = c$, and hence Eq. 216 may be written

$$y = ce^{-\beta x}(\cos \beta x + \sin \beta x) \tag{218}$$

The value of c may be determined by using the equation of equilibrium $\Sigma F = 0$ which states that the total upward pressure (force) on the beam in Fig. 114a is equal to P.   Thus

$$2\int_0^\infty q\,dx = 2\int_0^\infty ky\,dx = P \tag{219}$$

If the value of y from Eq. 218 is substituted in Eq. 219 and the integration is performed, the value of c is found to be

$$c = P\beta/2k \tag{220}$$

Thus the elastic curve equation (Eq. 216) for the very long beam subjected to a concentrated load P becomes

$$y = (P\beta/2k)e^{-\beta x}(\cos \beta x + \sin \beta x) \tag{221}$$

which gives the deflection for any positive value of x.   The values of the slope, the bending moment, and the shear for any positive value of x (to the right of the load) may now be obtained from the successive derivatives of Eq. 221.   The expressions for slope, moment, and shear are

$$dy/dx = \theta = -(P\beta^2/k)e^{-\beta x}\sin \beta x \tag{222}$$

$$EI(d^2y/dx^2) = M = (P/4\beta)e^{-\beta x}(\cos \beta x - \sin \beta x) \tag{223}$$

$$EI(d^3y/dx^3) = V = (P/2)e^{-\beta x}\cos \beta x \tag{224}$$

For convenience, Eqs. 221 to 224 may be written

$$y = (P\beta/2k)A_{\beta x} \qquad (221a)$$

$$\theta = -(P\beta^2/k)B_{\beta x} \qquad (222a)$$

$$M = (P/4\beta)C_{\beta x} \qquad (223a)$$

$$V = -(P/2)D_{\beta x} \qquad (224a)$$

in which $A_{\beta x} = e^{-\beta x}(\cos \beta x + \sin \beta x)$ $B_{\beta x} = e^{-\beta x}\sin \beta x$

$$(225)$$

$C_{\beta x} = e^{-\beta x}(\cos \beta x - \sin \beta x)$ $D_{\beta x} = e^{-\beta x}\cos \beta x$

The values of deflections, slopes, bending moments, and shears at any point in the beam are plotted from Eqs. 221a, 222a, 223a, and 224a, respectively, in Figs. 114c, 114d, 114e, and 114f. It should be noted, however, that in Fig. 114 and also in Table 7 $A_{\beta x}$, $B_{\beta x}$, etc., are represented by the symbols A_x, B_x, etc., that is, βx is represented by x; this makes it possible to use Fig. 114 and Table 7 for any value of β as explained later in this article. The maximum values of deflection, bending moment, and shear occur at $x = 0$, and their values as found from Eqs. 221a through 224a are

$$y_{max} = y_0 = P\beta/2k \qquad M_{max} = M_0 = P/4\beta \qquad V_{max} = V_0 = P/2 \quad (226)$$

It is important to note that in Fig. 114 the values of deflections, slopes, bending moments, and shears are all very small at the distance $x = \pi/\beta$ on either side of the load. Thus Eqs. 221a through 224a may be used for beams of lengths as short as $l = 2\pi/\beta$ without appreciable error. Many beams used on elastic supports have lengths equal to or greater than $l = 2\pi/\beta$; shorter beams are discussed in Art. 64.

It was stated in Art. 60 that the solution for the moment, the deflection, etc., in a very long beam subjected to a single concentrated load may be used as a basis for a solution when the long beam is subjected to various combinations of loading. For this reason the values of terms $A_{\beta x}$, $B_{\beta x}$, $C_{\beta x}$, and $D_{\beta x}$ in Eqs. 221a, 222a, 223a, and 224a have been computed for positive values of x up to $x = 8$, and are given in Table 7.[*]

For example, to find a value of $A_{\beta x}$ from Table 7, select a value in the column labeled x in the table which is equal to the value of βx, and read across horizontally to the value in the column under A_x; if, in a given problem, $\beta = 0.02$ in.$^{-1}$ and the distance of the section from the load is $x = 20$ in., $\beta x = 0.4$ radian, then by selecting a value of 0.4 in

[*] These values were first given by H. Zimmerman in *Die Berechnung des Eisenbahnoberbaues*, Berlin, 1888; 2nd edition, Berlin, 1930.

TABLE 7

Formulas

$$A_x = e^{-x}(\cos x + \sin x) \qquad B_x = e^{-x} \sin x$$

$$C_x = e^{-x}(\cos x - \sin x) \qquad D_x = e^{-x} \cos x$$

x	e^x	e^{-x}	A_x	B_x	C_x	D_x
0	1	1	1	0	1	1
0.001	1.0010	0.9990	1.0000	0.0010	0.9980	0.9990
0.002	1.0020	0.9980	1.0000	0.0020	0.9960	0.9980
0.003	1.0030	0.9970	1.0000	0.0030	0.9940	0.9970
0.004	1.0040	0.9960	1.0000	0.0040	0.9920	0.9960
0.005	1.0050	0.9950	1.0000	0.0050	0.9900	0.9950
0.006	1.0060	0.9940	1.0000	0.0060	0.9880	0.9940
0.007	1.0070	0.9930	0.9999	0.0070	0.9861	0.9930
0.008	1.0080	0.9920	0.9999	0.0080	0.9841	0.9920
0.009	1.0090	0.9910	0.9999	0.0087	0.9821	0.9910
0.010	1.0100	0.9900	0.9999	0.0099	0.9801	0.9900
0.011	1.0111	0.9891	0.9999	0.0109	0.9781	0.9890
0.012	1.0121	0.9881	0.9999	0.0119	0.9761	0.9880
0.013	1.0131	0.9871	0.9998	0.0129	0.9742	0.9870
0.014	1.0141	0.9861	0.9998	0.0138	0.9722	0.9860
0.015	1.0151	0.9851	0.9998	0.0148	0.9702	0.9850
0.016	1.0161	0.9841	0.9997	0.0158	0.9683	0.9840
0.017	1.0172	0.9831	0.9997	0.0167	0.9663	0.9830
0.018	1.0182	0.9822	0.9997	0.0177	0.9643	0.9820
0.019	1.0192	0.9812	0.9996	0.0187	0.9624	0.9810
0.02	1.0202	0.9802	0.9996	0.0196	0.9604	0.9800
0.03	1.0304	0.9704	0.9991	0.0291	0.9409	0.9700
0.04	1.0408	0.9608	0.9984	0.0384	0.9216	0.9600
0.05	1.0513	0.9512	0.9976	0.0476	0.9025	0.9501
0.10	1.1052	0.9048	0.9906	0.0903	0.8100	0.9003
0.15	1.1618	0.8607	0.9796	0.1283	0.7224	0.8510
0.20	1.2214	0.8187	0.9651	0.1627	0.6398	0.8024
0.25	1.2840	0.7788	0.9472	0.1927	0.5619	0.7546
0.30	1.3500	0.7408	0.9267	0.2189	0.4888	0.7078
0.35	1.4191	0.7047	0.9036	0.2416	0.4204	0.6620
0.40	1.4918	0.6703	0.8784	0.2610	0.3564	0.6174
0.45	1.5683	0.6376	0.8515	0.2774	0.2968	0.5742
0.50	1.6487	0.6065	0.8231	0.2908	0.2414	0.5323
0.55	1.7332	0.5770	0.7934	0.3016	0.1902	0.4918
0.60	1.8221	0.5488	0.7628	0.3099	0.1430	0.4529
0.65	1.9155	0.5220	0.7315	0.3160	0.0996	0.4156
0.70	2.0138	0.4966	0.6997	0.3199	0.0599	0.3798
0.75	2.1170	0.4724	0.6676	0.3220	0.0237	0.3456
$\frac{1}{4}\pi$	2.1933	0.4559	0.6448	0.3224	0	0.3224

TABLE 7 (Continued)

FORMULAS

$$A_x = e^{-x}(\cos x + \sin x) \qquad B_x = e^{-x}\sin x$$
$$C_x = e^{-x}(\cos x - \sin x) \qquad D_x = e^{-x}\cos x$$

x	e^x	e^{-x}	A_x	B_x	C_x	D_x
0.80	2.2255	0.4493	0.6353	0.3223	−0.0093	0.3131
0.85	2.3396	0.4274	0.6032	0.3212	−0.0391	0.2821
0.90	2.4596	0.4066	0.5712	0.3185	−0.0658	0.2527
0.95	2.5857	0.3867	0.5396	0.3146	−0.0896	0.2250
1.00	2.7183	0.3679	0.5083	0.3096	−0.1109	0.1987
1.05	2.8576	0.3499	0.4778	0.3036	−0.1294	0.1742
1.10	3.0042	0.3329	0.4476	0.2967	−0.1458	0.1509
1.15	3.1582	0.3166	0.4183	0.2890	−0.1597	0.1293
1.20	3.3201	0.3012	0.3898	0.2807	−0.1716	0.1091
1.25	3.4903	0.2865	0.3623	0.2719	−0.1815	0.0904
1.30	3.6693	0.2725	0.3355	0.2626	−0.1897	0.0729
1.35	3.8574	0.2592	0.3098	0.2530	−0.1962	0.0568
1.40	4.0552	0.2466	0.2849	0.2430	−0.2011	0.0419
1.45	4.2631	0.2346	0.2611	0.2329	−0.2045	0.0283
1.50	4.4817	0.2231	0.2384	0.2226	−0.2068	0.0158
1.55	4.7115	0.2122	0.2166	0.2122	−0.2078	0.0044
$\frac{1}{2}\pi$	4.8105	0.2079	0.2079	0.2079	−0.2079	0
1.60	4.9530	0.2019	0.1960	0.2018	−0.2077	−0.0059
1.65	5.2070	0.1920	0.1763	0.1915	−0.2067	−0.0152
1.70	5.4740	0.1827	0.1576	0.1812	−0.2046	−0.0236
1.75	5.7546	0.1738	0.1400	0.1720	−0.2020	−0.0310
1.80	6.0496	0.1653	0.1234	0.1610	−0.1985	−0.0376
1.85	6.3598	0.1572	0.1078	0.1512	−0.1945	−0.0434
1.90	6.6859	0.1496	0.0932	0.1415	−0.1899	−0.0484
1.95	7.0287	0.1423	0.0795	0.1322	−0.1849	−0.0527
2.00	7.3891	0.1353	0.0667	0.1230	−0.1793	−0.0563
2.05	7.7679	0.1287	0.0549	0.1143	−0.1737	−0.0594
2.10	8.1662	0.1225	0.0438	0.1057	−0.1676	−0.0619
2.15	8.5849	0.1165	0.0337	0.0975	−0.1613	−0.0638
2.20	9.0250	0.1108	0.0244	0.0895	−0.1547	−0.0652
2.25	9.4877	0.1054	0.0157	0.0820	−0.1482	−0.0663
2.30	9.9742	0.1003	0.0080	0.0748	−0.1416	−0.0668
2.35	10.4856	0.0954	0.0008	0.0679	−0.1349	−0.0671
$\frac{3}{4}\pi$	10.5507	0.0948	0	0.0671	−0.1342	−0.0671
2.40	11.0232	0.0907	−0.0056	0.0613	−0.1282	−0.0669
2.45	11.5884	0.0863	−0.0114	0.0550	−0.1215	−0.0665
2.50	12.1825	0.0821	−0.0166	0.0492	−0.1149	−0.0658
2.55	12.8071	0.0781	−0.0213	0.0435	−0.1083	−0.0648
2.60	13.4637	0.0743	−0.0254	0.0383	−0.1020	−0.0637
2.65	14.1540	0.0706	−0.0289	0.0334	−0.0956	−0.0623

TABLE 7 (*Continued*)

FORMULAS

$$A_x = e^{-x}(\cos x + \sin x) \qquad B_x = e^{-x} \sin x$$

$$C_x = e^{-x}(\cos x - \sin x) \qquad D_x = e^{-x} \cos x$$

x	e^x	e^{-x}	A_x	B_x	C_x	D_x
2.70	14.8797	0.0672	−0.0320	0.0287	−0.0895	−0.0608
2.75	15.6426	0.0639	−0.0347	0.0244	−0.0835	−0.0591
2.80	16.4446	0.0608	−0.0369	0.0204	−0.0777	−0.0573
2.85	17.2878	0.0578	−0.0388	0.0167	−0.0721	−0.0554
2.90	18.1742	0.0550	−0.0403	0.0132	−0.0666	−0.0534
2.95	19.1060	0.0523	−0.0415	0.0100	−0.0614	−0.0514
3.00	20.0855	0.0498	−0.0422	0.0071	−0.0563	−0.0493
3.05	21.1153	0.0474	−0.0427	0.0043	−0.0515	−0.0472
3.10	22.1980	0.0450	−0.0431	0.0019	−0.0469	−0.0450
π	23.1407	0.0432	−0.0432	0	−0.0432	−0.0432
3.15	23.3361	0.0428	−0.0432	−0.0004	−0.0424	−0.0428
3.20	24.5325	0.0408	−0.0431	−0.0024	−0.0383	−0.0407
3.25	25.7903	0.0388	−0.0427	−0.0042	−0.0343	−0.0385
3.30	27.1126	0.0369	−0.0422	−0.0058	−0.0306	−0.0365
3.35	28.5027	0.0351	−0.0417	−0.0073	−0.0271	−0.0344
3.40	29.9641	0.0334	−0.0408	−0.0085	−0.0238	−0.0323
3.45	31.5004	0.0318	−0.0399	−0.0097	−0.0206	−0.0303
3.50	33.1154	0.0302	−0.0388	−0.0106	−0.0177	−0.0283
3.55	34.8133	0.0287	−0.0378	−0.0114	−0.0149	−0.0264
3.60	36.5982	0.0273	−0.0366	−0.0121	−0.0124	−0.0245
3.65	38.4747	0.0260	−0.0354	−0.0126	−0.0101	−0.0227
3.70	40.4473	0.0247	−0.0341	−0.0131	−0.0079	−0.0210
3.75	42.5211	0.0235	−0.0327	−0.0134	−0.0059	−0.0193
3.80	44.7012	0.0224	−0.0314	−0.0137	−0.0040	−0.0177
3.85	46.9931	0.0213	−0.0300	−0.0139	−0.0023	−0.0162
3.90	49.4024	0.0202	−0.0286	−0.0140	−0.0008	−0.0147
$\frac{5}{4}\pi$	50.7540	0.0197	−0.0278	−0.0140	0	−0.0139
3.95	51.9354	0.0192	−0.0272	−0.0139	0.0005	−0.0133
4.00	54.5982	0.0183	−0.0258	−0.0139	0.0019	−0.0120
4.50	90.0171	0.0111	−0.0132	−0.0108	0.0085	−0.0023
$\frac{3}{2}\pi$	111.3178	0.0090	−0.0090	−0.0090	0.0090	0
5.00	148.4132	0.0067	−0.0046	−0.0065	0.0084	0.0019
$\frac{7}{4}\pi$	244.1511	0.0041	0	−0.0029	0.0058	0.0029
5.50	244.6919	0.0041	0.0000	−0.0029	0.0058	0.0029
6.00	403.4288	0.0025	0.0017	0.0007	0.0031	0.0024
2π	535.4917	0.0019	0.0019	0	0.0019	0.0019
6.50	665.1416	0.0015	0.0018	0.0003	0.0012	0.0018
7.00	1096.6332	0.0009	0.0013	0.0006	0.0001	0.0007
$\frac{9}{4}\pi$	1174.4832	0.0009	0.0012	0.0006	0	0.0006
7.50	1808.0424	0.0006	0.0007	0.0005	−0.0003	0.0002
$\frac{5}{2}\pi$	2575.9705	0.0004	0.0004	0.0004	−0.0004	0

the column labeled x in the table and reading across to the column headed A_x we find the value of $A_{\beta x}$ to be 0.8784.

Frequently in the solutions of problems it is necessary to use the derivatives of Eqs. 221a through 224a with respect to x. Referring to Eqs. 225 and differentiating each equation with respect to x, we obtain

$$dA_{\beta x}/dx = -2\beta B_{\beta x} \qquad dB_{\beta x}/dx = \beta C_{\beta x}$$

$$dC_{\beta x}/dx = -2\beta D_{\beta x} \qquad dD_{\beta x}/dx = \beta A_{\beta x}$$

$$(227)$$

Use of Principle of Superposition. It is noted in Eqs. 221a through 224a that the deflection, the slope, the bending moment, and the shear are all directly proportional to the concentrated load P. Therefore, if two or more concentrated loads act on the beam, the deflection, the slope, the bending moment, or the shear due to the action of any one of the loads may be assumed to be independent of all the other loads and hence may be calculated by Eqs. 221a through 224a, respectively. The value of the deflection resulting from all the concentrated loads may be obtained at any section of the beam (any value of x) by obtaining the algebraic sum of the deflections for the given value of x as computed by Eq. 221 or Eq. 221a for the various loads. A similar procedure may be used for the slope, the bending moment, and the shear at any section. This procedure is illustrated in Prob. 119.

Illustrative Problems

Problem 117. Compute the maximum bending moment and the maximum deflection for a railroad rail subjected to a single wheel load of 25,000 lb. The rail is supported by ties, ballast, and road bed which are assumed to act as an elastic support (see Art. 62) having a spring constant of $k = 2000$ lb per inch of length of beam per inch of deflection y (thus the unit of k is lb per sq in.). The rail is a 131-lb section for which $I = 88.6$ in.[4], $E = 30,000,000$ lb per sq in. Also calculate the maximum bending stress in the rail, assuming that the depth of the rail is $7\frac{1}{8}$ in. and that the distance of the centroidal axis of the cross section of the rail from the top surface is 3.90 in.

Solution. The equations for the bending moment and the deflection at the load point involve the value of the quantity β. From Eq. 216

$$\beta = \sqrt[4]{\frac{k}{4EI}} = \sqrt[4]{\frac{2000}{4 \times 30,000,000 \times 88.6}} = 0.0208 \text{ in.}^{-1}$$

From Eqs. 226, we have

$$M_{max} = M_0 = \frac{P}{4\beta} = \frac{25,000}{4 \times 0.0208} = 300,000 \text{ lb-in.}$$

$$y_{max} = y_0 = \frac{\beta P}{2k} = \frac{0.0208 \times 25,000}{2 \times 2000} = 0.130 \text{ in.}$$

The maximum bending stress is

$$\sigma_{max} = \frac{M_0 c}{I} = \frac{300,000 \times 3.90}{88.6} = 13,200 \text{ lb/in.}^2$$

In spite of the fact that a rail does not have a continuous support (the ties are spaced approximately 20 in. from center to center, and the width of the tie is approximately 8 in.), it has been found by measurement of the strains and deflection that the rail acts nearly the same as does a beam on a continuous elastic support (see Art. 62).

Problem 118. In investigating the stresses in railroad track it has been found that the value of the spring constant k of the track bed varies from $k = 1400$ to 2000 lb per sq in. What would be the effect on the value of the maximum bending stress in Prob. 117 if the value of k were assumed to be 1400 lb per sq in. instead of 2000 lb per sq in.?

Solution. The maximum bending stress is $\sigma_{max} = M_0 c/I$ in which $M_0 = P/4\beta$ $= (P/4)\sqrt[4]{4EI/k}$. Therefore

$$\sigma_{max} = (Pc/4I)\sqrt[4]{4EI/k}$$

Hence, the ratio of σ_{max} for $k = 2000$ to σ_{max} for $k = 1400$ is equal to $\sqrt[4]{2000/1400}$ $= 1.093$. Thus a 30 per cent reduction in the value of k causes an increase of only 9.3 per cent in the stress. This result is explained by the fact that the stress is inversely proportional to the fourth root of k, and hence a considerable error in determining the value of the constant k results in a much smaller error in the values of the bending stress.

Problem 119. As an illustration of the method to be used when more than one concentrated load acts on the beam, let it be required to determine the maximum resultant bending moment and deflection for the rail in Prob. 117 if three 25,000-lb wheel loads spaced 5.5 ft apart act on the rail. The other conditions are the same as in Prob. 117.

Solution. The three 25,000-lb wheel loads are shown in Fig. 115a with the wheel or load spacing $a = 5.5$ ft $= 66$ in. Three sets of axes are used as shown in Fig. 115a with origins at points O_1, O_2, and O_3, which lie under the three loads P_1, P_2 and P_3, respectively.

DEFLECTIONS. By use of the principle of superposition, the deflection of any point such as D of the rail is expressed as the algebraic sum of the deflections y_1, y_2, and y_3 caused by the loads P_1, P_2, and P_3, respectively. Thus, referring to Eq. 221a we may write

$$y_D = (P_1\beta/2k)A_{\beta x_1} + (P_2\beta/2k)A_{\beta x_2} + (P_3\beta/2k)A_{\beta x_3}$$

in which $P_1 = P_2 = P_3 = P = 25,000$ lb, $\beta = 0.0208$, and $k = 2000$ lb per sq in.; and the values $A_{\beta x_1}$, $A_{\beta x_2}$, and $A_{\beta x_3}$ may be found from Table 7 as explained in Art. 61. The distances of the point D from the loads P_1, P_2, and P_3 are $x_1 = 82.5$ in., $x_2 = 16.5$ in., and $x_3 = -49.5$ in., respectively; therefore $\beta x_1 = 1.72$, $\beta x_2 = 0.34$, and $\beta x_3 = -1.03$. From Table 7 the following values are found: $A_{\beta x_1} = 0.1505$, $A_{\beta x_2} = 0.9082$, and $A_{\beta x_3} = 0.4900$. It is well to recall that the deflection curve for a long beam caused by a single concentrated load may be considered to be symmetrical with respect to the Y axis for each load, and hence $A_{\beta x}$ for each load has the same value for a negative value of βx as it has for an equal positive value of βx. Thus the foregoing equation becomes

$$y_D = (P\beta/2k)(0.1505 + 0.9082 + 0.4900)$$

$$= 1.5487(P\beta/2k) = 1.5487 y_0$$

in which y_0 is the maximum deflection of the beam caused by any one of the three equal concentrated loads P (see Eqs. 226).

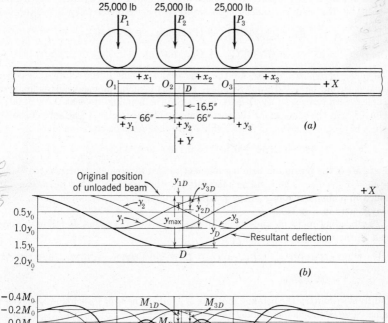

FIG. 115 Deflections and bending moments caused by three loads on beam on continuous elastic support.

The resultant deflection curve is shown by the heavy curve in Fig. 115b; it was obtained by drawing a smooth curve through points whose ordinates represent the deflections of various points on the beam as found by the same procedure as used in the foregoing solution for y_D. The maximum deflection y_{max} is at the point O_2 and is

$$y_{max} = (P\beta/2k)(A_{\beta x_1} + A_{\beta x_2} + A_{\beta x_3})$$

$$= (P\beta/2k)(0.2998 + 1.0000 + 0.2998) = 1.60 y_0$$

In Prob. 117 the maximum deflection y_0 caused by one concentrated load $P = 25,000$ lb was found to be $y_0 = 0.13$ in. The maximum deflection due to three such loads spaced 5.5 ft apart, therefore, is

$$y_{max} = 1.6 \times 0.13 = 0.208 \text{ in.}$$

MOMENTS. The bending moment at the section D along the rail is found by use of the principle of superposition to be the algebraic sum of the bending moments M_{1D}, M_{2D}, and M_{3D} at the section D caused by the loads P_1, P_2, and P_3, respectively. Equation 223a is used to compute the bending moment caused by each concentrated load. Thus the bending moment at the section D is given by the following expression:

$$M_D = (P_1/4\beta)C_{\beta x_1} + (P_2/4\beta)C_{\beta x_2} + (P_3/4\beta)C_{\beta x_3}$$
$$= (P/4\beta)(C_{\beta x_1} + C_{\beta x_2} + C_{\beta x_3})$$

The values of βx_1, βx_2, and βx_3 are the same as those found in the solution for deflections; it should be noted from Fig. 114e that the bending moment curves are symmetrical with respect to the Y axis, and hence the bending moment for a negative value of βx is the same as for the corresponding positive value. The substitution of values of $C_{\beta x_1}$, etc., as found from Table 7 into the foregoing equation gives

$$M_D = (P/4\beta)(-0.2036 + 0.4341 - 0.1160) = 0.1145(P/4\beta) = 0.1145M_0$$

where M_0 is the maximum bending moment caused by a single concentrated load $P = P_1 = P_2 = P_3$. The bending moments at other sections of the beam were obtained in a similar manner. The resultant bending moment curve is shown as the heavy curve in Fig. 115c.

The bending moment under each of the three loads is found as follows: Under load P_1 the bending moment M_{P_1} is

$$M_{P_1} = (P/4\beta)(C_{\beta x_1} + C_{\beta x_2} + C_{\beta x_3}) = (P/4\beta)(1.0000 - 0.1972 - 0.0845)$$
$$= 0.7183M_0$$

and from symmetry the bending moment M_{P_3} under the load P_3 is found to have the same value as the moment under the load P_1. The bending moment M_{P_2} under the load P_2 is

$$M_{P_2} = (P/4\beta)(C_{\beta x_1} + C_{\beta x_2} + C_{\beta x_3}) = (P/4\beta)(-0.1972 + 1.0000 - 0.1972)$$
$$= 0.6054M_0$$

The maximum bending moment caused by the three 25,000-lb loads spaced 5.5 ft apart is therefore $0.7183M_0$, where M_0 is the bending moment in the rail caused by only one 25,000-lb load. The foregoing solution shows that the addition of the two loads reduces appreciably the maximum value of the maximum bending moment but causes a large increase in the maximum deflection of the rail.

Problems

120. A long structural aluminum alloy H beam 4 in. deep rests on a horizontal, thick hard-rubber plate. The flange that is in contact with the rubber foundation is 4 in. wide. The value of E is 10,000,000 lb per sq in. and the moment of inertia I for the H section is 10.72 in.^{4}. The value of the spring constant k_0 of the hard rubber foundation is 1000 lb per cu in. If the beam has a concentrated vertical load of 13,000 lb acting on it near the center of the beam, compute the maximum deflection and the maximum bending stress in the beam. What will be the maximum pressure q per unit length between the flange and the rubber plate support?

121. If the maximum deflection of the beam in Prob. 120 must not exceed 0.1 in., what is the maximum concentrated load to which the beam may be subjected?

122. In the solution of Prob. 119 the resultant curve in Fig. 115c showing the distribution of the bending moment in a rail due to the three 25,000-lb wheel loads indicates that the maximum negative bending moment is at a section about 66 in. to the right of wheel 3 or to the left of wheel 1. Compute the bending moment at either of these sections in the rail.   *Ans.* $-0.28 M_0$

123. In Prob. 117 compute the approximate pressure per unit length of rail between the rail and the supporting elements of the roadbed directly beneath the load.   *Ans.*   260 lb/in.

124. In constructing a temporary foundation to support a heavy machine it is desired to select a long timber beam as a support which will carry a concentrated load near its mid-point and will rest upon a smooth, level, horizontal surface on the ground. The surface layer of the ground is silt, and below this layer is a thick layer of inorganic clay. The value of the spring constant for this ground is $k_0 = 100$ lb per cu in. If the beam is 8 in. wide and 12 in. deep, compute the maximum value of a concentrated load which may be supported by the beam if it is specified that the bending stress in the beam must not exceed 1500 lb per sq in. The value of $E = 1,200,000$ lb per sq in. for the timber.

62 Beam supported on equally spaced separate elastic supports.

It was pointed out in the solution of Prob. 117 that a very long beam supported on separate elastic supports may, within certain limitations, be assumed to rest on a continuous elastic foundation for the purpose of computing deflection, slope, bending moment, and shear. Figure 116a shows a very long beam that carries a concentrated load and rests on separate elastic supports. The solution for deflection, bending moment, etc., of such a beam usually is a rather lengthy statically indeterminate problem. The substitution of a beam on an equivalent continuous elastic support for the actual beam on separate supports makes the computation of deflections, moments, etc., much easier. The manner in which this substitution is made may be explained as follows.

It is assumed that the separate elastic supports are equally spaced, the distance between supports being l as shown in Fig. 116a, and that each elastic support has the same spring constant K; thus, if the reaction of one of the elastic supports on the beam is R and the corresponding deflection of the support is y (equal to the deflection of the beam at this support) the value of the reaction is

$$R = Ky \tag{228}$$

The units of K are force per unit deflection (lb per in.). The force exerted by each separate support will be considered to be distributed equally on the bottom of the beam over a distance $l/2$ on each side of the support, as shown in Fig. 116b. For example, the reaction R_1 will be replaced by a uniformly distributed pressure q_1 acting upward on the bottom of the beam as shown by ordinates to the line BC in Fig. 116b, provided that the total pressure thus exerted is equal to R_1.

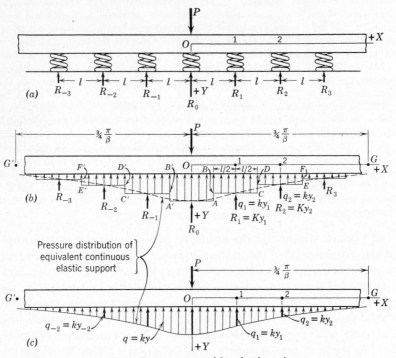

FIG. 116   Beam supported by elastic springs.

Therefore, the value of the equivalent pressure q_1 is given by the equation

$$q_1 = R_1/l \tag{229}$$

But from Eq. 228 $R_1 = Ky_1$, where y_1 is the deflection of the beam at this reaction. Thus Eq. 229 may be written

$$q_1 = (K/l)y_1 = ky_1 \tag{230}$$

in which the ratio K/l is represented by k. If the reaction R_2 is considered in a similar manner, a uniform pressure q_2 represented by the line DE in Fig. 116b extending over a distance $l/2$ on each side of the reaction R_2 is found whose value is

$$q_2 = (K/l)y_2 = ky_2 \tag{230a}$$

In this manner the reactions R_1, R_2, R_{-1}, R_{-2}, etc., are replaced by uniform pressures q_1, q_2, q_{-1}, q_{-2}, etc., which are represented by the ordinates to the broken line $E'D'C'B'A'A$, etc. The total pressure on the bottom of the beam is represented by the area between this broken line and the bottom line of the beam in Fig. 116b and is equal to the load P. The substitution of an equivalent continuous elastic support is made complete by assuming that the pressure distribution as represented by the broken line $E'D'C'B'$, etc., may be replaced by the dashed curve in Fig. 116b. This curve passes through the midpoint of each segment of the broken line and thus has ordinates at each reaction equal to the pressure q at that reaction. The total pressure on the bottom of the beam as represented by the area between the dashed curve and the bottom of the beam will be approximately equal to the total pressure as represented by the broken line $E'D'C'B'$, etc., provided that the spacing l of the separate elastic supports is not too large.

In Fig. 116c the pressure distribution on the bottom of the beam due to the equivalent continuous elastic support is shown; this is the dashed curve of Fig. 116b. The equivalent pressure q per unit length on the bottom of the beam at any section whose deflection is y is

$$q = ky \qquad (231)$$

in which the spring constant k of the equivalent continuous elastic support as given by Eq. 230 is

$$k = K/l \qquad (232)$$

The value of q from Eq. 231 is now used in Eq. 214 in deriving the elastic curve (Eq. 215) of a beam on a continuous elastic support. Therefore, the deflection, the slope, the bending moment, and the shear at any section of the beam on separate elastic supports as represented by Fig. 116a may be computed by using Eqs. 221a through 224a, respectively, in which the value of k is given by Eq. 232. This method of solving problems will be illustrated at the end of this article.

Length of Span l. It was pointed out in the preceding discussion that the error involved in the substitution of an equivalent continuous elastic support depends upon the length l of the span between the separate elastic supports. In general the larger the span l, the larger is the error in the computed values of deflection, bending moment, etc. But the error also depends upon the value of β which is equal to $\sqrt[4]{k/4EI}$. It is noted in Fig. 116c that the pressure of the support on the beam becomes zero at the points G and G' at distances $x = \pm\frac{3}{4}(\pi/\beta)$ from the load. The manner in which the load is supported at points beyond $x = \pm\frac{3}{4}(\pi/\beta)$ has negligible effect on the deflection, the moments, etc., near the load. It has been found (see reference 3 at the end of this chapter) that, if the span length l does not exceed $l = \pi/4\beta$, the error in the computed deflections, bending moments, etc., is negligible when these values are found by replacing the separate elastic supports by an equivalent continuous elastic support as previously described in this article.

Illustrative Problems

Problem 125. A machine base designed to prevent vibration consists partly of a standard aluminum alloy 3-in. 2.02-lb I beam 20 ft in length supported upon coil springs spaced $l = 30$ in. apart. The spring constant for each coil spring is $K = 600$ lb per in. The force exerted by the machine on the beam is a concentrated load of 2000 lb which acts at the mid-point of the beam. Compute the maximum deflection and the maximum bending stress in the beam. Assume that $E = 10,000,000$ lb per sq in. and $I = 2.52$ in.^{4} for the beam.

Solution. The value of k from Eq. 232 is

$$k = K/l = \tfrac{600}{30} = 20 \text{ lb/in.}^2$$

and

$$\beta = \sqrt[4]{\frac{k}{4EI}} = \sqrt[4]{\frac{20}{4 \times 10,000,000 \times 2.52}} = 0.0211 \text{ in.}^{-1}$$

In order to be considered as a long beam on an elastic foundation, the beam should be at least $\tfrac{3}{2}(\pi/\beta) = \tfrac{3}{2}(\pi/0.0211) = 223$ in. in length. The beam is 240 in. in length. The span length between spring supports is 30 in. and is less than $\pi/4\beta = \pi/(4 \times 0.0211) = 37.2$ in., which is the upper limit the spring spacing may have when using an equivalent continuous elastic support for the solution of this problem. It is assumed that the beam rests on an equivalent continuous elastic support whose spring constant $k = 20$ lb per sq in. as given by Eq. 232. Therefore, from Eq. 226 the maximum deflection is found to be

$$y_{\max} = \frac{P\beta}{2k} = \frac{2000 \times 0.0211}{2 \times 20} = 1.055 \text{ in.}$$

and the maximum bending moment is

$$M_{\max} = \frac{P}{4\beta} = \frac{2000}{4 \times 0.0211} = 23,700 \text{ lb-in.}$$

The maximum bending stress is

$$\sigma = \frac{Mc}{I} = \frac{23,700 \times 1.5}{2.52} = 14,100 \text{ lb/in.}^2$$

Problem 126. A long beam is suspended by a series of steel rods $\frac{7}{16}$ in. in diameter and 60 in. long, spaced 24 in. center to center. The beam is a 6-in. 12.5-lb steel I beam; the moment of inertia of the cross section of the beam is 21.8 in.^{4}, and hence its section modulus is 7.3 in.^{3}. If a 7000-lb vertical concentrated load is applied to the beam at its mid-point, compute the maximum bending stress in the beam and the maximum tensile stress in the hanger rods. The value of E for steel is 30,000,000 lb per sq in.

Solution. The spring constant K of a hanger rod is obtained from the equation for the elongation of a centrally loaded bar under tension. Thus $y = FL/aE$, where y is the elongation of the rod, F is the axial load on the bar, L is the length of the rod, a is the cross-sectional area, and E is the modulus of elasticity. The spring constant K of the rod is defined as

$$K = \frac{F}{y} = \frac{aE}{L} = \frac{0.150 \times 30{,}000{,}000}{60} = 75{,}000 \text{ lb/in.}$$

The value of the constant k of the equivalent continuous elastic support is found from Eq. 232 to be

$$k = K/l = 75{,}000/24 = 3120 \text{ lb/in.}^2$$

Hence
$$\beta = \sqrt[4]{\frac{k}{4EI}} = \sqrt[4]{\frac{3120}{4 \times 30{,}000{,}000 \times 21.8}} = 0.033 \text{ in.}^{-1}$$

Also $\pi/4\beta = \pi/(4 \times 0.033) = 24$ in., and hence the span length l between the suspension rods does not exceed $\pi/4\beta$. Therefore from Eq. 226 we obtain

$$M_{max} = \frac{P}{4\beta} = \frac{7000}{4 \times 0.033} = 53{,}000 \text{ lb-in.}$$

and
$$\sigma_{max} = \frac{M}{I/c} = \frac{53{,}000}{7.3} = 7260 \text{ lb/in.}^2$$

The stress in a rod is $\sigma_t = F/a = yE/L$. Therefore the maximum stress in the rods will be in the rod nearest the load where the deflection y of the beam (and hence of the rod) is a maximum. The maximum deflection as found from Eq. 226 is

$$y_{max} = \frac{P\beta}{2k} = \frac{7000 \times 0.033}{2 \times 3120} = 0.037 \text{ in.}$$

Therefore the maximum stress in the rods is

$$\sigma_t = \frac{y_{max}E}{L} = \frac{0.037 \times 30{,}000{,}000}{60} = 18{,}500 \text{ lb/in.}$$

Problems

127. In Prob. 126, let it be assumed that all the data remain the same except that the $\frac{7}{16}$-in. suspension rods are 72 in. long instead of 60 in. Compute the maximum bending stress in the beam and the maximum tensile stress in the suspension rods.

128. A long, welded steel pipe approximately $6\frac{1}{2}$ in. in outside diameter is suspended from a series of spring hangers each having a spring constant of $K = 94$ lb per in. The springs are spaced 10 ft center to center along the pipe. The moment of inertia of the cross section of the pipe is 28.1 in.^{4}, and its section modulus is 8.5 in.^{3}. The weight of the pipe is 19 lb per ft, and a concentrated load of 2000 lb is suspended from a point near the mid-length of the pipe. Compute the maximum bending stress and the maximum deflection of the pipe. Neglect the weight of pipe in computing stress but include it in computing deflection.

Ans. $\sigma = 15{,}000 \text{ lb/in.}^2$; $y_{max} = 7.00 \text{ in.}$

63 Uniformly distributed load over part of beam. In Fig. 117 a very long beam is supported on an elastic foundation and is subjected to a uniformly distributed force of w per unit length over a length h of the beam near the middle. Let it be required to determine the deflection, slope, bending moment, and shear in the beam at any section O within the length h. • The section O is located at a distance a from the left end of h and a distance b from the right end of h as shown in Fig. 117.

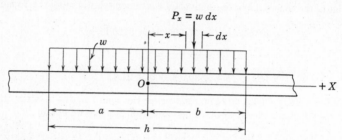

Fig. 117 Long beam on elastic support loaded over a portion of its length.

The problem will be solved by assuming that the distributed load is equivalent to a series of closely spaced concentrated loads P_x, each of which is equal to $w\,dx$, where dx is a differential length of the beam, and then using the principle of superposition as was done in Prob. 119.

Deflection. The deflection Δy of the point O due to the load $P_x = w\,dx$ shown in Fig. 117 is found from Eq. 221 to be

$$\Delta y = \frac{w\,dx\,\beta}{2k}\,e^{-\beta x}(\cos \beta x + \sin \beta x) \tag{233}$$

where x is the distance from the load $P_x = w\,dx$ to the point O, and β and k are constants as defined in Art. 61. The resultant deflection y of the point O caused by the entire distributed load will be equal to the algebraic sum of all the values of Δy as given by Eq. 233 for each of the loads $w\,dx$. Since the number of loads $w\,dx$ is indefinitely large and extends on both sides of the point $O(x = 0)$, the following two integrals are required to sum up the values of Δy.

$$y = \Sigma \Delta y = \int_0^a \frac{w\,dx}{2k}\,\beta e^{-\beta x}(\cos \beta x + \sin \beta x)$$

$a \neq b$

$$+ \int_0^b \frac{w\,dx}{2k}\,\beta e^{-\beta x}(\cos \beta x + \sin \beta x) \tag{234}$$

The value of a in Eq. 234 is negative, but it is given a positive sign here because Eq. 221, which is used in setting up Eqs. 233 and 234, gives the deflection only for positive values of x. This procedure is justified because the deflection of a beam under a single concentrated load has, because of symmetry, the same value at equal distances in the positive and negative directions of x. When integrated, Eq. 234 gives the following value of the deflection at O.

$$y = (w/2k)(2 - e^{-\beta a} \cos \beta a - e^{-\beta b} \cos \beta b) \qquad (235)$$

By reference to Eqs. 225 it is noted that the terms $e^{-\beta a} \cos \beta a$ and $e^{-\beta b} \cos \beta b$ may be replaced by the symbols $D_{\beta a}$ and $D_{\beta b}$, respectively, and therefore Eq. 235 may be written

$$y_0 = (w/2k)(2 - D_{\beta a} - D_{\beta b}) \qquad (236)$$

Values of $D_{\beta a}$ and $D_{\beta b}$ in Eq. 236 may be found in Table 7 by entering the x column with values of βa and βb, respectively. The maximum deflection of the beam occurs at the mid-point of the distributed load at the point where $a = b$.

Slope, Bending Moment, and Shear. The values of slope, bending moment, and shear at the point O produced by one load $P_x = w\,dx$ may be found by use of Eqs. 222, 223, and 224, respectively. The slope, bending moment, and shear at the point O produced by the entire distributed load are found by applying the principle of superposition. The resulting values of slope, bending moment, and shear at any section O under the distributed load are, respectively,

$$\theta = (w\beta/2k)(A_{\beta a} - A_{\beta b}) \qquad (237)$$

$$M = (w/4\beta^2)(B_{\beta a} + B_{\beta b}) \qquad (238)$$

$$V = (w/4\beta)(C_{\beta a} - C_{\beta b}) \qquad (239)$$

Values of the quantities within the second parentheses in Eqs. 237, 238, and 239 may be found from Table 7.

Maximum Bending Moment. The location of the point O which will result in the maximum bending moment in Eq. 238 is found as follows. If the loaded length h is short, that is, if h is less than $\pi/2\beta$, the maximum bending moment is at the mid-point of the distributed load. If h is greater than $\pi/2\beta$, there are two locations within the length h which give the same maximum moment. These two points are approximately at distances $\pi/4\beta$ from each end of the distributed load. These facts will be demonstrated in the illustrative problem which follows.

Illustrative Problems

Problem 129. A very long, wood beam whose cross section is 4 in. by 8 in. rests on an earth foundation. The modulus of elasticity of the wood is 1,500,000 lb per sq in., and the value of k_0 for the earth foundation is $k_0 = 160$ lb per cu in. A uni-

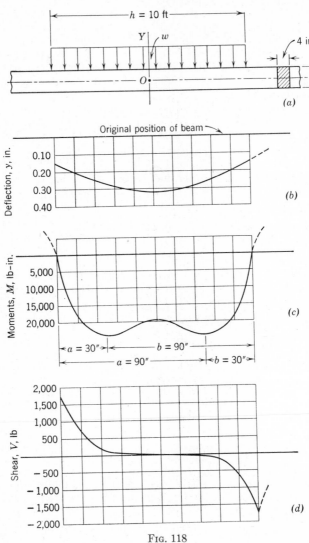

FIG. 118

formly distributed load of $w = 2400$ lb per ft extends over a length $h = 10$ ft of the beam near the middle of the beam as shown in Fig. 118a. Compute the maximum values of the deflection, the flexural stress, and the shearing stress in the beam and the maximum pressure per unit length between the beam and the earth foundation.

Solution. The value of $k = k_0$ times the width of the beam $= 160 \times 4 = 640$ lb per sq in. Therefore

$$\beta = \sqrt[4]{\frac{k}{4EI}} = \sqrt[4]{\frac{640}{4 \times 1,500,000 \times 170.6}} = 0.0281 \text{ in.}^{-1}$$

and $\beta h = 0.0281 \times 120 = 3.37$. Also, since a and b are the distances (see Fig. 117) over which the load is distributed on either side of any point under the load, $\beta a + \beta b = 3.37$.

DEFLECTION. From Eq. 236 the deflection of any point O in the beam under the distributed load is found to be

$$y = (w/2k)(2 - D_{\beta a} - D_{\beta b})$$

The maximum deflection is found by selecting O as the mid-point of the length h over which the load is distributed. Thus $\beta a = \beta b = 1.69$. The values of $D_{\beta a}$ and $D_{\beta b}$ corresponding to this value of βa and βb are found from Table 7 and then substituted in the preceding equation giving

$$y_{\max} = \frac{200}{2 \times 640} [2 - (-0.0219) - (-0.0219)] = 0.320 \text{ in.}$$

It is important to note that the values of $D_{\beta a}$ and $D_{\beta b}$ are quite small. If these values are neglected, $y_{\max} = w/k = \frac{200}{640} = 0.3125$ in. It may be concluded from this fact that an approximate value of the maximum deflection of a beam under a load distributed over a length βh which is greater than π (in this problem $\beta h = 3.37$) may be obtained from the equation $y_{\max} = w/k$.

The deflections of several other points under the distributed load have been obtained by the use of Eq. 236 and the results plotted as ordinates to the curve in Fig. 118b which shows that the maximum deflection occurs under the mid-point of the distributed load. The maximum pressure per unit length of beam and of the foundation is equal to $K y_{\max} = 640 \times 0.320 = 205$ lb per in.

BENDING MOMENT. The bending moment at various sections of the beam are computed from Eq. 238. The curve in Fig. 118c shows how the moment varies under the distributed load. The maximum value, $M_{\max} = 23,250$ lb-in., occurs at two sections, first where $a = 30$ in. and $b = 90$ in., and again where $a = 90$ in. and $b = 30$ in. If it is assumed that the maximum bending moment occurs at a section a distance $\pi/4\beta = \pi/(4 \times 0.0281) = 28$ in. from the left (or right) end of the distributed load, we have $\beta a = 0.0281 \times 28 = 0.79$, $\beta b = 0.0281 \times 92 = 2.58$. Thus we have from Eq. 238

$$M_{\max} = \frac{w}{4\beta^2} (B_{\beta a} + B_{\beta b}) = \frac{200}{4(0.0281)^2} (0.3224 + 0.0404) = 23,000 \text{ lb-in.}$$

Therefore the selection of the approximate location of the maximum bending moment at a distance $\pi/4\beta$ from the ends of the distributed load introduces only a small error. The maximum bending stress is

$$\sigma_{\max} = \frac{Mc}{I} = \frac{23,250 \times 4}{170.7} = 545 \text{ lb/in.}^2$$

SHEAR. The values of the vertical shear are computed by Eq. 239 and are designated by Q instead of V and shown as ordinates to the curve in Fig. 118d. The maximum value of the shear occurs at the ends of the distributed load and is $V_{\max}$

= 1730 lb. The maximum shearing stress in the beam is given by the formula for a rectangular section which is $\tau = \frac{3}{2}(V/A)$, where V is the vertical shear and A is the area of the rectangular cross section. Thus

$$\tau_{max} = \tfrac{3}{2}(V/A) = \tfrac{3}{2}\,\tfrac{1730}{32} = 81 \text{ lb/in.}^2$$

Problem 130. In Prob. 125 let it be assumed that the 2000-lb concentrated load is uniformly distributed over a length $h = 2$ ft, that is, $w = 83.3$ lb per in. If all the other data in the problem remain unchanged, compute the maximum deflection and the maximum bending stress in the beam.

Solution. The value of β from Prob. 125 is 0.0211 in.$^{-1}$. The length $h = 24$ in. over which the load is uniformly distributed is less than $\pi/2\beta = 74$ in., and therefore the maximum deflection and maximum bending moment are at the mid-point of the length h. The maximum deflection is found from Eq. 236 by taking $a = b = 12$ in. Then $\beta a = \beta b = 0.25$. The corresponding value of $D_{\beta a}$ and $D_{\beta b}$ are found from Table 7. The maximum deflection is

$$y_{max} = \frac{w}{2k}(2 - D_{\beta a} - D_{\beta b}) = \frac{83.3}{2 \times 20}(2 - 0.754 - 0.754) = 1.02 \text{ in.}$$

The maximum bending moment is at the mid-point of the distributed load for which $\beta a = \beta b = 0.25$ as before. The values of $B_{\beta a}$ and $B_{\beta b}$ as found from Table 7 are substituted into Eq. 238, and the maximum bending moment is found to be

$$M_{max} = \frac{w}{4\beta^2}(B_{\beta a} + B_{\beta b}) = \frac{83.3}{4(0.0211)^2}(1.93 + 1.93) = 18,000 \text{ lb-in.}$$

The maximum bending stress is

$$\sigma_{max} = \frac{Mc}{I} = \frac{18,000 \times 1.5}{2.52} = 10,700 \text{ lb/in.}^2$$

This maximum bending stress is about 25 per cent less than the maximum bending stress in Prob. 125 where the load is concentrated. Thus a distribution of a concentrated load over a short length of a beam supported on an elastic foundation provides a substantial reduction in the maximum bending stress. A comparison of the maximum deflections, however, shows that only a slight decrease occurs from distributing the load.

Problems

131. The beam in Prob. 129 is subjected to a uniformly distributed load of 1000 lb per ft over a length of 3 ft. (a) Compute the maximum deflection and the maximum bending stress. (b) Let it be assumed that the total distributed load is concentrated at one section, and compute the maximum deflection and the maximum bending stress.   *Ans.* (a) $y_{max} = 0.061$ in.; $\sigma = 360$ lb/in.^{2}.
(b) $y_{max} = 0.066$ in.; $\sigma = 620$ lb/in.^{2}.

132. A long concrete footing rests on an earth foundation for which the value of the spring constant $k_0 = 100$ lb per cu in. The footing has a cross section 8 in. wide and 8 in. deep. The footing supports a uniformly distributed load of $w = 100$ lb per inch of length which extends over a 10-ft length. Compute the approximate value of the maximum bending moment in the footing. Assume $E = 2,000,000$ lb per sq in. for the concrete.

64   Short beams.   In the preceding articles in this chapter relatively long beams supported on an elastic foundation were considered, a long beam being defined as one whose length is not less than $L = 3\pi/2\beta$. For beams shorter than $L = 3\pi/2\beta$ the expressions for deflection, bending moment, etc., as given in the preceding articles must be modified because the elastic curve equation (Eq. 218) for long beams is not applicable to short beams.   Although the modification of these equations consists in a rather simple procedure of superimposing additional fictitious loads on the beams, the equations when so modified are usually very complex.   These equations are given in Chapters 3 and 4 of reference 1 at the end of this chapter and will be presented here in the form of curves from which deflections and moments may be found.

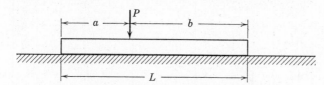

FIG. 119   Short beam on elastic support.

The simplest type of short beam supported on an elastic foundation is one which is subjected to a single concentrated load and which has free (unrestrained) ends.   For example, Fig. 119 shows a short beam of length $L(L < 3\pi/2\beta)$ subjected to a concentrated load P located at distances a and b from the ends of the beam which are free.   The deflection and bending moment at any section of this short beam are given as ordinates to the curves in Figs. 120 and 121 for various locations of the load.   In these figures y_0 and M_0 are the values of the maximum deflection and the maximum bending moment, respectively, under a concentrated load P on a *long* beam as found from Eq. 226; they are given by the expressions

$$y_0 = P\beta/2k \qquad \text{and} \qquad M_0 = P/4\beta \qquad (240)$$

The curves of Figs. 120 and 121 have been obtained from the equations for the deflection and bending moment given for this type of beam in Chapter 3 of reference 1 at the end of this chapter.   Curves for bending moments and deflections for four different lengths of beams, namely, $L = 2/\beta$, $3/\beta$, $4/\beta$, and $5/\beta$, have been plotted.

Bending Moments.   For each of the lengths shown in Figs. 120 and 121 curves are given in the upper diagrams for bending moments caused at any section by a single concentrated load P located at the left end and at a distance $L/12$, $L/6$, etc., from the left end, as indicated on the curves.

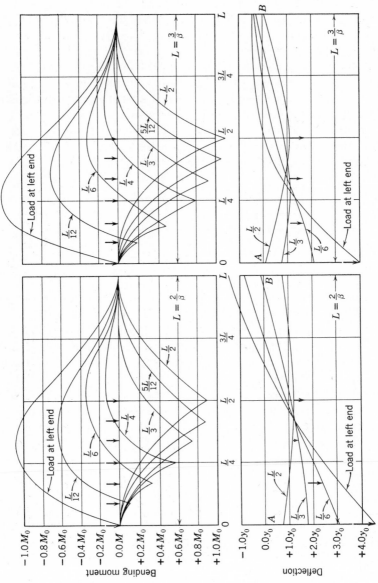

FIG. 120   Bending moment diagrams and deflection curves for short beam on elastic supports subjected to concentrated load located as shown on each curve. The ends of the beams are unrestrained (free).

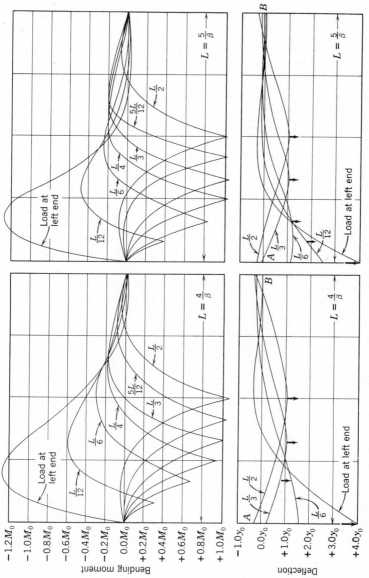

FIG. 121 Bending moment diagrams and deflection curves for short beam on elastic supports subjected to concentrated load located as shown on each curve. The ends of the beams are unrestrained (free).

If the bending moments caused by a single concentrated load located between the mid-point and the right end are desired, the curve corresponding to this distance from the left end may be used by exchanging ends of the beam. If the load P does not act exactly at one of the locations for which curves are given, the bending moment curve may be obtained easily by interpolation between the given curves; also, if the beam length is not equal to one of the lengths given in these diagrams, the bending moment at any section may be found for the lengths above and below the actual length of the beam, and then an interpolation will give an approximate value of the bending moment at this section in the actual beam.

Deflections. For each of the lengths shown in Figs. 120 and 121 curves are given in the lower diagrams for the deflection caused at any section by a single concentrated load P at the locations shown on the curve. The foregoing remarks with respect to bending moments concerning interpolation for loads P located at other sections apply also to deflections. These curves show the actual shape and position that the beam will assume as a result of the action of the load P in comparison to the original position of the beam as shown by the line AB in each diagram.

Limits of Length L. Short beams are those whose length L is less than about $5/\beta$ (about $3\pi/2\beta$). Curves for bending moment and deflection of short beams having four different lengths ranging from $L = 5/\beta$ to $L = 2/\beta$ are given in Figs. 120 and 121. If beams on elastic support shorter than $L = 2/\beta$ are encountered, it may be desirable to construct additional curves from the equations in reference 1. However, if approximate values of the bending moment and deflection will suffice, two alternative procedures are possible. First, if the length L is between $1/\beta$ and $2/\beta$, the curves for $2/\beta$ give approximate values for the bending moments and the deflection which are conservative. Second, if the beam and its elastic support are such that $L = 1/\beta$ or less, it may be assumed to be rigid, in which case the bending moments are negligible. If the beam is assumed to be rigid, the computation of the deflections is a statically determinate problem. The deflections then may be calculated by assuming a straight-line distribution of the reaction forces from the elastic supports and applying the equations of equilibrium to the system of forces acting on the beam.

Short Beam on Separate Elastic Supports. The problem of replacing separate elastic supports by an equivalent continuous elastic support has already been discussed for long beams in Art. 62. This same method may be applied to solving problems involving short beams on separate elastic supports. The moments, deflections, etc., are computed from the curves of Figs. 120 and 121. Unpublished results of experiments made in the Engineering Experiment Station at the University of Illinois confirm these facts.

Illustrative Problems

Problem 133. Solve Prob. 125 on the assumption that the length of the beam is 10 ft and that all the remaining data are unchanged.

Solution. The value of β from Prob. 125 is 0.0211 in.$^{-1}$. Therefore the value of $\beta L = 2.54$, that is $L = 2.54/\beta$, is between $2/\beta$ and $3/\beta$. From Fig. 121 the maximum bending moment for a beam of length $2/\beta$ is $0.9M_0$, and for a length $3/\beta$ is $1.1M_0$. Therefore, by interpolation between these values the maximum bending moment for the beam of length $2.54/\beta$ is $1.01M_0$. But, from Prob. 125, $M_0 = 23{,}700$ lb-in. Hence $M_{\max} = 1.01 \times 23{,}700 = 23{,}900$ lb-in. Therefore

$$\sigma = \frac{Mc}{I} = \frac{23{,}900 \times 1.5}{2.52} = 14{,}250 \text{ lb/in.}^2$$

The maximum deflection is found by a similar interpolation between the values $1.20y_0$ and $1.07y_0$ to be $1.13y_0$. From Prob. 125, y_0 is 1.055 in. Hence the maximum deflection is

$$y_{\max} = 1.13 \times 1.055 = 1.19 \text{ in.}$$

Problem 134. A load $P = 65$ tons is supported upon a structure consisting of nine 20-in. 70-lb steel I beams arranged as shown in Fig. 122. Three of the I beams lie parallel to each other across the other six I beams, which act as separate elastic supports for the three I beams; the three I beams are assumed to act as a unit in bending under the load P. Compute the maximum values of the deflection and bending stress in the three I beams and the maximum deflection and bending stress in the supporting beams AA (or BB) nearest the load P.

Solution. From a steel-maker's handbook the value of I for a 20-in. 70-lb I-beam is 1214 in.^{4}. The spring constant K of a separate elastic support such as beam AA is

$$K = \frac{48EI}{L_1{}^3} = \frac{48 \times 30 \times 10^6 \times 1214}{20^3 \times 12^3} = 126{,}500 \text{ lb/in.}$$

which comes from the equation $y = \frac{1}{48}(P_1 L_1{}^3/EI)$ for the deflection at the center of a simply supported beam such as AA in Fig. 122 of length L_1 supporting a load P_1 at its center. From Eq. 232 we find the spring constant k of the equivalent continuous elastic foundation is

$$k = \frac{K}{l} = \frac{48EI}{lL_1{}^3} = \frac{126{,}500}{60} = 2110 \text{ lb/in.}^2$$

Therefore $\quad \beta = \sqrt[4]{\dfrac{k}{4E(3I)}} = \sqrt[4]{\dfrac{48EI}{4E(3I)lL_1{}^3}} = \sqrt[4]{\dfrac{4}{lL_1{}^3}} = 0.00833 \text{ in.}^{-1}$

The value $3I$ used in computing β is for the three beams which are considered here as one beam on an elastic foundation. Note that the value of β depends only upon the distance l between elastic supports and the span length L_1 of the beams and is independent of the size of the I beams. For the purpose of getting the length L of the three I beams, they are shown extended beyond the elastic supports at the ends because it has been assumed in Eq. 232 that each separate elastic support exerts a uniform pressure on the beam for a distance of $l/2$ on either side of the support. Therefore $\beta L = 0.00833 \times 30 \times 12 = 3.00$. Thus $L = 3/\beta$, and the span length $l = 3/5\beta$ between the elastic supports is less than $\pi/4\beta$. Referring to the upper right diagram of Fig. 120 we find from the curve marked $L/2$ that for a beam of

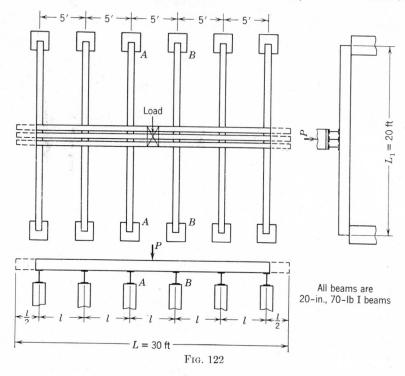

Fig. 122

length $L = 3/\beta$ loaded by a concentrated load at its mid-point the maximum moment is $1.1M_0$. But $M_0 = P/4\beta = 130,000/(4 \times 0.00833) = 3,900,000$ lb-in., and therefore

$$M_{max} = 1.1M_0 = 4,290,000 \text{ lb-in.}$$

The maximum stress in the three I beams is

$$\sigma_{max} = \frac{M_{max}c}{I} = \frac{4,290,000 \times 10}{3 \times 1214} = 11,800 \text{ lb/in.}^2$$

From the lower right-hand diagram of Fig. 120 we find by using the curve marked $L/2$ that the maximum deflection of the three I beams is $y_{max} = 1.08\,y_0$, but $y_0 = P\beta/2k = (130,000 \times 0.00833)/(2 \times 2110) = 0.256$ in. Therefore,

$$y_{max} = 1.08 \times 0.256 = 0.28 \text{ in.}$$

MAXIMUM DEFLECTION AND STRESS IN ELASTIC SUPPORTS. The beam AA (or BB) in Fig. 122 nearest the load P is subjected to the greatest stresses in the elastic supports. The deflection of beam AA at its mid-point is equal to the deflection of the three I beams at the section where these three beams rest on beam AA. This section is at a distance $0.4L$ from the left end of the three I beams, and the deflection is found to be $y = 1.0y_0$ from the curve in Fig. 120 previously used for finding the deflection. Therefore the maximum deflection of beam AA is

$$y_{AA} = 1.0y_0 = 0.256 \text{ in.}$$

This value of the deflection is substituted into the equation

$$y = \tfrac{1}{48}(P_1L_1{}^3/EI) = y_{AA} = 0.256$$

from which we find that the load at the center of beam AA is

$$P_1 = 48EI/L_1{}^3 \times 0.256 = 32,400 \text{ lb}$$

The maximum moment in beam AA is $P_1L_1/4 = 1,940,000$ lb-in., and the maximum stress in the beam AA is

$$\sigma = Mc/I = (1,940,000 \times 10)/1214 = 16,000 \text{ lb/in.}^2$$

Problems

135. In Prob. 126 the beam is 10 ft long, and the concentrated load is applied at the mid-point of the beam. Compute the maximum bending stress and the maximum deflection of the beam.

136. Solve Prob. 135 if the load is assumed to be applied at a point 40 in. from one end of the beam.

137. Solve Prob. 134, changing the size and weight of the nine I beams to 24-in. 79.9-lb steel I beams.

138. A steel bar of length $L = 20$ in. has a cross section 1 in. square. The beam is supported by five coil springs spaced a distance $l = 5$ in. apart. Each coil spring has a spring modulus $K = 75$ lb per in. (a) Compute the deflection of the beam at the mid-point if a concentrated load $P = 100$ lb acts at the mid-point. (b) If the concentrated load $P = 100$ lb acts at a distance of 8 in. from the left end, compute the deflection at each end of the beam. *Hint:* The beam is so short that it may be considered as rigid.   *Ans.* (a) 0.27 in. (b) Left end, 0.37 in.; right end, 0.16 in.

65 Concentrated load near one end of long beam. Figure 121

shows that, when the length L of a beam on an elastic foundation is greater than about $5/\beta$, the bending moment and the deflection caused by a load near one end are relatively large near that end, but that at distances equal to or greater than $L = 5/\beta$ from the loaded end the bending moment and deflection are negligibly small. Therefore, the bending moment and the deflection curves in Fig. 121 for $L = 5/\beta$ may be used for solving for the moments and deflections in a beam which has a length equal to or greater than $L = 5/\beta$ and which carries a concentrated load near one end of the beam; this means that, if the beam has a length greater than $L = 5/\beta$, this excess in length is ignored in the computation of moments and deflections.

66   Experimental procedure for determining the value of k.
It is important that the value of k to be used in solving problems of
beams on an elastic foundation should be determined experimentally
by a procedure that will duplicate as nearly as possible the main features of the actual beam and the actual elastic foundation.   For example, a value of k to be used for solving for the deflections and stresses
in railroad track should be obtained from tests on actual railroad track
(see Prob. 118 for values of k).   Figure 123a shows a rail of a railroad
track loaded by a concentrated load P.   A load P is applied to each rail,

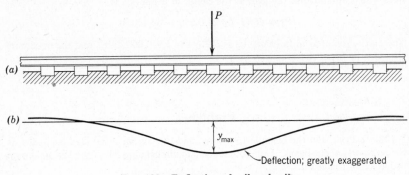

FIG. 123   Deflection of railroad rail.

and hence the total load on the track is $2P$.   The maximum deflection
y_{max} of the track under the loads P is shown in Fig. 123b.   According
to Eq. 226 the maximum deflection of the track under the loads is

$$y_{max} = \frac{P\beta}{2k} = \frac{P\sqrt[4]{k/4EI}}{2k} \tag{241}$$

If Eq. 241 is solved for k in terms of y_{max}, P, and EI, the value of k is

$$k = \frac{1}{4}\sqrt[3]{\frac{P^4}{EIy^4_{max}}} \tag{242}$$

The measured values of y_{max} and the load P are substituted into Eq.
242, and the value of k for the track bed is determined.

Other experimental procedures for determining the value of k are
discussed in references 2, 3, and 4 at the end of this chapter.   In reference 5 it is shown that the value of k_0 for soils depends somewhat upon
the size of the area of the surface of soil which is subjected to pressure and
upon the type of soil at different depths below the surface.   Therefore
much care should be exercised in the choice of a spring constant k_0 for a
soil which supports a beam or flat slab such as a runway pavement on an

air field. In some earth foundation problems the methods given in this chapter are not entirely satisfactory, and other procedures are used. In this connection see reference 6.

Selected References

1. Hetényi, M., *Beams on Elastic Foundation*, University of Michigan Press, 1946. This book gives a rather complete development of the theory of beams supported on an elastic foundation.

2. Talbot, A. N., "Progress Report of the Special Committee To Report on Stresses in Railroad Track," *Transactions of the American Society of Civil Engineers*, Vol. 82, 1918, pp. 1327–1332. This reference contains the results of experiments in which the spring modulus k of the foundation of railroad track was measured.

3. Wasiutynski, A., "Recherches expérimentales sur les déformations élastiques et le travail de la superstructure des chemins de fer," extract from *Annales de l'académie des sciences techniques à Varsovie*, Vol. IV, 1937, p. 1. On pp. 20–29 of this reference is given a discussion of a method of determining the spring modulus k of the foundation of railroad track. Also the results of a large number of experiments to determine k are reported.

4. Middlebrook, T. A., and G. E. Bertram, "Soil Tests for Design of Runway Pavements," *Proceedings of the Highway Research Board*, Vol. 122, 1942, pp. 152 and 170. The results of bearing tests of soils under a loaded circular plate 30 in. in diameter are given in this reference. Values of k_0 range from $k_0 = 100$ lb/in.^{3} for organic silt or inorganic clays up to a value of $k_0 = 800$ lb/in.^{3} for well-graded gravel or clay gravel.

5. Goldbeck, A. T., and M. J. Bussard, "The Supporting Value of Soil as Influenced by the Size of Bearing Area," *Public Roads*, Vol. 5, No. 11, January 1925, pp. 1–4.

6. Protzeller, H. W., "Track Stabilization—A Scientific Approach," *Railway Engineering and Maintenance*, Vol. 45, April 1949, p. 375. A discussion of the operating conditions affecting the railroad rail as a beam on a continuous elastic support.

Chapter 8

FLAT PLATES

§ 1 Introduction

67 General behavior of plates. A flat plate or flat slab such as
a bottom of a tank, floor panel, bulkhead, street manhole cover, etc.,
when supported around the edge and subjected to loads normal to the
surface, bends, but the bending differs from that of a beam in that the
plate bends in all planes normal to the plate whereas the beam may be
assumed to bend in one plane only. Furthermore, the bending of the
plate or slab in one plane is greatly influenced by the bending in all the
other planes, and hence the analysis of the stresses and deflections,
which takes into account these influences in a flat plate, is more difficult
than is that of a simple beam.

The values of the maximum stresses in flat plates as found by the
theory of flexure of flat plates are usually somewhat on the side of safety;
that is, as found from tests the maximum static loads that a plate will
resist without being structurally damaged are considerably greater than
are obtained from mathematical analysis based on the assumption that
the maximum load is reached when the maximum stress at any point
reaches the yield strength of the material. This fact is explained mainly
by observing that the portion of the plate where the maximum bending
stresses occur, as, for example, at the rim of a circular plate clamped or
fixed at the rim, yields slightly before the plate *as a whole* gives an indication of yielding, and thus there occurs a redistribution of stress which
gives the plate an added usable strength.

In fact, there may be three stages in the behavior of a medium-thick
flat plate in resisting loads, particularly in the case of a plate of ductile
metal that is restrained at its edges; *first*, the stage of purely elastic
strain when the deflection of the plate is strictly proportional to the
load and the deflection is due to bending only; *second*, the stage of
breakdown of elastic action when the yielding at the portions of high
stress becomes sufficient to permit a measurable permanent deflection

220

of the plate as a whole; during this stage the direct tension has become an appreciable factor in the resistance of the plate; *third*, the stage of direct tension in which the tension carries the greater part of the load; during this third stage the plate gradually takes a "dished" form. If the plate is thin, the major portion of the load may be carried by the direct tension even within the first or elastic stage. This fact will be discussed in Section 3 of this chapter.

Classification of Plates. Plates may be divided into three groups: (a) *thick* plates in which the shearing stresses are important, corresponding to short, deep beams; (b) *medium-thick* plates in which bending is the main action on which the useful resistance of the plate depends; the discussion in Section 2 of this chapter applies chiefly to this type of plate; (c) *thin* plates whose useful resistance depends in part on the direct tension accompanying the stretching of the middle plane. There are no sharp lines of division, however, between these classes of plates. A fourth group might be added, namely, membranes in which the resistance depends exclusively on the stretching of the middle plane and hence bending action is not present. Such a membrane, therefore, is not a plate as here considered.

It will be found that the elastic bending resistance of a relatively thin, flat plate is small, and that, if "dishing" the plate can be permitted, its usable strength is greatly increased since direct stresses then help resist the load. This fact explains why flat plates used where dishing must be prevented, such as flat boiler heads, are supported by stay bolts.

Methods of Determining the Elastic Stresses in Flat Plates. If it is assumed that the resistance of a plate to loads is limited by the magnitude of the stresses (normal or shearing) in the plate rather than by elastic deflection; in other words, if the strength of the plate rather than its stiffness is assumed to limit the maximum loads that may be applied to the plate, the main problem becomes one of finding a relationship between the loads acting upon the plate and the significant stresses caused by the loads.

In general, three methods have been employed in solving this problem for *medium-thick* plates; brief statements of the methods follow.

(a) The *strip method* in which the plate is assumed to be divided into two systems of strips at right angles to each other, each strip being assumed to act as a beam. This method is useful in a qualitative analysis of the behavior or action in a plate but is less satisfactory, in general, in obtaining reliable quantitative results.

(b) Another method is frequently designated as the *ordinary theory of flexure of flat plates*. This method is much the same in its general features as the theory of flexure for beams. In the first place it is assumed that bending is the dominant action in the (medium-thick) plate; it will be found (§ 3) that this assumption requires that the deflection of the plate be relatively small (of the order of one-half or less of the thickness of the plate); otherwise the direct tensile stresses in addition to the bending stresses will contribute substantially to the load resistance of the plate. It is also assumed that the plate is in equilibrium and is made of ideal elastic material for which the relations between stress and strain are as expressed in Chapter 3, just as is assumed in the theory of flexure of beams. In a beam, however, the assumption as to the strain behavior of the member, which must be made in accordance with the procedure outlined in Art. 8 in order to obtain the distribution of stress, states that a plane section before the beam is bent by the loads is a plane section after the beam is bent, and this assumption leads to a linear distribution of stress and to the simple flexure formula $\sigma = Mc/I$ and to the familiar differential equation $M = EI(d^2y/dx^2)$ of the elastic curve. The corresponding assumption for the flat plate is that every straight line drawn through the flat plate normal to its middle surface before the plate is bent by the loads remains straight and normal to the deflected middle surface after the plate is loaded.

In accordance with these assumptions Lagrange derived the differential equation for the deflection of a flat plate. If this differential equation can be solved for a given plate under a given loading, an expression for the deflection of any point in the plate is obtained, just as the deflection of a beam is obtained from the solution of the elastic curve equation of the beam. Furthermore, the bending moment per unit width in a plate may be found from the derivatives of the equation for the deflection of the plate just as the bending moment at any section of a beam can be obtained by differentiating the expression for the deflection of the beam, i.e., $M = EI(d^2y/dx^2)$. The bending stresses in the flat plate may then be found by substituting these bending moments in the flexure formula $\sigma = Mc/I$.

Except for simple types of loading and shapes of plates, such as a circular shape (see reference 3), the method of finding the bending moment by solving Lagrange's equation is somewhat complicated and will not be given here. However, the results obtained by means of this method can be reduced to tables or curves of coefficients for the maximum bending moments per unit width of a plate and for the maximum deflections of the plate, and some of these results are presented in this chapter.

The theory of flexure of plates, however, does not make allowance for the adjustments that take place when slight local yieldings at portions of high stress cause a redistribution of stress. This redistribution of stress, in turn, may give added usable strength to the plate as a whole which may often be counted on in the design of plates, particularly plates of ductile material. Nor does Lagrange's theory of flexure of plates take into account the added resistance of the plate resulting from the direct tensile stresses that accompany relatively large deflections.

(c) A third method is to obtain the total bending moment at the dangerous section from the equations of statics alone, the dangerous section being determined by observing the mode of failure from experiments. Likewise the factors by which the average stress corresponding to the total moment should be multiplied to obtain the maximum stress at the dangerous section are determined from experimental results, or in some cases these factors may be taken from the results found by applying the theory of flexure of plates as previously described. This third method, because of its simplicity and the direct experimental or physical basis of the formulas obtained, has been widely used; it is employed in several of the following articles. In this method, as in the theory of flexure, no attempt is made to include the effect of direct tensile stresses, which give the plate added strength as the deflection increases.

It should be noted that in methods (a) and (c) the attempt is made to reduce the problem of bending in more than one plane to an equivalent problem of bending in one plane only.

§ 2   Plates in Which Bending Action Is Dominant
Small Deflections

68   Stress in circular plate.   *Simply Supported at Edge; Load Uniformly Distributed.*   The third method stated in the preceding article will here be applied. Let a circular flat plate of radius r and of constant thickness t be subjected to a uniformly distributed load of w per unit area, and let the plate be simply supported on a circular rim around its edge.

The bending moment, about any diameter, of the forces that lie to one side of the vertical diametral plane (Fig. 124) is the moment of the reaction of the supporting rim minus the moment of the downward load. The magnitude of the load on the half-plate is $W = \frac{1}{2}\pi r^2 w$ and its action line passes through the centroid of the semicircular area; this centroid is at the distance $4r/3\pi$ from the diametral plane. The resultant R_1 of the reaction of the supporting rim must be equal in magnitude to the load, but its action line passes through the centroid of the semicircumference and hence acts at the distance $2r/\pi$ from the diametral plane as shown in Fig. 124. Therefore, the bending moment M about the diameter is

$$M = R_1 \frac{2r}{\pi} - W \frac{4r}{3\pi} = \frac{w\pi r^2}{2}\left(\frac{2r}{\pi} - \frac{4r}{3\pi}\right) \tag{243}$$

$$M = wr^3/3 \tag{244}$$

The bending moment may be equated to the resisting moment at the diametral section since the resisting moment holds the bending moment

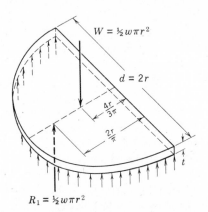

$W = \tfrac{1}{2}w\pi r^2$

$d = 2r$

$\dfrac{4r}{3\pi}$

$\dfrac{2r}{\pi}$

t

$R_1 = \tfrac{1}{2}w\pi r^2$

Fig. 124   Forces acting on circular flat plate.

in equilibrium, but the expression for the resisting moment in terms of the stress at any point in the section is unknown. If the expression for the resisting moment is assumed to be the same $(\sigma I/c)$ as that in a beam which bends in one plane only, that is, if the assumption is made that the stress at any point along a diameter is independent of the distance of the point from the center of the plate, we may write

$$wr^3/3 = \sigma I/c \tag{245}$$

But $I = \frac{1}{12}(2r)t^3$, and $c = t/2$. Therefore, this equation becomes

$$\sigma = w(r/t)^2 \tag{246}$$

The value of σ in Eq. 246 is the average bending stress at the surface of the plate at the diametral section.

Comparison with Results of Theory of Flexure of Plates. In Fig. 125 the curve CDE shows the stress distribution on the upper surface of a diametral section of the circular plate as obtained from the theory of flexure. The average stress σ as given by Eq. 246 is shown in Fig. 125 by the straight line AB. The maximum bending stress occurs at the center of the plate and is equal to $\frac{3}{8}(3 + \mu)w(r^2/t^2)$, where μ is Poisson's

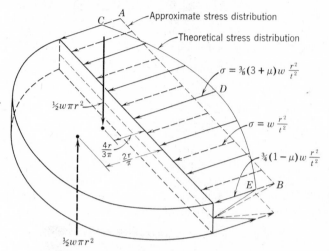

FIG. 125   Stress in circular flat plate under uniform load.

ratio. If the circular plate is made of steel for which $\mu = \frac{1}{4}$, the maximum bending stress is 22 per cent greater than the average stress as given by Eq. 246. However, experiments by Bach and others indicate that the readjustment of stress accompanying local yielding is such that Eq. 246 gives values of the significant or damaging stress, particularly if the plate is made of ductile material and the loads are static, and further if the deflection of the plate is small so that the direct tensile stress is negligible.

Simply Supported at Edge; Load Concentrated at Center. Let it be assumed first that the load P at the center is distributed over a small concentric circular area of radius r_0, as indicated in Fig. 126. The bending moment about a diametral plane AB may be found as in the above paragraph; the

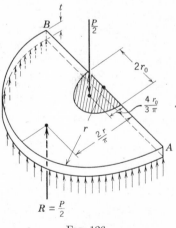

FIG. 126

total rim reaction R on one-half of the plate is $P/2$, and its moment arm is $2r/\pi$; the total load on the semicircular area of radius r_0 is $P/2$, and its moment arm is $4r_0/3\pi$. Therefore, the bending moment at the diametral section AB is

$$M = \frac{Pr}{\pi} - \frac{2Pr_0}{3\pi} = \frac{Pr}{\pi}\left(1 - \frac{2r_0}{3r}\right) \tag{247}$$

The average flexural stress σ at the top and bottom surfaces of the plate at the diametral plane as found from the flexure formula is

$$\sigma = \frac{Mc}{I} = \frac{\dfrac{Pr}{\pi}\left(1 - \dfrac{2r_0}{3r}\right)\dfrac{t}{2}}{\frac{1}{12}(2r)t^3} = \frac{3P}{\pi t^2}\left(1 - \frac{2r_0}{3r}\right) \tag{248}$$

in which t is the thickness of the plate and r is the radius of the plate.

Load Concentrated at the Center Point. If $r_0 = 0$ in the above equation, that is, if the load is concentrated on a very small area at the center of the plate, the expression for σ is

$$\sigma = 3P/\pi t^2 \tag{249}$$

The maximum bending stress in the plate is greater than the stress as given by Eqs. 248 and 249, particularly for small values of r_0; however, for plates made of ductile material and subjected to static loads, the value of σ in these equations may often be regarded as the significant stress. If the plate is made of brittle material, or if the plate is subjected to repeated stress even though it is made of ductile material, the value of the significant stress would be

$$\sigma = k(3P/\pi t^2)[1 - (2r_0/3r)] \tag{250}$$

where k may be assumed to be 1.5 for small values of r_0 and a lesser value for larger values of r_0. For the maximum theoretical values of stresses in circular plates as obtained by the theory of flexure of plates, see Table 8.

Circular Plates with Fixed Edges. If a circular plate is rigidly held (fixed) so that no rotation or radial displacement occurs at the edge, the average bending moment (and average bending stress) at any diametral section is less than that given by the equations in the foregoing articles, because the negative bending moment at the edge decreases the positive moment within the central portion of the plate in much the same way as in a beam that is fixed at its ends; furthermore, the negative moment at the edge of the plate is usually greater than the moment at the center, similar to the case of a beam with fixed ends.

TABLE 8

GRASHOF'S FORMULAS FOR VALUES OF MAXIMUM PRINCIPAL STRESSES AND MAXIMUM DEFLECTIONS IN CIRCULAR PLATES AS OBTAINED BY THEORY OF FLEXURE OF PLATES

r = radius of plate; r_0 = radius of central loaded area; t = thickness of plate; P = central load; w = uniform load per unit area; μ = Poisson's ratio.

Support and Loading	Principal Stress, σ_{max}	Point of Maximum Stress	Maximum Deflection, δ_{max}
Edge simply supported; load uniform.	$\dfrac{3}{8}(3+\mu)w\dfrac{r^2}{t^2}$	Center	$\dfrac{3}{16}(1-\mu)(5+\mu)\dfrac{wr^4}{Et^3}$
Edge fixed; load uniform.	$\dfrac{3}{4}w\dfrac{r^2}{t^2}$	Edge	$\dfrac{3}{16}(1-\mu^2)\dfrac{wr^4}{Et^3}$ *
Edge simply supported; load at center.	$\dfrac{3(1+\mu)P}{2\pi t^2}\left(\dfrac{1}{\mu+1}\right.$ $\left.+\log_e\dfrac{r}{r_0}-\dfrac{1-\mu}{1+\mu}\dfrac{r_0^2}{4r^2}\right)$	Center	$\dfrac{3(1-\mu)(3+\mu)}{4\pi}\dfrac{Pr^2}{Et^3}$
Fixed edge; load at center.	$\dfrac{3(1+\mu)P}{2\pi t^2}\left(\log_e\dfrac{r}{r_0}+\dfrac{r_0^2}{4r^2}\right)$ r must be $>1.7r_0$	Center	$\dfrac{3(1-\mu^2)P}{\pi Et^3}\dfrac{r^2}{4}$
Supported on central area; load uniform.	$\dfrac{3wr^2}{2t}\left[(1+\mu)\log_e\dfrac{r}{r_0}\right.$ $\left.+\dfrac{1}{4}(1-\mu)\left(1-\dfrac{r_0^2}{r^2}\right)\right]$	Center	$\dfrac{3}{16}(1-\mu)(7+3\mu)\dfrac{wr^4}{Et^3}$

* For thicker plates ($t/r > 0.1$) the deflection is $\delta_{max} = C\dfrac{3}{16}(1-\mu^2)(wr^4/Et^3)$, where the constant C depends upon the ratio t/r as follows: $C = 1 + 5.72(t/r)^2$.

Under service conditions, however, the edges of plates are seldom completely "fixed," although they usually are subjected to some restraint; furthermore, a slight amount of local yielding at the fixed edge may destroy much of the effect of the restraint and thereby transfer the moment to the central part of the plate. For these reasons, the restraint at the edges of a plate is considered of less importance, particularly if the plate is made of relatively ductile material, than would be indicated by the results of the theory of flexure of plates on the assumption of fixed edges. In general, a medium-thick plate with a restrained (so-called fixed) edge will be intermediate in strength between the plate with a simply supported edge and the plate with an ideally fixed edge. See Art. 81 for stresses in relatively thin plates having fixed edges.

Problem

139. A circular plate of radius r and thickness t is simply supported around its edge and is loaded along the circumference of a circle of radius r_0 concentric with the plate by a uniformly distributed load of w per unit length of the circumference. With the methods employed in Art. 68 derive an expression for the average bending stress at the surface of the plate on a diametral section in terms of the load and the dimensions of the plate.

$$Ans. \ \sigma = \frac{6r_0 w}{t^2}\left(1 - \frac{r_0}{r}\right) ; \text{ or } \sigma = \frac{3P}{\pi t^2}\left(1 - \frac{r_0}{r}\right), \text{ if } P \text{ is total load.}$$

69 Deflection of circular plate. Grashof's formulas given in Table 8 for the maximum deflection of circular plates of ideal, elastic material were obtained by the use of the theory of flexure of plates (see reference 3). Experiments by G. M. Russell have verified the formulas for uniformly distributed loads and a simply supported edge. His experiments with fixed-edged plates under uniformly distributed loads showed that Grashof's formula for the deflection was correct for thin and medium-thick plates $[(t/r) < 0.1]$ for deflections not larger than about one-half the plate thickness but that for thicker plates the measured values of deflection were much larger than those computed by the formula. Two reasons for this discrepancy were suggested: (a) lack of ideal fixity at the edge and (b) additional deflection in the thicker plates due to the shearing stresses. Russell and Clemmow suggested that for thicker $[(t/r) > 0.1]$ circular plates with fixed edges subjected to uniform loads the values as given by Grashof's formula be multiplied by a factor which depends on the ratio of the thickness t to the radius r. This factor is $C = 1 + 5.72(t/r)^2$. Russell's experiments on plates whose edges were securely clamped gave deflections that agreed closely with values computed by the use of Grashof's formula and the constant C.

Grashof's formulas for deflections give values that are too large when thin to medium-thick plates are loaded so that the deflections are larger than about one-half the plate thickness. See Arts. 81, 82, and 83 for discussion of plates having large deflections.

70 Stress in square plate; load uniformly distributed. *Simply Supported along Four Edges.* Experiments on square flat plates supported along the four edges indicate that the corners tend to curl up and that the dangerous section is approximately a diagonal section such as AC, Fig. 127. The bending moment, about the diagonal AC, of the forces that lie to one side of the diagonal may be found as follows. Let the load per unit area on the plate be w, and let b equal the side of the square. The total load on the plate is wb^2, the load W (Fig. 127) on one side of the diagonal is $W = \frac{1}{2}wb^2$, and its action line passes through the centroid of the triangular area ACB; the centroid lies on the median line at a perpendicular distance of $\frac{1}{3}h$ from AC. From the conditions

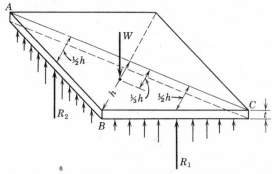

_FIG. 127   Forces acting on square flat plate under uniform load.

of symmetry and of equilibrium, the reactions R_1 and R_2 are found to be equal and each to have a magnitude of $\frac{1}{4}wb^2$. The bending moment about the diagonal AC is

$$M = (R_1 + R_2)(h/2) - W(h/3) = (wb^2h/4) - (wb^2h/6)$$

$$M = \tfrac{1}{12}wb^2h$$

(251)

and the average bending moment per unit width of the diagonal is

$$M_1 = \tfrac{1}{12}(wb^2h/AC) = \tfrac{1}{12}(wb^2h/2h)$$

$$M_1 = \tfrac{1}{24}wb^2 = 0.0417wb^2$$

(252)

The average stress σ at the surface of the plate at this diagonal section is then

$$\sigma = \frac{M_1 c}{I} = \frac{\tfrac{1}{24}wb^2 \times (t/2)}{\tfrac{1}{12}t^3} = \tfrac{1}{4}(wb^2/t^2)$$

(253)

The maximum stress is greater than σ in Eq. 253, but there is some justification (as given in the next paragraph) for assuming the moment (and stress) to be nearly constant along the diagonal and hence for assuming that σ is the significant stress.

Moment Coefficient. If the plate were supported along two parallel sides only, it would act approximately as a simple beam, and the average bending moment per unit width in a plane at the center of the plate perpendicular to the two sides would be $\frac{1}{8}wb^2$. The effect, therefore, of the supports along the additional two sides is to reduce the average bending moment per unit width from $\frac{1}{8}wb^2$ to $\frac{1}{24}wb^2$, the latter moment being in a plane perpendicular to a diagonal. The numbers by which wb^2 is multiplied to obtain the bending moment per unit width are called moment coefficients and are commonly used to indicate the intensity of the bending moment transferred across a section at any point along the given section of the plate.

By the theory of flexure of plates, several investigators have found moment coefficients for a homogeneous square flat plate. If such a plate is subjected to a uniformly distributed load and is simply supported along the four edges in such a way as to prevent its corners from curling up (this condition would require that the supports near the corners exert downward forces to keep the plate in contact with the supports at the corners), the bending moment at the corners A and C (Fig. 127) is $M_1 = 0.0463wb^2$, and at the center of the diagonal the bending moment is $M_1 = 0.0369wb^2$. This statement means that the moment coefficient along AC decreases from 0.0463 at the corners to 0.0369 at the center. The average of these coefficients is the value $\frac{1}{24}$ = 0.0417, given by Eq. 252.

This average value of $\frac{1}{24}$ (and Eq. 253) has been used widely as a basis of design and may be justified by the fact that the high stresses at the corners are localized stresses which do not affect appreciably the behavior of the plate as a whole even though they exceed the elastic strength of the material, and that when the material begins to yield in a part of the diagonal section the stresses are redistributed so that they become more nearly uniform along the diagonal.

Square Plate; Fixed at Edges, Uniform Load. If the plate is held rigidly (fixed) at the edges so that there is no rotation or displacement at the edges and is subjected to a uniformly distributed load w per unit area, the maximum moment is the negative moment at the center of each of the edges of the plate. The moment coefficient for the bending moment at the center of the plate as found from the theory of flexure of plates by several investigators is approximately 0.018; that is,

$$M_{center} = 0.018wb^2 \text{ per unit width of plate} \qquad (254)$$

and for the negative moment at the center of the edges the moment coefficient is approximately 0.050; that is,

$$M_{edge} = 0.050wb^2 \text{ per unit width of plate} \qquad (255)$$

Therefore the negative moment (and hence stress) at the edge is more than two and one-half times larger than that at the center. But since slight local yielding at the edges will redistribute the stress and give a more uniform distribution, the moment coefficient for use in design particularly with ductile material may be some value between those given in the above equations. If the average of these values (0.034) is used, the value of the stress is

$$\sigma = \frac{Mc}{I} = \frac{0.034wb^2(t/2)}{\frac{1}{12}t^3} = 0.20(wb^2/t^2) \text{ approximately} \qquad (256)$$

Nichols found, from experiments on square steel plates, a value of $\sigma = 0.141(wb^2/t^2)$ corresponding to the first measurable permanent set in the plate, and Bach obtained from experiments a value of $\sigma = 0.19(wb^2/t^2)$.

71 Stress in rectangular plate; load uniformly distributed. *Simply Supported along Four Edges.* Experiments on rectangular plates indicate that the dangerous section is approximately a diagonal section such as AC, Fig. 128, the same as in square plates, except for a plate in

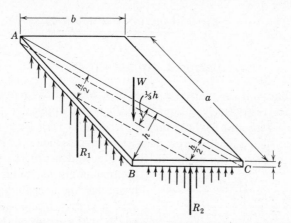

FIG. 128   Forces acting on rectangular flat plate under uniform load.

which one side is very much longer than the other side. The pressure along the supporting edges probably varies about as shown in Fig. 128, since the corners are known to tend to curl up, but the resultant pressure on each edge acts at the mid-point of the edge.

The average bending moment per unit width of diagonal may be found as was done with the square plate in the preceding article. Let the load per unit area on the plate be w. The total load on the plate then is wba, and the load W (Fig. 128) on one side of the diagonal is

$W = \frac{1}{2}wba$, and its action line passes through the centroid of the triangular area ACB; this centroid lies on the median line at a perpendicular distance of $\frac{1}{3}h$ from AC. Regardless of the values of R_1 and R_2, they have the same moment arm, and from the condition of symmetry and equilibrium their sum is equal to $\frac{1}{2}wba$. The bending moment M about the diagonal AC is

$$M = (R_1 + R_2)\tfrac{1}{2}h - W\tfrac{1}{3}h$$

$$= \tfrac{1}{2}wba\tfrac{1}{2}h - \tfrac{1}{2}wba\tfrac{1}{3}h = \tfrac{1}{12}wbah \tag{257}$$

The average bending moment per unit width of the diagonal is, therefore,

$$M_1 = \tfrac{1}{12}wbah/AC$$

But $\qquad h = ab/\sqrt{b^2 + a^2} \qquad$ and $\qquad AC = \sqrt{b^2 + a^2}$

Therefore $\qquad M_1 = \tfrac{1}{12}[a^2/(b^2 + a^2)]wb^2 \tag{258}$

and thus the coefficient of the average moment is $\tfrac{1}{12}[a^2/(b^2 + a^2)]$. Likewise, the average bending stress at the surface of the plate across the diagonal AC is

$$\sigma = \frac{M_1 c}{I} = \frac{\tfrac{1}{12}[a^2/(b^2 + a^2)]wb^2(t/2)}{\tfrac{1}{12}t^3}$$

$$\sigma = \tfrac{1}{2}[a^2/(b^2 + a^2)](wb^2/t^2) \tag{259}$$

If $a = b$, that is, if the plate is square, Eqs. 258 and 259 reduce to Eqs. 252 and 253, respectively. Equation 259 is not applicable to a plate that is very long and narrow, that is, when a is very large compared with b. For such a long, narrow plate the supports along the short sides have little effect on the action in the plate, and hence the plate acts

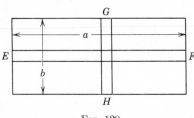

FIG. 129

approximately as would a simple beam having a span b; thus for such a plate the moment per unit width at the center of the plate in the direction of the shorter dimension would be $\frac{1}{8}wb^2$.

The stress at the center of the plate is always greater in the direction of the shorter span than in the direction of the larger span. This can be seen by considering two strips EF and GH (Fig. 129); the deflections of the two strips at the center are of course equal, but the shorter strip, being the stiffer, must carry the greater load, and hence the greater stress is developed in it.

In Fig. 130 are given the bending moment per unit width across the diagonal at the corner (denoted by M_{diag}), the bending moment per unit width at the center of the strip GH (Fig. 129) in the short span b (denoted by M_{bc}) and the bending moment per unit width at the center of the strip EF (Fig. 129) in the long span a (denoted by M_{ac}).

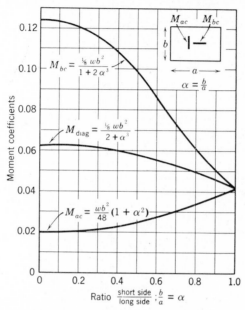

FIG. 130 Bending moment per unit width in rectangular plates with simply supported edges. Poisson's ratio μ assumed to be zero.

The curves and equations in Fig. 130 were obtained by Westergaard by making slight modifications in the results obtained from the theory of flexure of plates. The modifications were made in order to obtain relatively simple expressions, and in doing so allowance was made for some redistribution of stress accompanying slight yielding at the portions of high (and more or less localized) stresses. It will be noted that the moment coefficient for a square slab ($b/a = 1$) is $\frac{1}{24} = 0.0417$, and that for a long narrow slab ($b/a = 0$) the moment coefficient for the short span is $\frac{1}{8} = 0.125$. For intermediate values of b/a, the moment coefficient is always greater in the short span than elsewhere, and its value is intermediate between the limiting values of $\frac{1}{24}$ and $\frac{1}{8}$. But, as noted previously, the average moment coefficient given in Eq. 258 is probably, at least for ductile material, a better indication of the usable elastic strength of the plate than is the moment coefficient at the center of the short span.

Rectangular Plate with Fixed Edges, Uniform Load. If the plate is rigidly held (fixed) at the edges and is subjected to a uniformly distributed load, the maximum moment per unit width occurs at the centers of the long edges, that is, at the fixed ends of the central strip of the short span.

Two limiting cases of a fixed-edged rectangular slab will be considered first. If the plate is very long and narrow ($b/a = 0$), the forces at the

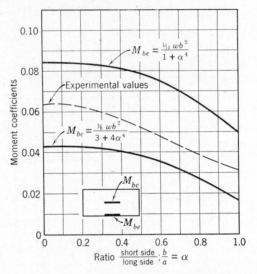

Fig. 131   Bending moment per unit width in rectangular plates with fixed edges. Poisson's ratio μ assumed to be zero.

short ends of the plate will have negligible effect on the moment in the central part of the plate, and hence the plate may be considered to be a fixed-ended beam with a span equal to the short dimension of the plate; therefore, the negative moment per unit width M_{be} at the fixed edges of the short span is $\frac{1}{12}wb^2$, and the positive moment M_{bc} at the center of the short span is $\frac{1}{24}wb^2$. The other limiting case is that of the square slab ($b/a = 1$) for which the moment coefficient at the center of the edges, as stated in Eq. 255, is approximately 0.05 and the moment coefficient at the center is 0.018.

For plates having other values of b/a, the maximum negative moment M_{be} and the maximum positive moment M_{bc} are given in Fig. 131. These values were obtained by Westergaard by simplifying the results obtained from the theory of flexure of flat plates. As explained in the preceding articles, owing to the advantageous redistribution of stresses accompanying slight yielding of the plate at points of maximum stress, the plate is somewhat stronger than is indicated by the results obtained from the theory.

For plates made of ductile metal, the maximum moment used in design should probably be about the average of the values of M_{be} and M_{bc} given in Fig. 131. Bach, from the results of experiments, recommends the moment coefficients given by the dotted line in Fig. 131. Montgomerie experimented on steel plates 24 in. by 48 in. $(b/a = 0.5)$ with the thicknesses varying from $\frac{1}{8}$ in. to $\frac{3}{4}$ in. and found the maximum moment per unit width to be approximately $0.042wb^2$. His results indicate that there is not much difference in the value of the stress at the center and at the end of the short span.

Other Types of Rectangular Flat Plates, Uniform Load. Formulas obtained by Westergaard giving approximate values of the moments per unit width in rectangular plates, including some of the formulas discussed in the preceding articles, are shown in Table 9. These formulas give results fairly close to those found from the theory of flexure of slabs, in which for convenience the value of Poisson's ratio $\mu = 0$ has been assumed. The effect of Poisson's ratio is to increase the bending moment per unit width in the plate. Let $M_{ac\mu}$ and $M_{bc\mu}$ represent the values of the bending moments at the center of a rectangular plate when the material has a Poisson's ratio μ not assumed to be zero. Approximate values of these bending moments are given by the expressions

$$M_{ac\mu} = M_{ac} + \mu M_{bc}$$

$$M_{bc\mu} = M_{bc} + \mu M_{ac}$$

(260)

in which M_{ac} and M_{bc} are values of the bending moments as given in Table 9, or subsequent tables, in which μ has been assumed to be zero. In using these formulas for plates made of ductile material, it should be borne in mind that they give results that probably err somewhat on the side of safety, as discussed in the preceding articles.

72 Deflection of rectangular plate; load uniformly distributed. The method used in the preceding articles for obtaining the average stress by treating the flat plate as though it bent in one plane only is *not* a satisfactory method for finding the deflection of a flat plate. For this problem, use is generally made of the solution of Lagrange's differential equation which, as explained in Art. 67, relates the deflection of the plate at any point to the loads on the plate. This differential equation for plates has been solved only for relatively simple shapes of plates and for certain simple types of loading. From the solution of this equation for rectangular plates subjected to uniformly distributed

TABLE 9

FORMULAS OBTAINED BY THEORY OF FLEXURE OF SLABS, GIVING APPROXIMATE VALUES OF BENDING MOMENTS PER UNIT WIDTH AND MAXIMUM DEFLECTIONS IN RECTANGULAR AND ELLIPTICAL SLABS UNDER UNIFORM LOAD w

(GIVEN BY WESTERGAARD)

Poisson's Ratio $\mu = 0$ (see Eq. 260)

b = shorter side; a = longer side; $b/a = \alpha$

	Moments in Span b		Moments in Span a		Maximum Deflection $\Delta_{max} = C(1-\mu^2)(wb^4/Et^3)$
	At Center of Edge $-M_{be}$	At Center of Slab M_{bc}	At Center of Edge $-M_{ae}$	Along Center Line of Slab M_{ac}	Values of C
Rectangular Slabs — Four edges simply supported.	0	$\dfrac{\frac{1}{8}wb^2}{1+2\alpha^3}$	0	$\dfrac{wb^2}{48}(1+\alpha)^2$	$\dfrac{0.16}{1+2.4\alpha^3}$
Span b fixed; span a simply supported.	$\dfrac{\frac{1}{12}wb^2}{1+0.2\alpha^4}$	$\dfrac{\frac{1}{24}wb^2}{1+0.4\alpha^4}$	0	$\dfrac{wb^2}{80}(1+0.3\alpha^2)$	$\dfrac{0.032}{1+0.4\alpha^4}$
Span a fixed; span b simply supported.	0	$\dfrac{\frac{1}{8}wb^2}{1+0.8\alpha^2+6\alpha^4}$	$\dfrac{\frac{1}{8}wb^2}{1+0.8\alpha^4}$	$0.015wb^2\dfrac{1+3\alpha^2}{1+\alpha^4}$	$\dfrac{0.16}{1+\alpha^2+5\alpha^4}$
All edges fixed.	$\dfrac{\frac{1}{12}wb^2}{1+\alpha^4}$	$\dfrac{\frac{1}{8}wb^2}{3+4\alpha^4}$	$\dfrac{1}{24}wb^2$	$0.009wb^2(1+2\alpha^2-\alpha^4)$	$\dfrac{0.032}{1+\alpha^4}$
Elliptical slab with fixed edges; diameters a and b. $b/a = \alpha$	$\dfrac{\frac{1}{12}wb^2}{1+\frac{2}{3}\alpha^2+\alpha^4}$	$\dfrac{\frac{1}{24}wb^2}{1+\frac{2}{3}\alpha^2+\alpha^4}$	$\dfrac{\frac{1}{12}wb^2\alpha^2}{1+\frac{2}{3}\alpha^2+\alpha^4}$	$\dfrac{\frac{1}{24}wb^2\alpha^2}{1+\frac{2}{3}\alpha^2+\alpha^4}$	

loads the maximum deflection $\delta_{\max}$ at the center of the plate is given by the equation

$$\delta_{\max} = C(1 - \mu^2)(wb^4/Et^3) \tag{261}$$

where w is the uniformly distributed load per unit of area, b is the short span length, E is the modulus of elasticity of the material in the plate, t is the plate thickness, μ is Poisson's ratio, and C is a dimensionless constant whose value depends upon the ratio b/a of the sides of the plate and upon the type of support at the edge of the plate.

Several investigators have computed values of the constant C in Eq. 261; some of the values are as follows: For a uniformly loaded square ($b/a = 1$) plate simply supported at its edges, $C = 0.047$; if the plate is very long and narrow ($b/a = 0$, approximately), $C = 0.16$. Thus the deflection of a long narrow plate is over three times that of a square plate having the same thickness as the narrow plate; in fact, the supports at the short ends of a narrow plate ($b/a < \frac{1}{3}$) have very little effect in preventing deflection at the center of the plate. If all the edges of a uniformly loaded square plate are fixed, the constant in Eq. 261 is $C = 0.016$. A comparison of this value of C with the value 0.047 for simply supported edges shows that if the edges of a square plate are held rigidly (fixed) the deflection at the center of the plate is about one-third of the deflection for simply supported edges. However, the edges of a plate are seldom if ever clamped rigidly, and therefore the deflection at the center of a plate having partial restraint at its edges would be given by a value of C between 0.016 and 0.047.

Values of the constant C in Eq. 261 for various ratios of b/a and for various conditions at the supports are given in Table 9. From Montgomerie's experiments on plates 48 in. by 24 in. with the edges carefully clamped the measured deflections on relatively thin plates ($b/t \leq 0.02$) agrees very closely up to values of deflections not greater than about one-half the plate thickness with those given by the formulas for deflection in Table 9. The formulas for deflection in this table give values which are too large when the direct tensile stresses in the plate are appreciable; this condition begins when the maximum deflection of the plate reaches a value of about one-half the thickness of the plate.

Illustrative Problem

Problem 140. A water tank 12 ft deep and 9 ft square is to be made of structural steel plate. The sides of the tank are divided into nine panels by two vertical supports or stiffeners and two horizontal supports; that is, each panel is 3 ft wide and 4 ft high, and the average head of water on a lower panel is 10 ft (see Fig. 132). Determine the thickness of the plate for the lower panels, using a working stress of 18,000 lb per sq in. Also calculate the maximum deflection of the panel.

Solution. The mean pressure on a bottom panel is $w = (10 \times 62.4)/144 = 4.33$ lb per sq in., and this pressure will be assumed to be uniform over the panel.

(*a*) If the panel is assumed to be simply supported around the edges, the average moment coefficient for a diagonal section is, according to Eq. 258,

$$\tfrac{1}{12}[a^2/(b^2 + a^2)] = \tfrac{1}{12}[16/(9 + 16)] = 0.0534$$

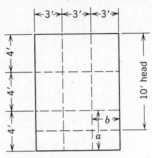

FIG. 132

From Fig. 130 it will be noted that this coefficient is considerably less than that at the center of the short span, but, as stated in Art. 70, it is probably the more significant value. Accordingly, the significant stress across a diagonal is (see Eq. 259)

$$\sigma = \tfrac{1}{2}[a^2/(a^2 + b^2)](wb^2/t^2)$$

and hence

$$t = ab\sqrt{w/[2(a^2 + b^2)\sigma_w]}$$

Therefore

$$t = 48 \times 36\sqrt{4.33/[2(3600)18,000]} = 0.315 \text{ in.}$$

(*b*) If the panel is assumed to be fixed at the edges, Fig. 131 gives approximately, for $b/a = \tfrac{3}{4} = 0.75$,

$$M = 0.042wb^2 = 0.042 \times 4.33 \times (36)^2 = 236 \text{ lb-in./in.}$$

and

$$\sigma = M/(I/c) = 6M/t^2$$

Hence

$$t = \sqrt{6M/\sigma_w} = \sqrt{(6 \times 236)/18,000} = 0.280 \text{ in.}$$

The plate is probably restrained somewhat at the edges but not fixed, and a value of t between 0.282 in. and 0.318 in. would be adequate for strength, but a commercial size and other considerations, such as rusting, etc., might dictate a larger thickness. Furthermore, some allowance for the error in the assumption that the water pressure is uniform on the panel might be made.

Maximum Deflection. (*a*) For edges supported, Table 9 gives

$$\delta_{\max} = C(1 - \mu^2)\frac{wb^4}{Et^3} \qquad C = \frac{0.16}{1 + 2.4(0.75)^3} = 0.080$$

$$\delta_{\max} = 0.080 \left(1 - \frac{1}{16}\right)\frac{4.33(36)^4}{30 \times 10^6} \times \frac{1}{(0.315)^3}$$

$$= 0.080 \times 0.226 \times (1/0.0313) = 0.58 \text{ in.}$$

(*b*) For fixed edges: $\quad C = 0.032/[1 + (0.75)^4] = 0.0243$

$$\delta_{\max} = 0.0243 \times 0.226 \times 1/(0.281)^3 = 0.247 \text{ in.}$$

These deflections are more than one-half the thicknesses, respectively, and are, therefore, considerably larger than would be expected to occur in the plates under these loads, owing to the effect of direct tensile stress in the plate as will be discussed later in Art. 80.

Problems

141. The cylinder of a steam engine is 16 in. in diameter, and the maximum steam pressure is 100 lb per sq in. Find the thickness of a steel flat plate cylinder head, assuming that the working stress is 12,000 lb per sq in. Calculate the maximum deflection of the cylinder head.

142. A structural steel trap door is 6 ft long, 3 ft wide, and $\frac{3}{8}$ in. thick. How large a uniform load will it support without being given a permanent deformation? Assume that the elastic strength of the material is 35,000 lb per sq in. When supporting this load, what will be the maximum deflection of the door?

143. A rectangular water tank is 12 ft deep and 12 ft square. It is divided into two compartments by a vertical steel flat plate. This flat plate is divided into four square panels by a vertical and a horizontal stiffener in addition to the stiffener across the top. What thickness should the plate have for a working stress of 20,000 lb per sq in.? One compartment may be full, and one empty.

144. A cast-iron flat disk valve 12 in. in diameter is subjected to a water pressure equivalent to a head of 200 ft. Find the thickness of the disk, using a working stress of 2000 lb per sq in.

73   Stress in square plate; concentrated load at center. *Simply Supported along Four Edges.* Experiments on square plates simply supported along the four edges have shown that a concentrated load P at the middle of the plate deforms the plate in somewhat the same manner as does a uniform load; that is, the corners have a tendency to curl up and the dangerous section is approximately a diagonal section such as AC in Fig. 133; but a concentrated load produces high stresses in the plate near the load. This fact makes the use of the average moment per unit width of the diagonal AC less reliable for obtaining the strength of the plate than it is in the case of the uniformly loaded plate.

Figure 133 shows the forces which act on one-half of a square plate having a central concentrated load P. The load P is assumed to be distributed over the area of a small circle whose diameter is d_0. From the conditions of symmetry and of equilibrium the reactions R_1 and R_2 are equal, and each has a magnitude of $\frac{1}{4}P$. The bending moment about the diagonal AC then is

$$M = (R_1 + R_2)\frac{h}{2} - \frac{P}{2}\frac{4d_0}{6\pi} = \frac{P}{2}\left(\frac{h}{2} - \frac{2d_0}{3\pi}\right) \tag{262}$$

and the average bending moment per unit length of the diagonal is

$$M_1 = \frac{M}{2h} = \frac{P}{4}\left(\frac{1}{2} - \frac{\sqrt{2}}{3\pi}\frac{d_0}{b}\right) \tag{263}$$

If the load is concentrated at the center of the plate, d_0 is zero and M_1 in Eq. 263 is equal to $\frac{1}{8}P$. The line EF in Fig. 133 represents the average bending stress in the surface of the plate across the diagonal section. The curved line in Fig. 133 represents the distribution of bending stress along this diagonal surface as determined from the theory of flexure of plates by Nadai and Westergaard. This curve shows that the bending stress per unit of length of diagonal near the load P increases sharply to a maximum value of $2.64(P/t^2)$ which corresponds to

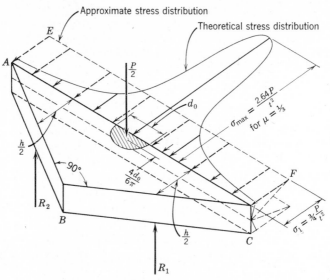

FIG. 133   Stresses in square flat plate with concentrated load at center.

a value of maximum bending moment per unit width of $0.44P$. This maximum stress is nearly four times as great as the average stress of $\frac{3}{4}(P/t^2)$ (Fig. 133) obtained by using the average bending moment of $\frac{1}{8}P$ per unit of width. Experiments by Sturm and Moore on square plates of aluminum supported at the edges show that, for a central load distributed over a very small area ($d_0/b = \frac{1}{24}$), the maximum bending moment per unit of width is approximately $0.43P$. For flat plates made of ductile material the relatively large difference between the maximum bending moment $0.44P$ and the average bending moment $\frac{1}{8}P$ is not highly significant because of the fact that the maximum bending moment is confined to the local region in the immediate neighborhood of the load P at which local yielding can occur without damaging the plate as a whole. If, however, the plate is made of brittle material or if P is a repeated load, the significant stress in the plate may correspond more nearly to the maximum bending moment per unit of width, 0.44P.

Square Plate with Fixed Edges, Concentrated Load at Center. If the plate is clamped rigidly (fixed) at the edges and subjected to a concentrated load P at the center, the maximum moment is the positive moment at the center of the plate rather than the negative moment at the middle of the edge. The moment coefficient for the bending moment at the center of the plate and at the edge have been found by the use of the theory of flexure of plates. For a material having a Poisson's ratio of $\frac{1}{3}$ and a central load P on a small area $(d_0/b = \frac{1}{24})$ the bending moment coefficient by this analysis is approximately 0.37. Therefore

$$M_{\text{center}} = 0.37P \qquad (264)$$

whereas the negative bending moment at the middle of an edge is only 0.125P.

Sturm and Moore found from experiment that the moment for aluminum plates $(\mu = \frac{1}{3})$ clamped at the edges and loaded at the center over a small area $(d_0/b = \frac{1}{24})$ is $M_{\text{center}} = 0.35P$.

Thus it will be seen that clamping or fixing the edges of a square plate carrying a central concentrated load P results in only a moderate benefit in reducing the bending moment at the center of the plate, since the reduction is from 0.44P for simply supported edges to 0.37P for fixed edges.

74   Stress in rectangular plate; concentrated load at center. *Simply Supported at Edges.* The average bending moment per unit of length of diagonal of a rectangular plate loaded at the center and simply supported at the edges can be found from the conditions of equilibrium, but the diagonal section is the dangerous section only when the rectangular plate is approximately square. The reason for this fact is that the supporting forces at the short ends of the rectangular plate have little or no effect on the moment at the center of the plate if $b/a < 0.5$. Thus the plate acts approximately as if it were supported on the long sides only, and therefore the moment M_{bc} per unit width at the center of the plate in a strip across the short span, such as GH in Fig. 129, is the maximum bending moment in the plate.

In Fig. 134 are given the bending moment per unit width M_{bc} at the center in the short span, and the bending moment per unit width M_{ac} at the center in the long span. The curves and equations in Fig. 134 were obtained by making slight modifications in the results obtained from the theory of flexure of plates. The modifications were made in order to obtain relatively simple expressions for the bending moment. These moments are given for a material in which Poisson's ratio has been assumed, for convenience in computation, to be zero; Eq. 260 may be used to compute the values of bending moments $M_{ac\mu}$ and $M_{bc\mu}$ from the values of M_{ac} and M_{bc} given in Fig. 134 or in Table 10.

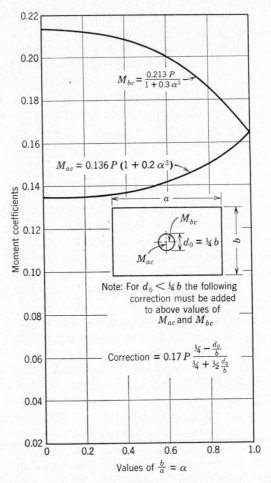

$$M_{bc} = \frac{0.213\,P}{1 + 0.3\,\alpha^3}$$

$$M_{ac} = 0.136\,P\,(1 + 0.2\,\alpha^3)$$

Note: For $d_0 < \frac{1}{4}\,b$ the following correction must be added to above values of M_{ac} and M_{bc}

$$\text{Correction} = 0.17\,P\,\frac{\frac{1}{4} - \frac{d_0}{b}}{\frac{1}{4} + \frac{1}{2}\frac{d_0}{b}}$$

Moment coefficients

Values of $\frac{b}{a} = \alpha$

FIG. 134 Bending moment per unit width in rectangular plates with simply supported edges, $\mu = 0$.

These maximum bending moments are more or less localized near the load; that is, the bending moments at a short distance from the load P are materially less than these maximum values. As a consequence of this fact, the maximum moments as given by these equations probably err on the side of safety, especially for plates of ductile material subjected to static loads.

TABLE 10

FORMULAS OBTAINED BY THEORY OF FLEXURE OF SLABS GIVING APPROXIMATE VALUES OF MAXIMUM BENDING MOMENTS PER UNIT WIDTH AND MAXIMUM DEFLECTIONS IN RECTANGULAR SLABS LOADED AT CENTER BY A LOAD P DISTRIBUTED OVER A CIRCULAR AREA OF DIAMETER d_0

b = shorter side; a = longer side; $b/a = \alpha$; $\mu = 0$ (see Eq. 260)

Kind of Support at Edge	Moments in Span b		Moments in Span a		Maximum Deflection $\delta_{max} = C(1-\mu^2)(Pb^2/Et^3)$
	At Center of Edge $-M_{be}$	At Center of Slab for Load on Central Area $d_0 = 0.25b$ * M_{bc}	At Center of Slab for Load on Central Area $d_0 = 0.25b$ * M_{ac}	At Center of Edge $-M_{ae}$	Values of C
Four edges simply supported.	0	$\dfrac{0.213P}{1+0.3\alpha^3}$	$0.136P(1+0.2\alpha^3)$	0	$\dfrac{0.2}{1+0.45\alpha^4}$
Span b fixed; span a simply supported.	$\tfrac{1}{6}P$	$0.148P$	$0.106P(1+0.1\alpha^5)$	0	0.087
Span a fixed; span b simply supported.	0	$\dfrac{0.213P}{1+0.9\alpha^3}$	$\dfrac{P}{100}\left(14-\cos\dfrac{4}{3}\pi\alpha\right)$	$\dfrac{P}{12}(1-\cos\pi\alpha)$	$\dfrac{0.2}{1+0.1\alpha^4+1.2\alpha^5}$
All edges fixed.	$\dfrac{\tfrac{1}{6}P}{1+\tfrac{1}{3}\alpha^5}$	$\dfrac{0.158P}{1+0.1(1-\alpha)^2}$	$\dfrac{0.158P}{1+0.5(1-\alpha)^2}$		$\dfrac{0.087}{1+0.3\alpha^4}$

* If d_0 is less than $0.25b$ the following correction must be added to each of the above values of M_{ac} and M_{bc}:

$$\text{Correction} = 0.17P\,\frac{\tfrac{1}{4}-(d_0/b)}{\tfrac{1}{4}+\tfrac{1}{2}(d_0/b)}$$

Fixed-Edged Rectangular Plates; Concentrated Load at Center. By rigidly clamping or fixing the edges of a rectangular plate subjected to a central concentrated load, the maximum bending moments given in the preceding articles for simply supported edges are reduced only slightly. If the edges are only partially restrained, as will nearly always be the case in practice, the reduction of moment at the center will be even less.

In Table 10 are given formulas for approximate values of the bending moments per unit width in rectangular flat plates with various conditions of support at the edges, including those already discussed. These formulas give values which are very close to the results obtained through the use of the theory of flexure of plates by Nadai, Westergaard, Newmark, Jensen, and Sturm and Moore. The moments are given for $\mu = 0$, but Eq. 260 may be used for computing values of bending moments for any value of μ.

75 Rectangular plate with one fixed edge, unsupported on other edges. *Concentrated Load at Mid-Point of Free Edge Parallel to the Fixed Edge.* Such a flat plate is shown in Fig. 135a, in which the long edge a is assumed here to be at least twice as long as the width b of the plate. An example of such a plate is described in Fig. 135b, in which a section of an I beam is shown loaded by a concentrated load at the edge of a lower flange, as sometimes occurs when an I beam is used to support the rollers of an overhead lift. MacGregor and Holl, using the theory of flexure of plates, have shown that the maximum transverse and longitudinal bending moments per unit of length (M_{be} and M_{ae}) at the fixed edge at a point directly opposite the location of the load P have the values

$$M_{be} = 0.51P \qquad M_{ae} = 0.15P \tag{265}$$

where M_{be} and M_{ae} are defined as in Table 9. The maximum deflection occurs at the load and is

$$\delta_{\max} = 2(1 - \mu^2)(Pb^2/Et^3) \tag{266}$$

Concentrated Load near Fixed Edge. In Fig. 135c the plate is shown with the load acting at a point near to the fixed edge and at the middle of the length a of the plate. In this location the load P produces a maximum bending moment per unit width at the fixed edge given by the expression

$$M_{be} = 0.31P \tag{267}$$

Thus, as the load P is moved from the unsupported edge of the plate across the plate to a point near the fixed edge, the maximum (transverse) bending moment M_{be} at the fixed edge decreases from $0.51P$ to

0.31P. If the load P approaches a concentrated load (distributed over a very small area) the bending moment (and hence the stresses) per unit of length on a section directly under the load may be much higher than the maximum value of 0.51P at the fixed edge, but these high stresses usually are not significant because of the local yielding, which can take place without damage to the plate as a whole. If, however,

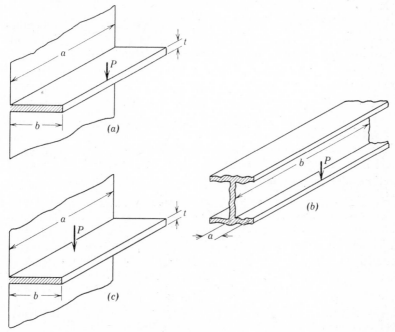

Fig. 135   Rectangular flat plate fixed on one edge and free on all others.

the length a is very long, as it is in the flange of the I beam in Fig. 135b, and if the load P moves along the free edge, such as the wheel load of a moving overhead lift supported by the I beam, the localized yielding which occurs at each point over which the load moves may result in large plastic distortion of the flange. Furthermore, when P is near the fixed edge, the contact stresses (see Chapter 11), due to the small area over which P acts, may combine with the high bending stresses at the fixed edge.

76 Deflection of rectangular plate; concentrated load at center. From the theory of flexure of plates the maximum deflection $\delta_{\max}$ of a rectangular plate subjected to a concentrated load P at the center is given by the equation

$$\delta_{\max} = C(1 - \mu^2)(Pb^2/Et^3) \tag{268}$$

in which P is the concentrated load at the center, b is the short span length, E is the modulus of elasticity of the material in the plate, t is the plate thickness, μ is Poisson's ratio, and C is a dimensionless constant whose value depends upon the ratio b/a of the sides of the plate and upon the type of support at the edges of the plate.

Square Plates. For a square plate with simply supported edges the constant in Eq. 268 is $C = 0.138$; with the four edges held rigidly (fixed), $C = 0.067$. However, the edges are rarely completely fixed, so that the significant value of C lies between 0.138 and 0.067. The value of C will depend upon the amount of restraint that exists at the edges; for instance, if the restraint is designated as 0.5 (which means that the slope at the edge of the plate is one-half as much as if the plate were simply supported), a value of C equal to the average of 0.138 and 0.067 ($C = 0.102$) will be used.

Experimenting on aluminum alloy plates with simply supported edges and with completely fixed edges, Sturm and Moore found very good agreement for small deflections between measured values of deflections and values computed by the use of Eq. 268 in which the foregoing values of C were used.

Other Types of Rectangular Plates. Formulas giving the values of the constant C in Eq. 268 for the deflection of rectangular plates are listed in Table 10. These formulas yield results that are very close to those found by use of the theory of flexure of plates. However, when the computed value of the deflection is more than about one-half the thickness of the plate, it is likely that this computed value is larger than the actual maximum deflection of the plate, since the direct tensile stresses which occur at the larger deflections will help the bending stresses resist the loads.

77 Stress in rectangular plate supported on two opposite edges by beams. *Uniformly Distributed Load.* In Fig. 136 is shown a rectangular flat plate simply supported along its two sides a by elastic (flexible) beams and simply supported along its two sides b by rigid foundations, as in one type of highway bridge slab where the curbs are equivalent to elastic beam supports. Let the load carried by this flat plate be uniformly distributed.

The deflection of the supporting beams causes the reactions on the plate to be smaller along the beams and to be larger along the rigid supports than would occur if all four edges were on rigid supports. As a result of this difference in the reactions, the bending moment at the center in span a is increased, and at the center in span b the moment is decreased.

For example, if the two beams are very light and slender and hence offer little or no resistance in supporting these two edges of the plate, the plate will be supported nearly wholly by the rigid foundations along the other two edges and thus act approximately as a simple beam. The moment per unit of width at the center of span a then would be $M_{ac} = wa^2/8$. If, on the other hand, the two beams are very stiff, these two edges may also be considered to be supported on rigid foundations. This type of plate has been considered in Art. 71, and the maximum moments per unit of width are given in Table 9. For example, if the plate is square, the moment per unit width at the center of span a is $M_{ac} = wa^2/24$. Thus, when all four edges of a square plate rest on rigid supports, the

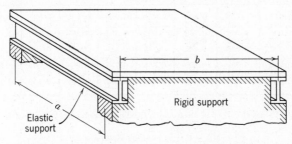

FIG. 136   Rectangular flat plate with two edges on elastic supports.

maximum bending moment is only one-third as much as when two edges are unsupported. When two edges are partially supported by elastic beams, the maximum bending moment will be between the values $wa^2/8$ and $wa^2/24$.

V. P. Jensen has shown (reference 2) by the use of the theory of flexure of plates that the bending moments in a plate supported as shown in Fig. 136 depend upon the ratio of the stiffness of the beams to the stiffness of the plate, the stiffness of the plate as used here being a measure of the tendency of the plate to transmit the load to the two beams. This ratio will be denoted by H. The stiffness of the beam is given by the expression EI, where E is the modulus of elasticity of the material in the beam and I is the moment of inertia of the cross section of the beam. The plate may be said to have two stiffnesses, that is, a stiffness in the direction of each span. The stiffness desired here is that related to the tendency of the plate to transmit the loads through the plate to the beams, since, as already noted, the deflection of the beams caused by these loads influences the bending moments in the plate. This action is of sufficient importance to discuss it further. Let it be assumed that the rigid supports are removed, in which case the plate would act as a simply supported beam of span length b transmitting all the load on the plate to the elastic beam supports. The stiffness of the

TABLE 11

RECTANGULAR PLATES SUPPORTED ON FLEXIBLE BEAMS ON TWO OPPOSITE EDGES AND ON RIGID SUPPORTS ON THE OTHER TWO EDGES (SEE FIG. 136). THE PLATE IS SUBJECTED TO A UNIFORMLY DISTRIBUTED LOAD w PER UNIT AREA.

(a) Values of C Used in Determining Bending Moment M_{ac} from Equation

$$M_{ac} = C\,\frac{wa^2}{8}\;;\;\text{Poisson's Ratio } \mu = 0.*$$

Values of b/a	Values of C								
	$H=0$	$H=0.05$	$H=0.10$	$H=0.20$	$H=0.50$	$H=1.0$	$H=2.0$	$H=4.0$	$H=\infty$
0.33	1.015	0.751	0.625	0.452	0.250	0.145	0.081	0.045	0.006
0.5	1.008	0.834	0.713	0.555	0.342	0.222	0.136	0.088	0.035
0.6	1.004	0.856	0.748	0.603	0.394	0.267	0.180	0.129	0.071
0.8	0.997	0.886	0.802	0.681	0.496	0.373	0.286	0.232	0.171
1.0	0.992	0.908	0.843	0.745	0.588	0.481	0.402	0.353	0.295
1.2	0.990	0.925	0.874	0.796	0.669	0.579	0.512	0.470	0.418
1.4	0.990	0.939	0.899	0.838	0.739	0.664	0.609	0.574	0.532
1.6	0.991	0.951	0.920	0.873	0.793	0.735	0.691	0.662	0.628
1.8	0.991	0.961	0.936	0.900	0.837	0.791	0.757	0.735	0.707

(b) Values of C Used in Determining Bending Moment M_{bc} from Equation

$$M_{bc} = C\,\frac{wa^2}{8}\;;\;\text{Poisson's Ratio } \mu = 0.*$$

Values of b/a	Values of C								
	$H=0$	$H=0.05$	$H=0.10$	$H=0.20$	$H=0.50$	$H=1.0$	$H=2.0$	$H=4.0$	$H=\infty$
0.33	−0.125	−0.052	−0.038	0.001	0.039	0.100	0.085	0.091	0.101
0.5	−0.098	−0.045	−0.009	0.037	0.101	0.138	0.167	0.177	0.197
0.6	−0.092	−0.032	+0.005	0.054	0.126	0.169	0.198	0.217	0.236
0.8	−0.055	−0.009	+0.026	0.076	0.152	0.203	0.239	0.262	0.287
1.0	−0.035	−0.060	+0.037	0.082	0.155	0.207	0.243	0.268	0.295
1.2	−0.021	+0.012	+0.039	0.080	0.145	0.192	0.227	0.250	0.275
1.4	−0.012	+0.016	+0.038	0.073	0.129	0.170	0.199	0.219	0.242
1.6	−0.007	+0.016	+0.035	0.063	0.110	0.144	0.170	0.186	0.206
1.8	−0.003	+0.016	+0.031	0.053	0.091	0.120	0.140	0.154	0.171

(c) Values of C Used in Determining Deflection at Center of Plate from Equation

$$\Delta = C(1 - \mu^2)\,\frac{wa^4}{Et^3}\;;\;\text{Poisson's Ratio } \mu = 0.15.$$

Values of b/a	Values of C								
	$H=0$	$H=0.05$	$H=0.10$	$H=0.20$	$H=0.50$	$H=1.0$	$H=2.0$	$H=4.0$	$H=\infty$
0.33	0.1591	0.1214	0.0983	0.0714	0.0398	0.0234	0.0135	0.0079	0.0019
0.5	0.1579	0.1310	0.1122	0.0879	0.0549	0.0358	0.0233	0.0160	0.0079
0.6	0.1573	0.1345	0.1180	0.0956	0.0636	0.0439	0.0307	0.0228	0.0140
0.8	0.1563	0.1394	0.1264	0.1080	0.0796	0.0609	0.0476	0.0395	0.0301
1.0	0.1557	0.1428	0.1327	0.1179	0.0940	0.0776	0.0656	0.0581	0.0493
1.2	0.1554	0.1455	0.1314	0.1258	0.1064	0.0927	0.0825	0.0761	0.0684
1.4	0.1553	0.1476	0.1415	0.1322	0.1167	0.1057	0.0974	0.0921	0.0856
1.6	0.1554	0.1495	0.1446	0.1374	0.1253	0.1165	0.1098	0.1056	0.1004
1.8	0.1556	0.1509	0.1473	0.1416	0.1321	0.1252	0.1200	0.1165	0.1125
2.0	0.1557	0.1521	0.1493	0.1449	0.1375	0.1321	0.1280	0.1253	0.1222
3.0	0.1565	0.1557	0.1551	0.1543	0.1528	0.1517	0.1509	0.1503	0.1496

TABLE 11 (*Continued*)

RECTANGULAR PLATES SUPPORTED ON FLEXIBLE BEAMS ON TWO OPPOSITE EDGES AND ON RIGID SUPPORTS ON THE OTHER TWO EDGES (SEE FIG. 136). THE PLATE IS SUBJECTED TO A UNIFORMLY DISTRIBUTED LOAD w PER UNIT AREA.

(d) Values of C Used in Determining Maximum Bending Moment in Flexible Beam Support (see Fig. 136) from Equation $M_{\text{beam}} = Cwa^3$; Poisson's Ratio $\mu = 0.15$.

Values of b/a	Values of C								
	$H=0$	$H=0.05$	$H=0.10$	$H=0.20$	$H=0.50$	$H=1.0$	$H=2.0$	$H=4.0$	$H=\infty$
0.33	0	0.0033	0.0052	0.0076	0.0103	0.0117	0.0126	0.0131	0.0134
0.5	0	0.0040	0.0067	0.0103	0.0152	0.0180	0.0199	0.0210	0.0217
0.6	0	0.0055	0.0095	0.0150	0.0228	0.0276	0.0308	0.0328	0.0349
0.8	0	0.0057	0.0101	0.0164	0.0261	0.0325	0.0370	0.0398	0.0430
1.0	0	0.0058	0.0104	0.0172	0.0282	0.0357	0.0412	0.0446	0.0487
1.2	0	0.0059	0.0106	0.0177	0.0294	0.0376	0.0438	0.0477	0.0524
1.4	0	0.0059	0.0107	0.0179	0.0301	0.0388	0.0454	0.0496	0.0546
1.6	0	0.0060	0.0108	0.0181	0.0305	0.0395	0.0463	0.0507	0.0560
1.8	0	0.0060	0.0108	0.0182	0.0308	0.0399	0.0469	0.0514	0.0568
2.0	0	0.0060	0.0108	0.0182	0.0309	0.0402	0.0472	0.0518	0.0573
∞	0	0.0060	0.0109	0.0183	0.0311	0.0405	0.0477	0.0523	0.0579

(e) Values of C Used in Determining Maximum Deflection of Flexible Beam Support from Equation

$$\Delta = C(1 - \mu^2)\frac{wa^4}{Et^3}\text{; Poisson's Ratio } \mu = \tfrac{1}{4}.$$

Values of b/a	Values of C								
	$H=0$	$H=0.05$	$H=0.10$	$H=0.20$	$H=0.50$	$H=1.0$	$H=2.0$	$H=4.0$	$H=10.0$
0.33	0.146	0.1265	0.1013	0.0724	0.0390	0.0221	0.0118	0.0061	0.0049
0.5	0.170	0.1381	0.1162	0.0882	0.0512	0.0301	0.0165	0.0087	0.0070
0.6	0.172	0.1425	0.1220	0.0947	0.0567	0.0340	0.0189	0.0100	0.0081
0.8	0.174	0.1482	0.1296	0.1037	0.0648	0.0398	0.0225	0.0120	0.0098
1.0	0.175	0.1515	0.1341	0.1090	0.0698	0.0436	0.0249	0.0134	0.0109
1.2	0.175	0.1534	0.1366	0.1121	0.0728	0.0460	0.0265	0.0143	0.0117
1.4	0.176	0.1546	0.1382	0.1140	0.0747	0.0474	0.0274	0.0149	0.0121
1.6	0.176	0.1553	0.1391	0.1150	0.0757	0.0482	0.0280	0.0152	0.0124
1.8	0.176	0.1557	0.1396	0.1156	0.0763	0.0487	0.0283	0.0154	0.0125
2.0	0.176	0.1559	0.1399	0.1160	0.0767	0.0490	0.0285	0.0155	0.0126
3.0	0.189	0.1562	0.1403	0.1165	0.0772	0.0494	0.0287	0.0156	0.0127

* The values of M_{ac} and M_{bc} for any value of μ may be found by using Eq. 260.

plate then would be $E_1 I_1$, where E_1 is the modulus of elasticity of the material in the plate and $I_1 = \frac{1}{12}at^3$ is the moment of inertia of the cross section of the plate considered as a beam supported only by the two elastic beams. But the plate actually bends in all directions, and this fact makes it necessary to correct this stiffness by dividing by the quantity $1 - \mu^2$. Therefore the stiffness of the plate is $E_1 I_1/(1 - \mu^2)$. The ratio H, then, is

$$H = (1 - \mu^2)(EI/E_1 I_1) \tag{269}$$

The significant values of bending moments per unit width in the plate occur at the center of the plate. Values of these bending moments may be found by using Table 11a and b in which M_{ac} is the moment per unit width in span a and M_{ac} is the corresponding value for span b. Table 11c gives values of the maximum deflection of the plate. Table 11d gives the maximum bending moment in the elastic beam support, which occurs at the mid-point of the beam. Table 11e gives the maximum deflection of the elastic beam support which also occurs at its mid-point.

Central Concentrated Load. In Tables 12a and 12b are given values of the bending moments M_{bc} and M_{ac} at the center of a plate supported as shown in Fig. 136 and loaded by a central (concentrated) load distributed

TABLE 12

RECTANGULAR PLATES SUPPORTED ON FLEXIBLE BEAMS ON TWO OPPOSITE EDGES AND ON RIGID SUPPORTS ON THE OTHER TWO EDGES (SEE FIG. 136). THE PLATE IS SUBJECTED TO A CONCENTRATED LOAD P AT CENTER WHICH IS UNIFORMLY DISTRIBUTED OVER A CIRCLE WHOSE DIAMETER * IS $d_0 = a/4$.

(a) Values of C Used in Determining Bending Moment M_{ac} from Equation
$M_{ac} = CP$; Poisson's Ratio $\mu = 0$.

Values of b/a	Values of C								
	$H=0$	$H=0.05$	$H=0.10$	$H=0.20$	$H=0.50$	$H=1.0$	$H=2.0$	$H=4.0$	$H=\infty$
0.33	0.686	0.521	0.421	0.305	0.171	0.101	0.060	0.037	0.010
0.5	0.468	0.396	0.348	0.284	0.200	0.148	0.119	0.100	0.080
0.6	0.398	0.350	0.314	0.268	0.202	0.161	0.133	0.117	0.098
0.8	0.318	0.292	0.274	0.246	0.204	0.176	0.158	0.145	0.132
1.0	0.274	0.260	0.249	0.232	0.207	0.189	0.176	0.168	0.159
1.2	0.248	0.242	0.236	0.225	0.209	0.198	0.190	0.184	0.177
1.4	0.235	0.230	0.225	0.220	0.210	0.204	0.198	0.195	0.199
1.6	0.225	0.223	0.221	0.217	0.211	0.207	0.204	0.202	0.200
1.8	0.220	0.218	0.217	0.215	0.211	0.208	0.207	0.205	0.204
2.0	0.217	0.216	0.215	0.214	0.211	0.210	0.209	0.208	0.207
3.0	0.212	0.212	0.212	0.212	0.212	0.212	0.212	0.212	0.212

(b) Values of C Used in Determining Bending Moment M_{bc} from Equation
$M_{bc} = CP$; Poisson's Ratio $\mu = 0$.

Values of b/a	Values of C								
	$H=0$	$H=0.05$	$H=0.10$	$H=0.20$	$H=0.50$	$H=1.0$	$H=2.0$	$H=4.0$	$H=\infty$
0.33	−0.0185	0.0276	0.0553	0.0864	0.124	0.142	0.154	0.160	0.168
0.5	0.0307	0.0522	0.0687	0.0870	0.114	0.130	0.139	0.144	0.151
0.6	0.0543	0.0717	0.0840	0.101	0.124	0.138	0.147	0.163	0.160
0.8	0.0850	0.0963	0.104	0.117	0.135	0.144	0.152	0.158	0.164
1.0	0.103	0.111	0.116	0.123	0.135	0.143	0.149	0.153	0.159
1.2	0.114	0.118	0.121	0.126	0.134	0.140	0.144	0.147	0.150
1.4	0.120	0.123	0.125	0.128	0.133	0.137	0.140	0.142	0.144
1.6	0.123	0.126	0.127	0.129	0.132	0.135	0.136	0.138	0.139
1.8	0.127	0.127	0.129	0.130	0.132	0.134	0.135	0.135	0.136
2.0	0.129	0.130	0.130	0.131	0.132	0.133	0.134	0.135	0.135
3.0	0.131	0.131	0.131	0.131	0.131	0.131	0.131	0.131	0.131

* In Table 11a and 11b, if d_0 is less than $a/4$, a correction of $0.17P \left(\frac{1}{4} - \frac{d_0}{a} \right) \Big/ \left(\frac{1}{4} + \frac{1}{2} \frac{d_0}{a} \right)$ must be added to both M_{ac} and M_{bc}. Also, the values of M_{ac} and M_{bc} for any value of μ are found from Eq. 260.

TABLE 12 (*Continued*)

(c) Values of C Used in Determining Maximum Deflection at Center of Plate from Equation

$$\Delta = C(1 - \mu^2)\frac{Pa^2}{Et^3} \text{ ; Poisson's Ratio } \mu = 0.15.$$

Values of b/a	Values of C								
	$H=0$	$H=0.05$	$H=0.10$	$H=0.20$	$H=0.50$	$H=1.0$	$H=2.0$	$H=4.0$	$H=\infty$
0.33	0.7593	0.5810	0.4718	0.3449	0.1957	0.1187	0.0718	0.0456	0.0174
0.5	0.5076	0.4250	0.3677	0.2932	0.1925	0.1340	0.0958	0.0736	0.0489
0.6	0.4264	0.3693	0.3280	0.2720	0.1910	0.1429	0.1098	0.0902	0.0689
0.8	0.3305	0.3004	0.2774	0.2446	0.1942	0.1610	0.1374	0.1230	0.1063
1.0	0.2789	0.2619	0.2485	0.2290	0.1975	0.1758	0.1600	0.1501	0.1385
1.2	0.2491	0.2391	0.2312	0.2195	0.2000	0.1863	0.1761	0.1696	0.1619
1.4	0.2312	0.2253	0.2206	0.2135	0.2016	0.1930	0.1866	0.1826	0.1776
1.6	0.2202	0.2167	0.2139	0.2096	0.2024	0.1972	0.1932	0.1907	0.1877
1.8	0.2135	0.2114	0.2097	0.2071	0.2028	0.1996	0.1972	0.1957	0.1938
2.0	0.2093	0.2081	0.2071	0.2055	0.2029	0.2010	0.1996	0.1887	0.1975
3.0	0.2031	0.2030	0.2030	0.2029	0.2028	0.2027	0.2027	0.2026	0.2026

(d) Values of C Used in Determining Maximum Bending Moment in Flexible Beam Support

(see Fig. 136) from Equation $M_\text{beam} = C\dfrac{Pa}{4}$; Poisson's Ratio $\mu = 0.15.$

Values of b/a	Values of C								
	$H=0$	$H=0.05$	$H=0.10$	$H=0.20$	$H=0.50$	$H=1.0$	$H=2.0$	$H=4.0$	$H=\infty$
0.33	0	0.105	0.169	0.242	0.328	0.372	0.399	0.413	0.423
0.5	0	0.072	0.122	0.185	0.271	0.320	0.352	0.371	0.383
0.6	0	0.060	0.103	0.161	0.242	0.292	0.325	0.345	0.368
0.8	0	0.043	0.076	0.122	0.193	0.240	0.273	0.293	0.316
1.0	0	0.032	0.057	0.094	0.153	0.193	0.223	0.241	0.263
1.2	0	0.024	0.044	0.073	0.120	0.154	0.179	0.195	0.213
1.4	0	0.019	0.033	0.057	0.094	0.121	0.142	0.155	0.170
1.6	0	0.015	0.026	0.044	0.074	0.095	0.111	0.121	0.134
1.8	0	0.011	0.020	0.034	0.057	0.074	0.087	0.095	0.104

(e) Values of C Used in Determining Maximum Deflection of Flexible Beam Support from Equation

$$\Delta = C(1 - \mu^2)\frac{Pa^2}{Et^3} \text{ ; Poisson's Ratio } \mu = 0.15.$$

Values of b/a	Values of C								
	$H=0$	$H=0.05$	$H=0.10$	$H=0.20$	$H=0.50$	$H=1.0$	$H=2.0$	$H=4.0$	$H=\infty$
0.33	0.7641	0.5805	0.4681	0.3375	0.1837	0.1044	0.0558	0.0291	0
0.5	0.5008	0.4104	0.3477	0.2664	0.1565	0.0928	0.0511	0.0269	0
0.6	0.4110	0.3454	0.2979	0.2336	0.1412	0.0857	0.0479	0.0254	0
0.8	0.2937	0.2541	0.2240	0.1810	0.1150	0.0715	0.0407	0.0219	0
1.0	0.2189	0.1923	0.1715	0.1409	0.0919	0.0582	0.0335	0.0182	0
1.2	0.1665	0.1475	0.1324	0.1098	0.0727	0.0465	0.0271	0.0150	0
1.4	0.1278	0.1137	0.1024	0.0855	0.0571	0.0368	0.0215	0.0117	0
1.6	0.0985	0.0879	0.0793	0.0664	0.0446	0.0288	0.0169	0.0092	0
1.8	0.0760	0.0679	0.0614	0.0515	0.0347	0.0235	0.0142	0.0082	0
2.0	0.0596	0.0534	0.0484	0.0408	0.0279	0.0194	0.0112	0.0066	0
3.0	0.0156	0.0140	0.0126	0.0106	0.0072	0.0047	0.0027	0.0015	0

over a small circular area of diameter d_0. Table 12c gives the value of the maximum deflection of the plate, which occurs at its center. Table 12d gives the value of the maximum bending moment in the elastic beam support, which occurs at the mid-point of the beam. Table 12e gives the maximum deflection of the elastic beam support, which also occurs at the mid-point. It will be noted that, in Tables 11c and 11d and 12c, 12d, and 12e, values of $\mu = 0.15$ for the plate have been used in computing the values of the constant C, whereas in Table 11e, $\mu = 0.25$. However, the effect on the deflection of changing the value of μ is small so that the values of C in these tables may be used for a plate having any value of μ.

Problems

145. A rectangular plate of steel is 72 in. square and ¾ in. thick. Two opposite edges are simply supported on a rigid foundation (see Fig. 136), and the other two edges are supported on 3-in. I beams of steel. ($I = 2.71$ in.[4], and the section modulus $I/c = 1.81$ in.[3]) The plate supports a uniformly distributed load of 4 lb per sq in.

Assume that $E = 30{,}000{,}000$ lb per sq in. and $\mu = \frac{1}{4}$. Compute the following quantities:

    (a) The maximum bending stress in the plate.   *Ans.*   15,000 lb per sq in.
    (b) The maximum deflection of the plate.   *Ans.*   0.62 in.
    (c) The maximum bending stress in the beams.   *Ans.*   29,000 lb per sq in.
    (d) The maximum deflection of the beams.   *Ans.*   0.35 in.

146. Solve Prob. 145, assuming that the 3-in. I beams are removed, leaving these two edges unsupported. *Hint*: The value of $H = 0$, since the value of EI for elastic beam, which is not present, is zero.

    Ans.   (a) 27,200 lb per sq in.   (b) 1.25 in.   (c) deflection of plate at edge 1.4 in.

147. Solve Prob. 145, assuming that all four edges are simply supported on rigid foundations. *Hint*: The value of $H = \infty$, since the value of EI for the rigid beam is assumed to be indefinitely large.   *Ans.*   (a) 10,200 lb per sq in.   (b) 0.39 in.

78   Continuous plate divided into square panels by circular supports.

Let a flat plate such as a flat slab floor attached to circular columns, or a flat steel plate stayed by rods and reinforced where each rod is attached to the plate by a circular disk or washer welded to the plate, be subjected to a uniformly distributed load; and let the supports be placed so that the plate is divided into square panels, the distance between centers of supports measured along the side of the square being L (Fig. 137).

The equilibrium of a quarter-panel (Figs. 137 and 138) will be considered. We wish to find the bending moment at the circular section A (Fig. 137) adjoining the support, also at each of the central sections C and D between the supports, and at each of the sections B and E joining the centers of the supports. The following simple method yielding approximate results is due to J. R. Nichols (reference 5). The assumption will be made that the shearing stress on the section A is uniformly distributed; the error, if any, in this assumption will have only a small effect on the results. The assumption is also made that the shearing stresses on the other four boundary sections are negligible. The forces acting on the quarter-panel are then as shown in Fig. 138, in which the resultant load on the quarter-panel considered is denoted by R_1. From the condition of equilibrium, the resultant R_2 of vertical shearing forces on section A is equal and opposite to R_1.

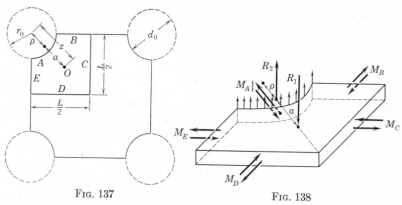

FIG. 137   FIG. 138

The bending moment applied to the plate is the moment of the couple consisting of the forces R_1 and R_2. This moment is

$$M = R_1 a \tag{270}$$

where a is the distance between the action lines of R_1 and R_2. Further, this moment is held in equilibrium by the resisting moments at the sections A, B, C, D, and E. Values of R_1 and a will now be found. It is evident that the magnitude of R_1 is

$$R_1 = \tfrac{1}{4}w(L^2 - \pi r_0^2) \tag{271}$$

and that it acts through the centroid of the top area of the plate at the distance z from the center line of the support. The value of z is found by the principle of moments of areas to be

$$z = \frac{[(L^3/16) - (r_0^3/3)]\sqrt{2}}{\tfrac{1}{4}(L^2 - \pi r_0^2)} \tag{272}$$

The resultant R_2 of the shearing forces on section A acts at the centroid of the circular line of section A which is at the distance ρ from the center of support; the value of ρ is

$$\rho = (2r_0/\pi)\sqrt{2} \tag{273}$$

The expression for a may be found from

$$a = z - \rho \tag{274}$$

Substituting the expressions for R_1 and a in Eq. 270, we find

$$M = R_1 a = w\sqrt{2}[(L^3/16) - (L^2 r_0/2\pi) + (r_0^3/6)] \tag{275}$$

$$M = wL^3(\sqrt{2}/16)[1 - 2.55(r_0/L) + 2.67(r_0^3/L^3)] \tag{276}$$

This moment is held in equilibrium by the resisting moments at the five edges of the plate. The component of the applied bending moment or couple in a plane perpendicular to each straight edge of the quarter panel is

$$M_x = M \cos 45° = wL^3/16[1 - 2.55(r_0/L) + 2.67(r_0^3/L^3)] \tag{277}$$

and the bending moment perpendicular to one whole side of the panel is $2M_x$; let this moment be denoted by M_0, then

$$M_0 = (wL^3/8)[1 - 2.55(r_0/L) + 2.67(r_0^3/L^3)] \tag{278}$$

But this may be shown to be approximately equal to the following relatively simple expression, where $d_0 = 2r_0$,

$$M_0 = (WL/8)[1 - \tfrac{2}{3}(d_0/L)]^2 \tag{279}$$

in which W is the total load on the square panel.

From the conditions of equilibrium, the algebraic sum of all the components of the moments acting on the quarter panel (Fig. 138) perpendicular to each edge must be equal to zero. Hence

$$M_x = M_B + M_D + M_A \cos 45°$$

or for one *whole side* this may be written

$$M_0 = 2(M_B + M_D + M_A \cos 45°) \tag{280}$$

Similarly $\qquad M_0 = 2(M_E + M_C + M_A \cos 45°)$

And from symmetry $\quad M_B = M_E \quad$ and $\quad M_C = M_D$

But the values of M_B, M_D, and M_A cannot be found from these equations of statics alone; in other words, the problem is statically indeterminate, and, even if these mean values of M_A, M_B, and M_D could be found from the conditions of equilibrium alone, the variation of the moment along each edge would still be unknown.

From the results of his own investigations using the theory of flexure and from those of several other investigators, Westergaard found the following values for the moments per unit width across the sections indicated in Fig. 139. The average moment per unit width for one

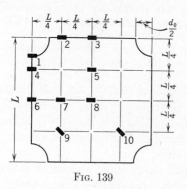

FIG. 139

whole side is M_0/L, and the moment per unit width at the sections designated is

$$\text{Moment per unit width} = k(M_0/L) = k\tfrac{1}{8}w(L - \tfrac{2}{3}d_0)^2 \quad (281)$$

in which k has the following values, where $q = d_0/L$.

Section	Values of k for $q = 0.15$ to 0.30
1	$-0.2\left(\dfrac{1}{q} + 4\right)$
2	$-0.5 - 1.5q^2$
3	-0.028
4	$0.23 - 4.5q^2$
5	0.02
6	0.46
7	0.34
8	0.25
9	$0.23 - 1.8q^2$
10	$0.125 - 0.50q^2$

Flat Plate Supported at Points. The following formula, given by Unwin, has been used widely for the stress in flat plates supported at points which divide the plate in equal square panels, such as stayed flat plates in boiler heads, etc.,

$$\sigma = \tfrac{2}{9}(a^2/t^2)w \quad (282)$$

where σ = stress, pounds per square inch.
   t = thickness of plate, inches.
   a = distance between points of support in any row, inches.
   w = uniformly distributed load, pounds per square inch.

Problem

148. A flat steel plate ½ in. thick is stayed by steel rods, the points of attachment dividing the plate into square panels 2 ft on each side. The plate at the points of attachment are reinforced with circular washers welded to the plate. The washers are ¾ in. thick and 8 in. in diameter. Find the maximum allowable gas pressure for such a plate, assuming a working stress of 14,000 lb per sq in.

79   Stress in elliptical plate.

An expression giving an approximate value for the maximum stress in an elliptical plate may be found by writing an expression that will satisfy the values for the stresses in the two limiting forms of an elliptical plate, namely, a circular plate and a very long narrow strip.

Let an elliptical plate have major and minor axes of $2a$ and $2b$, respectively, and let it be simply supported around the edge and be subjected to a uniform load of w per unit area.

If the plate is very long and narrow, it may be regarded as a simple beam of span $2b$, and hence the maximum moment per unit width is $\frac{1}{2}wb^2$; therefore, the maximum stress in the plate is

$$\sigma = \frac{Mc}{I} = \frac{\frac{1}{2}wb^2 \times (t/2)}{\frac{1}{12}t^3} = 3w\frac{b^2}{t^2} \tag{283}$$

If the plate is circular, its radius is b and the maximum stress is $\sigma = w(b^2/t^2)$ (see Eq. 246). The general expression for the maximum stress may be assumed, therefore, to be

$$\sigma = kw(b^2/t^2) \tag{284}$$

in which $k = 1$ when $b/a = 1$, and $k = 3$ when $b/a = 0$. A continuous relation for k that satisfies these conditions is

$$k = 3 - 2(b/a) \tag{285}$$

which may be used for approximate results. Hence

$$\sigma = \frac{(3a - 2b)}{a} w \frac{b^2}{t^2} \tag{286}$$

The maximum stress is in the direction of the shorter axis.

Fixed Edges. Expressions for bending moments per unit width in elliptical plates as found from the theory of flexure of slabs are given in Table 9. The remarks in Art. 75 concerning fixed-ended plates and redistribution of stress after slight yielding occurs applies also in general to elliptical plates with fixed edges.

Problem

149. A cast-iron manhole cover consists of a flat plate and is elliptical in form. It covers an opening 3 ft long and 1½ ft wide. If the plate is ¾ in. thick, what uniform pressure is it designed to resist if a working stress of 2500 lb per sq in. is used?

§ 3 Plates in Which Bending and Direct Tension Are Significant Large Deflections

80 Plate behavior when deflections are large. In Section 2 it was assumed that the maximum deflection of the plate was relatively small and hence that the direct tensile stresses in the plate were negligible. For some flat plates which are relatively thin, a maximum deflection which is equal to several thicknesses of the plate may still be relatively small as compared to the other dimensions of the plate; furthermore, the maximum stresses in thin plates subjected to such relatively large deflections may still be within the elastic strength of the material. Under these conditions the resistance of the plate to loads is greatly increased by the direct tensile stresses which begin to have a significant influence in resisting the loads (in addition to the bending stresses) when the maximum deflection exceeds about one-half the thickness of the plate. In many applications of flat plates, especially for relatively thin plates, maximum deflections equal to several thicknesses of the plate may be permitted without causing interference with the structural (load-resisting) use of the plate. The analysis of plates given in the foregoing sections of this chapter take into account the bending stresses only and therefore take into account only a part of the maximum utilizable strength of relatively thin plates. In this section methods are given for including the additional load resistance of plates arising from the direct tensile stresses in the plate.

Method of Analysis. The procedure for obtaining the stresses and deflections of a plate subjected to loads which cause relatively large elastic deflections is very similar to that described in Art. 67. The differential equation of the plate is derived so that the effects of the direct tensile stress are included in addition to the bending stress. The method of deriving and solving these differential equations may be found in reference 8 at the end of this chapter and will not be included in this discussion. The results for only a few types of plates are presented here, mainly to give some idea of the magnitudes of the additional resistance to loads which may be expected from the direct tensile stresses.

Caution: The conditions of support at the edges of a plate (simply supported, clamped, etc.) have a large influence on the load resistance which is contributed by the direct tensile stresses in the plate. If full advantage is to be made of the direct tensile stresses, it is necessary that the edges of the plate be very securely clamped and fixed. In a plate which is simply supported at its edges there are no direct tensile stresses *at the edge.* However, at all other points of the plate there *are* direct tensile stresses, increasing with the distance from the edge, which can develop because of the compressive stresses in a circumferential direction near the edges of the plate. Evidence of these compressive stresses is seen in the buckling or wrinkling of the plate near the edges, which sometimes occurs. The direct tensile stresses near the center of a plate which is simply supported at the edge are of such magnitude as to add considerable load resistance to the plate, though, of course, not so much as would occur if the edges were fixed.

81   Circular plate with large elastic deflections; edges clamped. *Load Uniformly Distributed.* In Fig. 140*a* is shown a circular plate whose edge is clamped so that rotation and radial displacement are prevented at the edge. The plate has radius r and thickness t and is loaded by a uniformly distributed load w per unit of area that causes a maximum deflection which is large relative to the thickness of the plate as shown in Fig. 140*c*. In Fig. 140*d* a diametral strip of one unit width is shown cut from the plate to show the bending moments per unit of width and the direct tensile forces which act in this strip at the edge and at the center of the plate. The direct tensile forces arise from two sources: first, the fixed support at the edge prevents the edge at opposite ends of a diametral strip from moving radially, thereby causing the strip to stretch as it deflects. Second, if the plate is not clamped at its edge but is simply supported as shown in Figs. 140*e* and 140*f*, radial stresses arise out of the tendency for outer concentric rings of the plate such as shown in Fig. 140*h* to retain their original diameter as the plate deflects. In Fig. 140*h* the concentric ring at the outer edge is shown cut from the plate. This ring tends to retain the original outside diameter of the unloaded plate; the radial tensile stresses acting on the inside of the ring as shown in Fig. 140*h* cause the ring diameter to decrease, and in doing so they introduce compressive stresses on every diametral section such as xx. These compressive stresses in the circumferential direction sometimes cause the plate to wrinkle or buckle near the edge, particularly if the plate is simply supported. The radial stresses are usually larger in the central portion of the plate than near the edge.

Thus when the plate is deflected more than about one-half the thickness there are direct tensile stresses in addition to bending stresses; as will be found later, the significant values of these stresses occur either at the edge or at the center of the plate. Let the bending stresses in a radial plane at the edge and center of the plate be designated by σ_{be} and σ_{bc},

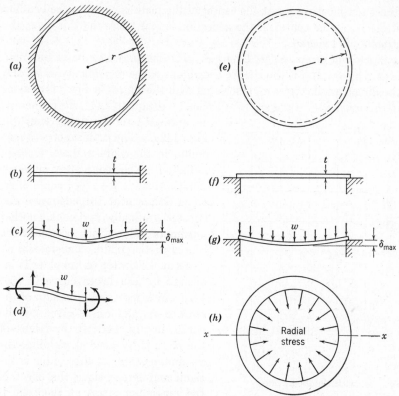

FIG. 140 Thin plates having large deflections in which direct tension is significant.

respectively, and let the corresponding direct tensile stresses be σ_{te} and σ_{tc}, respectively. Values of these stresses for a plate having a radius r and thickness t and made of a material having a modulus of elasticity E have been determined by the methods described in Art. 67 and are given in Fig. 141. In Fig. 141 the ordinates are values of the stress multiplied by the quantity r^2/Et^2 (to make dimensionless ordinates), and the abscissas are values of the maximum deflection δ_{max} divided by the thickness t (See reference 8.) It will be noted that the dimensionless ordinates and abscissas make it possible to use the curves for plates of any dimensions, provided that other conditions are the same. It will be noted that the bending stress σ_{be} at the fixed edge is the largest of these four stresses. The direct tensile stresses, though small for small deflections (deflections less than about one-half the plate thickness), become relatively much larger as the deflection increases. For example, if the deflection is equal to twice the plate thickness, the direct tensile stress σ_{tc} at the center of the plate is equal to the bending stress σ_{bc} at the center; if the deflection is four times the thickness, the stress σ_{tc} is twice σ_{bc}.

Significant Stress; Edges Clamped. The maximum stress in the plate is at the edge and is the sum of the values of the bending stress σ_{be} and the direct tensile stress σ_{te} associated with the curves in Fig. 141; values of this maximum stress σ_{max} multiplied by the quantity r^2/Et^2 are shown

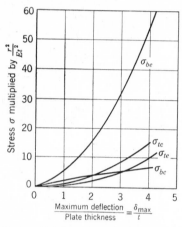

FIG. 141 Stresses in thin plates having large deflections; circular plate with clamped edges.

as ordinates to the upper curve in Fig. 142a. The values of σ_{max} at points in the plate a short distance radially from the edge are very much smaller than at the edge; a minimum value occurs near the edge, and the stresses gradually approach another maximum value which occurs at the center of the plate. The maximum stress at the center of the plate is indicated by the lower curve in Fig. 142a which represents the sum of the stresses σ_{bc} and σ_{tc} as given by the curves in Fig. 141. If the failure of the plate is by general yielding, the maximum stress at the center is the significant stress, since the effect of the maximum stress at the edge is localized. However, if the failure of the plate is by progressive fracture resulting from repeated applications of loads, or if the plate is made of brittle material and hence fails by sudden fracture under static loads, the stress at the edge would be the significant stress.

Load on Plate; Edges Clamped. In Fig. 142b the values of the load w on the plate with fixed edges multiplied by the quantity r^4/Et^4 are represented as ordinates, and maximum deflections divided by the plate thickness are abscissas, thus giving a dimensionless curve. The dashed line represents values of load and maximum deflection as computed by neglecting the effect of direct tensile stresses. A significant increase in the load w is indicated by the upward trend of the curve above the straight line for deflections larger than about one-half the plate thickness, which shows that the plate is much stronger than is indicated by the analysis in which the strength contributed by the direct tensile stress is neglected.

The relation between the load w and the stresses in the plate is obtained by using Figs. 142a and 142b jointly. For example, if the dimensions and the modulus of elasticity of the plate and the load w are given, the quantity wr^4/Et^4 can be computed. In Fig. 142b the abscissa δ_{max}/t corresponding to this value of wr^4/Et^4 is found from the curve. The value of δ_{max}/t thus found is now used as the abscissa in Fig. 142a, and the stress at the center or the edge of the plate is found by reading

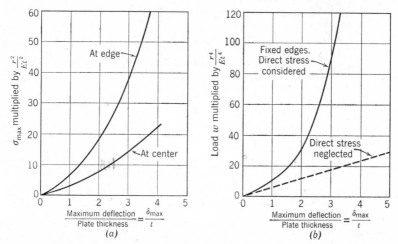

FIG. 142 Maximum stresses and deflections in thin plates having large deflections; circular plate with clamped edges.

the ordinate corresponding to this abscissa to the appropriate curve in Fig. 142a and dividing it by r^2/Et^2. This procedure is used in the following illustrative problem.

Illustrative Problem

Problem 150. A circular plate of aluminum alloy is 20 in. in diameter and 0.2 in. thick. The plate is subjected to a uniformly distributed load w lb per sq in. and is fixed at its edge. If the maximum utilizable strength of the plate is assumed to be the load that causes a significant tensile stress equal to the tensile yield strength of the material which is 40,000 lb per sq in., determine the magnitude of the load w which will develop not more than one-half the maximum utilizable strength of the plate, and also compute the maximum deflection corresponding to this (allowable) load w. The modulus of elasticity of the aluminum alloy is $E = 10,000,000$ lb per sq in.

Solution. It is noted in Fig. 142 that neither the load w nor the stress σ is directly proportional to the deflections; likewise, the stress σ at the edge or at the center of the plate is not directly proportional to the load w. We must therefore apply the reduction factor (factor of safety) to the load rather than to the stress (see Art. 2 in Chapter 1).

Under the conditions stated in the problem it may be assumed that the failure of the plate will be by general yielding which will occur soon after the maximum stress at the center of the plate reaches the yield strength of the material. We therefore seek the value of the load w which will cause a stress of 40,000 lb per sq in. at the center of the plate; this value of w will then be reduced by the factor 2.

We compute the quantity

$$\frac{\sigma r^2}{Et^2} = \frac{40,000 \times (10)^2}{10,000,000 \times (0.2)^2} = 10$$

and use this value as an ordinate in Fig. 142a to the curve for σ_{max} at the center of the plate and obtain the corresponding abscissa $\delta_{max}/t = 2.4$. We use the abscissa 2.4 in Fig. 142b and find that the corresponding ordinate to the curve is $wr^4/Et^4 = 50$. Hence

$$\frac{w(10)^4}{10,000,000 \times (0.2)^4} = 50$$

$$w = 80 \text{ lb/in.}^2$$

This value of w represents the maximum load that the plate will withstand without yielding over a considerable portion of the plate. Therefore one-half of w or 40 lb per sq in. is considered as one-half the maximum utilizable strength of the plate.

For finding the maximum deflection we first compute the quantity $\frac{wr^4}{Et^4} = \frac{40 \times 10^4}{10,000,000 \times (0.2)^4} = 25$. In Fig. 142b we find that the abscissa $\delta_{max}/t = 1.8$ corresponds to this ordinate. Therefore the deflection $\delta_{max} = 1.8t = 0.36$ in.

Problems

151. A circular opening in the flat end of a pressure vessel is 10 in. in diameter. A circular plate 0.1 in. thick made of a steel which has a tensile yield point of 35,000 lb per sq in. is used as a cover for the opening, and when in place over the opening has its edge securely clamped so that its edge may be considered fixed. Compute the maximum internal pressure for the vessel if the pressure must not exceed one third the pressure which will cause the cover plate to fail by general yielding.

Ans. $w = 14$ lb/in.^{2}.

152. A circular plate whose diameter is 10 in. is made of an aluminum alloy whose tensile yield strength 40,000 lb per sq in. The plate is to have its edge fixed and is to be subjected to a uniformly distributed load $w = 6$ lb per sq in. Compute the required thickness of the plate so that the load $w = 6$ lb per sq in. is two-thirds of the maximum load which the plate will withstand without any yielding at any place in the plate.

Hint: In this plate the maximum stress at the edge of the plate is the significant stress since no yielding of the plate is permitted. Use Figs. 142a and 142b, solving for t by trial and error, using a value of $w = \frac{3}{2} \times 6 = 9$ lb per sq in., and $\sigma = 40,000$ lb per sq in.   *Ans.* $t = 0.05$ in.

82 Circular plate with large elastic deflections; edges simply supported. *Load Uniformly Distributed.* In Art. 81 it was found that, when the edge of a circular plate as shown in Fig. 140 is fixed and the plate is subjected to a uniformly distributed load, there exist direct

radial tensile stresses in addition to the bending stresses. If a circular plate has its edge simply supported instead of fixed, the direct tensile stresses have somewhat smaller magnitudes, but they are still very effective in increasing the load resistance of the plate, particularly when the deflections are large relative to the thickness of the plate.

In Fig. 143a the ordinates to the curve marked σ_{tc} represent the direct tensile stresses at the center of the simply supported plate where these

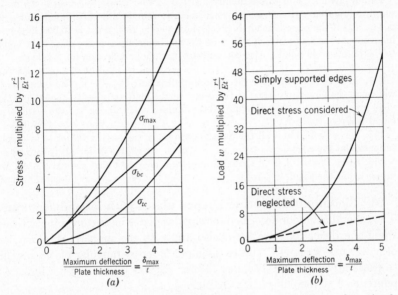

FIG. 143   Stresses in thin circular plates having large deflections; edges simply supported.

stresses are a maximum, and the ordinates to the curve marked σ_{bc} represent the bending stresses at the center of the plate which also have a maximum value at the center. The coordinates to the curves in Fig. 143a and b have the same meaning as those for Figs. 142a and 142b for a plate whose edge is fixed. In Fig. 143a the ordinates to the curve marked σ_{max} represent the sum of the stresses σ_{tc} and σ_{bc} which occur on the tensile side of the plate at the center. In Fig. 143b the curve represents the relation between the load and the maximum deflection, and the dashed line represents this relationship if the direct tensile stresses are neglected in the analysis. The solid curve in Fig. 143b, which rises above the dashed line when the maximum deflection becomes greater than one-half to one times the thickness of the plate, shows the influence of the direct tensile stress in increasing the elastic load resistance, especially of relatively thin plates for which the deflections are likely to be large in comparison with the thickness. Figures 143a and 143b are used in solving problems in a manner similar to the use of Figs. 142a and 142b as described in Art. 81.

Problems

153. A circular plate whose diameter is 100 in. and whose thickness is 0.5 in. is simply supported at its edge and is subjected to a uniformly distributed load w lb per sq in. If the plate is made of steel whose tensile yield point is 30,000 lb per sq in., compute the load w which will cause the maximum stress in the plate to be equal to the tensile yield point. Also compute the maximum deflection for this load.

Ans. $w = 7.2$ lb/in.^{2}; $\delta_{max} = 1.82$ in.

154. In Prob. 153 solve for the uniformly distributed load w on the plate which will cause the maximum stress at the center of the plate to be equal to one-half the yield point stress. Is the value of w thus obtained equal to one-half the value of w found in Prob. 153? Why? *Ans.* $w = 1.95$ lb/in.^{2}.

155. Solve Prob. 150 if all the data are the same except that the plate is simply supported at the edge. *Ans.* $w = 18.5$ lb/in.^{2}; $\delta_{max} = 0.72$ in.

156. Solve Prob. 151 if all the data are the same except that the plate is simply supported at the edge. *Ans.* 5 lb/in.^{2}.

83   Rectangular or other shaped plates with large deflections. The general behavior described for circular plates in the foregoing articles when the deflections are large also apply to rectangular, elliptical, or other shapes of plates. Curves giving data for rectangular plates similar to those given in Figs. 142 and 143 for circular plates may be found in reference 9 at the end of this chapter.

Selected References

1. Bach, C., *Elastizität und Festigkeit*, 8th edition, Julius Springer, Berlin, 1920, p. 598.
2. Jensen, V. P., "Moments in Simple Span Bridge Slabs with Stiffened Edges," *Bulletin* 315, Engineering Experiment Station, University of Illinois, 1939.
3. Morley, A., *Strength of Materials*, 8th edition, Longmans, Green and Co., 1935. Gives derivation of Grashof's equations for circular plates.
4. Newmark, N. M., "A Distribution Procedure for the Analysis of Slabs Continuous over Flexible Beams," *Bulletin* 304, Engineering Experiment Station, University of Illinois, 1938.
5. Nichols, J. R., "Statical Limitations upon Steel Requirement in Reinforced Concrete Flat Slab Floors," *Transactions of the American Society of Civil Engineers*, Vol. 77, 1914, p. 1670.
6. Sturm, R. G., and R. L. Moore, "The Behavior of Rectangular Plates under Concentrated Load," *Journal of Applied Mechanics*, Vol. 4, June 1937, pp. A75–85.

7. Westergaard, H. M., "Moments and Stresses in Slabs," *Proceedings of the American Concrete Institute*, Vol. 17, 1921.

8. Prescott, J., *Applied Elasticity*, Dover Publications, New York, 1946, pp. 455–469.

9. Ramberg, W., A. E. McPherson, and S. Levy, "Normal Pressure Tests of Rectangular Plates," *Report* 748, National Advisory Committee for Aeronautics, 1942.

Chapter 9

TORSIONAL RESISTANCE OF BARS HAVING NON-CIRCULAR CROSS SECTIONS

84 Introduction. If a bar having a constant circular cross section of diameter d is subjected to twisting couples T at its ends, the shearing stress at any point on a transverse cross section varies directly as the distance of the point from the center of the section (see Art. 11) and is expressed by the equation

$$\tau = Tc/J \tag{287}$$

in which c is the distance to the point, and $J = \pi d^4/32$ is the polar moment of inertia of the cross section. Furthermore, in accordance with Art. 17, a shearing stress of equal magnitude acts at the same point on a longitudinal plane. It should be recalled also that the angle of twist θ of the cylindrical bar is

$$\theta = Tl/JG \qquad \text{or} \qquad \phi = \theta/l = T/JG \tag{288}$$

in which l is the length of the bar, G is the shearing modulus of elasticity of the material, and ϕ is the angle of twist per unit of length.

Equations 287 and 288 apply only to bars or shafts having constant circular cross sections, for which plane cross sections remain plane as the bar is twisted, and are valid only when the shearing stress in the shaft does not exceed the shearing elastic strength of the material.

Non-circular Section. In 1853, St. Venant in his classical memoir on the torsion of prismatic bars showed that, if a bar whose transverse cross section is *not* circular is twisted by applying moments at its ends, a plane transverse section before twisting does *not* remain a plane section after twisting; it becomes a warped surface, and this warping is accompanied by an increase of shearing stress in some parts of the section and a decrease in other parts as compared with stresses that would occur if the section did not warp but remained a plane, as in a bar having a circular cross section.

For example, in a bar with an elliptical section the shearing stress has its maximum value at the ends of the minor axis, that is, at the points on the surface *nearest* to the axis of the bar; whereas, if the plane section remained plane so that the elastic shearing strain (and also stress) at any point were proportional to the distance of the point from the axis of twist, the strain and stress on the surface of the bar would have their *minimum* values at the end of the minor axis.

Similarly, the maximum shearing stress in a bar with a rectangular section is at the center of the long side, that is, at a point on the surface *nearest* to the axis of the bar; and the shearing stress at each corner of the section is zero. Furthermore, the polar moment of inertia of the cross-sectional area of a bar with a non-circular section has a very different effect on the torsional stiffness and strength of the bar than on those of a bar with a circular cross section. This fact is brought out by a statement often referred to as St. Venant's paradox; namely, if two solid bars of the same ideal elastic material have non-circular cross-sectional areas that are equal but different in shape, the one with the smaller polar moment of inertia has the greater torsional stiffness; it also has the greater strength, provided that the areas are everywhere convex (do not have re-entrant angles).

If a section has a sharp internal corner (re-entrant angle) such as that caused by a keyway in a shaft, the warping of a transverse section causes at the internal corner a shearing stress which theoretically is infinitely large.

As a rule, structural members such as I beams, channels, etc., are used to resist bending loads, but frequently these members are subjected to torsion in addition to bending, and, although the torsional moment may be relatively small, the lack of torsional strength and stiffness of such members makes their torsional behavior of importance.

The analysis given in the next article of the torsional stresses in a bar having a rectangular section is an approximate but very useful and relatively simple solution, due mainly to Bach.

85 Torsion of bar having a rectangular cross section. In Fig. 144*a* is shown a portion of a bar having a rectangular cross section, the bar being subjected to twisting moments T at its ends. In order to find the shearing stresses in the bar in terms of the twisting moment T and the dimensions b and h of the cross section, the procedure outlined in Art. 8, Chapter 2, is employed.

A plane is passed through the bar, cutting it in a direction perpendicular to the longitudinal axis (the axis of twist). The portion of the body lying on the left side of this plane is shown in Fig. 144*a*. The internal forces $\tau_x\, da$ and $\tau_y\, da$ are the components in the x and y directions, respectively, of the shearing force $\tau\, da$ on the area da. The equations of equilibrium require that the external twisting moment T shall be equal and opposite to the internal twisting moment, and hence

$$T = \int [y\tau_x\, da + x(-\tau_y)\, da] \tag{289}$$

in which x, y, τ_x, and τ_y must be given signs in accordance with the conventions shown in Fig. 144.

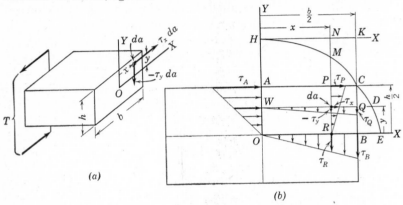

(a)

(b)

FIG. 144   Torsional shearing stresses in rectangular bar.

In order to integrate Eq. 289, the distribution of the stresses τ_x and τ_y must be obtained. In accordance with Art. 8, this distribution is obtained by making a study of the strains in the bar. When a bar having a rectangular section is twisted, it takes the form shown in Fig. 145a. The warping of the sections causes the shearing strain (and hence shearing stress) to be maximum at the center of the long side (at A, Figs. 145a and 144b) and to be zero at the corners, at C. These facts are obtained from a study of Figs. 145a and 145b, which show that the greatest distortion of the squares occurs at the middle of the long side and the least (zero) at the edge of the bar. Figure 145c shows the warping of the cross section. Points in the quadrants marked plus move in one direction longitudinally; those in quadrants marked minus move in the opposite direction. The fact that the shearing stress must be zero at the corner may also be shown as follows. The shearing stress on any transverse section at any point in the surface must be tangent to the surface; therefore, since C is a point on the side AC (Fig. 144b) and also on the side CB, the stress at C must be zero since it could not be tangent to both sides.

As shown in Fig. 145a, the strain (and hence stress) is assumed to vary from A to C (Fig. 144b) approximately as the ordinates of a parabola. Thus in Fig. 144b the stresses along AC are indicated by the ordinates to the parabola HMC having its vertex at H. In Fig. 144b, let τ_A represent the stress at A, and τ_P represent the stress at any point P on the

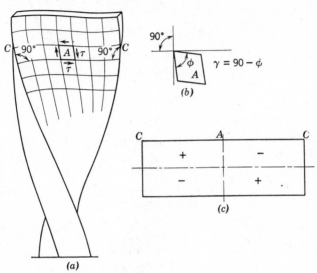

FIG. 145   Views showing warping of sections of bars having non-circular cross sections.   (From Bach, reference No. 1.)

periphery between A and the corner C. If HMC is a parabola in which AH represents τ_A and PM represents τ_P, we have from the equation of a parabola

$$\frac{MN}{CK} = \frac{x^2}{(b/2)^2}$$

thus

$$(\tau_A - \tau_P)/\tau_A = (2x/b)^2 \tag{290}$$

or

$$\tau_P = \tau_A[1 - (2x/b)^2] \tag{291}$$

Similarly, using the parabola CDE to represent the stresses along the periphery CB, we have

$$\tau_Q = \tau_B[1 - (2y/h)^2] \tag{292}$$

It will be assumed that the stress component τ_x (Fig. 144b) along any line (such as WQ) parallel to AC varies in the same way as does the stress along AC, but that the value of τ_x decreases directly from the value τ_P on the surface at P to zero at R on the major axis; a similar assumption is made with respect to τ_y. That is, if τ_x and τ_y denote the components of the stress at any point in the bar,

$$\tau_x = \frac{y}{h/2}\tau_P = \frac{2y}{h}\tau_A\left[1 - \left(\frac{2x}{b}\right)^2\right] \tag{293}$$

and

$$-\tau_y = \frac{x}{b/2}\tau_Q = \frac{2x}{b}\tau_B\left[1 - \left(\frac{2y}{h}\right)^2\right] \tag{294}$$

Further, it is assumed that τ_A and τ_B are inversely proportional to the distances of A and B from the center of the bar. That is,

$$\tau_B = (h/b)\tau_A \tag{295}$$

These assumptions are in accord with the general behavior of the bar as indicated by Fig. 145a, although they must be regarded only as approximate since the exact manner of variation of stress cannot be determined in this way. By use of Eqs. 293, 294, and 295, the right-hand member of Eq. 289 may be expressed in terms of the maximum stress τ_A and the dimensions of the area. Thus,

$$T = \frac{2\tau_A}{h}\left(\int y^2\,da - \frac{4}{b^2}\int x^2y^2\,da\right) + \frac{2h}{b^2}\tau_A\left(\int x^2\,da - \frac{4}{h^2}\int x^2y^2\,da\right) \tag{296}$$

But

$$\int y^2\,da = I_x = \tfrac{1}{12}bh^3 \qquad \int x^2\,da = I_y = \tfrac{1}{12}hb^3 \qquad \int x^2y^2\,da = \frac{b^3h^3}{144} \tag{297}$$

Hence Eq. 296 becomes

$$T = \tfrac{2}{9}bh^2\tau_A \qquad \text{or} \qquad \tau_A = \tfrac{9}{2}(T/bh^2) \tag{298}$$

in which τ_A is the maximum shearing stress in the bar when subjected to a twisting moment T, provided that h is not greater than b and that the stress does not exceed the shearing elastic strength of the material. If T is expressed in pound-inches and b and h in inches, τ_A will be expressed in pounds per square inch.

The above expression for the maximum stress must not be expected to give reliable results for a very thin section, that is, when b is very large compared to h. When b has a value of $1h$ to $2h$, the value of τ_A, though only approximate, may be considered to be reliable. If Eq. 298 is written

$$T = \alpha bh^2\tau_A \qquad \text{or} \qquad \tau_A = (1/\alpha)(T/bh^2) \tag{298a}$$

the values of α given in Table 13 will make the values of τ_A nearly the same as those given by St. Venant's analysis (see Appendix II).

From St. Venant's analysis the angle of twist ϕ per unit length is given by the equation

$$\phi = (1/\beta bh^3)(T/G) \tag{299}$$

where β has the values given in Table 13.

TABLE 13

$b/h = 1$	1.5	2	2.5	3	4	6	10	∞
$\alpha = 0.208$	0.231	0.246	0.256	0.267	0.282	0.299	0.312	0.333
$\beta = 0.141$	0.196	0.229	0.249	0.263	0.281	0.299	0.312	0.333

Problems

157. A steel bar having a rectangular cross section $\frac{1}{2}$ in. wide and $1\frac{1}{2}$ in. long is subjected to a twisting moment of 1000 lb-in. The shearing elastic strength of the material is 12,000 lb per sq in. (a) Calculate by Eq. 298 the maximum shearing stress, and state where in the bar it occurs. (b) Calculate the shearing stress at the center of the short side.   *Ans.* (a) Max. $\tau = 12{,}000$ lb/in.^{2}; (b) $\tau = 4000$ lb/in.^{2}.

158. Solve Prob. 157 by making use of the values of α given in Table 13.
Ans. Max. $\tau = 10{,}000$ lb/in.^{2}.

159. A bar of spring steel has a tensile elastic strength of 50,000 lb per sq in. and a shearing elastic strength equal to 0.6 of the tensile. The bar has a rectangular cross section and is subjected to a twisting moment of 5000 lb-in. If the working stress is two-thirds of the shearing elastic strength and the width of the section is $\frac{3}{4}$ in., what should be the length of the section?

160. A rectangular bar having a cross section such that $b/h = k$ and a cylindrical bar having a diameter d are subjected to the same twisting moment T. Using Eq. 298, show that when $d = 1.042h\sqrt[3]{k}$ the maximum shearing stresses in the two bars are equal, if the elastic strength of the material is not exceeded.

161. If the cross section of a rectangular bar is $1\frac{1}{2}$ in. thick, what must be its width in order that the maximum shearing stress produced in it shall be the same as that in a cylindrical shaft 2 in. in diameter, both shafts being subjected to the same twisting moment? Use Eq. 298a.

162. Two bars, one with a square cross section and the other with a circular cross section, have equal cross-sectional areas and are subjected to equal twisting moments. Show by use of Eq. 298 that the maximum torsional shearing stress in the square bar is 1.27 times that in the circular shaft.

86 Elastic-membrane (soap-film) analogy.

St. Venant in his analysis by the procedure discussed in Appendix II showed that, for a prismatic bar subjected to a twisting moment T, the shearing stresses on any plane cross section of the bar can be interpreted by the slopes of a dome-like surface over the cross section, such as is shown in Fig. 146. For example, suppose that this surface is represented for the section $ABCD$ of the bar by the surface whose cross sections in the yz and

xz planes are the arcs AEB and DEC, respectively; St. Venant showed that the slope of any line tangent to this surface at a point P, such as the line mn, is proportional to the shearing stress at the point P', the projection of P, in a direction perpendicular to the projection of the line mn in the cross section. Hence, if the Y axis is the projection of mn, the shearing stress, τ_x at P' in the x direction is proportional to the tangent of the angle that mn makes with the Y axis.

Furthermore, St. Venant showed that the volume beneath this surface is proportional to one-half of the twisting moment. The equation

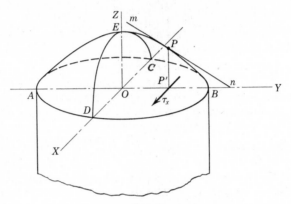

FIG. 146   Soap-film surface.

for this surface is called a *stress function*. Although St. Venant showed that such a surface (or stress function) always existed for a prismatic bar of any type of solid cross section, he actually found the stress function for only a relatively few sections such as ellipses, rectangles, equilateral triangles, etc. Weber has found the stress function for some other more irregular sections, but the mathematical equation for the stress function is very complicated for many of the technically important sections such as angle, channel, and I sections.

However, a close approximation to the surface representing the stress function for almost any shape of cross section can be made by the use of the soap-film analogy. A rather detailed description of the soap-film analogy is given in Appendix II. It was pointed out by Prandtl that the differential equation for the stress function of the twisted bar is of the same form and has the same boundary conditions as that of the surface of an elastic membrane stretched over an opening of the same shape as that of the cross section of the bar and distended by being subjected to a slight difference of pressure on its two sides. In 1917, A. A. Griffith and G. I. Taylor made use of this analogy for determining the torsional strength and stiffness of airplane propeller blades and various structural shapes (see reference 3 for apparatus used). The desired shaped hole is cut in a thin metal plate, and a circular hole of a certain predetermined diameter is also cut in the same plate. The plate is then clamped between the two halves of a cast-iron box, and soap films are stretched across the two holes. Air is then forced into the lower compartment of the box, thereby causing the soap films to be distended into a dome-like surface by the uniform pressure. The following statements apply only to so-called solid areas and not to the cross sections of hollow bars such as hollow cylinders, hollow rectangles, etc. (thin-walled hollow sections are discussed in Art. 88):

(a) The slope of a tangent line at any point on the soap film (see Fig. 146) is proportional to the shearing stress at the corresponding point in the bar in a direction at right angles to the projection in the section of the tangent line. The uniform pressure which causes the film to distend is proportional to the angle of twist; therefore, if soap films are stretched over two openings representing the cross sections of two bars and are subjected to the same uniform pressure, the stresses represented by the slopes of the soap films are stresses which would occur in the bars if they were subjected to the same angle of twist per unit of length.

Thus, if one of the two bars has a circular cross section, in which the stress at any point can be calculated satisfactorily, the stress at any point in a bar of irregular cross section may be found if the slopes to the films at corresponding points are determined experimentally.

(b) The volume under the soap film is proportional to the twisting moment acting on the bar. Thus, if the two bars are given the same angle of twist per unit of length, the twisting moment required to cause the given angle of twist of the irregular-shaped bar may be found if the ratio of the volumes under the two soap films is found experimentally.

Much of the importance of the soap-film analogy is based on the fact that, by visualizing the shape or form that the soap film will take, many valuable deductions may be made without the necessity of performing experiments. Figures 147 and 148 show views of the approximate forms of the soap films for several sections. These models were obtained by using a very thin sheet of rubber in place of the soap film and pouring plaster of Paris over the plate containing the holes, thereby causing the rubber membrane to deflect. The forms of these models are close approximations to the forms of the soap films for the same areas and will help the reader in visualizing the forms of the soap film for other areas. It will be noted that at outstanding corners, as at A, the slope to the soap film is practically zero, denoting zero stress; at inward projecting corners, as at C, the slope is very steep, denoting very high stress; and along a long straight edge the slope is nearly constant. Further, it will be noted that at the intersection of two rectangular areas, as at B, the volume is increased as shown by the dome or hump, denoting increased twisting moment to produce a given angle of twist. The shadows on the models distort somewhat the true shape of the models; for example, the slopes at some of the outstanding corners do

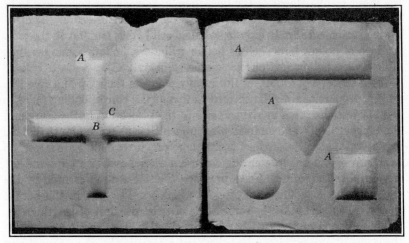

FIGS. 147 and 148   Plaster models of soap films.

not appear to be zero, etc. The reader should carefully visualize the form of the soap films and verify the following statements:

I. *Stiffness.* Since the twisting moment required to produce a given angle of twist is proportional to the volume under the film, it is evident that:

(*a*) A torsional member having a long, thin, rectangular cross section is not as stiff as one having a square section of the same area.

(*b*) The torsional stiffness of a member with a long, straight, thin rectangular cross section is approximately the same as that of a member having an L-shaped or U-shaped section, etc., provided that the width of the section and the length of median line remain constant.

(*c*) Any cut in the section, such as a keyway in a shaft, reduces the stiffness of the shaft more than the cut reduces the area of the section.

(*d*) Any addition to the area of the given section increases its stiffness.

II. *Stress.* Since the stress at any point in a section for a given angle of twist is proportional to the slope of the film at the corresponding point on the film, it is evident that:

(*a*) The stress at a point on the boundary of the section where the section is convex outward (as at A, Fig. 149) is less than it would be if the boundary of the section were straight; and at a sharp outwardly projecting corner the stress is zero.

(b) The stress at a point on the boundary of the section where the section has a concave curvature (as at B, Fig. 149) is greater than it would be if the section were straight; and the stress at an inward projecting sharp corner would be theoretically infinite if stress remained proportional to strain. However, if the material is ductile, it will deform

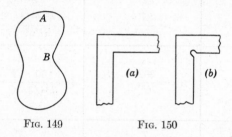

FIG. 149   FIG. 150

and the stress will be distributed to the adjacent material. The stress at a re-entrant angle may be reduced by cutting away some of the material in the corner, as indicated in Fig. 150.

(c) The maximum shearing stress in a section occurs at or near one of the points of contact of the largest inscribed circle, not, in general, at the point on the boundary nearest the centroid of the section, as has sometimes been assumed. If, however, the boundary is more concave at some other point, the maximum stress may occur at the point of greater concavity. For example, in a rectangle (Fig. 151a) the slope

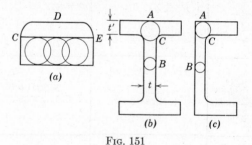

FIG. 151

to the film would be approximately constant along the greater part of the long side CE, and hence the shearing stress is nearly constant along this side. Therefore, the shearing stress probably varies about as indicated by the ordinates to the curve CDE rather than by the ordinates to a parabola as was assumed in the method of solution in Art. 85. For the I section and the channel section (Figs. 151b and 151c) with the

TABLE 14

APPROXIMATE FORMULAS FOR TORSIONAL SHEARING STRESS AND ANGLE OF TWIST, OBTAINED FROM MATHEMATICAL ANALYSIS

Cross Section	Relation between Shearing Stress and Twisting Moment	Relation between Angle of Twist per Unit Length and Twisting Moment
 Fig. A	$\tau_A = \dfrac{2T}{ab}$ $= \dfrac{2T}{\pi h b^2}$	$\phi = 4\pi^2 \dfrac{J}{a^4} \cdot \dfrac{T}{G}$ $= \dfrac{h^2 + b^2}{\pi h^3 b^3} \cdot \dfrac{T}{G}$
 Equilateral triangle Fig. B	$\tau_A = \dfrac{20T}{b^3}$	$\phi = \dfrac{80}{b^4 \sqrt{3}} \cdot \dfrac{T}{G} = \dfrac{46.2}{b^4} \cdot \dfrac{T}{G}$
 Fig. C	$\tau_A = \dfrac{T}{\alpha b h^2}$	$\phi = \dfrac{1}{\beta b h^3} \cdot \dfrac{T}{G}$ For values of α and β, see Table 13.
 Equvalent to rectangle with $\frac{b}{h}$ = large Fig. D	$\tau = \dfrac{3T}{2\pi r t^2}$ $= \dfrac{3r}{t} \cdot \dfrac{T}{2\pi r^2 t}$	$\phi = \dfrac{3}{2\pi r t^3} \cdot \dfrac{T}{G}$ $= \dfrac{3r^2}{t^2} \cdot \dfrac{1}{2\pi r^3 t} \cdot \dfrac{T}{G}$
 Fig. E	$\tau = \dfrac{Tr}{J}$ $= \dfrac{T}{2\pi r^2 t}$	$\phi = \dfrac{T}{JG}$ $= \dfrac{1}{2\pi r^3 t} \cdot \dfrac{T}{G}$
 Fig. F	$\tau_A = \dfrac{T}{2\pi b h t}$	$\phi = \dfrac{\sqrt{2(b^2 + h^2)}}{4\pi b^2 h^2 t} \cdot \dfrac{T}{G}$
 Fig. G	$\tau_A = \dfrac{T}{2bht_1}$ $\tau_B = \dfrac{T}{2bht}$	$\phi = \dfrac{bt + ht_1}{2tt_1 b^2 h^2} \cdot \dfrac{T}{G}$

T = twisting moment. ϕ = angle of twist per unit of length. a = area of cross section. J = polar moment of inertia. G = shearing modulus of elasticity.

thickness of the flange greater than that of the web, the slope of the film (and hence the stress) would be greater at A than at B; but the slope at C would be greater than at either A or B.

(*d*) For a given angle of twist the stress in a bar at the points of contact of an inscribed circle is always greater than the stress in a circular bar whose radius is equal to that of the inscribed circle. The more nearly the boundary of the section coincides with the arc of the circle at the point of contact, the nearer the stress at the point approaches that in the inscribed circular bar.

87   Special formulas obtained from mathematical analysis for solid cross sections.   As noted in the preceding article, a mathematical analysis of the torsion of a bar has been made by St. Venant only for the simpler cross sections, and the results even for most of these sections are too complicated for convenient use.   In Appendix II St. Venant's method of analysis is discussed and illustrative problems are given which show how his method is applied.   Stresses for bars having the first four cross sections shown in Table 14 were obtained by St. Venant's analysis for bars having solid cross sections.   The maximum shearing stress τ in each case occurs along the central portion of the longest side of the cross section, as at A in the figures of Table 14.   By visualizing the slopes to the soap films for the so-called *solid* areas in Table 14 the point or region of maximum shearing stress can easily be determined. In the expressions for the angle of twist per unit length in the third column of Table 14 the ratio T/G is multiplied by a constant which depends upon the shape and dimensions of the cross-sectional area.   This constant, sometimes called the torsion constant, is a measure of the torsional rigidity and corresponds to the polar moment of inertia J in Eq. 288 which applies to a circular section.   The method of obtaining the stresses and angle of twist in the *hollow thin-walled* tubes included in Table 14 is given in the next paragraph.

Problems

163. Solve Prob. 157 by use of the equations in Table 14.   Also calculate the angle of twist of the bar described in Prob. 157, assuming its length to be 4 ft.

164. A steel bar 2 in. by 2 in. by 6 ft long is subjected to twisting moments at its ends that cause a maximum shearing stress equal to one-half of the shearing elastic strength of the material.   Calculate the angle of twist of one end of the bar relative to the other.   Assume the shearing elastic strength of the steel to be 30,000 lb per sq in.

165. A steel bar having a slender rectangular cross section ($\frac{1}{4}$ in. by 4 in.) is subjected to twisting couples of 1000 lb-in. at its ends.   Find the maximum shearing stress and the angle of twist per unit length.

88   Formulas obtained from mathematical analysis for hollow thin-walled tubes. In Art. 195 of Appendix II is given a method of finding the torsional stresses in a thin-walled tube based on a modification of St. Venant's analysis for solid sections. The stress function for a thin-walled tube such as is shown in Fig. 152a is represented by the surface ABCD in Fig. 152b. The surface representing the stress function rises from the outer edge just as it does for a solid section in Fig. 146; but beginning at the inner edge and extending over the hollow portion the surface is a flat horizontal plane. Thus an approximate value of the volume underneath the surface representing the stress function is aH, where a is the area enclosed by the mean perimeter of the wall of the tube and H is the height of the flat part of the surface above the hollow portion of the cross section. By use of the membrane analogy the twisting moment may be written

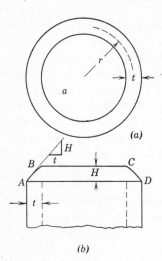

(a)

(b)

Fig. 152

$$T = 2aH \quad \text{or} \quad H = T/2a \quad (300)$$

If the tube is circular, Eq. 300 becomes

$$H = T/2\pi r^2 \quad (301)$$

An approximate value of the shearing stress is obtained by computing the slope of a line joining A and B in Fig. 152b. This line is very nearly parallel to the tangent line at the mid-thickness of the wall of the tube to the surface representing the stress function. The slope, and hence the shearing stress, is

$$\tau = H/t = T/2at \quad (302)$$

For a circular tube Eq. 302 becomes

$$\tau = T/2\pi r^2 t \quad (303)$$

This method of computing the stresses does not consider the fact that failure of a thin-walled tube may occur as an elastic buckling of the thin wall. Also the stresses are computed at the mid-thickness of the wall and the stress at the outside has a somewhat higher value which may be significant in thicker walled tubes.

Shear Flow. It should be noted in Eqs. 300, 301, and 302 that the quantity H has units of force per unit length; that is, H represents the resisting force per unit length along the mean perimeter of the thin-walled section. H is sometimes called the *shear flow* at a point (see

Art. 35) and is a convenient quantity for use in computing the torsional resistance of thin-walled sections such as are often used in aircraft construction.

Angle of Twist. In accordance with the discussion in Appendix II the angle of twist per unit length is given by the equation

$$\phi = \frac{H}{2Ga}\Sigma\frac{l}{t} = \frac{\Sigma(l/t)}{4a^2}\cdot\frac{T}{G} \tag{304}$$

In this equation the term $\Sigma(l/t)$ represents the sum of the various ratios of the length of the mean perimeter of each part of a thin-walled tube divided by its respective thickness. For example, assume that a hollow tube has a rectangular cross section of sides b and h in which side b has a thickness t_1 and side h a thickness t (Fig. G, Table 14); then for this cross section $\Sigma(l/t) = (2b/t_1) + (2h/t)$. For a circular tube, $l = 2\pi r$, and hence $\Sigma(l/t) = 2\pi r/t$. Therefore, the angle of twist per unit of length of the tube with a circular cross section is

$$\phi = \frac{H}{2Ga}\frac{2\pi r}{t} = \frac{T}{2\pi r^3 tG} \tag{305}$$

which is in accordance with Eq. 288 and the result given in Table 14.

Illustrative Problems

Problem 166. A hollow steel tube of rectangular cross section whose dimensions are as shown in Fig. 153a is subjected to a twisting moment of 100,000 lb-in. Find the maximum shearing stress and the angle of twist per unit of length.

Solution. The stress function is represented by the surface $ABCD$ in Fig. 153b. Therefore the twisting moment is, approximately,

$$T = 2aH = 2 \times 46H = 100,000 \text{ lb-in.}$$

Thus $\qquad H = 1090 \text{ lb-in.}$

The shearing stress along each side having a wall thickness of 0.25 in. is

$$\tau = H/t = 1090/0.25 = 4360 \text{ lb/in.}^2$$

The shearing stress along the side having a wall thickness of 0.5 in. is

$$\tau = H/t = 1090/0.50 = 2180 \text{ lb/in.}^2$$

The angle of twist per unit length is

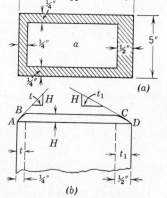

(a)

(b)

Fig. 153

$$\phi = \frac{H}{2Ga}\Sigma\frac{l}{t} = \frac{1090}{2 \times 12 \times 10^6 \times 46}\left(\frac{24}{0.25}+\frac{4.75}{0.50}\right) = 0.000104 \text{ radian/in.}$$

Problem 167. A hollow steel tube has two compartments as shown by Fig. 154a, in which a_1 is the area of the left compartment and a_2 the area of the right compartment. The tube is subjected to a twisting moment $T = 1,000,000$ lb-in. Find the maximum shearing stress and the angle of twist per unit of length.

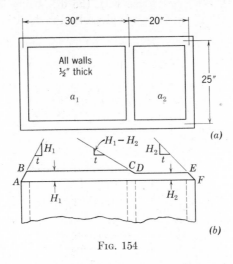

Fɪɢ. 154

Solution. In Fig. 154b the surface $ABCDEF$ represents the stress function. Twice the volume under the stress function surface is the twisting moment T, and hence

$$T = 2a_1H_1 + 2a_2H_2 = 1,000,000 \text{ lb-in.} \tag{1}$$

In order to solve this equation for H_1 and H_2 one other equation involving H_1 and H_2 must be obtained. This may be done by writing the equation for the angle of twist of each compartment. This angle will, of course, be equal to the angle of twist of the whole tube. For compartment a_1 the angle of twist per unit length is

$$\phi = \frac{H_1}{2Ga_1} \sum_{30''} \frac{l}{t} + \frac{H_1 - H_2}{2Ga_1} \sum_{25''} \frac{l}{t} = \frac{H_1}{2Ga_1} \cdot \frac{85}{0.5} + \frac{H_1 - H_2}{2Ga_1} \cdot \frac{25}{0.5}$$

$$\phi = (110H_1 - 25H_2)/Ga_1 \tag{2}$$

For compartment a_2,

$$\phi = \frac{H_2}{2Ga_2} \sum_{20''} \frac{l}{t} + \frac{H_2 - H_1}{2Ga_2} \sum_{25''} \frac{l}{t} = \frac{H_2}{2Ga_2} \cdot \frac{65}{0.5} + \frac{H_2 - H_1}{2Ga_2} \cdot \frac{25}{0.5}$$

$$\phi = (90H_2 - 25H_1)/Ga_2 \tag{3}$$

Equations 1, 2, and 3 contain the three unknown quantities H_1, H_2, and ϕ. Solving these equations for the unknowns, we have

$$H_1 = 413 \text{ lb/in.} \qquad H_2 = 380 \text{ lb/in.} \qquad \phi = 0.000004 \text{ radian/in.}$$

The shearing stress along any outside wall of compartment a_1 is

$$\tau = H_1/t = 413/0.5 = 826 \text{ lb/in.}^2$$

The shearing stress along any outside wall of compartment a_2 is

$$\tau = H_2/t = 380/0.5 = 760 \text{ lb/in.}^2$$

The shearing stress along the wall which is common to both compartments is

$$\tau = (H_1 - H_2)/t = (413 - 380)/0.5 = 66 \text{ lb/in.}^2$$

Problems

168. A hollow thin-walled brass tube has an equilateral triangular cross section. The length of the side of the triangle is 1.0 in., and the wall thickness is 0.1 in. The tube is subjected to a twisting moment of $100\sqrt{3}$ in.-lb. Find the maximum shearing stress and the angle of twist per unit length. $G = 4,000,000$ lb per sq in.

Ans. $\tau_{\max} = 2000$ lb/in.^{2}; $\phi = 0.0017$ radian/in.

169. A hollow thin-walled steel tube has the cross section and dimensions shown in Fig. 155. The twisting moment applied to the tube is $T = 1,000,000$ lb-in. Find the maximum shearing stress and the angle of twist per unit of length.

Ans. $\tau_{\max} = 6660$ lb/in.^{2}; $\phi = 0.000074$ radian/in.

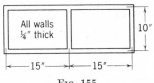

FIG. 155

170. In Prob. 169 let the partition separating the tube into two compartments (Fig. 155) be removed. Compute the maximum shearing stress and the angle of twist per unit length.   *Ans.* $\tau_{\max} = 6660$ lb/in.^{2}; $\phi = 0.000074$ radian/in.

Torsional Resistance of Hollow Thin-walled Tubes Having a Longitudinal Slit. The strength and stiffness of a hollow thin-walled tube are very greatly reduced if a longitudinal slit is cut in the tube. A tube with a longitudinal slit is practically like a thin plate with a rectangular cross section whose length is the perimeter of the tube and whose width is the wall thickness of the tube. For example, in Table 14 the tube with the longitudinal slit acts practically the same as a bar or plate having a slender rectangular cross section of length $2\pi r$ and thickness t and therefore has very small strength and stiffness. The soap-film analogy as adapted to thin-walled tubes helps to explain the great difference in the stiffness of a hollow tube without a slit and a tube with a longitudinal slit. The tube with the slit is a solid section consisting of a long narrow rectangle, and the volume of the soap film stretched over such an opening is very small. The soap film for the hollow tube without a slit encloses a much larger volume, since for the hollow tube the inner boundary of the tube is raised a distance H (see Appendix II) above the outside boundary, and the total volume under the soap film and the raised plane representing the inner boundary is much greater than the volume under the soap film for the long narrow rectangle.

Problems

171. A seamless cylindrical steel tube has an outside diameter of 3 in. and a wall thickness of ¼ in. If this tube is split longitudinally along one element, what twisting moment applied at its ends will cause a shearing stress of 12,000 lb per sq in.? If the tube were not split, what twisting moment would be required to produce the same stress?

172. A hollow cylindrical tube having an outside diameter of 10 in. and an inside diameter of 9 in. is subjected to twisting moments at its ends, the angle of twist being α. How many times greater will be the angle of twist if the tube is split longitudinally along one element?

89   Torsion of sections composed of narrow rectangles. The

approximate angle of twist per unit of length of a member whose cross section is a relatively narrow rectangle may be found from an expression similar to that applicable to a circular cross section, namely,

$$\phi = T/JG \qquad (306)$$

except that, in the place of the true polar moment of inertia J of the section, a modified value is used. St. Venant found from his analysis of the torsion of bars having rectangular cross section that for large ratios of b/h the value of J was given by the expression $J = \frac{1}{3}(b - 0.63h)h^3$, in which b is the length and h the width of the rectangular section. For a narrow rectangle $0.63h$ may be neglected. Hence

$$J = \tfrac{1}{3}bh^3 \qquad \text{(approximately)} \qquad (307)$$

For a rolled-steel section such as an I section or channel, etc., which may be regarded as made up of narrow rectangles, the value of J would be expected (on the basis of the soap-film analogy) to be $J = \frac{1}{3}\Sigma bh^3$, approximately. Experimental results for rolled-steel channels indicate that the value is approximately

$$J = 1.10 \times \tfrac{1}{3}\Sigma bh^3 \qquad (308)$$

The maximum torsional shearing stress in a bar having a narrow rectangular section likewise may be found from an expression similar in form to that of the torsion formula, $\tau = Tc/J$, for circular sections.

The maximum shearing stress in a narrow rectangle in which the ratio b/h is large as given by Eq. 298a is

$$\tau = T/\tfrac{1}{3}bh^2 \tag{309}$$

By multiplying both numerator and denominator by h, the right side of Eq. 309 becomes

$$\tau = Th/\tfrac{1}{3}bh^3 = Th/J \tag{310}$$

in which J has the value given by Eq. 307, and h is the short dimension of the rectangle. The stresses for a section composed of narrow rectangles such as a channel and I section are given approximately by Eq. 310 in which $J = \tfrac{1}{3}\Sigma bh^3$, and h is the thickness or short dimension of the web or flange, using the larger of the two values to obtain the maximum stress in the section. The maximum shearing stress is at the center of one of the long sides of the rectangular part that has the greatest thickness; this fact is also evident from the soap-film analogy.

Strain gage measurements at the center of the web and of the flange on a number of rolled steel channel sections indicate that the above formula is reliable. The shearing stress at the inwardly projecting corners will be greater than that given by the above equation unless the fillets at such corners have ample radii; these localized stresses are discussed in Part III.

Problems

173. Find the maximum shearing stress and the angle of twist per unit of length of a bar having the cross section shown in Fig. 156 when subjected to twisting moments at its ends of 12,000 lb-in. each. At what point in the area does this maximum calculated shearing stress occur? Assume $E = 10 \times 10^6$ lb per sq in.

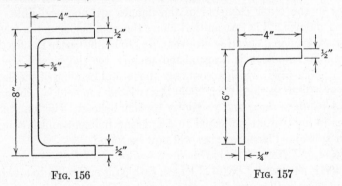

FIG. 156   FIG. 157

174. A bar having a cross section shown in Fig. 157 is subjected to twisting couples of 2000 lb-in. at its ends. The bar is 4 ft long. Find the angle of twist of one end relative to the other. Also find the maximum shearing stress and show in Fig. 157 where it acts. Assume the material to be steel.

175. Compare the twisting moments required to give the same angle of twist per unit length to the two sections shown in Fig. 158. Also compare the twisting moments required to cause the same maximum shearing stress, not considering the localized stress at the fillets.

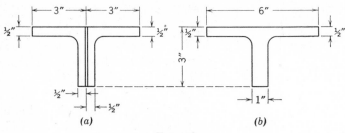

(a)   (b)

FIG. 158

90   Torsion of channel or I beam with one section restrained from warping. *General Behavior.* If all the cross sections in a bar subjected to twisting are free to warp (as has been assumed in the preceding articles) the longitudinal elements (lines) of the surface of the twisted bar remain practically straight lines with negligible change in their lengths unless the angle of twist per unit length is very large and the cross sections are unusually extended; likewise, longitudinal stresses which accompany the small changes in length in rolled shapes such as channels, I beams, etc., may usually be neglected.

If, however, one or more cross sections of a channel or I beam subjected to a twisting moment T (Fig. 159) is restrained from warping, then the longitudinal elements of the surface become decidedly curved with marked changes in their lengths, and the accompanying longitudinal stresses in the outer elements of the flanges are not negligible. The twisting moment T is transmitted along the member near the free end mainly by torsional shearing stresses (Fig. 159c), but near the fixed end the twisting moment is transmitted mainly by the lateral shearing forces V (Fig. 159a) which accompany the lateral bending of the flanges. At intermediate sections (Fig. 159b) the twisting moment is transmitted partly by lateral shear and partly by torsional shear. The longitudinal stresses in an I beam subjected to a twisting moment and having one section restrained from warping will now be found.

Torsion of I Beam Having One Section Restrained from Warping. In Fig. 160a is shown an I beam of length l which is subjected to a twisting moment T such that one of its cross sections is restrained from warping (the fixed end). The outer longitudinal elements (fibers) of the flanges near the fixed end where warping is prevented are decidedly curved, and the marked changes in their lengths are accompanied by longitudinal stresses in the outer edges of the flanges as a result of the lateral bending of the flanges; these stresses are not negligible at or near the section which is restrained from warping. This fact means that at any cross section of the beam such as AB in Fig. 160a there exist lateral shearing

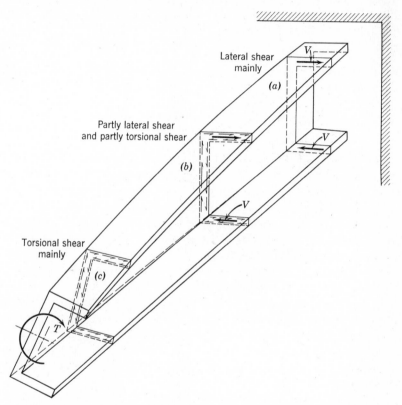

FIG. 159   General torsional effect of twisting moment on channel beam.

forces V in the flanges which bend the flanges in lateral directions as shown in Fig. 160b. Therefore the twisting moment T is transmitted along the member at each cross section, such as AB, in two ways as pointed out in Fig. 159. First, a twisting moment T_1 is produced by the lateral shearing forces which constitute a couple with moment arm h so that

$$T_1 = Vh \tag{311}$$

Second, a twisting moment T_2 is produced by the pure torsional shearing stresses in the cross section which are assumed to occur as if *all* cross sections of the beam were free to warp. The value of T_2 is found from Eq. 306 to be

$$T_2 = JG\phi \tag{312}$$

where ϕ is the angle of twist per unit length of the beam. The values of T_1 and T_2 are unknown since the values of V and ϕ at any section are not known. Values of these quantities must be found before the lateral

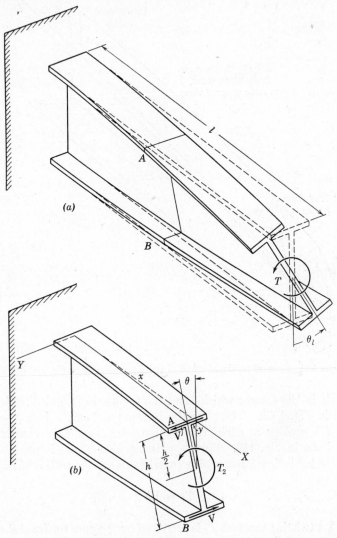

FIG. 160   Effect of twisting moment applied to I beam with one end fixed.

bending stresses in the flanges or the torsional shearing stresses in the I beam can be computed. For this purpose two equations are needed. From the condition of equilibrium, one of these equations is

$$T_1 + T_2 = T$$

which by using Eqs. 311 and 312 may be written

$$Vh + JG\phi = T \tag{313}$$

For the additional equation we may use the elastic curve equation for bending in the lateral direction of the upper flange in Fig. 160b, which is

$$(EI/2)(d^2y/dx^2) = -M \tag{314}$$

in which the X and Y axes are chosen with positive directions as shown in Fig. 160b; M is the lateral bending moment in the flange at any section producing lateral bending in the flange; I is the moment of inertia of the entire cross section of the beam with respect to the axis of symmetry in the web so that $\frac{1}{2}I$ closely approximates the value of the moment of inertia of a flange cross section. But Eq. 314 does not contain either of the desired quantities V and ϕ. These quantities are introduced into Eq. 314 as follows: In Fig. 160b the deflection of the flange at section AB is

$$y = (h/2)\theta \tag{315}$$

Differentiation of Eq. 315 twice with respect to x gives

$$d^2y/dx^2 = (h/2)(d^2\theta/dx^2) \tag{316}$$

and since $d\theta/dx = \phi$, Eq. 315 may be written

$$d^2y/dx^2 = (h/2)(d\phi/dx) \tag{317}$$

The substitution of this value of d^2y/dx^2 into Eq. 314 gives

$$(EIh/4)(d\phi/dx) = -M \tag{318}$$

In order to introduce V into Eq. 318, use is made of the fact that $dM/dx = V$. Thus by differentiating both sides of Eq. 318 with respect to x we obtain

$$(EIh/4)(d^2\phi/dx^2) = -V \tag{319}$$

Equations 313 and 319 are simultaneous equations in V and ϕ. The value of V obtained from Eq. 319 is substituted into Eq. 313, which then becomes

$$-(EIh^2/4JG)(d^2\phi/dx^2) + \phi = T/JG \tag{320}$$

For convenience let

$$a = (h/2)\sqrt{EI/JG} \qquad (321)$$

so that Eq. 320 may be written

$$-a^2(d^2\phi/dx^2) + \phi = T/JG \qquad (322)$$

The solution of this equation as given in textbooks on differential equations is

$$\phi = Ae^{x/a} + Be^{-x/a} + (T/JG) \qquad (323)$$

Two known pairs of values of x and ϕ or its derivative are used in finding values of the constants A and B in Eq. 323. At the fixed end where $x = 0$, $\phi = d\theta/dx = (h/2)(dy/dx) = 0$ (since the slope is zero). At the free end where $x = l$, $d\phi/dx = 0$ (see Eq. 318) since at the free end the bending moment M in the flange is zero. The values of A and B are determined from these two conditions and are substituted in Eq. 323, which gives the angle of twist per unit length:

$$\phi = \frac{T}{JG}\left[1 - \frac{\cosh\,(l-x)/a}{\cosh\,(l/a)}\right] \qquad (324)$$

The total angle of twist at the free end is

$$\theta = \int_0^l \phi\,dx = \frac{T}{JG}\left(l - a\tanh\frac{l}{a}\right) \qquad (325)$$

The twisting moment T_2 at any section of the beam is obtained by substituting the value of ϕ from Eq. 324 into Eq. 312 which gives

$$T_2 = T\left[1 - \frac{\cosh\,(l-x)/a}{\cosh\,(l/a)}\right] \qquad (326)$$

The torsional shearing stresses at any section are computed by substituting this value of T_2 into Eq. 310. The lateral bending moment M in the flanges of the beam at any section is obtained by substituting $d\phi/dx$ from Eq. 324 into Eq. 318, which gives

$$M = -\frac{T}{h}a\,\frac{\sinh\,(l-x)/a}{\cosh\,(l/a)} \qquad (327)$$

It will be noted that Eq. 327 shows that the maximum value of M occurs at the fixed end, for $x = 0$, and is

$$M_{\max} = (T/h)a\tanh\,(l/a) \qquad (328)$$

For all except relatively short beams the length l is large as compared with the value of a, and the value of $\tanh\,(l/a)$ is approximately equal to 1 when $l/a > 2.5$. In Eq. 325 and Eq. 328 the substitution of tanh $(l/a) = 1$ gives

$$\theta = (T/JG)(l - a) \tag{329}$$

$$M_{\max} = (T/h)a \tag{330}$$

These approximate values of θ and $M_{\max}$ obtained from Eqs. 329 and 330 lead to the following procedure for solving for the angle of twist and

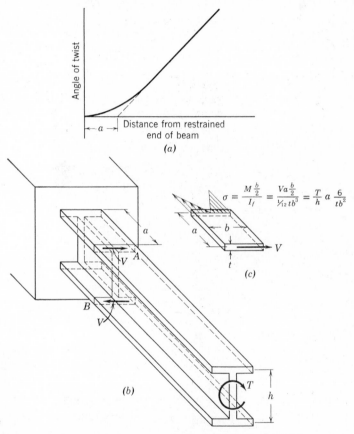

Fig. 161   Lateral bending stresses at fixed section in flange of I beam caused by torsion.

the maximum longitudinal stresses resulting from a twisting moment in an I beam with one section restrained from warping. Let Fig. 161 represent an I beam which is fixed at one end and loaded at the free end by the twisting moment T. Figure 161a represents a typical curve showing the relation between the angle of twist of the I beam and the distance from the fixed section of the beam. In Fig. 161a the distance from the fixed section to the section AB at which the straight-line portion of the curve intersects the horizontal axis is very nearly equal to the distance a as given by Eq. 321. Thus, from this fact and from Eq. 329 the length $l - a$ of the beam between the free end and section AB may be considered as being twisted under pure torsion for the purpose of computing the angle of twist. From Eq. 330 the sections of the beam within the length a from the fixed section to section AB may be considered as transmitting the entire twisting moment T by means of the lateral shears V in the flanges. Therefore

$$T = Vh \qquad \text{or} \qquad V = T/h \tag{331}$$

The force V causes each flange of length a to bend laterally, producing a longitudinal stress at each edge of the flange, tensile stress at one edge, and compressive stress at the other, Fig. 161c. Assuming that the lateral bending of each flange is in accordance with the flexure formula, and that each flange has a rectangular cross section, we have at the fixed end

$$\sigma = \frac{M\frac{1}{2}b}{I_f} = \frac{T}{h} a \frac{\frac{1}{2}b}{\frac{1}{12}tb^3} = \frac{6Ta}{htb^2} \tag{332}$$

The value for a is given by Eq. 321, in which E and G are the tensile and shearing moduli of elasticity, respectively, I is the moment of inertia of the entire section with respect to a centroidal axis parallel to the web, and J is an equivalent polar moment of inertia of the section. Values of a calculated by this equation check closely with values obtained from actual tests. For a section made up of slender, approximately rectangular areas, such as a rolled-steel channel, angle, or I section, J is given approximately by the expression (see Eq. 307).

$$J = \frac{1}{3}\Sigma bt^3 \tag{333}$$

in which b is the long dimension of each rectangular area, and t is the mean thickness, or mean short dimension. All equations in this article have been derived for an I beam, but they apply as well to channels or Z sections.

Various Loads and Supports for Beams in Torsion. The solution of Eq. 322 given by Eq. 323 is for the particular beam shown in Fig. 160. However, solutions of the equation have been obtained for beams loaded and supported as shown in Figs. A, B, C, and D in Table 15 by arranging the particular solution of the differential equation to suit the conditions of loading and support for each beam. The values of the maximum lateral bending moment M_{max} given in Table 15 may be used in Eq. 332

to compute the maximum lateral bending stress in the beam. The formulas in Table 15 in which I beams are shown may also be used for channels or Z bars.

TABLE 15

BEAMS SUBJECTED TO TORSION

Type of Loading and Support	Maximum Lateral Bending Moment in Flange	Angle of Twist of Beam of Length l
Fig. A	$M_{max} = \dfrac{Ta}{h} \tanh \dfrac{l}{2a}$ $= \dfrac{Ta}{h}$, if $\dfrac{l}{2a} > 2.5$	$\theta = \dfrac{T}{JG}\left(l - 2a \tanh \dfrac{l}{2a}\right)$ $= \dfrac{T}{JG}(l - 2a)$ Error is small if $\dfrac{l}{2a} > 2.5$
$T = wle$ Fig. B	$M_{max} = \dfrac{Ta}{2h}\left(\coth \dfrac{l}{2a} - \dfrac{2a}{l}\right)$ $= \dfrac{Ta}{h}$, if $\dfrac{l}{2a}$ is large	$\theta = \dfrac{T}{2JG}\left(\dfrac{l}{4} - a \tanh \dfrac{l}{4a}\right)$ $= \dfrac{T}{2JG}\left(\dfrac{l}{4} - a\right)$ Error is small if $\dfrac{l}{4a} > 2.5$
w $T = wle$ Fig. C	$M_{max} = \dfrac{Ta}{h}\left(\coth \dfrac{l}{a} - \dfrac{a}{l}\right)$ $= \dfrac{Ta}{h}$, if $\dfrac{l}{a}$ is large	$\theta = \dfrac{T}{JG}\left(\dfrac{l}{2} - a \tanh \dfrac{l}{2a}\right)$ $= \dfrac{T}{JG}\left(\dfrac{l}{2} - a\right)$ Error is small if $\dfrac{l}{2a} > 2.5$
Fig. D	$M_{max} = \dfrac{Ta}{h}\dfrac{\sinh \dfrac{l_1}{a}\sinh \dfrac{l_2}{a}}{\sinh \dfrac{l}{a}}$ $= \dfrac{Ta}{2h}$, if $\dfrac{l_1}{a}$ and $\dfrac{l_2}{a} > 2$ Error is small	Approximate value $\theta = \dfrac{1}{2}\dfrac{T}{JG}\left(\dfrac{l}{2} - a \tanh \dfrac{l}{2a}\right)$ $= \dfrac{1}{2}\dfrac{T}{JG}\left(\dfrac{l}{2} - a\right)$ Error is small if $\dfrac{l}{2a} > 2.5$

Problems

176. A wide-flange steel I beam having a depth of 10 in., a web thickness of 0.845 in., a flange thickness of 1.368 in., and a flange width of 10.5 in. is 20 ft long and weighs 124 lb per ft. It is fixed at one end and free at the other. A twisting moment of $T = 20,000$ lb in. is applied to the beam at its free end. Compute the maximum lateral bending stress in the flanges at the fixed end and the angle of twist of the beam at the free end. A steelmaker's handbook gives the following properties for the cross section: I about the centroidal axis parallel to the web of the section is 264.8 in.^{4}, $E = 30,000,000$ lb per sq in., and $G = 12,000,000$ lb per sq in.

Ans. $\sigma = 2300$ lb/in.^{2}; $\theta = 0.0177$ radian.

177. Let the beam described in Prob. 176 be simply supported at each end; that is, the supports prevent rotation but do not restrain the section from warping.

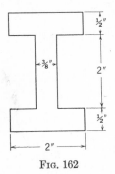

FIG. 162

The twisting moment $T = 20,000$ lb per in. is applied at the mid-point of the beam. Compute the maximum lateral bending stress in the flanges and the angle of twist at the mid-section of the beam.

Ans. $\sigma = 1130$ lb/in.^{2}; $\theta = 0.0038$ radian.

178. A steel connecting rod in an engine has an I-shaped cross section whose dimensions are as shown in Fig. 162 except at its ends where bearing connections are provided. The length of the rod having this I section is 12 in. In addition to the axial loads which the rod carries it is noted that at one place in its cycle of operation the rod is twisted through an angle of $\frac{1}{4}$ of a degree due to a deflection of the crank shaft. Assume that the sections at the ends of the rod are not free to warp, and compute the maximum lateral bending stress in the flanges produced by the twisting moment accompanying the angle of twist. See Fig. A, Table 15.   *Ans.* $\sigma = 8040$ lb/in.^{2}.

91 Transverse loads not through shear center.

If a channel beam having one section restrained from warping is subjected to a transverse load that does not act through the shear center of the section (Fig. 163a), the maximum longitudinal (bending) stress at the restrained section will be considerably greater than that given by the transverse bending moment because of the lateral bending of each flange due to the twisting moment Pm (Fig. 163a).

The maximum longitudinal stress as indicated in Fig. 163b may be found approximately by the expression

$$\sigma = \sigma_1 + \sigma_2$$

$$= \frac{M\frac{1}{2}h}{I} + \frac{Va\frac{1}{2}b}{I_f} = \frac{M\frac{1}{2}h}{I} + \frac{Pm}{h}\, a\, \frac{\frac{1}{2}b}{\frac{1}{12}tb^3} \tag{334}$$

in which $M = Pl$ is the transverse bending moment, I is the moment of inertia of the whole cross section of the beam with respect to the horizontal centroidal axis, and I_f is the moment of inertia of one flange with respect to the vertical centroidal axis of the flange.

In a rolled-steel channel and I beam the additional longitudinal stress caused by the lateral bending resulting from the twisting moment which arises from eccentricity of the transverse loads may be large. However, since the torsional stiffness of such sections is very small, a relatively small lateral restraint at a number of points along the beam is

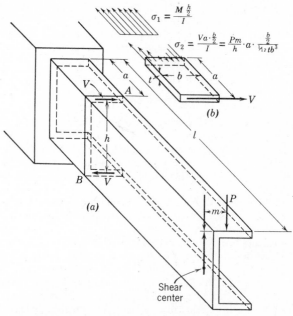

$$\sigma_1 = \frac{M\frac{h}{2}}{I}$$

$$\sigma_2 = \frac{Va \cdot \frac{b}{2}}{I} = \frac{Pm}{h} \cdot a \cdot \frac{\frac{b}{2}}{\frac{1}{12}tb^3}$$

FIG. 163   Approximate analysis of longitudinal stress in channel when load is not applied through shear center.

sufficient to prevent the twisting. Thus, in many uses of such members, even though the loads are not applied through the shear center, the lateral restraint supplied by attached portions of the structure along the length of the member may justify the assumption that the longitudinal bending stresses are the same as though the transverse loads were applied through the shear center.

When channel and I beams, however, are used so that they can twist as they bend, it is important that they be loaded through the shear center, or, if this is impossible, they should be designed to resist longitudinal stresses considerably in excess of those required by the flexural formula, in accordance with the above analysis. In any case, it is important to understand the limitations of the flexure formula as applied to channel and I beams.

Problems

179. A 6-in. 8.2-lb channel beam used as a cantilever beam 84 in. long is subjected to a concentrated load of 800 lb at the free end acting through the centroid of the section. Calculate the maximum longitudinal stress in the beam.

Ans. $\sigma_1 = 15,600$ lb/in.^{2}; $\sigma_2 = 10,600$ lb/in.^{2}; $\sigma = \sigma_1 + \sigma_2 = 26,200$ lb/in.^{2}

180. A 6-in. 15.3-lb ship channel is used as a simple beam on a span of 14 ft. It is subjected to a concentrated load of 3200 lb at mid-span acting through the centroid of the section. Calculate the maximum longitudinal stress at the restrained (mid-span) section. *Hint:* From the conditions of symmetry the mid-span section of the beam is not free to warp and is therefore restrained. A half-length of the beam therefore can be treated as a cantilever beam such as Fig. 163.

Selected References

1. Bach, C., *Elastizität und Festigkeit*, 8th edition, Julius Springer, Berlin, 1920. Gives the derivation of the torsion formula for elliptical and rectangular sections based on the observed strains of a model of plastic material.
2. Baron, F. M., "Torsion of Multiconnected Thin-walled Cylinders," *Transactions of the American Society of Mechanical Engineers*, Vol. 9, No. 2, June 1942, p. A-72.
3. Griffith, A. A., and G. I. Taylor, "The Use of Soap Films in Solving Torsion Problems," *Proceedings of the Institute of Mechanical Engineers (London)*, 1917, p. 755.
4. Pletta, D. H., and F. J. Maher, "The Torsional Properties of Round-Edged Flat Bars," *Bulletin* 50, Engineering Experiment Station, Virginia Polytechnic Institute.
5. Todhunter, I., and K. Pearson, *A History of the Elasticity and Strength of Materials*, Vol. II, Part I, Chapter X, Cambridge University Press, 1886. This chapter gives an interesting discussion of St. Venant's contributions to the solution of the problem of the torsion of prismatic bars.
6. Trayer, G. W., and H. W. March, "The Torsion of Members Having Sections Common in Aircraft Construction," *Report* 334, National Advisory Committee for Aeronautics, Superintendent of Documents, Washington, D. C.
7. Moore, R. L., and A. D. Paul, "Torsion Tests of 24ST Aluminum-Alloy Non-circular Bar and Tubing," *Technical Note* 885, National Advisory Committee for Aeronautics, 1942.

Chapter 10

THICK-WALLED CYLINDERS

92 The problem defined. By the term *thin-walled* or *thin-shelled cylinder* is meant a hollow cylinder in which the circumferential stress (frequently called hoop tension) in the shell may, without introducing appreciable errors in the stress analysis, be assumed to be constant throughout the thickness of the shell when the cylinder is subjected to an internal fluid pressure. Many boilers, tanks, steam and water pipes, etc., may be treated satisfactorily as thin-walled circular cylinders.

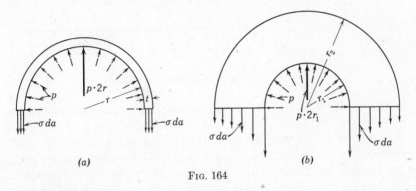

(a) (b)

FIG. 164

The circumferential stress σ in a thin-walled cylinder subjected to an internal pressure p per unit area is found by applying an equation of equilibrium to the forces acting on the half-cylinder shown in the Fig. 164a. For convenience the length of cylinder is assumed to be unity, and the wall thickness is denoted by t. The resulting equation is

$$p \cdot 2r = 2 \int \sigma \, da \qquad (335)$$

But under the assumed conditions, $\int \sigma \, da = a\sigma = t\sigma$. Hence,

$$\sigma = pr/t \qquad (336)$$

295

If, however, the wall thickness of the cylinder is relatively large, as in the case of guns, pipe to hydraulic presses, and similar high-pressure hydraulic and steam machinery (Fig. 164b), the variation in the stress from the inner surface to the outer surface is relatively large, and the value of the stress found from Eq. 336 is not a satisfactory measure of the significant circumferential stress in the cylinder.

Equation 335, however, applies to a thick-walled cylinder as well as to one with a thin shell; this fact will be evident from a consideration of the equilibrium of the forces acting on the thick-walled cylinder shown

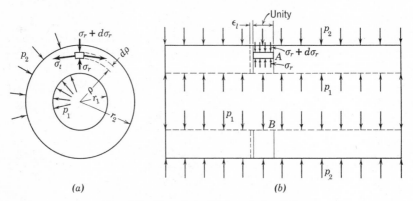

(a) (b)

Fig. 165 Stresses in thick-walled cylinder.

in Fig. 164b. The manner of distribution of the stress σ on the area, however, is not known, and hence the procedure outlined in Art. 8 (Chapter 2) is not directly applicable to the situation in Fig. 164b. Furthermore, a satisfactory solution of the thick-walled cylinder problem requires the determination not only of the circumferential stress at any point in the cylinder, but of both of the principal stresses whose vectors lie in the plane of the paper, namely, the circumferential or tangential stress σ_t and the radial stress σ_r as indicated in Fig. 165. The procedure in Art. 8, however, can be made to give a satisfactory solution by making a different approach to the problem as is illustrated in the next article. After these two principal stresses at any point in the cylinder wall have been found, the shearing stress, the maximum strain, the strain energy per unit volume, and the radial displacement or deflection of the point can also be obtained, by use of the equations developed in Chapter 3.

93 Lamé's solution for principal stresses. Figure 165 represents a relatively long open-ended thick-walled cylinder subjected to internal and external fluid pressures p_1 and p_2, respectively. Let it be required to find the circumferential stress σ_t and the radial stress σ_r at a point at any distance ρ from the central axis of the cylinder, as indicated in Fig. 165. From the conditions of symmetry, it is known that there is no shearing stress on the planes on which σ_t and σ_r act, and hence they are principal stresses.

Since both σ_t and σ_r are to be found, the procedure outlined in Art. 8 (Chapter 2) requires that sections be passed through the body in such a way that the portion of the body isolated by the sections shall be acted on by forces that involve the two stresses σ_t and σ_r. Such a portion is

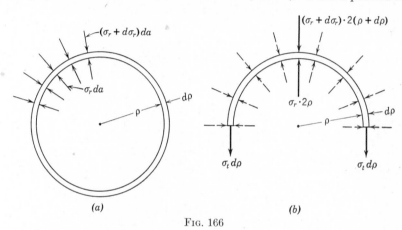

(a)   (b)

FIG. 166

obtained by first passing two concentric sections through the body and thus isolating a thin-walled cylinder; this element with the forces acting on it is shown in Fig. 166a. A diametral plane is then passed through the element, thereby isolating one-half of the element on which are acting forces that may be expressed in terms of the two stresses to be found, as indicated in Fig. 166b.

By applying one of the equations of equilibrium to the forces in Fig. 166b, namely, that the algebraic sum of the vertical components of the forces is equal to zero, the following equation is obtained:

$$2\sigma_t \, d\rho = -2\sigma_r \, d\rho - 2\rho \, d\sigma_r - 2 \, d\rho \, d\sigma_r \qquad (337)$$

The term $2 \, d\rho \, d\sigma_r$ is negligibly small. Hence

$$\sigma_t = -\sigma_r - \rho(d\sigma_r/d\rho) \qquad (338)$$

If the stresses σ_r and σ_t in Fig. 166b have been assumed to be positive, that is, if both stresses have been assumed to be tensile stresses, Eq. 338 would be

$$\sigma_t = \sigma_r + \rho(d\sigma_r/d\rho) \qquad (338a)$$

In accordance with the procedure outlined in Art. 8, the next step is to observe the strain behavior of the body under the loading specified, and then to express the relation between the strains and the stresses σ_t and σ_r, as developed in § 2 of Chapter 3.

A rational assumption concerning the strains in the thick-walled cylinder is that longitudinal strains of the (longitudinal) fibers are equal (denoted as plane strain). This means that plane transverse (parallel) sections before the fluid pressures P_1 and P_2 are applied remain plane and parallel after the pressures are applied; this will be true at least for a cylinder with open ends, and it will also be nearly true for a closed cylinder at sections well removed from the ends of the cylinder.

The relation between the longitudinal strain ϵ_l of any longitudinal fiber (Fig. 165) and the stresses acting on the fiber in an open-ended thick-walled cylinder is

$$\epsilon_l = \mu(\sigma_r/E) - \mu(\sigma_t/E) \tag{339}$$

as given by Eq. 39 of Chapter 3, and in accordance with the above assumption ϵ_l is a constant. Furthermore, Poisson's ratio μ and the modulus of elasticity E are constants of the (assumed) material. Hence

$$\sigma_t - \sigma_r = \text{Constant} = 2\alpha \tag{340}$$

The constant is denoted by 2α for convenience. Equations 338 and 340 give two relations between σ_t and σ_r. From these two equations we obtain

$$2\alpha = -2\sigma_r - \rho(d\sigma_r/d\rho)$$

But the right-hand member of this equation when multiplied by ρ becomes the derivative, with respect to ρ, of $-(\rho^2\sigma_r)$, and hence Eq. 340 may be written

$$d(\rho^2\sigma_r)/d\rho = -2\alpha\rho$$

The integration of this equation gives

$$\rho^2\sigma_r = -\alpha\rho^2 + \beta \tag{341}$$

where β is a constant of integration. Therefore

$$\sigma_r = (\beta/\rho^2) - \alpha \tag{342}$$

and, from Eq. 340,

$$\sigma_t = (\beta/\rho^2) + \alpha \tag{343}$$

The values of the constants α and β are found by substituting in Eq. 342 known pairs of values of σ_r and ρ as obtained from the physical conditions stated in the problem. For example, assuming the cylinder to be subjected to both internal and external pressures p_1 and p_2, respectively, we observe that

$$\sigma_r = p_1 \quad \text{when } \rho = r_1 \quad \text{and} \quad \sigma_r = p_2 \quad \text{when } \rho = r_2$$

and hence from Eq. 342 we obtain

$$p_1 = -\alpha + (\beta/r_1^2) \quad \text{and} \quad p_2 = -\alpha + (\beta/r_2^2) \qquad (344)$$

from which α and β are found to be

$$\alpha = \frac{p_1 r_1^2 - p_2 r_2^2}{r_2^2 - r_1^2} \quad \text{and} \quad \beta = \frac{r_1^2 r_2^2}{r_2^2 - r_1^2}(p_1 - p_2) \qquad (345)$$

The substitution of these values of α and β in Eqs. 342 and 343 gives

$$\sigma_t = \frac{p_1 r_1^2 - p_2 r_2^2 + (r_1^2 r_2^2/\rho^2)(p_1 - p_2)}{r_2^2 - r_1^2} \qquad (346)$$

and

$$\sigma_r = \frac{p_2 r_2^2 - p_1 r_1^2 + (r_1^2 r_2^2/\rho^2)(p_1 - p_2)}{r_2^2 - r_1^2} \qquad (347)$$

It is evident from Eq. 346 that the maximum value of σ_t occurs at the inner surface where ρ has its minimum value r_1. The maximum value of σ_r will always be the larger of the two pressures p_1 and p_2.

Signs. Both σ_t and σ_r were considered to be positive in the above derivation, and hence when the expression for σ_t gives a positive value σ_t is a tensile stress, and when it gives a negative value σ_t is a compressive stress; whereas when the expression for σ_r gives a positive value σ_r is a compressive stress, and it will always be positive.

Maximum Stresses with Both Internal and External Pressures. By making ρ in the above equations equal to r_1, the maximum stresses (at the inner surface) are found to be

$$\text{Maximum } \sigma_t = \frac{p_1(r_1^2 + r_2^2) - 2p_2 r_2^2}{r_2^2 - r_1^2} \qquad (348)$$

$$\text{Maximum } \sigma_r = p_1 \quad \text{if } p_1 > p_2 \qquad (349)$$

Special Cases: Maximum Stresses

Internal Pressure Only. If the internal pressure is p_1 and the external pressure is zero ($p_2 = 0$), as in most hydraulic pipes, tanks, etc., Eqs. 346 and 347 reduce to

$$\sigma_t = p_1 \frac{r_1^2}{r_2^2 - r_1^2}\left(\frac{r_2^2}{\rho^2} + 1\right) \qquad (350)$$

$$\sigma_r = p_1 \frac{r_1^2}{r_2^2 - r_1^2}\left(\frac{r_2^2}{\rho^2} - 1\right) \qquad (351)$$

These equations show that the maximum values of σ_t and σ_r occur at the inner surface, that is, when ρ has its least value r_1; they also show that, for any value of ρ, σ_t is always greater than σ_r. The maximum value of σ_t, as found from Eq. 350 by making $\rho = r_1$, is

$$\text{Maximum } \sigma_t = p_1 \frac{r_2{}^2 + r_1{}^2}{r_2{}^2 - r_1{}^2} \tag{352}$$

and the maximum value of σ_r for this case is p_1; these maximum stresses are indicated in Fig. 167.

It is important to note that Eq. 352 shows that σ_t is always greater than p_1, and hence p_1 cannot exceed a value greater than the elastic or utilizable strength of the material; therefore, when large internal pressures are required, as in guns, hoops are shrunk on the cylinder to cause initial compressive stresses but the value of p_1 is still limited to a value less than the compressive elastic limit of the material in order to prevent permanent set in the radial strain; or the material near the bore of an underbored gun is strained (plastically) beyond the elastic strength of the material by hydraulic pressure so that, as the pressure is released, the metal for a short depth from the inner surface or bore is put in a state of initial compression by the outer understressed elastic layers as they attempt to return to their unstrained condition. This procedure of pre-stressing as applied to guns is frequently called autofrettage. Several methods of pre-stressing are discussed in Arts. 99 to 101.

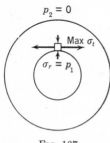

FIG. 167

In Table 16 are given values of the ratio of the maximum circumferential stress in a cylinder subjected to internal pressure only, as obtained

TABLE 16

$\dfrac{r_2}{r_1} = 1$	1.1	1.2	1.4	1.6	1.8	2.0	2.5
$\dfrac{\sigma_{\text{thick}}}{\sigma_{\text{thin}}} = 1$	1.05	1.10	1.23	1.37	1.51	1.67	2.07

from the thick-cylinder formula (Eq. 352) to that obtained by the thin-cylinder formula (Eq. 336) for various values of r_2/r_1. For example, the maximum circumferential stress in a thick-walled cylinder in which $r_2 = 1.4r_1$, is 1.23 times the value of σ obtained from the thin-cylinder formula, if the cylinder is subjected to an internal pressure only. (Figure 169 shows the variation of circumferential stress across a section for which $r_2 = 2r_1$.)   The thick-cylinder formula is specified by the A.P.I.–A.S.M.E. code * for calculating stresses in steel pipe when the thickness of the wall is greater than 10 per cent of the inside *diameter*, that is, when r_2/r_1 is greater than 1.2; and by the A.S.M.E. Power Boiler code when the wall thickness exceeds 10 per cent of the inside *radius*, that is, when r_2/r_1 is greater than 1.1.

External Pressure Only. If the external pressure is p_2 and the internal pressure is zero ($p_1 = 0$), Eqs. 346 and 347 reduce to

$$\sigma_t = -p_2 \frac{r_2^2}{r_2^2 - r_1^2}\left(1 + \frac{r_1^2}{\rho^2}\right) \tag{353}$$

$$\sigma_r = p_2 \frac{r_2^2}{r_2^2 - r_1^2}\left(1 - \frac{r_1^2}{\rho^2}\right) \tag{354}$$

These equations show that the maximum value of σ_t occurs at the inner surface (when $\rho = r_1$), and that it is a compressive (negative tensile) stress; its value is

$$\sigma_t = -2p_2 \frac{r_2^2}{r_2^2 - r_1^2} \tag{355}$$

The maximum value of σ_r is, of course, at the outer surface, and its value is p_2; as indicated in Fig. 168, the maximum value of σ_t and of σ_r do not occur at the same point in the cylinder for this case.

Longitudinal Stress in Cylinder with Closed Ends. If the thick-walled cylinder has closed or capped ends and is subjected to an internal pressure p_1 and an external pressure p_2, the longitudinal stress (on a transverse section) may be assumed to be uniformly distributed on any transverse section which is not close to the ends of the cylinder. By applying the conditions of equilibrium to the forces acting on the portion of the cylinder that lies to one side of a transverse plane, and assuming that p_2 acts on the capped ends, the longitudinal stress on such a section is found to be

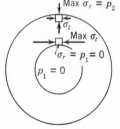

Fig. 168

$$\sigma_l = \frac{p_1 r_1 - p_2 r_2}{r_2^2 - r_1^2} \tag{356}$$

---

* This code was formulated by a joint committee of the American Petroleum Institute (A.P.I.) and the American Society of Mechanical Engineers (A.S.M.E.).

In such a cylinder there are three principal stresses at any point in the cylinder wall, namely, σ_t, σ_r, and σ_l. In many cases σ_l is small relative to σ_t and σ_r.

Barlow's Formula. Barlow's formula for the maximum circumferential stress in a thick-walled cylinder was the first formula to gain wide acceptance. The formula is $\sigma_t = pr_2/t$, where p is the internal pressure, r_2 is the external radius, and t is the wall thickness. The main difference between Lamé's formula (Eq. 352) for σ_t and Barlow's formula lies in the assumptions made concerning the manner in which the cylinder as a whole strains under the internal pressure. The Barlow formula applies to cylinders subjected to internal pressures only and depends upon the assumption that the cylinder strains in such a manner that the transverse cross-sectional area remains constant (see reference 3 at the end of this chapter). This assumption is known to be incorrect. The stresses calculated by the formula are always higher than the stresses calculated by the Lamé's formula for the same loading; therefore, Barlow's formula gives results on the side of safety, and hence thick-walled cylinders designed by the Barlow formula are likely to be uneconomical of material. Although Barlow's formula is still sometimes used, Lamé's formula, which rests on a sounder theoretical foundation, has gained wide acceptance.

Concentration of Stress in Pressure Vessels. In the preceding discussion the primary stresses in the cylinder wall have been assumed to be the significant stresses. This assumption is substantially correct for steel pressure vessels if corrosion is minimized, if elevated temperatures accompanied by creep or very low temperatures conducive to brittle fracture are avoided, and if the pressure is approximately a static load. However, around reinforced openings of high-pressure vessels and at points of rather sharp curvature and at points of support, etc., there may occur stress concentrations both in thin-walled and in thick-walled cylinders which under some conditions (especially under repeated applications of the pressure) may be the cause of failure and hence may be the significant stresses. For a discussion of stress concentrations in pressure vessels see reference 11 at the end of this chapter, and for a discussion of the design and construction of the ends of thick-walled cylinders see reference 12.

Stresses Caused by Temperature Gradient. If the temperature of the wall of a thick-walled cylinder varies throughout the wall, the uneven expansion or contraction of the material resulting from such temperature gradients will induce stresses in the wall which are superimposed on the stresses caused by the internal pressure in the cylinder. For a discussion of the significance of stresses due to temperature gradients and of methods for computing the stresses, see p. 74 of reference 11 at the end of this chapter.

Illustrative Problem

Problem 181. The barrel or hollow cylinder of a field gun is made of steel and has an internal diameter of 4.70 in. and an external diameter of 7.72 in. The tensile and compressive elastic strength of the material σ_e is 50,000 lb per sq in. (a) Find the maximum internal pressure to which the cylinder may be subjected (assuming the external pressure to be zero) without stressing the material above three-quarters of its elastic strength. (b) Find the maximum external pressure (assuming the internal pressure to be zero) that may be applied (by shrinking on hoops) without causing a stress greater than three-quarters of the tensile elastic strength of the material, as obtained from a tensile test. Thus a factor of safety of $\frac{4}{3}$ based on the tensile (or compressive) elastic strength is to be used in each case.

Solution. (a) By use of Eq. 352 we have

$$\frac{3}{4} \times 50,000 = p_1 \frac{(3.86)^2 + (2.35)^2}{(3.86)^2 - (2.35)^2} = 2.18p_1$$

$$p_1 = 37,500/2.18 = 17,250 \text{ lb/in.}^2$$

Hence, the maximum internal pressure that may be applied when the external pressure is zero is 17,250 lb per sq in.

(b) By use of Eq. 355 we have

$$-\frac{3}{4} \times 50,000 = -2p_2 \frac{(3.86)^2}{(3.86)^2 - (2.35)^2} = -3.18p_2$$

$$p_2 = 37,500/3.18 = 11,760 \text{ lb/in.}^2$$

Hence, the maximum external pressure that may be applied when the internal pressure is zero is 11,760 lb per sq in.

Problems

182. A hollow cylinder with closed ends has an internal diameter of 8 in. and an external diameter of 24 in. It is subjected to an internal pressure, only, of 10,000 lb per sq in. Find the maximum circumferential, radial, and longitudinal stresses at a section some distance from the ends, and state at what point on the section each stress occurs. *Ans.* $\sigma_t = 12,500$ lb/in.^{2}; $\sigma_r = 10,000$ lb/in.^{2}; $\sigma_l = 1,250$ lb/in.^{2}.

183. If the cylinder in Prob. 182 is subjected to an external pressure of 10,000 lb per sq in. and no internal pressure, find the maximum circumferential and radial stresses, and state where in the cylinder they occur. *Ans.* $\sigma_t = -22,500$ lb/in.^{2}.

184. A steel tank having an internal diameter of 5 ft is required to resist an internal air pressure of 5000 lb per sq in. The tensile and compressive elastic strength of the material is 30,000 lb per sq in. What should be the thickness of the wall if the working value of the circumferential stress is two-thirds of the tensile elastic strength (that is, a so-called factor of safety of 1.5 based on the tensile elastic strength as obtained from a tension test is used). *Ans.* $t = 8.80$ in.

185. A thick-walled cylinder is to be designed to resist an internal pressure of 12,000 lb per sq in. without being subjected to a maximum tensile stress greater than one-half the tensile elastic strength of the material; the internal radius is specified to be 4 in., and the outside radius 8 in. Four grades of steel are available; their tensile elastic strengths are 30,000, 40,000, 50,000, and 60,000 lb per sq in. Could each of these steels be used? If not, which of the four would *not* satisfy the requirements specified in the problem?

186. A hollow cylinder is acted on by an external pressure of 3000 lb per sq in. and an internal pressure of 10,000 lb per sq in. The internal diameter of the cylinder is 3 in., and the external diameter is 5 in. Calculate the maximum circumferential stress in the cylinder, assuming that the tensile elastic strength of the material is not exceeded.   *Ans.*   11,900 lb/in.[2].

187. Plot a curve (similar to AB in Fig. 169), the ordinates to which show the values of the circumferential stress at various distances from the center of the cylin-

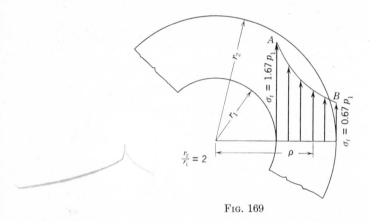

Fɪɢ. 169

der: (a) Let $r_1 = 1$ in., $r_2/r_1 = 1.2$, $p_1 = 1000$ lb per sq in., and $p_2 = 0$; (b) Plot a similar curve, using the value $r_2/r_1 = 4$, the other data remaining the same. In obtaining the curve in Fig. 169, the value used for r_2/r_1 was 2.

94   Radial deflection. In some thick-walled cylinders such as guns it is required to determine the deflection (displacement) in the radial direction of any point in the cylinder wall. For example, the radial displacement is an important quantity to determine in a thick-walled cylinder that is made by shrinking an outer thick-walled cylinder (frequently called a tube, hoop, or jacket) over an inner hollow cylinder. The computation of the stresses in such a composite hollow cylinder is a statically indeterminate problem, the solution of which involves the radial deflections of the two cylinders.

The radial deflection or displacement of a point in the cylinder wall is found by first computing the increase (or decrease) in the length of the circumference of a circle passing through the point. Let the cylinder to be considered be represented in Fig. 170, and let the point A be any point on a circle whose radius is ρ. The pressures p_1 and p_2 produce radial and tangential stresses σ_r and σ_t at the point A. The strain in the tangential direction at the point A and at all points on the circle, expressed in terms of these stresses, is given by Eq. 39 and is

$$\epsilon_t = (1/E)(\sigma_t - \mu\sigma_r) \tag{357}$$

in which a tensile stress is considered to be positive and a compressive stress negative. The change in the length of the circumference of the

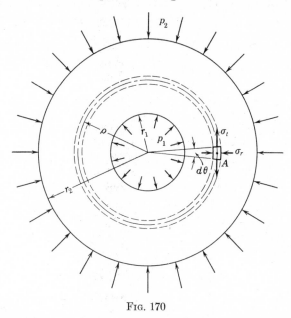

FIG. 170

circle whose radius is ρ is $2\pi\rho\epsilon_t$, and hence the change in the length of ρ which is also the radial deflection or displacement δ_A of each point on the circle is

$$\delta_A = 2\pi\rho\epsilon_t/2\pi = \rho\epsilon_t \tag{358}$$

Combining Eqs. 357 and 358 we obtain

$$\delta_A = (\rho/E)(\sigma_t - \mu\sigma_r) \tag{359}$$

In Eq. 359 σ_t and σ_r are the stresses at the point whose deflection is desired. For example, if the cylinder is subjected to an internal pressure p_1 only, the increase in the length of the internal radius is (see Eq. 352)

$$\delta_1 = \frac{r_1}{E}\left[p_1 \frac{r_2{}^2 + r_1{}^2}{r_2{}^2 - r_1{}^2} - \mu(-p_1) \right]$$

$$= \frac{p_1 r_1}{E}\left(\frac{r_2{}^2 + r_1{}^2}{r_2{}^2 - r_1{}^2} + \mu \right) \tag{360}$$

If the cylinder is subjected to an external pressure p_2 only, the change in length of the external radius is (see Eq. 353)

$$\delta_2 = -\frac{p_2 r_2}{E}\left(\frac{r_2{}^2 + r_1{}^2}{r_2{}^2 - r_1{}^2} - \mu\right) \tag{361}$$

in which the negative sign indicates a decrease in the radius r_2.

Illustrative Problem

Problem 188. In part (b) of Prob. 181 it was found that the required value of the external pressure was $p_2 = 11,760$ lb per sq in. A hollow thick-walled cylinder of steel whose external diameter is 12 in. is shrunk on the main or inner hollow cylinder described in Prob. 181 in order to produce this external pressure. The outer cylinder which is shrunk on the inner cylinder is usually called a jacket or a hoop. (a) Compute the difference that must exist between the external diameter of the cylinder and the internal diameter of the jacket in order that the pressure p_2 of 11,760 lb per sq in. will occur between the jacket and the cylinder after the jacket has been shrunk on the cylinder and the two hollow cylinders have reached the same (room) temperature. (b) How many degrees of temperature (Fahrenheit) will the jacket have to be heated above the temperature of the cylinder in order that the jacket will just slip on the cylinder?

Solution. (a) The radii of the hollow cylinders are

$$r_1 = 2.35 \text{ in.} \qquad r_2 = 3.86 \text{ in.} \qquad r_3 = 6.00 \text{ in.}$$

r_3 is the external radius of the jacket. Let it be assumed that $r_2 = 3.86$ in. is also approximately equal to the internal radius of the jacket. The pressure p_2 acting on the inside surface of the jacket causes an increase in length of its internal radius r_2 which is given by Eq. 360. Thus

$$\delta_1 = \frac{p_2 r_2}{E}\left(\frac{r_3{}^2 + r_2{}^2}{r_3{}^2 - r_2{}^2} + \mu\right)$$

$$= \frac{11,760 \times 3.86}{30,000,000}\left[\frac{(6.00)^2 + (3.86)^2}{(6.00)^2 - (3.86)^2} + \frac{1}{4}\right] = 0.0040 \text{ in.}$$

The pressure p_2 acting on the exterior surface of the cylinder causes a decrease in the external radius r_2, the magnitude of which may be found from Eq. 361. Thus,

$$\delta_2 = -\frac{p_2 r_2}{E}\left(\frac{r_2{}^2 + r_1{}^2}{r_2{}^2 - r_1{}^2} - \mu\right)$$

$$= -\frac{11,760 \times 3.86}{30,000,000}\left[\frac{(3.86)^2 + (2.35)^2}{(3.86)^2 - (2.35)^2} - \frac{1}{4}\right] = -0.0029 \text{ in.}$$

The negative sign indicates that r_2 is shortened. The difference between the outer radius of the cylinder and the inner radius of the jacket must be made equal to the numerical sum of δ_1 and δ_2. Thus $\delta_1 + \delta_2 = 0.0069$ in. Therefore the inner diameter of the jacket must be made equal to $2(3.86 - 0.0069) = 7.706$ in.

(b) The coefficient of thermal expansion of steel is $\alpha = 0.0000066$ in. per in. per degree Fahrenheit. Let Δt be the change in temperature required. The equation $\delta_A = \rho\epsilon_t$ may be written

$$\delta_A = \rho\alpha\,\Delta t$$

In order to provide for a sliding fit in placing the heated jacket over the cylinder, 0.002 in. is added to the required value of δ_A, thus making 0.0089 in. instead of 0.0069 in.

$$0.0089 = 3.86 \times 0.0000066\Delta t$$

and hence $\qquad\qquad \Delta t = 348° \text{ F}$

Problems

189. Compute the radial deflection or displacement of a point on the internal surface of the cylinder described in Prob. 182.

190. A thick-walled steel cylinder has an interior radius of 2 in. and an exterior radius of 3.5 in. This cylinder is to be subjected to an internal pressure of 36,000 lb per sq in., but the maximum circumferential (tensile) stress must not exceed 40,000 lb per sq in. If a cylindrical jacket or hoop of the same material is shrunk on the thick-walled cylinder in order to prevent the stress from exceeding 40,000 lb per sq in., what should be the difference between the internal diameter of the jacket and the external diameter of the cylinder before the jacket is expanded by heating so that it will slip on the cylinder. *Ans.* Difference in diameters = 0.0037 in.

95 Maximum shearing stress, octahedral shearing stress, maximum strain, and energy of distortion.

The design of a thick-walled cylinder, as discussed in the next article, in accordance with the various theories of the breakdown of elastic behavior (so-called theories of failure), requires expressions for the quantities listed in the title of this article. As previously noted, these quantities may be expressed in terms of the principal stresses which in turn may be expressed in terms of the loads (internal and external pressures) acting on the cylinder and the dimensions of the cylinder, by means of the equations developed in the preceding articles of this chapter.

It may seem that it should be unnecessary to apply to thick-walled cylinders each of the several theories of the beginning of inelastic deformation. If the one criterion or theory which is considered to be the most reliable or acceptable were used, much work would be avoided. The fact is, however, that all the several theories that were discussed in Arts. 30 through 33 are used in the design of thick-walled cylinders, and some confusion has arisen in interpreting the results of the various theories. It is desirable, therefore, to discuss the application of all these theories.

Maximum Shearing Stress. As shown in Art. 20 (Chapter 3) the maximum shearing stress at any point in a stressed body is equal to one-half the algebraic difference of the maximum and minimum principal stresses at the point. Thus at any point in the thick-walled cylinder

$$\tau_{\max} = \tfrac{1}{2}(\sigma_t - \sigma_r) \tag{362}$$

in which a tensile stress is regarded as positive and a compressive stress as negative.

For a cylinder subjected to both internal and external pressure, the value of $\tau_{\max}$ at a point whose distance from the center of the cylinder is ρ may be found by making use of Eqs. 346 and 347. The value is

$$\tau_{\max} = \frac{(p_1 - p_2)r_1{}^2 r_2{}^2}{\rho^2(r_2{}^2 - r_1{}^2)} \tag{363}$$

The greatest value of $\tau_{\max}$ occurs at a point on the inner surface, that is where $\rho = r_1$. Further, if the cylinder is subjected to internal pressure only, the greatest value of $\tau_{\max}$ may be found from Eq. 363 by making $\rho = r_1$ and $p_2 = 0$. The value is

$$\tau_{\max} = p_1[r_2{}^2/(r_2{}^2 - r_1{}^2)] \tag{364}$$

This stress occurs on each of two planes, making an angle of 45° with the planes on which the principal stresses act as shown in Fig. 171.

Octahedral Shearing Stress. It was shown in Art. 24 (Chapter 3) that at any point in a stressed body shearing stresses of equal magnitude occur on each of the octahedral planes passing through the point. These stresses are called octahedral shearing stresses and can be expressed conveniently in terms of the three principal stresses at the point.

In the thick-walled cylinder the principal stresses are σ_t, σ_r, and σ_l, and in accordance with Eq. 26 (Art. 24) the expression for the octahedral shearing stress τ_G is

$$\tau_G = \tfrac{1}{3}\sqrt{(\sigma_t - \sigma_r)^2 + (\sigma_r - \sigma_l)^2 + (\sigma_l - \sigma_t)^2} \tag{365}$$

in which a tensile stress is regarded as positive and a compressive stress as negative.

If σ_l is small relative to σ_t and σ_r and may be neglected, Eq. 365 reduces to

$$\tau_G = \tfrac{1}{3}\sqrt{(\sigma_t - \sigma_r)^2 + \sigma_r{}^2 + \sigma_t{}^2} \tag{366}$$

The values of σ_t, σ_r, and σ_l may be obtained from the loads on the cylinder, and its dimensions by use of the equations developed in the preceding articles of this chapter.

Maximum Strain. The most severe straining action in the thick-walled cylinder occurs at the inner fibers where the circumferential stress has its maximum value, and the direction of the maximum strain is the same as that of the circumferential stress σ_t. The stresses acting on a longitudinal fiber of a closed cylinder are shown in Fig. 172, the stresses being indicated only on one face of each pair of faces of the fiber. The value of the maximum (circumferential) strain is (see Eq. 39 of Chapter 3)

$$\epsilon_{\max} = (\sigma_t/E) - \mu(\sigma_r/E) - \mu(\sigma_l/E) \tag{367}$$

in which a tensile stress is regarded as positive and a compressive stress as negative.

For a cylinder with open ends, σ_l is equal to zero, and for a cylinder with closed ends, σ_l is given by Eq. 356. The values of σ_t and σ_r for use

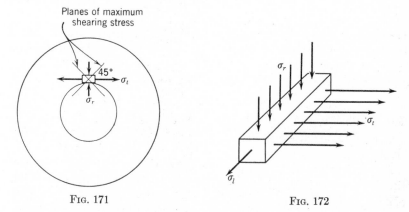

Planes of maximum shearing stress

FIG. 171 FIG. 172

in Eq. 367 are given in Art. 93 for various combinations of internal and external pressures. Thus Eq. 367 can be made to express the maximum strain $\epsilon_{\max}$ in the cylinder in terms of the external loads and dimensions of the cylinder. This will be done for special cases as follows.

Internal Pressure Only. Let it be assumed that the cylinder has *open* ends ($\sigma_l = 0$) and that the external pressure p_2 is zero. Then, from Eqs. 352 and 367, we obtain

$$\epsilon_{\max} = \frac{p_1}{E} \left(\frac{r_2^2 + r_1^2}{r_2^2 - r_1^2} + \mu \right) \tag{368}$$

which sometimes is referred to as *Birnie's formula.*

If the cylinder has *closed* ends and hence σ_l is not equal to zero, Eq. 367 becomes

$$\epsilon_{\max} = \frac{p_1}{E} \left[\frac{r_2^2 + (1 - \mu)r_1^2}{r_2^2 - r_1^2} + \mu \right] \tag{369}$$

which sometimes is referred to as *Clavarino's formula.*

Maximum Energy of Distortion. As shown in Art. 29, Chapter 3, Eq. 60 is an expression for the energy of distortion per unit volume (absorbed in changing the shape of a unit volume). In a thick-walled cylinder in which the three principal stresses are σ_t, σ_r, and σ_l, Eq. 60 gives

$$w_d = \frac{1+\mu}{6E} [(\sigma_t - \sigma_r)^2 + (\sigma_r - \sigma_l)^2 + (\sigma_l - \sigma_t)^2] \qquad (370)$$

in which a tensile stress is assumed to be positive and a compressive stress negative. If the cylinder has an open end, as for example in the case of a gun, the longitudinal stress σ_l is zero, and Eq. 370 becomes

$$w_d = \frac{1+\mu}{6E} [(\sigma_t - \sigma_r)^2 + \sigma_r{}^2 + \sigma_t{}^2]$$

$$= \frac{1+\mu}{3E} (\sigma_t{}^2 - \sigma_t \sigma_r + \sigma_r{}^2) \qquad (371)$$

The values of σ_t and σ_r for any condition of loading and type of cylinder can be obtained from the equations in the preceding articles of this chapter.

As previously noted, the foregoing expressions for the several quantities that are considered, in the various theories of failure, to be the cause of structural damage to material when they reach certain limiting values, are needed in the next article. The use of the expressions and the significance of the limiting values of the several quantities are illustrated in the following problem.

Illustrative Problem

Problem 191. A thick-walled steel cylinder is subjected to an internal pressure p only ($p_1 = p$, $p_2 = 0$). The dimensions of the cylinder are $r_2 = 4$ in. and $r_1 = 2$ in. The limiting values, as found from a tension test, of the several quantities that are considered to be the cause of structural damage are as follows (see Table 1, Chapter 3; these are the values of the several quantities when inelastic deformation is observed to start in the specimen of the material used in the tension test): Tensile stress $\sigma_e = 50,000$ lb per sq in.; maximum shearing stress $\tau_e = \frac{1}{2}\sigma_e = 25,000$ lb per sq in.; octahedral shearing stress $\tau_G = (\sqrt{2}/3)\sigma_e = 0.47\sigma_e = 23,500$ lb per sq in.; tensile strain $\epsilon_e = \sigma_e/E = 50,000/30,000,000 = 0.00166$ in. per in.; energy of distortion per unit volume $w_d = \dfrac{1+\mu}{3E}\sigma_e{}^2 = \dfrac{1+0.25}{3 \times 3 \times 10^7}(50,000)^2 = 34.7$ in.-lb per cu in. Use a factor of safety of 1.5, and calculate p_w, the working value of p, in accordance with each of the criteria of structural damage.

Solution. Tensile Stress. Equation 352 gives

$$\sigma_w = \frac{50,000}{1.5} = p_w \frac{(4)^2 + (2)^2}{(4)^2 - (2)^2} = \frac{5}{3} p_w$$

$$p_w = 20,000 \text{ lb/in.}^2$$

Maximum Shearing Stress. Equation 364 gives

$$\tau_w = \frac{25,000}{1.5} = p_w \frac{(4)^2}{(4)^2 - (2)^2}$$

$$p_w = 12,500 \text{ lb/in.}^2$$

Octahedral Shearing Stress. Equations 366 and 352 gives

$$\tau_{Gw} = \frac{0.47\sigma_e}{1.5} = \frac{23,500}{1.5} = \frac{1}{3} \sqrt{(\sigma_t - \sigma_r)^2 + \sigma_r^2 + \sigma_t^2}$$

in which $\sigma_t = \frac{5}{3}p_w$ and $\sigma_r = -p_w$. Hence

$$15,650 = 1.10p_w \quad \text{and} \quad p_w = 14,300 \text{ lb/in.}^2$$

Tensile Strain. Equation 368 gives

$$\epsilon_w = \frac{0.00166}{1.5} = \frac{p_w}{3 \times 10^7} \left[\frac{(4)^2 + (2)^2}{(4)^2 - (2)^2} + \frac{1}{4} \right]$$

$$p_w = 17,300 \text{ lb/in.}^2$$

Energy of Distortion. Referring to Eqs. 371 and 352, and to *Caution* in Art. 2, Chapter 1, we proceed as follows.

$$w_d = 34.7 = \frac{1 + \mu}{3E} (\sigma_t^2 - \sigma_t\sigma_r + \sigma_r^2)$$

in which $\sigma_t = \frac{5}{3}(1.5p_w)$ and $\sigma_r = -1.5p_w$, $\mu = 0.25$.

$$34.7 = \frac{1.25}{3 \times 3 \times 10^7} \times \frac{49}{4} p_w^2$$

$$p_w = 14,300 \text{ lb/in.}^2$$

As shown in Art. 31 of Chapter 3, this method should give the same result as that found by the use of the octahedral stress.

In this problem it is found that the working or allowable value for the internal pressure would be limited to 12,500 lb per sq in. if the maximum shearing stress were considered to be the cause of the beginning of inelastic deformation; whereas the allowable value could be 20,000 lb per sq in. if inelastic deformation is considered to be caused by the tensile principal stress. The other criteria of inelastic action give values for the allowable internal pressure between these two values. The reliability of the various criteria is discussed in Art. 32 of Chapter 3 and in the next article.

Problems

192. Find the maximum shearing stress in the cylinder described in Prob. 182, and state where this stress is located in the cylinder and the direction of the plane on which the stress acts.   *Ans.* $\tau_{max} = 11,250$ lb/in.^{2}.

193. The shearing elastic strength of the material of the tank described in Prob. 184 is $\tau_e = 0.5\sigma_e = 15,000$ lb per sq in. If the maximum allowable value of the shearing stress is two-thirds the shearing elastic strength, what should be the thickness of the tank wall?

194. Derive the expression for the maximum shearing stress when the cylinder is subjected to (a) external pressure only, and (b) both internal and external pressures.

$$Ans. \quad (a)\ \tau_{max} = \frac{-p_2 r_2^2}{r_2^2 - r_1^2}. \quad (b)\ \tau_{max} = \frac{(p_1 - p_2) r_2^2}{r_2^2 - r_1^2}.$$

195. In Prob. 191 let $\sigma_e = 40,000$ lb per sq in., and calculate the allowable internal pressure on the assumption that (a) the tensile strain is the criterion for the beginning of inelastic deformation, and (b) that the tensile principal stress is the criterion.

196. Let the tensile elastic strength of the material of the gun described in Prob. 181 be 40,000 lb per sq in.; also let $\mu = 0.25$, and $E = 30,000,000$ lb per sq in. Use a factor of safety of 2 (see *Caution* in Art. 2, Chapter 1), and calculate the allowable internal pressure, assuming that the criterion for the beginning of inelastic deformation is the energy of distortion. Check the answer by calculating the allowable pressure based on the assumption that the criterion for the beginning of inelastic deformation is the octahedral stress.

96   Application of various theories of the breakdown of elastic action. For convenience in design and for the purpose of making comparisons of the results obtained by applying the various criteria for the beginning of inelastic behavior, it is convenient to find expressions for the thickness of the wall of a thick-walled cylinder in terms of the allowable value of the stress or strain or energy, according to the criterion of strength used, and of the pressures applied and the radii of the cylinder. Frequently it is convenient to obtain the ratio t/r_1 (or r_2/r_1) in terms of the ratio p/σ_w. The expressions for the wall thickness (or for the ratio t/r_1) will here be found *for the case in which a cylinder with closed ends is subjected to an internal pressure only* ($p_2 = 0$, $p_1 = p$).

Maximum Principal Stress Theory. Equation 352 may be written

$$\frac{p}{\sigma_w} = \frac{r_2^2 - r_1^2}{r_2^2 + r_1^2} \tag{372}$$

in which the allowable or working value σ_w of the tensile stress must not exceed σ_e. Equation 372 may be written

$$\frac{r_2}{r_1} = \sqrt{\frac{\sigma_w + p}{\sigma_w - p}} \tag{373}$$

or
$$\frac{r_1 + t}{r_1} = 1 + \frac{t}{r_1} = \sqrt{\frac{\sigma_w + p}{\sigma_w - p}} \tag{374}$$

Thus
$$t = r_1 \left[\sqrt{\frac{\sigma_w + p}{\sigma_w - p}} - 1 \right] \tag{375}$$

Equation 375 may be rewritten in terms of two dimensionless ratios as follows:

$$\frac{t}{r_1} = \sqrt{\frac{1 + (p/\sigma_w)}{1 - (p/\sigma_w)}} - 1 \tag{376}$$

In Fig. 173 values of the ratio p/σ_w are represented as ordinates and values of t/r_1 as abscissas. The coordinates of points on the upper curve in this figure satisfy Eq. 376. In Eqs. 375 and 376, if $\sigma_w = p$, the thickness t required is indefinitely large.

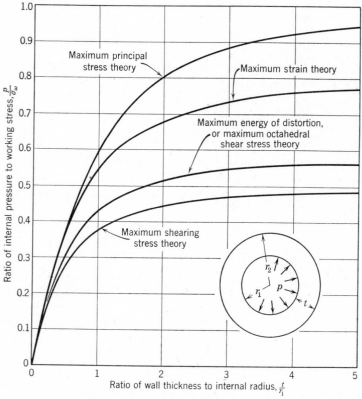

Fig. 173 Relation between internal pressure and thickness of wall as determined by various theories of failure.

Maximum Shearing Stress Theory. Equation 364 may be written

$$\left(\frac{r_2}{r_1}\right)^2 = \frac{\tau_w}{\tau_w - p} \tag{377}$$

in which τ_w must not exceed τ_e. Equation 377 may be written

$$\frac{r_2}{r_1} = 1 + \frac{t}{r_1} = \sqrt{\frac{\tau_w}{\tau_w - p}} \tag{378}$$

$$t = r_1 \left[\sqrt{\frac{\tau_w}{\tau_w - p}} - 1 \right] \tag{379}$$

According to the maximum shearing stress theory of failure, the shearing elastic strength is one-half of the tensile elastic strength, and, therefore, $\tau_w = \frac{1}{2}\sigma_w$. Hence Eq. 379 may be written

$$\frac{t}{r_1} = \sqrt{\frac{1}{1 - 2(p/\sigma_w)}} - 1 \tag{380}$$

In Fig. 173 this equation is represented by the lowest curve. In Eq. 379, if $\tau_w = p$, the required thickness t is indefinitely large as it is also in Eq. 380 if $p/\sigma_w = \frac{1}{2}$. Sometimes the value of τ_w is taken as $0.6\sigma_w$ because the results of torsion tests indicate that $\tau_e = 0.6\sigma_e$. If $\tau_w = 0.6\sigma_w$, Eq. 379 becomes

$$\frac{t}{r_1} = \sqrt{\frac{1}{1 - 1.67(p/\sigma_w)}} - 1 \tag{380a}$$

Maximum Strain Theory. If the values of σ_t, σ_r, and σ_l are substituted in Eq. 367, we obtain

$$\epsilon_w = \frac{p}{E}\left(\frac{r_2^2 + r_1^2}{r_2^2 - r_1^2} + \mu - \mu\frac{r_1^2}{r_2^2 - r_1^2}\right) \tag{381}$$

in which ϵ_w must not exceed the value of the strain ϵ_e at which inelastic deformation of the material starts as determined in the tension test. Equation 381 may be written

$$\frac{r_2}{r_1} = \sqrt{\frac{E\epsilon_w + (1 - 2\mu)p}{E\epsilon_w - (1 + \mu)p}}$$

and hence

$$t = r_1 \left[\sqrt{\frac{E\epsilon_w + (1 - 2\mu)p}{E\epsilon_w - (1 + \mu)p}} - 1 \right] \tag{382}$$

For the purpose of comparing the results obtained from Eq. 382 with those from Eqs. 376 and 380, we may replace $E\epsilon_w$ with its equivalent value σ_w and rewrite the equation in the form

$$\frac{t}{r_1} = \sqrt{\frac{1 + (1 - 2\mu)(p/\sigma_w)}{1 - (1 + \mu)(p/\sigma_w)}} - 1 \tag{383}$$

This equation is represented in Fig. 173 by the curve second from the top.

Maximum Energy of Distortion. If the values of σ_t, σ_r, and σ_l are substituted in Eq. 370, we obtain, after collecting terms,

$$w_{dw} = \frac{1 + \mu}{E}\left(\frac{pr_2{}^2}{r_2{}^2 - r_1{}^2}\right)^2 \tag{384}$$

in which w_{dw} must not exceed the value

$$w_{de} = \frac{1 + \mu}{3E}\sigma_e{}^2 \tag{385}$$

which is the value of the energy of distortion per unit volume in the material of a tension specimen when inelastic deformation starts. Equation 384 may be written

$$(q - 1)\frac{r_2{}^4}{r_1{}^4} - 2q\frac{r_2{}^2}{r_1{}^2} + q = 0 \tag{386}$$

in which the terms involving w_{dw}, E, μ, and p^2 are collected into one quantity and represented by q, that is,

$$q = \frac{Ew_{dw}}{p^2(1 + \mu)} \tag{387}$$

Equation 386 is a quadratic in $r_2{}^2/r_1{}^2$, and hence

$$\frac{r_2{}^2}{r_1{}^2} = \frac{2q \pm \sqrt{(2q)^2 - 4q(q - 1)}}{2(q - 1)} \tag{388}$$

An examination of the magnitude of the quantity q shows that in order that the right-hand side of Eq. 388 be positive the plus sign in front of the square root must be chosen. Thus

$$\frac{r_2{}^2}{r_1{}^2} = \frac{q + \sqrt{q}}{q - 1} = \frac{\sqrt{q}(\sqrt{q} + 1)}{(\sqrt{q} - 1)(\sqrt{q} + 1)} = \frac{\sqrt{q}}{\sqrt{q} - 1}$$

Therefore

$$t = r_1\left[\sqrt{\frac{\sqrt{q}}{\sqrt{q} - 1}} - 1\right] \tag{389}$$

An allowable or working value q_w must now be selected for q. This is done by applying the factor of safety N to the load p (see *Caution* in Art. 2, Chapter 1). Thus a load Np is considered to act on the cylinder and to cause the maximum energy of distortion to be equal to the value w_{de}. Hence Eq. 387 becomes

$$q_w = \frac{Ew_{de}}{(Np)^2(1 + \mu)} = \frac{[E(1 + \mu)/3E]\sigma_e^2}{(Np)^2(1 + \mu)} = \frac{1}{3p^2}\left(\frac{\sigma_e}{N}\right)^2 \quad (390)$$

But $\sigma_e/N = \sigma_w$ is the working value of the circumferential stress as used previously in this article. Hence

$$q_w = \tfrac{1}{3}(\sigma_w/p)^2 \quad (391)$$

Equation 389 may now be written

$$\frac{t}{r_1} = \frac{1}{\sqrt{1 - \sqrt{3}(p/\sigma_w)}} - 1 \quad (392)$$

This equation is represented in Fig. 173 by the curve labeled energy of distortion theory (or octahedral shearing stress theory, since as previously noted these two theories lead to the same results).

Comparison of Theories. The curves in Fig. 173 apply to thick-walled cylinders subjected to internal pressure *only*. They may be used for determining by each of the theories of the breakdown of elastic deformation the allowable internal pressure p for a thick-walled cylinder of given dimensions (r_1 and t) made of a material for which the given allowable circumferential stress is σ_w. Or they may be used for determining, by the various theories of elastic breakdown, the dimensions of the cylinder required for insuring that the significant quantity (which according to the theory is the cause of the inelastic deformation) is equal to the allowable value of this quantity when the cylinder is resisting the given internal pressure p.

The reader should study Fig. 173 and compare the results obtained by the various theories of elastic failure. A brief discussion of the reliability of the several theories is given in Art. 32, Chapter 3, and in the next article of this chapter.

One fact of special importance is revealed by the curves in Fig. 173, namely, that for the larger values of the ratio p/σ_w each of the curves shows that a small increase in the pressure p requires a large increase in the wall thickness. And, since much of the material in a cylinder having a very thick wall is ineffectively used because of the low stress in the outer portion of the cylinder, it is desirable to select a material such that σ_w will make the ratio p/σ_w reasonably small. When this cannot be done, one of several methods of increasing the strength of a thick-walled cylinder (discussed in Arts. 98 to 101) may be used which makes possible more effective use of the material.

Illustrative Problem

Problem 197. A pipe is made of steel having a tensile elastic strength of $\sigma_e = 40,000$ lb per sq in., a shearing elastic strength of $\tau_e = \frac{1}{2}\sigma_e = 20,000$ lb per sq in., and a tensile modulus of elasticity of $E = 30,000,000$ lb per sq in. The pipe is subjected to an internal fluid pressure of $p = 10,000$ lb per sq in. The internal radius is $r_1 = 2$ in. Find the proper thickness of the wall, according to each of the four most widely used theories of failure, using a factor of safety of $\frac{4}{3}$ in each case.

Solution. Maximum Principal Stress Theory. The value of the working stress is $\sigma_w = 30,000$ lb per sq in., and hence the ratio $p/\sigma_w = 0.33$ is small so that effective use of the material is possible. The substitution of this value of p/σ_w into Eq. 376 gives

$$\frac{t}{r_1} = \sqrt{\frac{1 + 0.33}{1 - 0.33}} - 1 = 0.41$$

$$t = 0.41 r_1 = 0.82 \text{ in.}$$

Maximum Shearing Stress Theory. The value of the working shearing stress is $\tau_w = 15,000$ lb per sq in. Equation 379 then gives

$$t = 2\left[\sqrt{\frac{15,000}{15,000 - 10,000}} - 1\right] = 1.46 \text{ in.}$$

Maximum Strain Theory. If in Eq. 382 $\mu = 0.25$, the equation becomes

$$t = r_1\left[\sqrt{\frac{4E\epsilon_w + 2p}{4E\epsilon_w - 5p}} - 1\right]$$

Since $\epsilon_w = \frac{3}{4}(40,000/E)$ or $E\epsilon_w = \frac{3}{4}(40,000)$.

$$t = r_1\left(\sqrt{\frac{120,000 + 20,000}{120,000 - 50,000}} - 1\right) = 2(1.414 - 1) = 0.83 \text{ in.}$$

Maximum Energy of Distortion Theory. If in Eq. 392 $p/\sigma_w = 0.33$ is substituted, the equation becomes

$$\frac{t}{r_1} = \frac{1}{\sqrt{1 - 0.33\sqrt{3}}} - 1 = 0.54$$

$$t = 0.54 r_1 = 1.08 \text{ in.}$$

In this problem the required wall thickness varies from $t = 0.82$ in. as required by the maximum principal stress theory of elastic breakdown to $t = 1.46$ as required by the maximum shearing stress theory. It is clear from these values and from Fig. 173 in general that the theory of failure used in the design of thick-walled cylinders under internal pressure is of real importance. See Art. 97 for brief comments on the significance of the several theories.

Problem

198. Find, by each of the four theories of failure used in Prob. 197, the thickness of the wall of a steel hollow cylinder to which the following data apply: internal diameter = 6 in.; internal pressure = 10,000 lb per sq in.; external pressure = 0; tensile elastic strength = 50,000 lb per sq in.; tensile modulus of elasticity = 30,000,-000 lb per sq in.; factor of safety = 2.

97 Comments on the theories of failure. The discussion of the theories of the breakdown of elastic action given in Art. 32 (Chapter 3) should here be reviewed. It is well to emphasize the following facts in connection with the thick-walled cylinder problem.

(a) The theories of failure of elastic action give no information as to the value of the stresses in the cylinder; the stresses are fixed solely by the conditions of equilibrium and the manner of distribution of strain in the cylinder, as obtained from Lamé's solution, etc.

(b) This distribution of strain according to Lamé's solution is assumed to be that the longitudinal strains of the fibers are equal; since this could not be true near the ends of a closed cylinder owing to the restraint (bending action) of the ends, the values of the stresses given in Lamé's formulas should be modified (largely, at present, by judgment after studying the nature of the restraints) in obtaining the significant stress when the conditions do not justify Lamé's assumption.

(c) The theories of failure as used in this chapter refer to the theories that predict the beginning of yielding, and hence they apply mainly to ductile material such as low and medium carbon steels, aluminum, brass, etc. In such materials the mode of failure of elastic action is that of yielding and not fracture, since the limiting value predicted by each of the theories is obtained from the simple tensile test in which the end of elastic behavior is followed by yielding and not by fracture (separation). Thus it is understood that in each of the theories the value which is assumed to represent the limit of elastic action (whether the value is stress, strain, or strain energy) is an average or statistical value for the material in the neighborhood of the point at which inelastic strains are assumed to start, and that the member is subjected to static loads and so-called normal temperatures. The stress, strain, or strain energy in a metal member may vary in different grains according to the properties and orientation of the different grains, but because of the ductility of the parts the statistical value is a significant value for estimating failure of elastic action since such failure brings into action the material surrounding the point at which the failure is assumed to occur, provided the material is ductile and is subjected to static loads.

Applicability of the Theories. If the pressure in a thick-walled cylinder is a static load (and not a repeatedly applied load which might lead to fatigue failure), the following general conclusions may be stated.

Brittle Material; Failure by Fracture. If the material is relatively brittle, and hence the internal pressure is limited by fracture of the material, that is, the strains are essentially elastic until fracture occurs, the wall thickness is given by the maximum principal stress theory of elastic failure (Eq. 375), since tensile stress is probably the best criterion of fracture.

Ductile Material; Failure by Small Inelastic Strains. In some thick-walled cylinders such as gun tubes a very small amount of inelastic strain in the cylinder wall will cause unsatisfactory operation of the gun. Hence no (or only very small) inelastic strains can be permitted if (functional) failure of the cylinder is to be avoided. The wall thickness of such cylinders is given by the maximum shearing stress theory or by the octahedral shearing stress theory of elastic failure, that is, by Eq. 380 or 380a and Eq. 389, because these theories are the most reliable in predicting when inelastic strains in the cylinder wall will start as the internal pressure is increased. The maximum shearing stress theory gives a slightly larger value of the wall thickness than is given by the octahedral stress theory.

Ductile Material; Failure by General Yielding. There are many applications of thick-walled cylinders, such as some types of pressure vessels, in which the cylinder functions satisfactorily, with respect to strength until inelastic deformation spreads completely through the wall of the cylinder. Such an amount of inelastic deformation is referred to as general yielding. Under these conditions none of the theories of failure (which predict only the beginning of inelastic strain) will apply. Inelastic deformation in the cylinder wall is accompanied by a redistribution of stress which increases the capacity of the cylinder to resist internal pressure considerably greater than the pressure which initiates inelastic deformation (see Art. 101). Thus, if, for such a cylinder, use is made (erroneously) of the maximum shearing stress theory or the octahedral shearing stress theory of failure for determining wall thicknesses, the value obtained will be much larger than is required to resist the given pressure. For the design of cylinders in which some inelastic strains are permissible probably the most rational procedure would be to use the results of an analysis of the stresses in the cylinder based on the existence of inelastic strains as discussed in Art. 101. However, it will be seen from the discussion in Art. 101 that the maximum principal stress theory of failure, which most engineers prefer for designing cylinders in which general yielding is permitted, employs some, though not all, of the increased resistance to internal pressure which accompanies the general yielding of the cylinder wall. One reason why the maximum principal stress has been rather widely used for designing such thick-walled cylinders is that, in most tests that have been made of cylinders under internal pressure, the instruments for measuring inelastic strains were such that measurements were made only at the external surface of the cylinder and were not sufficiently sensitive to detect the starting of yielding which occurs at the bore or internal surface and spreads to the outer surface. The load at which yielding actually started, therefore, was not obtained. This difficulty in detecting the test value of the pressure at which inelastic strains started lead to an erroneous interpretation of the test results which indicated that the test results were predicted by the maximum principal stress theory of failure.

Thus, although the use of the maximum principal stress theory is irrational as applied to thick-walled cylinders which fail by general yielding, it may perhaps be justified as an empirical method which gives results reasonably consistent with test results. As pointed out in the last two paragraphs of Art. 101, the internal pressures predicted by this (empirical) method lie about midway between the pressures found by taking full account of the redistribution of stresses accompanying yielding which extends completely through the cylinder wall and the pressures required merely to initiate inelastic strain at the inner surface.

98 Methods of increasing the elastic strength by prestressing. It was pointed out in the preceding articles (see especially Fig. 173) that for large internal pressures in thick-walled cylinders the wall thickness required becomes very large. This means that much of the (outer) material is subjected to low stresses and is, therefore, ineffectively used. Furthermore, when the pressure becomes equal to the value of the working or allowable circumferential stress for the material, the required wall thickness becomes indefinitely large.

In order to construct thick-walled cylinders that will resist elastically relatively large internal pressures and will make relatively effective use of the material near the outer portion of the cylinder, several methods of prestressing are employed. Stated differently, several methods are used for creating prestresses (called initial, residual, or deformation stresses, see Art. 7) in the cylinder so that when the load stresses produced by applying the internal pressure are superimposed on these initial stresses the resultant stress distribution is more favorable than would exist without the presence of the initial stresses.

Three methods of prestressing are discussed briefly in the following articles, namely, (a) shrinking on a hollow cylinder (hoop, jacket or shell) over the main cylinder, (b) constructing the thick-walled cylinder of a number (nest) of prestressed thin-walled cylinders, called a multi-layer or laminated cylinder, and (c) autofrettage or self-hooping.

99   Analysis of effects on stresses of shrinking a hollow cylinder over the main cylinder.   The outer thick-walled cylinder or jacket is made so that its inner radius is slightly smaller than the outer radius of the main cylinder.   When the jacket is heated, it expands sufficiently to allow it to just slip over the main cylinder.   As the jacket cools, it tends to contract, thereby exerting an external pressure on the inner or main cylinder.   This pressure p_s on the outer surface of the cylinder and on

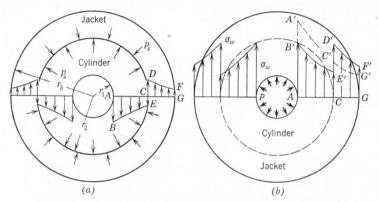

Fig. 174   Effect of shrinking on a jacket.   (a) Stresses due to shrink pressure. (b) Stresses due to shrink pressure and internal working pressure p.

the inner surface of the jacket causes circumferential stresses in the cylinder and in the jacket which are distributed approximately as shown in Fig. 174a; compressive stresses are produced in the inner cylinder and tensile stresses in the jacket.

The Value of p_s.   Before these initial stresses can be computed the shrinkage pressure p_s on the surface of contact between the two cylinders must be found.   In Fig. 174a let r_1, r_2, and r_3 denote the three radii. The radius r_2 will denote the outer radius of the cylinder and also the inner radius of the jacket before the jacket is shrunk on the cylinder, since these radii will differ by only a few thousandths of an inch.   Let δ denote this small difference in the original two values of the inner radius of the jacket and the outer radius of the cylinder.   After the jacket has been shrunk on the cylinder, the length of the inner radius of the jacket will be larger than its initial value by an amount δ_1 which is given by Eq. 360, namely,

$$\delta_1 = \frac{p_s r_2}{E}\left(\frac{r_3{}^2 + r_2{}^2}{r_3{}^2 - r_2{}^2} + \mu\right) \tag{393}$$

and the length of the outer radius of the cylinder will be changed (decreased) by an amount given by Eq. 361, namely,

$$\delta_2 = -\frac{p_s r_2}{E}\left(\frac{r_2^2 + r_1^2}{r_2^2 - r_1^2} - \mu\right) \tag{394}$$

At the completion of the shrinkage process the difference δ in these radii disappears as a result of the changes in length δ_1 and δ_2. Therefore, the sum of the magnitudes (ignoring the signs) of δ_1 and δ_2 is equal to δ. This fact is expressed by the following equations.

$$\delta = \delta_1 + \delta_2 \tag{395}$$

Hence

$$\delta = \frac{p_s r_2}{E}\left(\frac{r_3^2 + r_2^2}{r_3^2 - r_2^2} + \frac{r_2^2 + r_1^2}{r_2^2 - r_1^2}\right) \tag{396}$$

provided that the cylinder and jacket are made of materials having the same values of μ and E. The solution of Eq. 396 gives

$$p_s = \frac{E\delta}{2r_2^3}\frac{(r_3^2 - r_2^2)(r_2^2 - r_1^2)}{r_3^2 - r_1^2} \tag{397}$$

Residual Circumferential Stress. The residual or initial circumferential stress may now be found in terms of the known pressure p_s as given by Eq. 397. In Fig. 174a the maximum initial circumferential stress in the inner cylinder occurs at a point A on the inner surface, and its value as represented by AB is given by Eq. 355, namely,

$$AB = -2p_s\frac{r_2^2}{r_2^2 - r_1^2} \tag{398}$$

Similarly for the outer cylinder or jacket, CD in Fig. 174a is given by Eq. 352, namely,

$$CD = p_s\frac{r_3^2 + r_2^2}{r_3^2 - r_1^2} \tag{399}$$

Resultant Stresses after the Composite Cylinder Is Subjected to Internal Pressure p. In determining the stresses caused by the pressure p, the composite cylinder consisting of the inner cylinder and the jacket may be considered to be a single thick-walled cylinder. The maximum value of the circumferential stress caused by p, as shown by AA' in Fig. 174b, occurs at a point A on the inner surface of the cylinder; its value is given by Eq. 352, namely

$$AA' = p\frac{r_3^2 + r_1^2}{r_3^2 - r_1^2} \tag{400}$$

Similarly CC' is found from Eq. 350 to be

$$CC' = p\,\frac{r_1^2(r_3^2 + r_2^2)}{r_2^2(r_3^2 - r_1^2)} \tag{401}$$

The stresses must now be superposed on the residual stresses at A and C, respectively, as given by Eqs. 398 and 399. The actual or resultant stress at A is

$$\sigma_A = AA' - AB = p\,\frac{r_3^2 + r_1^2}{r_3^2 - r_1^2} - 2p_s\,\frac{r_2^2}{r_2^2 - r_1^2} \tag{402}$$

and that at C is

$$\sigma_C = CC' + CD = p\,\frac{r_1^2(r_3^2 + r_2^2)}{r_2^2(r_3^2 - r_1^2)} + p_s\,\frac{r_3^2 + r_2^2}{r_3^2 - r_2^2} \tag{403}$$

The distribution of the resultant stress on section AG is shown by the ordinates to the solid line $B'E'D'F'$ in Fig. 174b. It will be noted that the stress at A has been reduced from AA' to AB'. In an ideal design * the values of σ_A and σ_C should each be equal to the allowable stress σ_w. A method of satisfying this condition will now be discussed.

Most Effective Proportions of Cylinder and Jacket. The desired condition is expressed by the equations

$$\sigma_A = p\,\frac{r_3^2 + r_1^2}{r_3^2 - r_1^2} - 2p_s\,\frac{r_2^2}{r_2^2 - r_1^2} = \sigma_w \tag{404}$$

$$\sigma_C = p\,\frac{r_1^2(r_3^2 + r_2^2)}{r_2^2(r_3^2 - r_1^2)} + p_s\,\frac{r_3^2 + r_2^2}{r_3^2 - r_2^2} = \sigma_w \tag{405}$$

Three unknowns, r_2, r_3, and p_s, are involved in these two equations in which the known quantities are p, r_1, and σ_w. A third equation, therefore, is needed. This may be obtained from Eq. 397 in which the value of δ may be chosen arbitrarily within the practical limits of the temperature which may be used in the heating and shrinking without causing residual stresses greater than the elastic strength of the material. This means that for each choice of a value for δ (and hence of p_s) there is a set of values of r_2 and r_3 which will satisfy the two simultaneous Eqs. 404 and 405. It is required to find the set of values of r_2 and r_3 in which r_3 has its minimum value. It will be shown that this set of values is

---

* If the jacket and cylinder combination must resist a high internal pressure without *any* inelastic strain occurring at the bore, it would be better at this point to use the maximum shearing stress theory of failure and set the stresses τ_A and τ_C each equal to τ_w. This is done in Prob. 202, the answers to which give the desired results by this method.

$r_2 = Cr_1$ and $r_3 = C^2 r_1$ in which C (see Eq. 413) is a constant for a given set of values of p and σ_w. This will be done by first solving Eq. 404 for p_s, which gives

$$p_s = \frac{r_2^2 - r_1^2}{2r_2^2}\left(p\,\frac{r_3^2 + r_1^2}{r_3^2 - r_1^2} - \sigma_w\right) \tag{406}$$

and substituting its value in Eq. 405, thereby obtaining a quadratic equation in r_3^2 in the form

$$ar_3^4 + br_3^2 + c = 0 \tag{407}$$

in which the coefficients a, b, and c have the values

$$a = (p - 3\sigma_w)r_2^2 + (p + \sigma_w)r_1^2$$

$$b = (p + \sigma_w)(r_2^4 - r_1^4) + 4\sigma_w r_1^2 r_2^2$$

$$c = -(p + \sigma_w)(r_1^2 + r_2^2)r_1^2 r_2^2$$

The solution of Eq. 407 for r_3^2 gives

$$r_3^2 = \frac{-b \pm \sqrt{b^2 - 4ac}}{2a} \tag{408}$$

If the expressions for a, b, and c are substituted in Eq. 408 and the negative sign in front of the radical is used, the equation obtained is

$$r_3^2 = r_2^2\left[\frac{1 + \dfrac{p}{\sigma_w}}{\dfrac{3r_2^2 - r_1^2}{r_2^2 + r_1^2} - \dfrac{p}{\sigma_w}}\right] \tag{409}$$

If the positive sign is used in Eq. 408, the value of r_3^2 is found to be equal to r_1^2, which means that the wall thickness is zero; this is the trivial solution of the problem. Hence, Eq. 409 represents the relationship between r_3 and r_2, since the values of r_1, p, and σ_w are given. The main problem, however, is to find the minimum value of r_3. Therefore, in Eq. 409 the square root of both sides of the equation is taken and the derivative dr_3/dr_2 is obtained by differentiation of the expression with respect to r_2. The expression for dr_3/dr_2 is set equal to zero, giving the equation

$$(p - 3\sigma_w)r_2^4 + 2r_1^2(p + \sigma_w)r_2^2 + (p + \sigma_w)r_1^4 = 0 \tag{410}$$

Equation 410 represents the condition which will make the radius r_3 in

Eq. 409 have its minimum value. Equation 410 is a quadratic in $r_2{}^2$, and the solution of this quadratic gives

$$r_2{}^2 = r_1{}^2 \frac{p + \sigma_w + 2\sqrt{p\sigma_w + \sigma_w{}^2}}{3\sigma_w - p} \tag{411}$$

which is the value of $r_2{}^2$ needed in Eq. 409 to give the minimum value of r_3. In solving for the minimum value, let the numerator and denominator of the right side of Eq. 411 be divided by σ_w; the equation then becomes

$$r_2{}^2 = r_1{}^2 \frac{1 + (p/\sigma_w) + 2\sqrt{1 + (p/\sigma_w)}}{3 - (p/\sigma_w)} \tag{412}$$

In Eq. 412 let

$$C^2 = \frac{1 + (p/\sigma_w) + 2\sqrt{1 + (p/\sigma_w)}}{3 - (p/\sigma_w)} \tag{413}$$

Equation 412 may then be written

$$r_2 = Cr_1 \tag{414}$$

If this value of r_2 is substituted into Eq. 409, the minimum value of r_3 is found to be

$$r_3 = C^2 r_1 \tag{415}$$

The values of r_2 and r_3 as given by Eqs. 414 and 415 are such as to satisfy the two simultaneous requirements: first, that the maximum circumferential stresses in the cylinder and the jacket are each equal to the working stress σ_w when the allowable internal pressure p is reached; and, second, that the radius r_3 has its minimum possible value, thereby making the most effective use of the material. It is interesting to note that the values of r_2 and r_3 are, respectively, equal to Cr_1 and $C^2 r_1$ which shows that the magnitudes of the three radii are terms in a geometrical progression and that the value of C as given by Eq. 413 does not depend on the internal radius r_1.

The benefit obtained by shrinking a jacket on a thick-walled cylinder is shown conveniently by rewriting Eq. 415 in the form

$$t/r_1 = C^2 - 1 \tag{416}$$

in which t is the total wall thickness, and C depends only upon p/σ_w as shown by Eq. 413. The relation between corresponding values of t/r_1 and p/σ_w as expressed by Eq. 416 is represented in Fig. 175 by the curve labeled B. The lower curve labeled A represents the relationship between values of p/σ_w and t/r_1 for a solid-wall cylinder as is given by the top curve in Fig. 173. These curves show that for a given value of p/σ_w the total wall thickness of a thick-walled cylinder composed of two

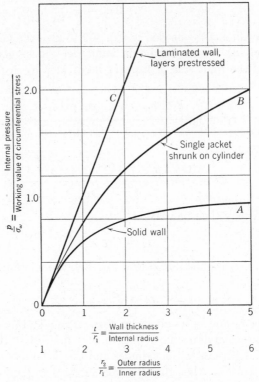

FIG. 175   Comparison of effects of single jacket and prestressed laminated wall construction.

hollow cylinders with one shrunk on the other can be much smaller than that of a single (solid-wall) cylinder. For example, if the internal pressure is such that $p/\sigma_w = 0.8$, the value of $t/r_1 = 1.02$ for the composite cylinder as compared with $t/r_1 = 2.00$ for a single cylinder having a so-called solid wall.

This means that a solid-walled cylinder would require nearly four times as much material as the equivalent cylinder composed of a jacket shrunk on a cylinder, since the volume of the cylinder is nearly proportional to the square of the wall thickness. Thus a significant saving in weight of material may be made by use of a jacket shrunk on a cylinder.

Attention, however, should be directed to the fact that the curves A and B in Fig. 175 are based on the maximum principal stress theory of elastic failure. Curves based on each of the other theories of failure would give somewhat different results (see Prob. 202). In general, however, by all the theories given here the relationship among r_1, r_2, and r_3 is represented by a geometric progression. The ratio of succeeding terms in this progression will be different for each theory of failure (see Prob. 202).

In a few instances thick-walled cylinders have been constructed by shrinking on two or more separate jackets in an effort to obtain a more even distribution of stress in the wall. However, it can be shown that the addition of more than one jacket gives much less additional strength per jacket to the cylinder, assuming a given value of total wall thickness, than does the use of the first jacket. This means that one jacket is very effective whereas additional ones are much less effective than the first jacket. However, if the cylinder is constructed by shrinking on many layers, each having only a small thickness, the strength of the cylinder is substantially larger than for one jacket. This fact is shown by a line marked C in Fig. 175. The laminated or multilayered construction is discussed in the next article.

Illustrative Problem

Problem 199. A cylindrical steel pressure vessel having an internal radius of $r_1 = 6$ in. is required to resist an internal pressure of $p = 22,500$ lb per sq in. The tensile and compressive elastic strength of the material is $\sigma_e = 50,000$ lb per sq in. Determine the required wall thickness (a) if the vessel is made with a solid continuous wall, and (b) if the vessel is constructed by shrinking a jacket on a hollow cylinder. Use a factor of safety of $N = 2$ and the maximum principal stress theory of failure of elastic behavior.

Solution. (a) *Solid wall.* Equation 376, in which $p/\sigma_w = 22,500/25,000 = 0.9$ gives

$$t = 6\left(\sqrt{\frac{1 + 0.9}{1 - 0.9}} - 1\right) = 20.16 \text{ in.}$$

Such a large wall thickness would result in very ineffective use of much of the outer portion of the cylinder.

(b) *Jacket Shrunk on Hollow Cylinder.* Equations 414 and 413 give

$$r_2 = Cr_1 = 6C$$

$$C^2 = \frac{1 + 0.9 + 2\sqrt{1 + 0.9}}{3 - 0.9} = 2.22$$

$$C = \sqrt{2.22} = 1.49$$

$$r_2 = 6 \times 1.49 = 8.95 \text{ in.}$$

Thus the wall thickness of the main cylinder is $8.95 - 6.0 = 2.95$ in. Equation 415 gives

$$r_3 = (1.49)^2 \times 6 = 13.30 \text{ in.}$$

Hence the total wall thickness of the cylinder and jacket is $13.30 - 6 = 7.3$ in., in contrast to 20.16 in. for a single solid-wall cylinder.

The interface pressure p_s caused by shrinking on the jacket is given by Eq. 406; thus

$$p_s = \frac{(8.95)^2 - (6.00)^2}{2 \times (8.95)^2} \left[22{,}500 \, \frac{(13.30)^2 + (6.00)^2}{(3.30)^2 - (6.00)^2} - 25{,}000 \right] = 2470 \text{ lb/in.}^2$$

The difference δ in the outer radius of the cylinder and the inner radius of the jacket before the tube is shrunk on the cylinder is found from Eq. 396. Thus

$$\delta = \frac{2470 \times 8.95}{30{,}000{,}000} \left[\frac{(13.30)^2 + (8.95)^2}{(13.30)^2 - (8.95)^2} + \frac{(8.95)^2 + (6.00)^2}{(8.95)^2 - (6.00)^2} \right] = 0.0038 \text{ in.}$$

The temperature difference Δt required between the jacket and the cylinder so that the jacket will just slip over the cylinder is given by the equation

$$\delta = r_2 \alpha \, \Delta t \qquad \text{in which } \alpha = 0.0000066$$

In order to provide clearance for a sliding fit of the heated jacket over the cylinder, let it be assumed that a value of 0.004 in. is added to δ, making it 0.0078 in. instead of 0.0038 in. Therefore,

$$\Delta t = \frac{0.0078}{8.95 \times 0.0000066} = 132° \text{ F}$$

Problems

200. Solve Prob. 199 if the material has an elastic strength in tension and a compression of 45,000 lb per sq in.

201. A thick-walled steel cylinder (hoop or jacket) is shrunk on an inner cylinder. The inner cylinder is to be subjected to an internal pressure of 36,000 lb per sq in., and the maximum circumferential stress must not exceed 40,000 lb per sq in. If the dimensions of the cylinders are $r_1 = 2$ in., $r_2 = 2.5$ in., and $r_3 = 5$ in., what should be the difference between the internal diameter of the jacket and the external diameter of the inner cylinder before the jacket is heated?

202. A thick-walled cylinder is constructed by shrinking a jacket on a hollow cylinder. The hollow cylinder is to be subjected to an internal pressure p. Determine the values of r_2 and r_3 to satisfy the following conditions: The maximum shearing stress in the cylinder and in the jacket shall each be equal to the shearing working stress τ_w, and the radius r_3 shall be the minimum value. It should be noted from the answers to this problem that r_1, r_2, and r_3 are values in a geometric progression in which the ratio of the succeeding terms is $\sqrt{\dfrac{1}{1 - \frac{1}{2}(p/\tau_w)}}$ and corresponds to the value of C in Eq. 413. This value of C obtained from the maximum shearing stress theory gives a much larger wall thickness for given values of p and σ_w than that given by the maximum stress theory.

$$Ans. \quad r_2 = r_1 \sqrt{\frac{1}{1 - \frac{1}{2}(p/\tau_w)}} \, ; \; r_3 = r_1 \frac{1}{1 - \frac{1}{2}(p/\tau_w)} \, ; \; p_s = \frac{p^2}{2(4\tau_w - p)} .$$

100 Analysis of stresses in hollow cylinder made of thin-walled shells or laminations. As each metal shell or layer is added in constructing the laminated cylinder, it is stressed in tension and is then welded along a longitudinal seam as indicated in Fig. 176a (see reference 5 at the end of this chapter). It therefore exerts an external

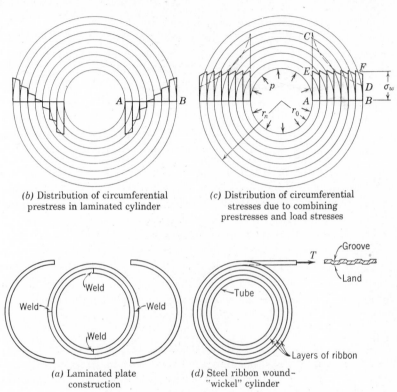

(b) Distribution of circumferential prestress in laminated cylinder

(c) Distribution of circumferential stresses due to combining prestresses and load stresses

(a) Laminated plate construction

(d) Steel ribbon wound-"wickel" cylinder

Fig. 176   Distribution of stress in laminated cylinder.

pressure on the layer directly beneath it. If these wrapping pressures are such that they cause prestresses in the layers which vary on any section approximately as shown on section AB in Fig. 176b, the load stresses caused by the internal pressure p when superposed on these prestresses will result in nearly a uniformly distributed stress as indicated by the sawtoothed line EF in Fig. 176c. The load stresses in the layers are shown by the ordinates to the dashed curve CD in Fig. 176c. It will be noted that in Fig. 176b the prestresses in several layers in the inner portion of the cylinder are compressive stresses, and those in the layers in the outer portion are tensile stresses. The algebraic addition of the load stress and the prestress on each layer gives a nearly constant stress. Such a uniform stress distribution would, of course, make the most effective use of the material in the cylinder. The problem is to show how this condition may be obtained. It should be noted, however, that, if the completed cylinder is subjected to the customary annealing process for welded sections, much of the beneficial effects of the favorable residual stresses may be lost.

Let h denote the wall thickness of each shell in a laminated thick-walled cylinder; for steel pressure vessels h frequently is about 0.25 in. Let t denote the total wall thickness. If the stress in each shell is the allowable stress σ_w when the laminated cylinder is subjected to the internal pressure p, we may write

$$\sigma_w = pr_0/t \qquad \text{or} \qquad p/\sigma_w = t/r_0 \qquad (417)$$

in which r_0 is the internal radius of the laminated cylinder. This equation is represented in Fig. 175 by the straight (top) line; the internal radius in Fig. 175 is indicated by r_1 instead of r_0. Let $n = t/h$ denote the number of shells or layers; if t/h is fractional, n is taken as the nearest whole number larger than t/h. Further, let $r_1, r_2, r_3, \cdots, r_n$ be the radii to the outer surface, respectively, of layers 1, 2, 3, $\cdots$, n. Also let $x_1, x_2, x_3, \cdots, x_n$ be the distance to the mid-thicknesses of the corresponding layers. Finally let $p_1, p_2, p_3, \cdots, p_{n-1}$ be the wrapping pressures; that is, p_1 is the external pressure on layer 1 caused by the wrapping of layer 2, p_2 is the external pressure on layer 2 resulting from the addition of layer 3, etc.; the last layer n exerts the pressure p_{n-1} on the layer $n - 1$.

There are, then, $n - 1$ of these unknown wrapping pressures which must be determined in order that each layer may be wrapped with the correct pressure to give the desired uniform stress distribution when the internal pressure is applied to the finished laminated cylinder. The equations from which these unknowns may be found are obtained by writing an equation for the stress at the mid-thickness of each layer and setting this expression equal to σ_w. The stress at the mid-thickness of any intermediate layer, say the mth layer, may be expressed as the algebraic sum of several component stresses as follows: First, a tensile stress σ' at the mid-thickness of the mth layer caused by the internal pressure p which is found from Eq. 350 to be

$$\sigma' = p \frac{r_0{}^2(r_n{}^2 + x_m{}^2)}{x_m{}^2(r_n{}^2 - r_0{}^2)} \qquad (418)$$

Second, a tensile stress σ_m in the mth layer due to the wrapping pressure

p_{m-1} which acts as an internal pressure on the mth layer. This stress is found by using the equation for a thin-walled cylinder. Thus

$$\sigma_m = \frac{p_{m-1} \cdot r_{m-1}}{h} \tag{419}$$

Third, compressive stresses at the mid-thickness of the mth layer caused by each of the wrapping pressures p_m, p_{m+1}, p_{m+2}, etc., through p_{n-1}. The first of these stresses, the stress σ_m due to the wrapping pressure p_m, is found from Eq. 353 to be

$$\sigma_m = -\left(1 + \frac{r_0^2}{x_m^2}\right) \frac{p_m r_m^2}{r_m^2 - r_0^2} \tag{420}$$

Similarly, the next stress σ_{m+1} in the mth layer, caused by p_{m+1}, is found from Eq. 353 to be

$$\sigma_{m+1} = -\left(1 + \frac{r_0^2}{x_m^2}\right) \frac{p_{m+1} \cdot r_{m+1}^2}{r_{m+1}^2 - r_0^2} \tag{421}$$

An inspection of Eqs. 420 and 421 reveals that the total compressive circumferential stress caused at the mid-thickness of the mth layer by all these wrapping pressures is given by the equation

$$\sigma_{m \text{ through } n-1} = -\left(1 + \frac{r_0^2}{x_m^2}\right) \sum_{m=m}^{n-1} \frac{p_m r_m^2}{r_m^2 - r_0^2} \tag{422}$$

Therefore, the total or resultant circumferential stress at the mid-thickness of the layer m is the algebraic sum of the stresses as given by Eqs. 418, 419, and 422. But the circumferential stress at this point must be equal to σ_w. Hence

$$\sigma_w = p \frac{r_0^2(r_n^2 + x_m^2)}{x_m^2(r_n^2 - r_0^2)} + \frac{p_{m-1} \cdot r_{m-1}}{h} - \left(1 + \frac{r_0^2}{x_m^2}\right) \sum_{m=m}^{n-1} \frac{p_m r_m^2}{r_m^2 - r_0^2} \tag{423}$$

Equation 423 may be written for the stress at the mid-thickness of each layer. These equations are written starting with the outer layer first so that each equation will contain only one new unknown wrapping pressure. The laminated plate construction described here has been used in this country for several years. Recently cylinders have been constructed by wrapping a steel ribbon having lands and grooves as illustrated in Fig. 176d about a tube. The tube has a spiral groove machined to fit the lands of the first layer of ribbon. The lands of each succeeding layer of ribbon fit into the grooves of the preceding layer. The lands and grooves provide resistance to longitudinal stresses in the cylinder. After the final layer of ribbon is in place, a thin tube is shrunk over it to protect the ribbon (see reference 12 at the end of this chapter). The use of Eq. 423 for determining the wrapping pressures is illustrated in the following problem. The wrapping tension in each layer may be found from Eq. 419 by substituting the values of the wrapping pressures as found by applying Eq. 423. See p. 61 of reference 11 at the end of this chapter for the method of applying the maximum shearing stress theory in prestressing laminated cylinders.

Illustrative Problem

Problem 203. A laminated thick-walled cylinder is required to have an internal radius $r_0 = 3$ in. and to withstand an internal working pressure $p = 9000$ lb per sq in. The laminated cylinder is to be constructed of steel plate laminations of $h = \frac{1}{4}$-in. thickness. Determine the total wall thickness of the cylinder and the required wrapping pressure for each layer so that each layer or shell will be stressed to the working stress $\sigma_w = 18,000$ lb per sq in.

Solution. The wall thickness is given by Eq. 417.

$$t = pr_0/\sigma_w = (9000 \times 3)/18,000 = 1.5 \text{ in.}$$

The required number of layers is $n = t/h = 1.5/0.25 = 6$. The wrapping pressures are designated as p_1, p_2, p_3, p_4, and p_5. The pressure p_5 is exerted by the sixth or last layer on the fifth layer; its value is given by Eq. 423.

$$18,000 = 9000 \frac{3^2(\overline{4.5^2} + \overline{4.375^2})}{4.375^2(\overline{4.5^2} - 3^2)} + p_5 \frac{4.25}{0.25}$$

$$p_5 = 187.2 \text{ lb/in.}^2$$

The pressure p_4 exerted by the fifth layer on the fourth layer likewise is given by Eq. 423.

$$18,000 = 9000 \frac{3^2(\overline{4.5^2} + \overline{4.125^2})}{4.125^2(\overline{4.5^2} - 3^2)} + p_4 \frac{4.00}{0.25} - \left(1 + \frac{3^2}{4.125^2}\right) \frac{187.2 \times \overline{4.25^2}}{4.25^2 - 3^2}$$

$$p_4 = 175 \text{ lb/in.}^2$$

Similarly p_3 is found from Eq. 423.

$$18,000 = 9000 \frac{3^2(\overline{4.5^2} + \overline{3.875^2})}{3.875^2(\overline{4.5^2} - 3^2)}$$
$$+ p_3 \frac{3.75}{0.25} - \left(1 + \frac{3^2}{3.875^2}\right)\left(\frac{175.4 \times \overline{4.00^2}}{4.00^2 - 3^2} + 373.1\right)$$

$$p_3 = 155.2 \text{ lb/in.}^2$$

The value of p_2 is obtained in the same manner.

$$18,000 = 9000 \frac{3^2(\overline{4.5^2 + 3.625^2})}{3.625^2(\overline{4.5^2 - 3^2})}$$

$$+ p_2 \frac{3.50}{0.25} - \left(1 + \frac{3^2}{3.625^2}\right)\left(\frac{155.2 \times \overline{3.75^2}}{\overline{3.75^2 - 3^2}} + 400.9 + 373.1\right)$$

$$p_2 = 123.9 \ \text{lb/in.}^2$$

and the pressure p_1 exerted by the second layer on the first or inner layer is also obtained from Eq. 423. Thus,

$$18,000 = 9000 \frac{3^2(\overline{4.5^2 + 3.375^2})}{3.375^2(\overline{4.5^2 - 3^2})}$$

$$+ p_1 \frac{3.25}{0.25} - \left(1 + \frac{3^2}{3.375^2}\right)\left(\frac{123.9 \times \overline{3.50^2}}{\overline{3.50^2 - 3^2}} + 431.1 + 400.9 + 373.1\right)$$

$$p_1 = 76.3 \ \text{lb/in.}^2$$

As a check on these values of the wrapping pressures we may write Eq. 423 for the first layer (the first layer has the value $p_{m-1} = 0$ in Eq. 423). This equation is

$$18,000 = 9000 \frac{3^2(\overline{4.5^2 + 3.125^2})}{3.125^2(\overline{4.5^2 - 3^2})}$$

$$+ 0 \frac{3.00}{0.25} - \left(1 + \frac{3^2}{3.125^2}\right)\left(\frac{76.3 \times \overline{3.25^2}}{\overline{3.25^2 - 3^2}} + 467.0 + 431.1 + 400.9 + 373.1\right)$$

or $\qquad$ $18,000 = 17,930$, which is a satisfactory check

The wrapping tensions in the layers are found from Eq. 419. Thus the wrapping tension in the outer or sixth layer is

$$\sigma_6 = \frac{p_5 r_5}{h} = \frac{187.2 \times 4.25}{0.25} = 3180 \ \text{lb/in.}^2$$

In like manner

$$\sigma_5 = \frac{p_4 r_4}{h} = \frac{175 \times 4.00}{0.25} = 2800 \ \text{lb/in.}^2$$

$$\sigma_4 = \frac{p_3 r_3}{h} = \frac{155.2 \times 3.75}{0.25} = 2330 \ \text{lb/in.}^2$$

$$\sigma_3 = \frac{p_2 r_2}{h} = \frac{123.9 \times 3.50}{0.25} = 1730 \ \text{lb/in.}^2$$

$$\sigma_2 = \frac{p_1 r_1}{h} = \frac{76.3 \times 3.25}{0.25} = 990 \ \text{lb/in.}^2$$

Problem

204. Solve Prob. 203 if the thick-walled cylinder is required to resist an internal pressure of $p = 12,000$ lb per sq in.

101   Analysis of effects of autofrettage. As noted in Art. 98, one method of prestressing thick-walled cylinders is called autofrettage or self-hooping. It consists of subjecting the inner surface or bore of the hollow cylinder to a fluid pressure which causes inelastic deformation to start in the portion of the material near the bore where the stresses are relatively large and to extend outward as the internal pressure is increased. When the pressure is released, the outer portion of the cylinder exerts radial pressure on the inner portion, which in turn causes circumferential compressive residual stresses near the bore and tensile stresses near the outer surface.

If a certain autofrettage pressure produces a given amount of inelastic deformation, the same internal pressure may be applied to the cylinder in service without causing appreciable additional inelastic strains. However, if in service this autofrettage pressure is exceeded, further inelastic deformation in the cylinder wall will occur. The maximum increase in internal pressure which can be applied to a thick-walled cylinder as a result of the self-hooping effect is equal to the pressure required to cause inelastic strains to progress from the inner surface or bore just to the outer surface. In this statement it is assumed that no increase in strength of the material occurs as the result of the cold working of the material and that the residual stresses do not cause yielding in the reverse direction when the pressure is released. This assumption would be substantially correct for a material which possesses a well-defined yield point and for a cylinder wall for which the ratio r_2/r_1 has small to medium values.

A substantial increase in resistance to internal pressure may be obtained in the autofrettage process if sufficiently large strains are allowed to occur to permit cold working (strain hardening) of the material to take place. This increase is in addition to that obtained from the presence of residual stresses (self-hooping effect) after autofrettaging. The self-hooping effect reaches its full value when yielding has just spread to the outer wall; any further yielding (within limits) does not change the magnitude or distribution of the residual stresses which cause the self-hooping effect. The cylinder is said to reach the fully plastic state or condition when the inelastic strains just extend to the outer surface (see Chapter 17 for a further discussion of the fully plastic condition) and the pressure required to just cause the fully plastic condition to develop will be called the fully plastic pressure and will be denoted by p_f; as already noted, p_f represents the maximum pressure that can be obtained from the self-hooping action caused by the residual stresses resulting from the autofrettage process.

Fully Plastic Pressure. The fully plastic internal pressure referred to in the preceding paragraph may be found by the same general procedure as was used in obtaining Lamé's solution for principal stresses in Art. 93 even though Lamé's solution is valid only when the stresses are accompanied by *elastic* strains. The procedure consists in using the following equation of equilibrium which was derived previously (see Eq. 338a)

$$\sigma_t = \sigma_r + \rho(d\sigma_r/d\rho) \qquad (424)$$

and which is valid when the stresses are accompanied either by inelastic or elastic strains. Although the term for the internal pressure does not occur directly in the foregoing equation, it will be noted that σ_r is equal to the pressure when $\rho = r_1$.

An additional equation is needed for use with Eq. 424 in order to determine the stresses σ_t and σ_r that exist at any point in the cylinder when the fully plastic autofrettage pressure is acting. This equation is obtained by making the assumption that, when the maximum shearing stress at each point in the cylinder wall reaches the shearing yield point τ_e, it remains equal to this value as further yielding occurs at the point. This assumption is expressed by the equation

$$\tau_e = \tfrac{1}{2}(\sigma_t - \sigma_r) \qquad (425)$$

This assumption is acceptable when considered on a statistical basis. Tests of thick-walled cylinders made of a steel having a yield point show that the fully plastic pressure is reached before inelastic strains have spread to every point in the wall, that is, strain patterns called Lüders' lines first appear and spread as spiral-like bands across the cylinder wall, leaving elastic material between the bands. It is hardly possible that under these conditions the shearing stress is uniform across the wall. However, if the fully plastic pressure is maintained for several hours, the elastic material between the inelastic bands will yield, and this yielding will cause the shearing stresses finally to have an approximately uniform distribution. It should be realized that during the spread of this delayed inelastic straining the diameter of the bore will increase appreciably, but this does not affect the strength of the cylinder. Equation 425 is the additional relationship between σ_t and σ_r needed for solving Eq. 424. From Eqs. 424 and 425 we obtain

$$d\sigma_r/d\rho = 2\tau_e/\rho \qquad (426)$$

The solution of this differential equation is

$$\sigma_r = 2\tau_e \log_e \rho + C \qquad (427)$$

The constant of integration C is obtained from the fact that, when $\rho = r_2$, $\sigma_r = 0$. Thus $C = -2\tau_e \log_e r_2$, and hence

$$\sigma_r = 2\tau_e \log_e (\rho/r_2) \qquad (428)$$

From Eq. 428 the radial stress at the inner surface, where $\rho = r_1$, is found to be

$$\sigma_r = 2\tau_e \log_e (r_1/r_2)$$

But at the inner surface σ_r is equal to the internal pressure. Hence

$$p_f = -2\tau_e \log_e (r_1/r_2) = 2\tau_e \log_e (r_2/r_1) \tag{429}$$

The negative sign is used in order to give p_f a positive sign, since the $\log_e (r_1/r_2)$ is always negative.

Circumferential Stress. The distribution of the circumferential stress when the cylinder acts wholly elastically was obtained in Art. 93. For

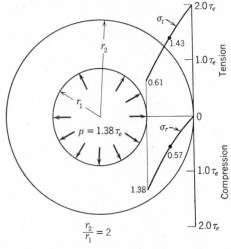

Fig. 177　Stress distribution in cylinder due to internal pressure causing fully plastic condition.

comparison with this stress distribution it is desirable to find the distribution of the stresses σ_t that corresponds to the foregoing assumption that the shearing stress is uniformly distributed across the cylinder wall when the material is strained inelastically. The substitution of Eq. 428 into Eq. 425 gives the following equation for the circumferential stress at any point in the cylinder after inelastic strain has spread throughout the wall.

$$\sigma_t = 2\tau_e[1 + \log_e (\rho/r_2)] \tag{430}$$

The distributions of the stresses σ_t (and also σ_r) through the cylinder wall as given by Eqs. 428 and 430 are illustrated by the ordinates to the curves marked σ_t and σ_r in Fig. 177. It is noted that these stresses have the same values for both open-end and closed-end conditions at the end of the cylinder. The reason for this fact is that the maximum shearing stress is usually given by one-half the difference between σ_t and σ_r, and it is therefore not influenced by the longitudinal stress.

Significance of the Fully Plastic Autofrettage Pressure. Equation 429 gives the internal pressure required to cause inelastic strain to just extend to the outer fibers, which is called the fully plastic pressure. This equation may be written

$$p_f/2\tau_e = -\log_e (r_1/r_2) \quad (431)$$

For the purpose of comparing the results of Eq. 431 with the corresponding results for the elastic behavior of the thick-walled cylinder, let it be assumed that $\sigma_e = 2\tau_e$ (this assumption is true if σ_e and τ_e are determined from a tension test). Then Eq. 431 becomes

$$p_f/\sigma_e = -\log_e (r_1/r_2)$$
$$= \log_e (r_2/r_1) \quad (432)$$

Equation 432 can be represented graphically as shown by the upper curve in Fig. 178, which represents pairs of values of p_f/σ_e and r_2/r_1 which satisfy this equation. The lower curve has been plotted from Eq. 380 in which σ_w is replaced by σ_e. The ordinates to points on the lower curve represent values of the pressure which, according to the maximum shearing stress theory, will cause inelastic strains to be on

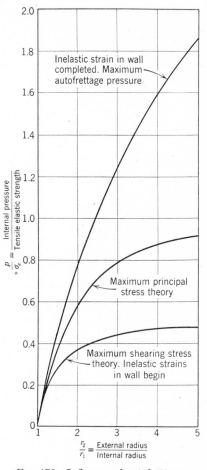

FIG. 178   Influence of autofrettage.

the verge of occurring at the inner surface of the wall. Thus it will be seen by comparing ordinates to points on the lower curve with those on the upper curve that a large increase in pressure is required to cause inelastic strains to spread throughout the cylinder wall after they have started at the inner surface. These increases in pressure are achieved without increasing the shearing stress anywhere in the wall above the shearing yield point τ_e. If some cold working of the metal is permissible (that is, if larger strains are permissible), the autofrettage pressure may be increased to even larger values than indicated by the upper curve. These two curves, therefore, furnish the basis for interpreting the beneficial effects of the autofrettage process, since it is usually assumed that the second and subsequent application of a pressure less than or equal to the fully plastic autofrettage pressure does not cause any additional inelastic strain.

Importance of Fig. 178 in Evaluating the Significance of the Results Found by Applying Maximum Principal Stress Theory of Strength. Apart from its use for interpreting the influence of autofrettage, Fig. 178 reveals information concerning the reliability of the results found by applying (though illogically) the maximum principal stress theory to the design of a thick-walled cylinder made of ductile material, when some inelastic deformation is permitted in the cylinder wall.

As pointed out in Art. 97, the use of the maximum tensile stress as a criterion of the beginning of inelastic action is theoretically unsound. Nevertheless, Fig. 178 shows that, if a small amount of inelastic strain is permitted to occur in the fibers of the inner surface and to spread to fibers a short distance through the wall, the capacity of the cylinder to resist internal pressure will be raised to values equal approximately to those predicted by the maximum principal stress theory to cause inelastic strain to start. Such a procedure is highly irrational and is essentially an empirical method which apparently leads to fairly satisfactory results; it has been used rather widely, frequently on the erroneous assumption that it has a sound theoretical basis.

Approximate Bursting Pressure. Equation 429 gives the pressure in the cylinder when the shearing stress at every point in the cylinder wall has reached the value of the shearing yield point τ_e. This pressure has been described as the fully plastic pressure, and in general it represents the maximum autofrettage pressure that need be applied. However, it is sometimes desirable for determining the amount of reserve strength in the cylinder to determine the bursting pressure which is, of course, somewhat higher than the autofrettage pressure unless there are flaws in the material in the cylinder wall.

One method sometimes used in computing the bursting pressure is based on the assumption that when the bursting pressure is reached the shearing stresses in the wall are again evenly distributed over the thickness of the wall and are everywhere equal to the shearing ultimate strength τ_{ult}. Therefore, Eq. 429 may be used for computing the bursting pressure by simply replacing τ_e by τ_{ult}. It then becomes

$$p_{ult} = 2\tau_{ult} \log_e (r_2/r_1) \tag{433}$$

In using Eq. 433 it is customary to assume that $2\tau_{ult}$ is equal to the tensile ultimate strength σ_{ult} of the material since the shearing ultimate strength is difficult to obtain. Therefore

$$p_{ult} = \sigma_{ult} \log_e (r_2/r_1) \tag{434}$$

Although Eq. 434 has been used to compute the bursting pressure and is based on fairly sound theoretical reasoning, it must be regarded as essentially empirical. One difficulty in predicting the bursting pressure arises from the fact that it is difficult to obtain reliable values of τ_{ult}. Furthermore, flaws in the cylinder wall such as blow holes, dirty material, etc., may substantially influence (decrease) the bursting pressure. In fact some cylinder walls containing such flaws burst even before the fully plastic autofrettage pressure is reached. Thus in those instances where x-ray inspections to determine the presence of flaws are not made, the autofrettage process may be regarded as a means of proof testing to eliminate poor cylinders before putting them in service.

Illustrative Problem

Problem 205. A thick-walled cylinder is to be constructed of a ductile steel for which the working stresses are $\sigma_w = 40,000$ lb per sq in. and $\tau_w = 24,000$ lb per sq in. The working pressure is $p = 37,000$ lb per sq in. The inner radius is $r_1 = 5$ in. Compute the wall thickness of the cylinder based on each of the following.

(a) The cylinder wall is of one thickness or layer (solid).

(b) A jacket is shrunk on an inner cylinder.

(c) The cylinder is of one thickness or layer and is to be autofrettaged before placing it in service.

Solution.

(a) The maximum principal stress theory (see Eq. 376) gives

$$\frac{t}{r_1} = \sqrt{\frac{1 + (p/\sigma_w)}{1 - (p/\sigma_w)}} - 1 = \sqrt{\frac{1 + 0.925}{1 - 0.925}} - 1 = 5.07 - 1 = 4.07$$

Therefore $t = 4.07r_1 = 20.35$ in.

(b) The wall thickness of the inner cylinder plus the jacket is given by Eq. 416. Thus

$$t/r_1 = C^2 - 1$$

in which C^2 is given by Eq. 413 to be

$$C^2 = \frac{1 + (p/\sigma_w) + 2\sqrt{1 + (p/\sigma_w)}}{3 - (p/\sigma_w)} = \frac{1.925 + 2\sqrt{1.925}}{3 - 0.925} = 2.23$$

Therefore $t/r_1 = 2.23 - 1 = 1.23$ and $t = 1.23r_1 = 6.15$ in.

(c) Equation 429 gives the maximum autofrettage pressure. Thus

$$p_f = -2\tau_e \log_e (r_1/r_2) = 2\tau_e \log_e (r_2/r_1)$$

If p_w denotes the allowable or working pressure and N the factor of safety, we may write

$$p_w = p_f/N = 2(\tau_e/N) \log_e (r_2/r_1)$$

since the autofrettage pressure is the maximum utilizable pressure for the cylinder. Likewise we may write $\tau_w = \tau_e/N$. The substitution of these values in the foregoing equation gives

$$p = 2\tau_w \log_e (r_2/r_1)$$

For the autofrettaged cylinder we have

$$37{,}000 = 2 \times 24{,}000 \log_e (r_2/5)$$

and therefore $\log_e r_2 = 2.38$

$$r_2 = 10.8 \text{ in.} \quad \text{and} \quad t = 5.8 \text{ in.}$$

The answers to this problem indicate the great benefits in saving of material which may result from methods of manufacture of cylinders that make use of locked-in or residual stresses such as occur in the shrinking on of a jacket or in autofrettaging.

Prestressing Is of Value Primarily for Increasing Elastic Strength Only. It may be wise to offer a further comment in the nature of a warning concerning the advantages of prestressing a thick-walled cylinder. The prestressing of such a cylinder, by any of the three methods previously discussed, will justify an increase in the allowable or working internal pressure if for satisfactory behavior in service the cylinder must strain only elastically; this would be true, for example, for gun tubes in which the inner or bore diameter must not be changed appreciably and permanently by the internal pressure.

If the service conditions will permit some inelastic straining of the wall of the cylinder to accompany the internal pressure, a prestressed cylinder will have little or no advantage in resisting the internal pressure over a similar one used in the natural or un-prestressed state. This statement follows from the following two facts. (a) For a thick-walled cylinder used under the stated conditions, the fully plastic internal pressure p_f (or a pressure somewhat less than p_f) would be the maximum utilizable pressure (the maximum internal pressure which could be applied to the cylinder without causing the cylinder to operate unsatisfactorily). (b) A thick-walled cylinder which is prestressed to increase its elastic strength has approximately the same value for p_f as it would have if it were not prestressed.

Selected References

1. Baugher, J. W., "Transmission of Torque by Means of Press and Shrink Fits," *Transactions of the American Society of Mechanical Engineers*, Vol. 53, 1931, p. 85, MSP53–10.

2. Cook, G., and A. Robertson, "The Strength of Thick Hollow Cylinders under Internal Pressure," *Engineering (London)*, Vol. 92, December 15, 1911, p. 786. Also "The Stresses in Thick-walled Cylinders of Mild Steel Over-strained by Internal Pressure," The Institution of Mechanical Engineers, 1934.

3. Goodman, J., *Mechanics Applied to Engineering*, 8th edition, Longmans, Green and Co., London, 1914, pp. 421–423. A derivation of Barlow's formula is given in this reference.

4. Harman, J. J., "Higher Pressures and Temperatures as They Affect the Design, Installation and Maintenance of Piping," *Heating, Piping and Air Conditioning*, Vol. 2, No. 12, December 1930, p. 985. Also see H. D. Wagner, comments on above article, *Heating, Piping and Air Conditioning*, Vol. 3, No. 8, August 1931, pp. 658–661.

5. Jasper, T. M., and N. F. Scudder, "Multi-layer Construction of Thick Wall Pressure Vessels, *Bulletin* 224, A. O. Smith Corp., Milwaukee, Vol. 37, 1941, p. 885.

6. Mesick, B. S., "The Cold Working of Cannon," *Mechanical Engineering*, Vol. 54, No. 10, October 1932, p. 703.

7. Nadai, A., "Plasticity," 2nd edition, McGraw-Hill Book Co., 1950. Chapters 28 and 29 of this book give a theoretical discussion of the relationship between the pressure and the stresses in a thick-walled cylinder subjected to inelastic strains.

8. Rossheim, D. B., and A. R. C. Marki, "The Significance of and Suggested Limits for the Stresses in Pipe Lines Due to Combined Effects of Pressure and Expansion," *Transactions of the American Society of Mechanical Engineers*, Vol. 62, 1940, p. 443.

9. "Symposium on Internal Stresses in Metals and Alloys," Institute of Metals (British), London, 1948. On pp. 209–218 of this book is given a discussion by A. G. Warren of the autofrettage process as applied to gun tubes.

10. "Welding Multilayer Steel Pressure Vessels," *Materials and Methods*, June 1946, pp. 1578–1582. In this article is given a pictorial description of building thick-walled cylinders by wrapping layers of thin plates.

11. Newitt, D. M., *High Pressure Plant and Fluids at High Pressures*, Clarendon Press, 1940. Pages 1–77 of this reference give a discussion of design principles for use in construction of thick-walled cylinders including end connections, valves, fittings, etc., for use under high pressure.

12. Holroyd, R., "Report on Investigations by Fuels and Lubricants Teams at the I. G. Farbenindustrie, A. G. Works, Ludwigshafen and Oppau." *U. S. Bureau of Mines Information Circular* 7375, August 1946. Pages 60–67 of this paper give a description of new developments in Germany in the construction of laminated-type thick-walled cylinders, described as Wickel pressure vessels. Also there are some descriptions of improved type of end connections for thick-walled cylinders.

Chapter 11

CONTACT STRESSES

102 Introduction. Contact stresses are caused by the pressure of one elastic solid on another at limited areas of contact. Most load-resisting members are designed on the basis of stress in the main body of the member, that is, in portions of the body not affected by the localized stresses at and near the surface of contact where the loads are applied to the body. In other words, the actions in most load-resisting members that cause failures (excessive elastic deflection, yielding, and fracture) of the members are associated with stresses and strains in portions of the body well-removed from the influence of the so-called "contact stresses" in the neighborhood of the points of application of the loads.

In some bodies, however, the contact stresses set up when curved surfaces of two bodies are pressed together by external loads are the significant stresses; that is, the stresses on or somewhat beneath the surface of the contact are associated with the failure of one or both of the bodies. For example, contact stresses may be significant at the area (a) between a locomotive wheel and the railroad rail (a rail head is curved across its top surface); (b) between a roller or a ball and its race in a roller or ball bearing; (c) between the teeth of a pair of gears in mesh; (d) between the cam and valve tappets of a gasoline engine; etc.

It will be noted that in each of these examples the members do not remain in fixed contact. In fact, the contact stresses are repeated a very large number of times, often resulting in a fatigue failure which starts as a localized fracture (crack) that is associated with localized stresses; the fact that contact stresses frequently lead to fatigue failure largely explains why they may limit the load-carrying capacity of the members in contact and hence may be the significant stresses in the bodies. For example, a railroad rail sometimes fails as a result of "contact stresses"; the failure starts as a localized fracture in the form of a minute transverse crack at a point in the head of the rail somewhat beneath the surface of contact between the rail and the locomotive wheel, and progresses outwardly under the influence of the repeated wheel loads until the whole

342

rail cracks or fractures. This fracture is called a transverse fissure failure.

On the other hand, ball bearings and gear teeth sometimes fail as a result of contact stresses by pitting at the surface of contact. The bottom of such pits is often located at the approximate depth to the point of maximum shearing stress. Steel tappets have been observed which failed by the initiation of microscopic cracks at the surface which then spread and caused flaking. Chilled cast-iron tappets have failed by cracks which start underneath the surface, where the shearing stress is highest, and spread to the surface, causing pitting failure.

The principal stresses at or on the contact area between the two curved surfaces that are pressed together are greater than at a point beneath the contact area; whereas the maximum shearing stress at a point on the contact area is usually less than that at a point a small depth from the contact surface.

The problem here considered is that of determining the maximum principal (compressive) and shearing "contact stresses" on and beneath the contact area between two ideal elastic bodies having curved surfaces that are pressed together by external loads. Several investigators have attempted to solve this problem. H. Hertz * was the first to obtain a satisfactory solution although his solution gave only the principal stresses on (within) the contact surface.

103   The problem of determining contact stresses. Figure 179 will aid the reader in visualizing the conditions involved in the problem. Two semicircular disks made of elastic material are pressed together by forces P. The two bodies are initially in contact at a single point. Sections of the boundaries of the two bodies at the point of contact are smooth curves before the loads are applied. The minimum and maximum radii of curvature of the surface of the upper disk at the point of contact are R_1 and R'_1, respectively. These are called principal radii of curvature of the surface. For the lower disk R_2 and R'_2 are the minimum and maximum radii of curvature, respectively, of the surface at the point of contact. The planes in which the minimum radii R_1 and R_2 (or the maximum radii) lie make an angle α. In Figs. 180a and 180b are shown elevation and plan views respectively of the two disks. The lines V_1 and V_2 which make the angle α lie in the plane sections containing the minimum radii R_1 and R_2, respectively. The load P lies along the axis which passes through the centers of the disks and through the

---

* Hertz published a paper in 1881 "On the Contact of Elastic Solids," and in the following year a paper "On the Contact of Rigid Elastic Solids and on Hardness." See H. Hertz, *Gesammelte Werke*, Vol. 1, Leipzig, 1895. English translation in *Miscellaneous Papers*, H. Hertz, Macmillan and Co., 1896.

point of contact and is perpendicular to a plane which is tangent to both disks at the point of contact. In other words, it is assumed that there is no tendency for one body to slide laterally with respect to the other, and hence there is no friction force in addition to the normal force P; the effect of a friction force is discussed in Art. 110.

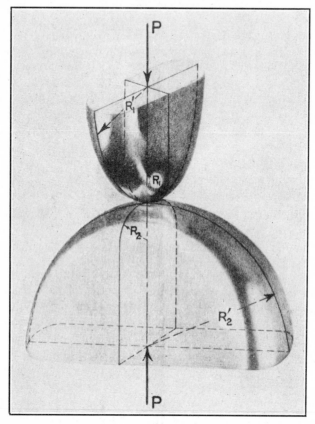

FIG. 179 Two curved surfaces of different radii pressed against each other.

The effect of the load P is to cause the surface of the disks to be deformed elastically over a region surrounding the initial point of contact, thereby bringing the two bodies into contact over a small area as shown in Fig. 180b. The problem is to determine a relation between the load P and the maximum compressive stress on this small area of contact and to determine the principal stresses at any point in either disk on the line of action of the load designated as the Z axis. The principal stresses σ_x, σ_y, and σ_z acting on a small cube at a point on the Z axis are shown in Fig. 180c. The maximum shearing stress at the point is $\tau_{max} = \frac{1}{2}(\sigma_z - \sigma_y)$, where σ_z and σ_y are the maximum and minimum principal stresses at the point.

Attempts to determine the contact stresses described in the foregoing paragraph by the method of mechanics of materials have not yielded satisfactory results; the main reasons are that the area of contact and the volume of material underneath the area of contact subjected to strains are both very small and likewise are practically inaccessible for making the observations of the strains as required in Step 2 of the procedure of mechanics of materials (see Art. 8, Chapter 2). Use will be made therefore of the results of the solution of this problem by the method of the theory of elasticity (see Appendix I). Although the solution of the problem will not be undertaken here, the main assumptions made in the solution of the problem are given in order that the limitations on the use of the results may be understood. After the assumptions are stated, a brief discussion will be given to explain and justify the assumptions.

104   Assumptions on which solution for contact stresses is based. The solution of the problem of the contact stresses in the neighborhood of the point of contact of two bodies as illustrated in Art. 103 is based on the following assumptions:

(a) *Properties of Materials.* The material of each of the two bodies is homogeneous, isotropic, and elastic in accordance with Hooke's law, but the two bodies are not necessarily made of the same material.

(b) *Shape of Surfaces near Point of Contact.* BEFORE LOADING. If two bodies are in contact at a point, there is a common tangent plane to the surfaces at the point of contact. In the solution for contact stresses there is a need for a mathematical expression for the distance between corresponding points on the surfaces near the point of contact, corresponding points being defined as points on the surfaces on a line perpendicular to the common tangent plane. Equations expressing the distances z to points on the surfaces from a common tangent plane at the point of contact are needed in setting up an equation for determining the deformations of the two bodies near the initial point of contact after loads are applied. Instead of using the exact equation for z for a given pair of surfaces, an equation which approximates the distances z between corresponding points on any two surfaces is used. This equation is

$$z = Ax^2 + By^2 \tag{435}$$

in which x and y are coordinates with respect to Y and X axes that pass through the point of contact and lie in the tangent plane, and A and B are constants which depend upon the maximum and minimum radii of curvature of the surfaces at the point of contact. The derivation of

Eq. 435 will be given later in this article. Figures 180*d* and 180*e* show that the curve representing Eq. 435 for a constant value of z is an ellipse. This fact will be important in considering the shape of the area of contact between the two bodies caused by the loads P applied to the bodies.

AFTER LOADING. When the loads P are applied to the bodies as described in Art. 103 and as illustrated in Fig. 180*a*, their surfaces deform

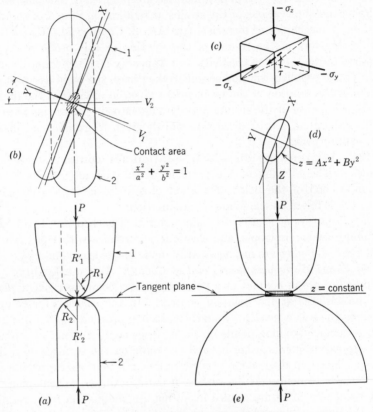

FIG. 180   Analysis of contact stresses.

elastically near the point of contact so that a small area of contact is formed. It is assumed that, as this small area of contact forms, the points which come into contact simultaneously will be points on the two surfaces which were originally equal distances apart. According to Eq. 435, equidistant points on the two surfaces lie on an ellipse. Hence the boundary line of the area of contact is assumed to be an ellipse whose equation is

$$x^2/a^2 + y^2/b^2 = 1 \qquad (436)$$

where x and y are coordinates referred to the same axes as were specified for Eq. 435. The contact area described by Eq. 436 is shown in Fig. 180b. Equation 435 is of sufficient importance to warrant further discussion of its validity, particularly since a method of determining the

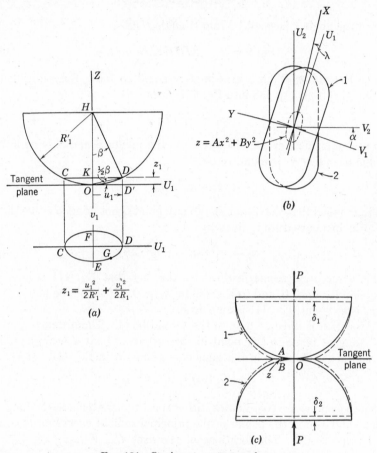

$$z_1 = \frac{u_1^2}{2R_1'} + \frac{v_1^2}{2R_1}$$

(a)

$$z = Ax^2 + By^2$$

(b)

(c)

FIG. 181 Strains at contact surface.

constants A and B is required in the solution of a problem of finding contact stresses.

Justification for Eq. 435. In order to obtain Eq. 435 an expression is derived first for the perpendicular distance z_1 from the tangent plane to any point on the surface of body 1 near the point of contact, assuming the bodies free from loads and in contact at a point. A portion of body 1 showing the distance z_1 is illustrated in Fig. 181a. Let the points considered lie in the planes of principal radii of curvature. Let U_1 and

V_1 be axes in the tangent plane which lie in the planes of principal radii of curvature of body 1. The distance z_1 to point C or D is found as follows. From triangle ODD'

$$z_1 = u_1 \tan \tfrac{1}{2}\beta = \tfrac{1}{2}u_1\beta \tag{437}$$

since the angle β is small. From triangle HKD

$$\tan \beta = \beta = KD/HK = u_1/R'_1 \tag{438}$$

since the radius R'_1 is approximately equal to HK. Substituting the value of β from Eq. 438 into Eq. 437 gives

$$z_1 = u_1{}^2/2R'_1 \tag{439}$$

In a similar manner the distance z_1 to the points E and F lying in the plane of radius R_1 is found to be

$$z_1 = v_1{}^2/2R_1 \tag{440}$$

It is assumed that the distance z_1 to any point G not lying in either plane of principal curvature is given by

$$z_1 = u_1{}^2/2R'_1 + v_1{}^2/2R_1 \tag{441}$$

This assumption seems justified by the fact that Eq. 441 reduces to Eq. 440 for $u_1 = 0$, and to Eq. 439 for $v_1 = 0$. It should be noted that, if z_1 is constant, Eq. 441 is an ellipse.

Attention is directed now to the second body. The distance z_2 from the tangent plane to any point in the surface of body 2 near the point of contact is obtained in the same way as was z_1 in Eq. 441. It is

$$z_2 = u_2{}^2/2R'_2 + v_2{}^2/2R_2 \tag{442}$$

where u_2 and v_2 are coordinates with respect to axes lying in the tangent plane and also in the planes of the principal radii of curvature R'_2, and R_2, respectively. The locations of the axes U_1, V_1 and U_2, V_2 are shown in Fig. 181b which is the same view of the disks as in Fig. 180b. The axes V_1 and V_2 are separated by the angle α which is the angle between the lines V_1 and V_2 of the disks as shown in Fig. 180b.

The distance z between points on the two surfaces near the point of contact is the numerical sum of z_1 and z_2 given by Eqs. 441 and 442. Hence

$$z = z_1 + z_2 = u_1{}^2/2R'_1 + v_1{}^2/2R_1 + u_2{}^2/2R'_2 + v_2{}^2/2R_2 \tag{443}$$

Equation 443 is now transformed into the form of Eq. 435. The first transformation is the elimination of the coordinates u_2 and v_2 by using the relationship

$$u_2 = u_1 \cos \alpha + v_1 \sin \alpha$$

$$v_2 = -u_1 \sin \alpha + v_1 \cos \alpha$$

(444)

When Eqs. 444 are substituted into Eq. 443 it becomes

$$z = A'u_1{}^2 + 2H'u_1v_1 + 2B'v_1{}^2$$

(445)

where

$$2A' = (1/R'_1) + (1/R'_2) \cos^2 \alpha + (1/R_2) \sin^2 \alpha$$

$$2H' = [(1/R'_2) - (1/R_2)] \sin \alpha \cos \alpha$$

(446)

$$2B' = (1/R_1) + (1/R'_2) \sin^2 \alpha + (1/R_2) \cos^2 \alpha$$

Equation 445 is an ellipse, as shown in Fig. 181b, whose center is at the point O. It is now desired to find the equation of the ellipse referred to a set of axes X and Y which coincide with its major and minor axes. The value of the angle λ through which the axes U_1 and V_1 must be rotated in order to eliminate the product term u_1v_1 in Eq. 445 is required for this transformation. The transformation is

$$u_1 = x \cos \lambda - y \sin \lambda$$

$$v_1 = x \sin \lambda + y \cos \lambda$$

(447)

If Eqs. 447 are substituted in Eq. 445, using the value of the angle λ which will eliminate the product term u_1v_1, Eq. 445 becomes

$$z = Ax^2 + By^2$$

(448)

which is also Eq. 435. In the transformation of Eq. 445 into Eq. 448 the constants A and B must be evaluated. In the process of making the transformation it is found that A and B are the roots of a quadratic equation and have the following values:

$$B = \frac{1}{4}\left(\frac{1}{R_1} + \frac{1}{R_2} + \frac{1}{R'_1} + \frac{1}{R'_2}\right) +$$

$$\frac{1}{4}\sqrt{\left[\left(\frac{1}{R_1} - \frac{1}{R'_1}\right) + \left(\frac{1}{R_2} - \frac{1}{R'_2}\right)\right]^2 - 4\left(\frac{1}{R_1} - \frac{1}{R'_1}\right)\left(\frac{1}{R_2} - \frac{1}{R'_2}\right)\sin^2 \alpha}$$

(449)

$$A = \frac{1}{4}\left(\frac{1}{R_1} + \frac{1}{R_2} + \frac{1}{R'_1} + \frac{1}{R'_2}\right) -$$

$$\frac{1}{4}\sqrt{\left[\left(\frac{1}{R_1} - \frac{1}{R'_1}\right) + \left(\frac{1}{R_2} - \frac{1}{R'_2}\right)\right]^2 - 4\left(\frac{1}{R_1} - \frac{1}{R'_1}\right)\left(\frac{1}{R_2} - \frac{1}{R'_2}\right)\sin^2 \alpha}$$

(450)

The constants A and B depend upon the principal radii of curvature of the two bodies at the point of contact and upon the angle α between the corresponding planes of the minimum (or maximum) principal curvatures. If the lines V_1 and V_2 of the disks in Fig. 180a are parallel, $\alpha = 0$ and Eqs. 449 and 450 reduce to

$$B = \tfrac{1}{2}[(1/R_1) + (1/R_2)] \qquad (449a)$$

$$A = \tfrac{1}{2}[(1/R'_1) + (1/R'_2)] \qquad (450a)$$

If $\alpha = 90°$ Eqs. 449 and 450 reduce to

$$B = \tfrac{1}{2}[(1/R_1) + (1/R'_2)] \qquad (449b)$$

$$A = \tfrac{1}{2}[(1/R'_1) + (1/R_2)] \qquad (450b)$$

Brief Discussion of Solution by Theory of Elasticity. It was pointed out earlier in this article that Eq. 435 or Eq. 448 is used to express the amount of deformation of points on the surfaces of the two bodies within the contact area. In Fig. 181c the solid outline shows the two disks of Fig. 179 in contact at one point, before the loads are applied, and the dashed lines show the new positions of the two bodies after the loads P are applied and the two disks are in contact over a flattened area around the original point of contact O. The centers of the disks move toward each other by amounts of δ_1 and δ_2, respectively, which means that the distance between points on the bodies not affected by the local deformation near O is shortened by an amount $\delta_1 + \delta_2 = \delta$. Points such as A and B move toward each other a distance z as given by Eq. 448, then meet each other. If they did not meet within the contact area, they might move the whole distance δ. Therefore, the deformation of the two bodies within the contact area is $\delta - z$. If w_1 and w_2 represent the deformations of each of the two bodies, at any point within the contact area, the sum of these deformations is given by

$$w_1 + w_2 = \delta - z$$

Furthermore, if the value for z is substituted from Eq. 448, the sum of the deformations of any two points which meet in the contact area is

$$w_1 + w_2 = \delta - Ax^2 - By^2 \qquad (451)$$

where δ is the approach of the two bodies or the distance they move towards each other. Equation 451 gives the deformation only at points on the surface and within the contact area; it does not furnish sufficient information concerning the deformation to solve the problem by the method of mechanics of materials. However, Eq. 451 does furnish the basis for a complete solution of the problem by the method of theory of elasticity. Hertz noted that Eq. 451 has the same form as that of the Newtonian potential equation for the attraction of a homogeneous mass M in the shape of an ellipsoid upon a unit of mass concentrated at a point P some distance from the ellipsoid. This Newtonian potential function satisfies the same differential equations which are required to be satisfied in the method of the theory of elasticity. The problem is solved by placing into the potential equation the stresses at the contact surface instead of the mass, etc., and the constants are evaluated. The complete solution is given in reference 1 at the end of this chapter. The solution is given in terms of elliptic integrals which have to be solved with tables, as will be illustrated later. The results are given in the following articles.

105 Notation and meaning of terms. The following notation and interpretations of terms are needed for an understanding of subsequent equations:

$P =$ total force or pressure exerted by body 1 on body 2, and vice versa.

$E_1, E_2 =$ tensile (or compressive) moduli of elasticity for bodies 1 and 2.

$\mu_1, \mu_2 =$ Poisson's ratio for bodies 1 and 2.

$a =$ semi-major axis of ellipse of contact.

$b =$ semi-minor axis of ellipse of contact.

$k = b/a = \cos \theta; k \gtrless 1$

$k' = \sqrt{1 - k^2} = \sin \theta$

$R_1, R'_1 =$ minimum and maximum numerical values of the radii, respectively, of the surface of body 1 at the point of contact. The plane sections in which R_1 and R'_1 lie are perpendicular to each other. See Fig. 179. The signs of R_1 and R'_1 are as follows: If the center of curvature is inside the body, the radius is positive; if outside the body, it is negative.

$R_2, R'_2 =$ same as R_1, R'_1, for body 2.

$\alpha =$ angle between planes of minimum (or maximum) curvatures at point of contact (see Fig. 180b).

$k(z/b) =$ relative depth below surface of contact to point on Z axis at which stresses are to be calculated. The reason that the depth is expressed in terms of $k(z/b)$ rather than by z directly is that, in evaluating the integrals obtained in the mathematical solution of the problem, the term

$k(z/b)$ can conveniently be replaced by a trigonometric function. Thus

$$\cot \phi = k(z/b)$$

z_s = depth in either body from surface to point on Z axis at which maximum shearing stress occurs.

In the expressions for the principal stresses two integrals (called elliptic integrals) are found which involve ϕ [or $k(z/b)$], θ, and k' (that is, b/a). These integrals are denoted as $F(\phi, k')$ and $H(\phi, k')$. Likewise, two integrals involving k' alone are encountered, denoted as $K(k')$ and $E(k')$. These integrals are

$$F(\phi, k') = \int_0^\phi \frac{d\theta}{\sqrt{1 - k'^2 \sin^2 \theta}} \qquad H(\phi, k') = \int_0^\phi \sqrt{1 - k'^2 \sin^2 \theta} \, d\theta$$

$$K(k') = F\left(\frac{\pi}{2}, k'\right) = \int_0^{\pi/2} \frac{d\theta}{\sqrt{1 - k'^2 \sin^2 \theta}}$$

$$E(k') = H\left(\frac{\pi}{2}, k'\right) = \int_0^{\pi/2} \sqrt{1 - k'^2 \sin^2 \theta} \, d\theta$$

106 Expressions for principal stresses. The analysis involving the assumptions and limitations indicated in Art. 104 yields the following expressions for the principal stresses σ_x, σ_y, and σ_z at a point on the Z axis; the point is at the distance z from the origin which lies in the surface of contact of the two elastic bodies; and the stresses act on planes perpendicular to the X, Y, and Z axes, respectively. The solution of this problem, from which these results are taken, is given in reference 1 at the end of this chapter.

$$\sigma_x = [M(\Omega_x + \mu\Omega'_x)] \frac{b}{\Delta} \tag{452}$$

$$\sigma_y = [M(\Omega_y + \mu\Omega'_y)] \frac{b}{\Delta} \tag{453}$$

$$\sigma_z = \left[\frac{M}{2}\left(\frac{1}{n} - n\right)\right] \frac{b}{\Delta} \tag{454}$$

in which
$$M = \frac{2k}{k'^2 E(k')} \qquad n = \sqrt{\frac{k^2 + k^2(z/b)^2}{1 + k^2(z/b)^2}}$$

$$\Delta = \frac{1}{A + B}\left(\frac{1 - \mu_1^2}{E_1} + \frac{1 - \mu_2^2}{E_2}\right)$$

where A and B are constants given by Eqs. 449 and 450.

$$\Omega_x = -\frac{1-n}{2} + k\frac{z}{b}[F(\phi, k') - H(\phi, k')]$$

$$\Omega'_x = -\frac{n}{k^2} + 1 + k\frac{z}{b}\left[\left(\frac{1}{k^2}\right)H(\phi, k') - F(\phi, k')\right]$$

$$\Omega_y = \frac{1}{2n} + \frac{1}{2} - \frac{n}{k^2} + k\frac{z}{b}\left[\frac{1}{k^2}H(\phi, k') - F(\phi, k')\right]$$

$$\Omega'_y = -1 + n + k\frac{z}{b}[F(\phi, k') - H(\phi, k')]$$

From all these equations representing the terms in Eqs. 452, 453, and 454 it will be noted that the stresses depend upon the variables A, B, k, k', μ_1, μ_2, E_1, E_2, b, and z. The first four variables depend only upon the shape of the surfaces near the point of contact. Of these four, A and B are found from Eqs. 449 and 450, and, from Art. 105, $k' = \sqrt{1 - k^2}$. Therefore, one additional equation is needed for finding the value of k. This equation is

$$\frac{B}{A} = \frac{(1/k^2)E(k') - K(k')}{K(k') - E(k')} \tag{455}$$

The second group of four variables, μ_1, μ_2, E_1, and E_2, depend only upon the physical properties of the two bodies in contact and are found by tests of the material. The next variable, b, the semi-minor axis of the area of contact, depends upon the eight variables previously listed, but it is important to note that it also depends upon the load P. The equation expressing this fact is

$$b = \sqrt[3]{\frac{3kE(k')}{2\pi} \cdot P\Delta} \tag{456}$$

Values of the last variable z, which represent the depth of a point below the surface of contact, may be chosen so that the three principal stresses at any point on the Z axis may be obtained.

107   Method of computing contact stresses.   *Principal Stresses.* In Art. 106 it is noted that the values of A and B must be computed first, and that in Eq. 455 the ratio B/A determines the value of k (and of k'). It should be remembered from Art. 104 that the values of A and B are related to the geometric shape and configuration of the two bodies. Thus, if two cylinders are crossed so that they are in point contact with their longitudinal axes perpendicular, the value of $B/A = 1$, but, if these cylinders are arranged so that their longitudinal axis are parallel (line contact), $B/A = \infty$. With the values of the four quantities A, B, k, and k' known, the terms in the brackets in Eqs. 452, 453, and 454 can be computed if some value of Poisson's ratio μ is assumed. Fortunately the value of μ in these bracket terms has only a small influence on the final values of the stresses; a value of $\mu = \frac{1}{4}$ will be assumed in computing these terms. The actual values of μ_1 and μ_2 of the two bodies are used later in computing Δ. Thus, since these terms within the brackets do *not* depend upon the elastic constants of the two bodies or on the load P, their magnitudes can be computed and tabulated for use as coefficients for the ratio b/Δ, which must also be computed before the magnitudes of the stresses can be found. As an example, let a value of the ratio $B/A = 1.24$ be chosen. From Eq. 455 it can be shown that the corresponding value of $k = 0.866$ and $k' = 0.5$. By choosing values of the ratio kz/b, the coefficients referred to can be found for computing the stresses at any depth z below the area of contact. The results of these computations are given in Fig. 182, in which the coefficients of b/Δ are plotted as abscissas, and the values of kz/b to the point at which the stresses occur are plotted as ordinates. The curves representing σ_x, σ_y, and σ_z show that their largest magnitudes occur when $z = 0$ (at the center of the surface of contact) and that all three stresses decrease as the depth z increases. The principal stress having the greatest magnitude is σ_z, and hence this stress would be the most significant one if the maximum principal stress theory of failure is accepted. In this example, in which $B/A = 1.24$, the value of $\sigma_{max} = 0.67b/\Delta$. The coefficient 0.67 of b/Δ is found at $z = 0$ from the curve σ_z.

Maximum Shearing Stress. The maximum shearing stress at any point is $\frac{1}{2}(\sigma_{max} - \sigma_{min})$. In Fig. 182 the curves show that the magnitudes of σ_x and σ_y decrease more rapidly than that of σ_z at points just beneath the surface of contact. Because of this fact the maximum shearing stress at points just beneath the surface of contact increases in magnitude and reaches its maximum value $\frac{1}{2}(\sigma_{z_s} - \sigma_{y_s})$ at the depth z_s, as shown by the curve marked τ. In this example in which $B/A = 1.24$, the value of $\tau_{max} = 0.22b/\Delta$, and the depth $kz_s/b = 0.44$, that is, $z_s = 0.44b/0.866 = 0.51b$. The coefficient 0.22 of b/Δ is the ordinate to the τ curve at the depth z_s.

Maximum Octahedral Shearing Stress. The maximum octahedral shearing stress τ_G is given by Eq. 33 in Chapter 3; in this example its value at any point is

$$\tau_G = \frac{1}{3}\sqrt{(\sigma_x - \sigma_y)^2 + (\sigma_y - \sigma_z)^2 + (\sigma_z - \sigma_x)^2}$$

The values of τ_G have been computed by this equation for several points beneath the surface of contact and are plotted as ordinates to the curve marked τ_G. In this example, for $B/A = 1.24$, the maximum value of

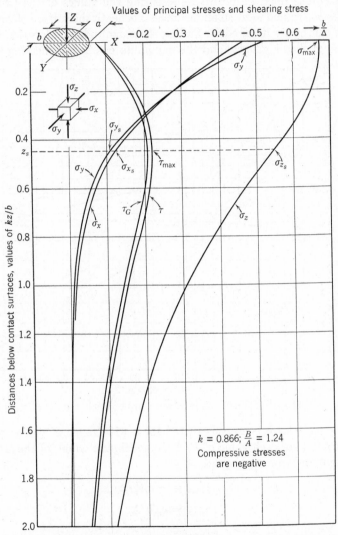

Fig. 182 Curves showing variation in principal stresses, maximum shearing stress, and octahedral shearing stress with variations in distance below contact surface; $\mu = 0.25$.

the octahedral shearing stress $\tau_{G\,max} = 0.21b/\Delta$, and it occurs at the same depth $z_s = 0.51b$ as the maximum shearing stress. The coefficient 0.21 of b/Δ is the ordinate to the τ_G curve at the depth z_s.

Curves for Computing Stresses for Any Value of B/A. The example in which $B/A = 1.24$ ($k = 0.866$) shows that for each value of B/A or k a set of curves must be drawn representing the values of the principal stresses σ_x, σ_y, and σ_z at small distances z beneath the surface of contact. These curves are required for finding the magnitude and location of the maximum shearing stress and the maximum octahedral shearing stress.

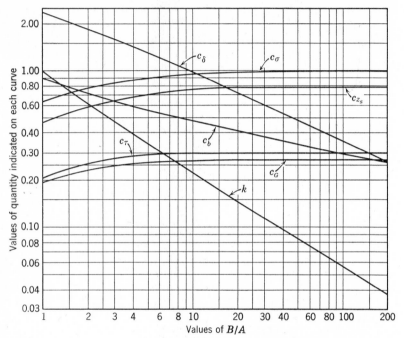

Fig. 183   Stresses and deflections between two bodies in contact at a point.

These curves have been constructed for a wide range of values of the ratio B/A. For each value of B/A the maximum values of the stresses may be found from the equations

$$\sigma_{max} = -c_\sigma(b/\Delta)$$

$$\tau_{max} = c_\tau(b/\Delta) \qquad (457)$$

$$\tau_{G\ max} = c_G(b/\Delta)$$

in which c_σ, c_τ, and c_G are the coefficients as found from curves such as shown in Fig. 182. In the example in which $B/A = 1.24$ the values of the coefficients have already been given as $c_\sigma = 0.67$, $c_\tau = 0.22$, and $c_G = 0.21$. In Figs. 183 and 184, values of these coefficients for use in Eq. 457 are given as ordinates to the curves marked c_σ, c_τ, and c_G for a

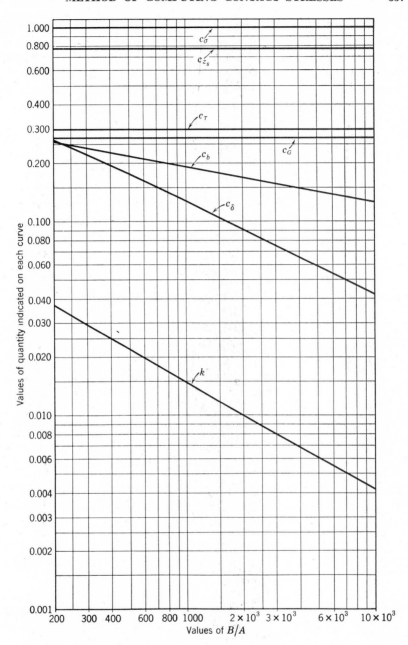

FIG. 184   Stresses and deflections between two bodies in contact at a point.

range of values B/A from 1 to 10,000 which are shown as abscissas. The values of k which are required in computing the semi-major axis a and the semi-minor axis b of the area of contact are given as ordinates to the curve marked k. The value of b which may be computed by using Eq. 456 is found as follows. Equation 456 is rewritten as

$$b = c_b \sqrt[3]{P\Delta} \qquad (458)$$

in which $c_b = \sqrt[3]{3kE(k')/2\pi}$. The values of k (and k') as found from the curve marked k have been used to compute the value of the coefficient c_b. These values of c_b to be used in Eq. 458 are given as ordinates to the curve marked c_b. The length of the semi-major axis is $a = b/k$. The depth z_s below the surface of contact to the location on the Z axis of the point at which the maximum stresses τ_{max} and $\tau_{G\,max}$ occur is

$$z_s = c_{zs}b \qquad (459)$$

in which the coefficient is given as ordinates to the curve marked c_{zs}. The use of the coefficients given in Figs. 183 and 184 in solving problems is now illustrated.

Illustrative Problems

Problem 206. In Fig. 179 the two semicircular disks are made of steel. The load $P = 1000$ lb. The radii of the surfaces at the point of contact are $R_1 = 2$ in., $R'_1 = 5$ in., and $R_2 = 3$ in., $R'_2 = 8$ in. The angle α between the planes of minimum curvature is 60°. Compute the maximum principal stress, the maximum shearing stress, and the maximum octahedral shearing stress in the disks due to the contact pressure, and state the location of the point where each of these stresses occur. Assume that $E_1 = E_2 = 30 \times 10^6$ lb per sq in., and $\mu_1 = \mu_2 = \frac{1}{4}$.

Solution. The values of the maximum principal stress, the maximum shearing stress, and the maximum octahedral shearing stress are obtained from Eq. 457 by using the coefficients which are found from the curves in Fig. 183 after computing the ratio B/A. From Eqs. 449 and 450 the values of B and A are found to be

$$B = \tfrac{1}{4}(\tfrac{1}{2} + \tfrac{1}{3} + \tfrac{1}{5} + \tfrac{1}{8}) + \tfrac{1}{4}\sqrt{[(\tfrac{1}{2} - \tfrac{1}{5}) + (\tfrac{1}{3} - \tfrac{1}{8})]^2 - 4(\tfrac{1}{2} - \tfrac{1}{5})(\tfrac{1}{3} - \tfrac{1}{8})\sin^2 60°}$$

$$= 0.356 \text{ in.}^{-1}$$

$$A = \tfrac{1}{4}(\tfrac{1}{2} + \tfrac{1}{3} + \tfrac{1}{5} + \tfrac{1}{8}) - \tfrac{1}{4}\sqrt{[(\tfrac{1}{2} - \tfrac{1}{5}) + (\tfrac{1}{3} - \tfrac{1}{8})]^2 - 4(\tfrac{1}{2} - \tfrac{1}{5})(\tfrac{1}{3} - \tfrac{1}{8})\sin^2 60°}$$

$$= 0.223 \text{ in.}^{-1}$$

and $B/A = 1.6$. The value of b/Δ is found by computing Δ and b separately. The value of Δ is

$$\Delta = \frac{1}{A + B}\left(\frac{1 - \mu_1^2}{E_1} + \frac{1 - \mu_2^2}{E_2}\right) = \frac{1}{A + B}\left[\frac{2(1 - \mu^2)}{E}\right]$$

$$= \frac{1}{0.356 + 0.223}\left[\frac{2(1 - \overline{0.25^2})}{30 \times 10^6}\right] = 1.08 \times 10^{-7} \text{ in.}^3/\text{lb}$$

The value of b is found from Eq. 458 by using the coefficient $c_b = 0.78$, as found from the curve in Fig. 183 for $B/A = 1.6$. Therefore

$$b = 0.78 \sqrt[3]{P\Delta} = 0.78 \sqrt[3]{1000 \times 1.08 \times 10^{-7}} = 0.037 \text{ in.}$$

Hence
$$\frac{b}{\Delta} = \frac{0.037 \times 10,000,000}{1.08} = 343,000 \text{ lb/in.}^2$$

From the curves for c_σ, c_τ, and c_G in Fig. 183, for $B/A = 1.6$, we obtain $c_\sigma = 0.73$, $c_\tau = 0.24$, and $c_G = 0.22$. Substitution of these values in Eq. 457 gives

$$\sigma_{max} = -0.73b/\Delta = -0.73 \times 343,000 = -251,000 \text{ lb/in.}^2$$

$$\tau_{max} = 0.24b/\Delta = 0.24 \times 343,000 = 82,500 \text{ lb/in.}^2$$

$$\tau_{G \text{ max}} = 0.22b/\Delta = 0.22 \times 343,000 = 75,500 \text{ lb/in.}^2$$

and from Eq. 459
$$z_s = c_{zs}b = 0.54 \times 0.037 = 0.02 \text{ in.}$$

The maximum principal stress acts normal to the area of contact at the center of the area. The maximum shearing stress occurs at a point on the Z axis, at a distance of 0.02 in. from the surface of contact.

Problem 207. *Crossed Cylinders, with Axes at Right Angles.* A steel railway car wheel 33 in. in diameter rolls on a steel rail whose top surface has a cross radius of 12 in., as indicated in Fig. 185. The wheel pressure on the rail head is 25,000 lb.

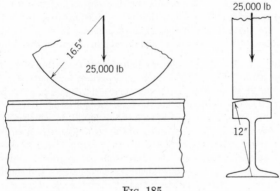

25,000 lb

16.5"

25,000 lb

12"

FIG. 185

Assume that $E = 30,000,000$ lb per sq in., and Poisson's ratio $\mu = 0.25$ for both wheel and rail. Calculate the maximum principal stress, the maximum shearing stress, and the maximum octahedral shearing stress in the rail head and the depth below the surface at which the maximum shearing stress occurs.

Solution. The values of σ_{max}, τ_{max}, and $\tau_{G \text{ max}}$ are obtained from Eq. 457 after computing B/A from Eqs. 449 and 450. Since R'_1 and R'_2 are infinite for the two cylinders, and the angle $\alpha = 90°$, Eqs. 449b and 450b reduce to

$$B = 1/2R_1 \qquad A = 1/2R_2$$

Hence $B/A = R_2/R_1$. The ratio B/A must be greater than or equal to unity in order that we may use the curves of Fig. 183 to solve this problem. Therefore, the wheel is selected as body 2 with the value of $R_2 = 16.5$ in., and the rail is body 1 with $R_1 = 12$ in. Therefore,

$$\frac{B}{A} = \frac{16.5}{12} = 1.375 \quad \text{and} \quad A + B = \frac{1}{2R_2} + \frac{1}{2R_1} = 0.0720 \text{ in.}^{-1}$$

$$\Delta = \frac{2(1 - \mu^2)}{(A + B)E} = \frac{2(1 - (\tfrac{1}{4})^2)}{0.0720 \times 30,000,000} = 8.68 \times 10^{-7} \text{ in.}^3/\text{lb}$$

From the curves in Fig. 183 for $B/A = 1.375$, we obtain

$$b = 0.82\sqrt[3]{P\Delta} \qquad \sigma_{max} = 0.70b/\Delta \qquad \tau_{max} = 0.23b/\Delta$$

$$\tau_{G \ max} = 0.21b/\Delta \qquad z_s = 0.51b$$

Hence

$$b = 0.82\sqrt[3]{25,000 \times 8.68 \times 10^{-7}} = 0.23 \text{ in.}$$

and

$$\frac{b}{\Delta} = \frac{0.23 \times 10,000,000}{8.68} = 265,000 \text{ lb/in.}^2$$

Therefore

$$\sigma_{max} = -0.70 \times 265,000 = -185,000 \text{ lb/in.}^2$$

$$\tau_{max} = 0.23 \times 265,000 = 61,000 \text{ lb/in.}^2$$

$$\tau_{G \ max} = 0.21 \times 265,000 = 56,000 \text{ lb/in.}^2$$

The maximum shearing stress and the maximum octahedral shearing stress occur at a distance from the contact surface of $z_s = 0.51b = 0.51 \times 0.23 = 0.12$ in.; they are repeated each time a 25,000-lb wheel load passes over the given section of the rail. It should be noted that the principal stresses in each of the two bodies in contact are equal at points on the Z axis that are equidistant from the contact surface, and likewise the maximum shearing stresses and maximum octahedral shearing stresses in the two bodies are equal at points equidistant from the point of contact.

Problem 208. In Fig. 186a is shown a ball bearing consisting of an inner race, an outer race, and 12 balls, $\frac{3}{8}$ in. in diameter, all parts being made of steel. A rated load of $P_0 = 935$ lb is given in a manufacturer's handbook for this bearing when operating at 3000 rpm. The load P on the topmost ball which bears the largest portion of the load is $P = 5P_0/n = (5 \times 935)/12 = 390$ lb, in which n is the number of balls (see reference 5). The dimensions of the bearing are given in Figs. 186b and 186c. At the region of contact between the inner race and the topmost ball, compute the maximum principal stress, the dimensions of the area of contact, the maximum shearing stress, the maximum octahedral shearing stress, and the distance from the point of contact to the point where these stresses occur. Use $\mu_1 = \mu_2 = \frac{1}{4}$; $E_1 = E_2 = 30,000,000$ lb per sq in.

Solution. Let the ball be designated as body 2 and the inner race as 1, so that R_2 and $R'_2 = \frac{3}{16}$ in., $R_1 = -0.1912$ in., and $R'_1 = 0.7180$ in. We substitute these values in Eqs. 449 and 450. In these equations it is noted that in the ball the radii of curvature are the same in all plane sections through its center so that the angle α may take any value whatsoever, but this fact does not influence the results since the term $\sin^2 \alpha$ is multiplied by $[(1/R_2) - (1/R'_2)]$, which is zero. The foregoing equations give

$$B = 3.3630 \text{ in.}^{-1} \qquad A = 0.0516 \text{ in.}^{-1}$$

$$B + A = 3.4146 \text{ in.}^{-1} \qquad B/A = 65.2$$

and

$$\Delta = \frac{2}{A + B}\left(\frac{1 - \mu^2}{E}\right) = 0.0183 \times 10^{-6} \text{ in.}^3/\text{lb}$$

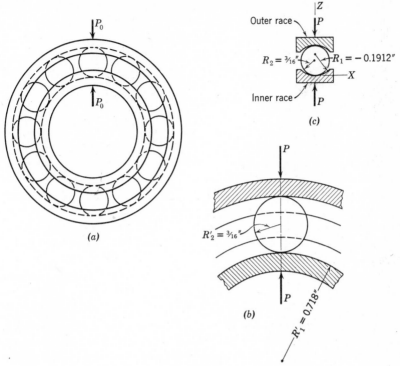

FIG. 186   Contact pressure in ball bearing.

From the curves in Fig. 183 we obtain the following coefficients: $c_b = 0.32$, $k = 0.07$, $c_\sigma = 1.00$, $c_\tau = 0.30$, $c_G = 0.27$, and $c_{zs} = 0.78$.   Hence

$$b \doteq 0.32\sqrt[3]{P\Delta} = 0.00084\sqrt[3]{P} = 0.0061 \text{ in.}$$

$$a = b/k = 0.0061/0.07 = 0.087 \text{ in.}$$

$$\frac{b}{\Delta} = \frac{0.00084 \sqrt[3]{P}}{0.0183 \times 10^{-6}} = 46,000\sqrt[3]{P} = 336,000 \text{ lb/in.}^2$$

$$\sigma_{max} = -1.00b/\Delta = -46,000\sqrt[3]{P} = -336,000 \text{ lb/in.}^2$$

$$\tau_{max} = 0.30b/\Delta = 13,800\sqrt[3]{P} = 101,000 \text{ lb/in.}^2$$

$$\tau_{G\ max} = 0.27b/\Delta = 12,500\sqrt[3]{P} = 91,000 \text{ lb/in.}^2$$

$$z_s = c_{zs}b = 0.78 \times 0.0061 = 0.0048 \text{ in.}$$

Significance of Stresses.   In the three preceding illustrative problems the magnitudes of the maximum principal stresses are quite large in comparison with values of this stress usually found in direct tension, bending, and torsion.   In these problems, as in all contact stress problems, the three principal stresses at the point where they have their maximum values have the same sense, that is, they are all compressive stresses. As a result of this fact the maximum shearing stress and the maximum octahedral shearing stress are always less than one-half the maximum principal stress; it will be recalled that for a state of uniaxial stress (one principal stress) the maximum shearing stress is one-half the principal stress. In fact by a comparison of the values of c_σ, c_τ, and c_G for various values of B/A in Figs. 183 and 184, it can be seen that, when $B/A = 1$, $c_\tau = 0.32c_\sigma$, and $c_G = 0.30c_\sigma$, and, when $B/A = 100$ or larger, $c_\tau = 0.30c_\sigma$, and $c_G = 0.27c_\sigma$. Thus τ_{max} and $\tau_{G\ max}$ are always slightly smaller than one-third of the maximum principal stress σ_{max}. This fact is of special importance if the maximum shearing stress or the octahedral shearing stress is considered to be the cause of structural damage (failure) of the member, for, if the shearing stresses are relatively small in comparison to the maximum principal stress, very high principal stresses can occur as has been pointed out in the foregoing illustrative problems. However, it should be stated that the maximum utilizable values of the maximum shearing stress or maximum octahedral shearing stress are not easily determined, owing to the fact that in many problems involving two bodies under pressure at a small area of contact, such as occurs in bearings, there are additional factors which affect the behavior of the material such as sliding friction (see Art. 110), the effect of a lubricant, the effect of repeated loads, the effect of variation in the metal near the surface of contact such as that due to case hardening, and the effects of metallurgical changes which often occur in such parts as the races of ball bearings due to the heat generated by repeated stressing.

Problems

209. In Prob. 207 compute the major and minor axes of the ellipse of contact.

210. In Prob. 207 compute τ_{max} if the wheel is cast iron, with $\mu = 0.25$ and $E = 20,000,000$ lb per sq in.   *Ans.* $\tau_{max} = 46,000$ lb per sq in.

211. In Prob. 207 the value of σ_z at the contact surface is 185,000 lb per sq in. How does this compare with the average surface normal (compressive) stress over the area of contact?

212. In Prob. 208 compute the maximum shearing stress in the ball and in the outer race due to the pressure between the two. The radii of the outer race are -1.093 in. and -0.1912 in.

213. Compute, in terms of P, the maximum principal stress, the maximum shearing stress, and the maximum octahedral shearing stress in a steel ball 4 in. in diameter for each of the following conditions: (a) The ball (sphere) is pressed against a plane steel surface by a force of P lb. (b) The ball is pressed against another steel ball of equal diameter by a force of P lb. (c) The ball is pressed against the inside of a steel spherical surface having a radius of 4 in. by a force of P lb.

214. A feed roll used in finishing steel shafts consists of two cylindrical steel rollers each 7 in. in diameter arranged with their longitudinal axes parallel. The shaft is fed between the rollers so that its axis is perpendicular to that of the rollers. If the shaft is 2 in. in diameter and the pressure between the shaft and the rollers is 1000 lb, compute the maximum shearing stress in the shaft and determine the distance from the point of contact to the point of maximum shearing stress.

Ans. $\tau_{\text{max}} = 133,000$ lb per sq in.

215. The feed roll in Prob. 214 is rearranged so that the angle between the longitudinal axes of the rollers is 30° and the angle between the longitudinal axes of each of the rollers and of the shaft is 15°. Compute the maximum shearing stress in the shaft if the pressure between the rolls and the shaft is 1000 lb. Determine the distance from the point of contact to the point in the shaft where the maximum shearing stress occurs. What percentage reduction in the maximum shearing stress as compared with the stress in the rollers of Prob. 214 is gained by the rearrangement of the rollers?

216. A cast-iron push rod in a valve gear is operated by a steel cam as shown in Fig. 187. The cam is cylindrical in shape and has a radius of curvature of ¼ in. at

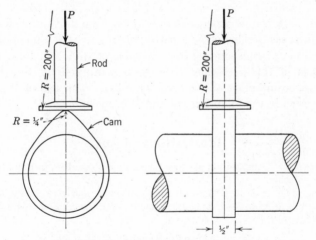

Fig. 187   Contact pressure in valve tappet.

its nose. The surface on the end of the push rod which follows the cam is part of a sphere whose radius of curvature is 200 in. so that the rod and cam are in point contact when under no load. If the allowable maximum principal stress for cast iron on steel is 200,000 lb per sq in., compute the allowable load P on the rod. Poisson's ratio for cast iron and steel is ¼, and the values for the modulus of elasticity for cast iron and steel are 17,000,000 lb per sq in. and 30,000,000 lb per sq in., respectively.

108   Deflection of bodies in point contact. In Eq. 451 is given an expression for the distance $\delta = \delta_1 + \delta_2$ through which two bodies in contact at a point move towards each other when acted upon by a load P as shown in Fig. 181c. The deflection δ is sometimes called the approach because it expresses the sum of the deflections of the two bodies as they approach each other. The expression for the value of δ has been found from this equation by Hertz and is given by

$$\delta = \frac{3kPK(k')}{2\pi}\left(\frac{A + B}{b/\Delta}\right) \tag{460}$$

in which P is the load, $K(k')$ is the complete elliptic integral described in Art. 105, and A, B, k, Δ, and b are defined in Arts. 105 and 106. In order to make convenient use of Eq. 460 a substitution of

$$c_\delta = 3kK(k')/2 \tag{461}$$

is made so that the equation becomes

$$\delta = c_\delta \frac{P}{\pi}\left(\frac{A + B}{b/\Delta}\right) \tag{462}$$

In Eq. 461 the value c_δ depends only upon k (and k'), and since from Eq. 455 there is a value of B/A corresponding to each value of k, there is a value of c_δ corresponding to each value of B/A. In Figs. 183 and 184 values of this coefficient have been computed by Eq. 461 and plotted as ordinates to the curve marked c_δ. The use of Eq. 462 is demonstrated in the following illustrated problem.

Illustrative Problem

Problem 217. Compute the distance the two disks described in Prob. 206 move towards each other.

Solution. The value of $B/A = 1.6$ from Prob. 206, and $B + A = 0.579$. The value of b/Δ from Prob. 206 is 343,000. From Fig. 183 the value of $c_\delta = 2.00$. Substitution of these values in Eq. 462 gives

$$\delta = 2.00 \frac{1000 \times 0.579}{\pi \times 343,000} = 0.0011 \text{ in.}$$

Problems

218. Compute the approach towards each other of the cross-cylinders described in Prob. 207.   *Ans.* $\delta = 0.0045$ in.

219. A steel ball 1 in. in diameter rests on a thick flat aluminum alloy plate. Compute the deflection of the ball and plate if a 300-lb force presses the ball against the plate.

109   Stresses for two bodies in contact over narrow rectangular area (line contact); loads normal to contact area. Two surfaces of contact may be cylindrical and be arranged so that they are in contact approximately along a straight line element before loads are applied. Figure 188a illustrates such an arrangement of two circular cylinders, the line of contact being perpendicular to the paper. Figure 188b also shows a line contact of a circular cylinder resting upon a plane. Figure 188c shows a line contact of a small circular cylinder resting inside a larger hollow cylinder. In the cylinders shown in Fig. 188 the radii R'_1 and R'_2, which lie in a plane perpendicular to the paper, are

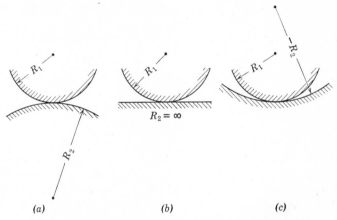

$R_2 = \infty$

(a)   *(b)*   *(c)*

Fig. 188   Line contact between cylindrical bodies.

each indefinitely large so that $1/R'_1$ and $1/R'_2$ are each equal to zero and also the angle $\alpha = 0$. Therefore, from Eqs. 449a and 450a the expressions for B and A are

$$B = \tfrac{1}{2}[(1/R_1) + (1/R_2)] \qquad\qquad A = 0$$

Hence the value of the ratio B/A is indefinitely large, and from Eq. 455 it is seen that the corresponding value of k approaches zero. But k is the ratio of the semi-minor axis b of the area of contact to semi-major axis a, and therefore a must be indefinitely large, which is the case of contact along a line between two bodies. The area of contact when a load of q lb per unit length is applied is a long narrow rectangle of width $2b$ in the y direction and length $2a$ in the x direction. When $k = 0$, Eqs. 452, 453, and 454 for the stresses at points on the Z axis at various distances z/b below the contact surface do not involve elliptic functions and are given by the following equations:

$$\sigma_x = -2\mu \left[\sqrt{1 + \left(\frac{z}{b}\right)^2} - \frac{z}{b} \right] \frac{b}{\Delta} \tag{463}$$

$$\sigma_y = - \left[\frac{(\sqrt{1 + (z/b)^2} - z/b)^2}{\sqrt{1 + (z/b)^2}} \right] \frac{b}{\Delta} \qquad (464)$$

$$\sigma_z = - \left[\frac{1}{\sqrt{1 + (z/b)^2}} \right] \frac{b}{\Delta} \qquad (465)$$

Furthermore the value of b from Eq. 456 for the limiting case in which $k = 0$ is

$$b = \sqrt{2q\Delta/\pi} \qquad (466)$$

in which q is the load per unit length of the contact area. The value of Δ is

$$\Delta = \frac{1}{(1/2R_1) + (1/2R_2)} \left(\frac{1 - \mu_1{}^2}{E_1} + \frac{1 - \mu_2{}^2}{E_2} \right) \qquad (467)$$

where R_1 and R_2 are the radii of curvature of the cylindrical surfaces as shown in Fig. 188. The values of the stresses at a point on the line of contact are obtained from Eqs. 463, 464, and 465 by setting $z = 0$.

Maximum Principal Stresses, $k = 0$. It may be readily seen from Eqs. 463, 464, and 465 that the principal stresses σ_x, σ_y, and σ_z have their maximum numerical value when $z/b = 0$, that is, at the surface of contact. These stresses are

$$\sigma_x = -2\mu(b/\Delta) \qquad \sigma_y = -b/\Delta \qquad \sigma_z = -b/\Delta \qquad (468)$$

Maximum Shearing Stress, $k = 0$. The shearing stress at any point on the Z axis is $\tau = \frac{1}{2}(\sigma_z - \sigma_y)$. If the expressions for σ_y and σ_z from Eq. 464 and 465 are substituted in this equation for τ and the first derivative of τ with respect to z is equated to zero, the value of z (or z/b) found from this equation will be the distance below the contact surface at which the greatest value τ_{max} of the shearing stress occurs. The value thus found is $z_s/b = 0.7861$. At this point the principal stresses are found from Eqs. 463, 464, and 465 to have the values

$$\sigma_x = -0.9718\mu b/\Delta \qquad \sigma_y = -0.1856b/\Delta \qquad \sigma_z = -0.7861b/\Delta \qquad (469)$$

and hence $\qquad \tau_{max} = \frac{1}{2}(\sigma_z - \sigma_y) = 0.300b/\Delta \qquad (470)$

It is well to note that, at the depth $z_s/b = 0.7861$, σ_y is smaller than σ_x for values of μ greater than about 0.24.

Maximum Octahedral Shearing Stress, $k = 0$. The maximum octahedral shearing stress occurs at the same point as the maximum shear and is found by substituting the values of σ_x, σ_y, and σ_z from Eq. 469 into Eq. 33 (see Chapter 3) which gives

$$\tau_{G\,max} = 0.27b/\Delta \qquad (471)$$

It should be noted that the coefficients for determining the quantities σ_{max}, τ_{max}, $\tau_{G\ max}$ and z_s as obtained from Figs. 183 and 184 for values of B/A greater than about 50 are 1.00, 0.30, 0.27, and 0.78, respectively, and these are the same coefficients found for the case of line contact between two bodies. This fact means that when the ratio B/A is about 50 or larger the area of contact between the two bodies is very nearly a long narrow rectangle.

Illustrative Problems

Problem 220. Two steel cylinders of equal radii R have their longitudinal axes parallel and are pressed against each other by a load of q lb per unit of length of the cylinders. Compute the maximum principal stress and the maximum shearing stress in terms of the load q.

Solution. The values of b and Δ are computed first. Since $R_1 = R_2 = R$, $\mu_1 = \mu_2 = \mu = \frac{1}{4}$, and $E_1 = E_2 = E = 30,000,000$ lb per sq in., the value of Δ as obtained from Eq. 467 is

$$\Delta = 2R\left(\frac{1 - \mu^2}{E}\right) = \frac{R}{16,000,000}$$

From Eq. 466 the half-width of the contact area is

$$b = \sqrt{2q\Delta/\pi} = 0.0002\sqrt{qR}$$

hence

$$b/\Delta = 3200\sqrt{q/R}$$

Therefore, from Eq. 468 the maximum principal stress is

$$\sigma_z = -b/\Delta = -3200\sqrt{q/R}$$

and from Eq. 470 the maximum shearing stress is

$$\tau_{max} = 0.300b/\Delta = 960\sqrt{q/R}$$

That is, within the elastic strength of the material, the maximum principal stress and the maximum shearing stress caused by the pressure q per unit length of the cylinders varies directly as the square root of the load and inversely as the square root of the radius of the cylinders. Thus, if the elastic strength of the material is doubled, the load-carrying capacity is quadrupled. Furthermore, if the ratio of the load per unit length of the cylinders to the radius of the cylinders remains constant, the maximum principal stress and the maximum shearing stress remain constant.

Problem 221. *Cylinder on a Plane.* In Prob. 207 let it be assumed that the top surface of the rail is flat and horizontal and that it has a width of 2 in. As in Prob. 207, $\mu = 0.25$, $E = 30,000,000$ lb per sq in., $P = 25,000$ lb, and $R = 16.5$ in. Calculate the maximum shearing stress in the rail head and the depth below the surface at which this shearing stress occurs.

Solution. From Eq. 470 we have for the special case of $k = 0$

$$\tau_{max} = 0.300b/\Delta$$

From the data given in the problem the load per unit length of the cylinder is

$$q = 25,000/2 = 12,500 \text{ lb/in.}$$

The radii R_2 (and R'_2) of the flat surface on the top of the rail are both indefinitely large. Therefore from Eq. 467, since $1/R_2 = 0$, we have

$$\Delta = 2R \left(\frac{1 - \mu_1^2}{E_1} + \frac{1 - \mu_2^2}{E_2} \right)$$

$$= 2 \times 16.5 \left[\frac{1 - (\frac{1}{4})^2}{30,000,000} + \frac{1 - (\frac{1}{4})^2}{30,000,000} \right] = 20.6 \times 10^{-7} \text{ in.}^3/\text{lb}$$

From Eq. 466 we have

$$b = \sqrt{\frac{2q\Delta}{\pi}} = \sqrt{\frac{2 \times 12,500 \times 20.6}{10,000,000\pi}} = 0.128 \text{ in.}$$

Hence

$$\frac{b}{\Delta} = \frac{0.128 \times 10,000,000}{20.6} = 62,200 \text{ lb/in.}^2$$

From Eq. 470

$$\tau_{max} = 0.300b/\Delta = 0.300 \times 62,200 = 18,660 \text{ lb/in.}^2$$

Depth from surface to point of maximum shearing stress is

$$z_s = 0.7861 \times 0.128 = 0.101 \text{ in.}$$

In the preceding solution of this problem the equation for shearing stress was based on the assumption that the cylinder was infinitely long.* The cylinder in this problem is in contact with the plane for a length of only 2 in., and hence the assumption is not fulfilled. However, H. R. Thomas has shown by tests that the formula gives a close approximation to the shearing stress, provided that the contact area is relatively long and narrow (k small).

Problem

222. A cylindrical steel roller is 1 in. in diameter and $\frac{1}{2}$ in. in length. The roller is used as a follower on a steel cam whose nose is a cylindrical surface with a radius of curvature of $\frac{1}{4}$ in. The follower and the cam are in line contact when under no pressure. Compute the maximum load which may be exerted between the roller and the cam when the nose is in contact with the roller if the maximum principal stress must not exceed 200,000 lb per sq in. If the maximum usable principal stress (the stress at which structural damage starts) is 215,000 lb per sq in., what factor of safety, based on the load, is represented by the stress of 200,000 lb per sq in.?

110 Stresses for two bodies in line contact; loads normal and tangent to contact area. In the preceding articles the contact stresses in two elastic bodies held in contact by forces normal to the area of

---

* For a discussion of the problem of the cylinder on a plane when the length of the contact area is not large compared to its width, see "Some Three-Dimensional Aspects of the Bridge Roller Problem," by V. P. Jensen, *Bulletin* 138, Iowa Engineering Experiment Station, 1937.

contact have been found. Frequently the normal force is accompanied by a tangential (frictional) force in the contact area such as occurs when the teeth of spur gears come into contact or when a shaft rotates in a bearing. The frictional force which results from the sliding contact lies in the plane of the area of contact in a direction perpendicular to the normal force. The presence of the frictional force causes the maximum values of the contact stresses in the two elastic bodies to become substantially larger than those produced by the normal force alone. Furthermore, the presence of a frictional force combined with a normal force causes certain changes in the nature of the stresses. For example, when a normal force acts alone, the three principal stresses are compressive stresses at every point in the body near the contact area, and this fact has made it difficult to understand how a crack could form and progressively spread to cause a separation type of failure such as occurs in pitting failures of some bearing surfaces. But, when a frictional force is introduced, two of the three principal stresses are changed into tensile stresses in the region immediately behind the frictional force (see Figs. 190*b* and 190*c*). If the coefficient of friction for the two surfaces of contact is sufficiently large, these tensile stresses are relatively large. However, if these tensile stresses are nominally small, as they probably are on well-lubricated surfaces, their values may be raised by stress concentration resulting from surface irregularities or to small microscopic cracks which usually exist in the surfaces of real materials. These tensile stresses, when considered in conjunction with the many other factors involved such as wear, non-homogeneity of the material, and type of lubrication, help in explaining why a crack may develop and progressively spread in the surface of contact of such parts as gear teeth, roller bearings, etc.

The addition of a frictional force to a normal force on the contact surface also causes a change in the shearing stresses in the region of the contact surface. One important change is that the location of the point at which the maximum shearing stresses occur moves from beneath the surface of contact towards the contact area. In fact, when the coefficient of friction is $\frac{1}{10}$ or greater, this point is located in the contact surface. The foregoing remarks also apply to the maximum octahedral shearing stress.

The facts described in the foregoing paragraphs will now be illustrated for an elastic cylindrical roller pressed against the plane surface of another elastic body.

Roller on Plane. Let Fig. 189*a* represent the cross section of a long roller of elastic material which rests upon a flat surface of a thick, solid elastic body. The roller is subjected to a force of q lb per unit length which presses it against the body over a long narrow area of contact whose width is $2b$. A lateral force of f lb per inch of length causes the roller to slide on the body. If the coefficient of sliding friction is designated as β, then $f = \beta q$. In Fig. 189b a part of the solid body is shown with the forces q and f acting on the contact area. In Fig. 189c, which

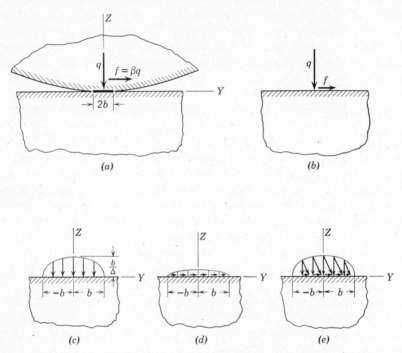

FIG. 189   Tangential (shearing) forces in addition to normal forces on the contact area.

is an enlarged view of the part near the contact area, the ordinates to the ellipse show the distribution of normal stresses over this area, and the maximum stress $-b/\Delta$ is given by Eq. 468. R. D. Mindlin has found that when sliding occurs the shearing stresses on the contact area due to the frictional force f are distributed as ordinates to an ellipse as shown in Fig. 189d, and the maximum shearing stress τ_{zy} at the center is $\tau_{zy} = \beta(b/\Delta)$. Figure 189$e$ shows the distribution of the combined normal and friction stresses on the contact surface. C. K. Liu *

* In his Doctor's Thesis at the University of Illinois entitled "Stresses and Deformations Due to Tangential and Normal Loads on an Elastic Solid with Applications to Contact Stresses."

has derived the equations for the stresses σ_z, σ_x, σ_y, and τ_{zy} at any point in the body. These equations are as follows:

$$\sigma_z = -\frac{b}{\pi\Delta}\left[z(b\phi_1 - y\phi_2) + \beta z^2\phi_2\right]$$

$$\sigma_y = -\frac{b}{\pi\Delta}\left\{z\left(\frac{b^2 + 2z^2 + 2y^2}{b}\phi_1 - \frac{2\pi}{b} - 3y\phi_2\right)\right.$$

$$\left. + \beta\left[(2y^2 - 2b^2 - 3z^2)\phi_2 + \frac{2\pi y}{b} + 2(b^2 - y^2 - z^2)\frac{y}{b}\phi_1\right]\right\}$$

$$\sigma_x = -\frac{2\mu b}{\pi\Delta}\left\{z\left(\frac{b^2 + y^2 + z^2}{b}\phi_1 - \frac{\pi}{b} - 2y\phi_2\right)\right.$$

$$\left. + \beta\left[(y^2 - b^2 - z^2)\phi_2 + \frac{\pi y}{b} + (b^2 - y^2 - z^2)\frac{y}{b}\phi_1\right]\right\}$$

$$\tau_{zy} = -\frac{b}{\pi\Delta}\left\{z^2\phi_2 + \beta\left[(b^2 + 2y^2 + 2z^2)\frac{z}{b}\phi_1 - 2\pi\frac{z}{b} - 3yz\phi_2\right]\right\}$$

(472)

In Eq. 472 the values of ϕ_1 and ϕ_2 must be computed for each value of y and z by making use of the equations

$$\phi_1 = \frac{\pi(M + N)}{MN\sqrt{2MN + 2y^2 + 2z^2 - 2b^2}}$$

$$\phi_2 = \frac{\pi(M - N)}{MN\sqrt{2MN + 2y^2 + 2z^2 - 2b^2}}$$

where $M = \sqrt{(b + y)^2 + z^2}$ and $N = \sqrt{(b - y)^2 + z^2}$. It should be noted that the values of stress as given by Eq. 472 do not depend on x because it is assumed that either a state of plane strain or of plane stress exists.

Principal Stresses. In Eq. 472 σ_x is a principal stress, say σ_3, but σ_z and σ_y are not principal stresses because of the presence of the shearing stress τ_{zy} which acts on these planes. Let the other two principal stresses at any point be designated by σ_1 and σ_2. These two stresses may be found by the substitution of the values of σ_z, σ_y, and τ_{zy} for the point into Eqs. 19 and 20. The principal stresses σ_1, σ_2, and σ_3 for points on the surface * and at a distance $z = b/4$ underneath the surface have been computed by these equations for a value of friction coefficient of $\frac{1}{3}$, and their values are represented by the ordinates to the curves in Figs. 190a, 190b, and 190c. Each principal stress has its maximum value in

---

* A special method of evaluating Eq. 472 must be used when solving for the stresses on the surface where $Z = 0$. (See Dr. C. K. Liu's Thesis.)

the surface of the body at a distance of about $0.3b$ from the center of the area of contact in the direction of the frictional force. These maximum values, all of which occur at the same point, are $\sigma_1 = -1.4b/\Delta$, σ_2

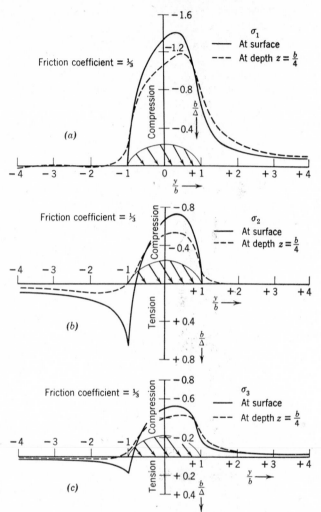

FIG. 190   Effect of tangential force on contact stresses.

$= -0.72b/\Delta$ and $\sigma_3 = -0.53b/\Delta$. These values are to be compared with $\sigma_1 = -b/\Delta$, $\sigma_2 = -b/\Delta$ and $\sigma_3 = -0.5b/\Delta$, as found from Eq. 468 for the normal force q only. This comparison shows that the frictional force corresponding to a coefficient of friction of $\frac{1}{3}$ increases the maximum principal stress by 40 per cent. Furthermore, the curves in

Fig. 190 show that the principal stresses σ_2 and σ_3 are tension stresses near the edge of the contact area opposite to the direction of the frictional force. The largest magnitudes of these stresses are $\frac{2}{3}(b/\Delta)$ and $\frac{1}{6}(b/\Delta)$, respectively, but these values are sometimes quite large. The presence of the tensile stresses in the surface aids in understanding the occurrence of fatigue failure by pitting, etc., of bearing surfaces subjected to repeated loads.

Maximum Shearing Stress. From the values of maximum and minimum principal stresses at a point in the surface of contact as given in the foregoing paragraph, the maximum shearing stress at the point on the surface is found to be

$$\tau_{\max} = \tfrac{1}{2}(-1.4b/\Delta + 0.53b/\Delta) = -0.43b/\Delta \tag{473}$$

But, before it can be stated that this value of the shear is the maximum value occurring in the body, it is necessary to compute the maximum shearing stress at other points, and especially at points underneath the surface, since in all previous paragraphs in this chapter the maximum shearing stress was found to be a sub-surface shear. The values of shearing stress at points on the surface and at points below the surface a distance of $z = b/4$ (where the maximum sub-surface shear occurs) have been computed by making use of the principal stresses in Fig. 190 and are represented as ordinates to the curves in Figs. 191a, 191b, and 191c. There are three maximum shearing stresses at each point, which are computed as follows:

$$\tau_{1\ \max} = \tfrac{1}{2}(\sigma_1 - \sigma_3)$$

$$\tau_{2\ \max} = \tfrac{1}{2}(\sigma_1 - \sigma_2) \tag{474}$$

$$\tau_{3\ \max} = \tfrac{1}{2}(\sigma_2 - \sigma_3)$$

From Figs. 191a and 191c it will be seen that the ordinates to the curves representing $\tau_{1\ \max}$ and $\tau_{3\ \max}$ at a depth $z = b/4$ underneath the surface are everywhere smaller than at the surface. This fact is true of the curves for these values at all depths. However, in Fig. 191b the curve for $\tau_{2\ \max}$ at $z = b/4$ rises above the curve representing values of $\tau_{2\ \max}$ at the surface. Such curves for values of $\tau_{2\ \max}$ have been plotted for several different depths, and it is found that the largest value of $\tau_{2\ \max}$ is $0.36b/\Delta$, and this occurs at a depth of about $b/4$ below the surface. Therefore the value of $\tau_{1\ \max} = 0.43b/\Delta$ as given by Eq. 473 is the maximum shearing stress, and it occurs at a point in the contact area about $0.3b$ from the center of the area. In Eq. 474 the maximum value of $\tau_{2\ \max}$, which always occurs below the surface, does not become larger than $\tau_{1\ \max}$ until the coefficient of friction has a value less than $\frac{1}{10}$.

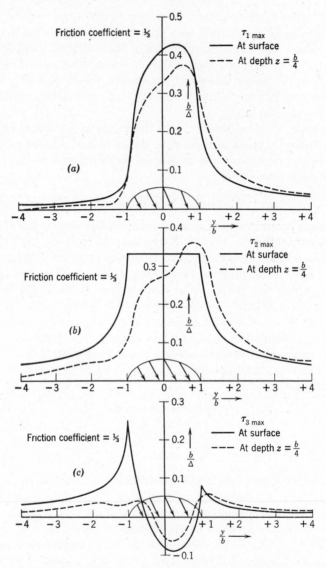

FIG. 191   Effect of tangential force on contact stresses.

Maximum Octahedral Shearing Stress.   In Fig. 192 the ordinates to the curves represent the values of the octahedral shearing stresses τ_{oct} which have been computed at each point from Eq. 33 by the substitution of the values of the principal stresses obtained from Fig. 190. Figure 192 shows that the maximum value of $\tau_{oct} = 0.37b/\Delta$ and that

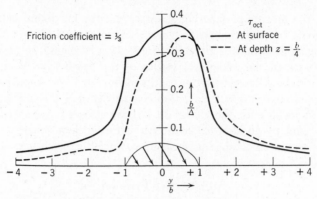

FIG. 192 Effect of tangential force on contact stresses.

this value occurs in the contact area at the same point that the maximum principal stress and maximum shearing stresses occur.

Effect of Magnitude of Friction Coefficient. The magnitude of the coefficient of friction determines the size of the frictional force f for a given value of q and therefore of the values of the maximum principal

TABLE 17

VALUES OF CONTACT STRESSES BETWEEN TWO LONG CYLINDRICAL BODIES
SLIDING AGAINST EACH OTHER WHILE IN LINE CONTACT
(NORMAL AND FRICTION FORCES)

Coefficient of Friction →	0	$\frac{1}{12}$	$\frac{1}{9}$	$\frac{1}{6}$	$\frac{1}{3}$
Kind of Stress and Its Location	Values of Stress in Terms of b/Δ Corresponding to the Above Friction Coefficients				
Maximum tensile principal stress which occurs in surface at $y = -b$	0	$\frac{2}{12}\frac{b}{\Delta}$	$\frac{2}{9}\frac{b}{\Delta}$	$\frac{2}{6}\frac{b}{\Delta}$	$\frac{2}{3}\frac{b}{\Delta}$
Maximum compressive principal stress which occurs in the surface between $y = 0$ and $y = 0.3b$	$-\frac{b}{\Delta}$	$-1.09\frac{b}{\Delta}$	$-1.13\frac{b}{\Delta}$	$-1.19\frac{b}{\Delta}$	$-1.40\frac{b}{\Delta}$
Maximum shearing stress *	$0.300\frac{b}{\Delta}$	$0.308\frac{b}{\Delta}$	$0.310\frac{b}{\Delta}$	$0.399\frac{b}{\Delta}$	$0.435\frac{b}{\Delta}$
Maximum octahedral shearing stress *	$0.272\frac{b}{\Delta}$	$0.265\frac{b}{\Delta}$	$0.255\frac{b}{\Delta}$	$0.277\frac{b}{\Delta}$	$0.368\frac{b}{\Delta}$

* Note that these stresses occur at the surface when friction coefficient is $\frac{1}{10}$ or larger.

stresses, the maximum shearing stresses, and the maximum octahedral shearing stress. The changes in the maximum contact stresses with the coefficient of friction are given by Table 17. It should be noted that the increases in the maximum values of the tensile and compressive principal stresses caused by the frictional force are very nearly proportional to the increases in the friction coefficient. For the smaller values of friction coefficients, the values of shearing stress are increased a very small amount by an increase in the friction coefficient, whereas there is a small decrease in octahedral shear up to a friction coefficient of $\frac{1}{6}$.

Illustrative Problem

Problem 223. Two steel cylindrical rollers each 3 in. in diameter and 6 in. in length are mounted on parallel shafts and are pressed together by a force of $q = 3000$ lb per inch of length. The two shafts are rotated at slightly different speeds so that the roller surfaces slide against each other along the contact area. Compute the values of the maximum tensile principal stress, the maximum compressive principal stress, the maximum shearing stress, and the maximum octahedral shearing stress if it is assumed that the coefficient of sliding friction is $\frac{1}{9}$.

Solution. From Table 17 the values of these stresses are found as follows:

$$\text{Maximum tensile stress} = \tfrac{2}{9}(b/\Delta)$$

$$\text{Maximum compressive stress} = -1.13b/\Delta$$

$$\text{Maximum shearing stress} = 0.31b/\Delta$$

$$\text{Maximum octahedral shearing stress} = 0.255b/\Delta$$

From Eq. 467 the value of Δ is found to be

$$\Delta = \frac{1}{\frac{1}{3} + \frac{1}{3}} \left[\frac{1 - (\tfrac{1}{4})^2}{30 \times 10^6} + \frac{1 - (\tfrac{1}{4})^2}{30 \times 10^6} \right] = 0.94 \times 10^{-7} \text{ in.}^3/\text{lb}$$

and from Eq. 466

$$b = \sqrt{\frac{2q\Delta}{\pi}} = \sqrt{\frac{2 \times 3000 \times 0.94 \times 10^{-7}}{\pi}} = 0.0134 \text{ in.}$$

Thus

$$\frac{b}{\Delta} = \frac{0.012}{0.94 \times 10^{-7}} = 143,000 \text{ lb/in.}^2$$

Therefore we have the following results:

$$\text{Maximum tensile stress} = \tfrac{2}{9}(143,000) = 31,800 \text{ lb/in.}^2$$

$$\text{Maximum compressive stress} = -1.13 \times 143,000 = -161,000 \text{ lb/in.}^2$$

$$\text{Maximum shearing stress} = 0.31 \times 143,000 = 44,300 \text{ lb/in.}^2$$

$$\text{Maximum octahedral shearing stress} = 0.255 \times 143,000 = 36,400 \text{ lb/in.}^2$$

111　Application of a factor of safety to contact loads. It was stated in Art. 2 (Chapter 1) that the real function of a factor of safety is to limit the *load* on the member to a safe or working value, that is, to a value that will not cause structural damage to the member. *Thus a factor of safety N should be applied in such a way that the working load could be increased to a load N times the working or safe value without causing structural damage to the member.*

In the design of a load-resisting member, however, it is customary, as explained in Art. 2 (Chapter 1), to attempt to insure a safe or working load by introducing in the design formula a safe or working stress obtained by applying a reducing factor to the stress that is considered to be the cause of structural damage (in the case of contact stresses this stress would in many cases be the endurance limit of the material). This reduction factor applied to the damaging value of a stress is usually called the factor of safety, but it is very important to note that such a reduction factor is not equal to the factor of safety N unless the significant stress as expressed in the design formula is directly proportional to the load P.

It has, however, been shown in the preceding articles of this chapter that contact stresses are expressed in terms of $\sqrt{P}$ or $\sqrt[3]{P}$, depending on the conditions of loading. Therefore, in a problem in which contact stresses are the significant stresses a reduction factor of $\sqrt{N}$ or $\sqrt[3]{N}$ should be applied to the stress that causes structural damage in order to apply a factor of safety of N to the load. This idea is illustrated further in the following problems.

Illustrative Problems

Problem 224. In Prob. 208 let it be assumed that the maximum usable value of the shearing stress (the value at which structural damage starts) for the material of which the bearing is made is 126,000 lb per sq in. Compute the load P to which the single ball at the top may be subjected without exceeding this value of the shearing stress. Compute the maximum shearing stress which will be produced in the ball by one-half the load P just computed, that is, by a load to which a factor of safety $N = 2$ has been applied. How does this shearing stress compare with the stress obtained by dividing the maximum usable shearing stress by $\sqrt[3]{2}$?

Solution. From Prob. 208

$$\tau_{\max} = 13,800\sqrt[3]{P} = 126,000 \text{ lb/in.}^2$$

Thus $\qquad\qquad P = 760 \text{ lb} \qquad \text{and} \qquad P/2 = 380 \text{ lb}$

Therefore the value of the shearing stress produced by a load of $P/2$ is

$$\tau = 13,800\sqrt[3]{P} = 13,800\sqrt[3]{380} = 100,000 \text{ lb/in.}^2$$

The shearing stress of 100,000 lb per sq in. is the same value that is obtained by applying a reduction factor of $\sqrt[3]{2}$ to 126,000 lb per sq in.

Problem 225. A flat-faced chilled cast-iron tappet is operated by a steel cam as shown in Fig. 187 (the tappet surface is flat instead of spherical). The radius of curvature of the nose on the cam is $R = \frac{1}{4}$ in. The maximum usable value of the maximum normal stress for chilled cast iron on steel is $\sigma_e = 120,000$ lb per sq in. Compute the working load for the tappet using a factor of safety $N = 1.2$ based upon the load. Assume $\mu = \frac{1}{4}$ for cast iron and also for steel. Assume $E = 20,000,000$ lb per sq in. for cast iron, $E = 30,000,000$ lb per sq in. for steel, and a coefficient of friction of $\frac{1}{9}$ for these lubricated surfaces.

Solution. Since the maximum principal stress is proportional to the square root of the load, the working stress is obtained by dividing the maximum usable stress by $\sqrt{1.2} = 1.1$. The working stress is $120,000/1.1 = 109,000$ lb per sq in. For a cylinder on a plane the value of Δ from Eq. 467 is

$$\Delta = 2R \left(\frac{1 - \mu_1^2}{E_1} + \frac{1 - \mu_2^2}{E_2} \right)$$

$$= 2 \times \frac{1}{4} \left[\frac{1 - (\frac{1}{4})^2}{20,000,000} + \frac{1 - (\frac{1}{4})^2}{30,000,000} \right] = 0.3906 \times 10^{-7} \text{ in.}^3/\text{lb}$$

From Eq. 466

$$b = \sqrt{\frac{2q\Delta}{\pi}} = \sqrt{\frac{2q \times 0.3906}{10^7 \pi}} = 0.000157 \sqrt{q} \text{ in.}$$

The maximum principal stress is σ_z, as given by Table 17, and is $\sigma_z = 1.13b/\Delta$. Therefore, using the working values of $\sigma_z = 109,000$, we have

$$109,000 = 1.13 \frac{0.000157 \sqrt{q}}{0.3906 \times 10^7}$$

Hence $q = 578$ lb/in., and $P = q/2 = 289$ lb.

Selected References

1. Thomas, H. R., and V. A. Hoersch, "Stresses Due to the Pressure of One Elastic Solid on Another," *Bulletin* 212, Engineering Experiment Station, University of Illinois, June 15, 1930.
2. Love, A. E., *Mathematical Theory of Elasticity*, 3rd edition, 1920, pp. 190–196.
3. Barish, Thomas, "A Theoretical Derivation of Ball Bearing Ratings," Paper 46-A-75, presented at the annual meeting of the American Society of Mecanical Engineers, December 2–6, 1946.
4. Turkish, M. C., "Valve Gear Design," Eaton Manufacturing Co., Wilcox-Rich Division, Detroit, 1946.
5. Allen, R. K., *Rolling Bearings*, Sir Isaac Pitman & Sons, London, 1945.
6. Palmgren, Arvid, "Ball and Roller Bearing Engineering," SKF Industries, Inc., Philadelphia, 1945.
7. Jones, A. B., "New Departure Engineering Data—Analysis of Stresses and Deflections," New Departure Division, General Motors Corp., Bristol, Conn., 1946.

PART THREE

Localized Stress
Stress Concentration

Chapter 12

VALUES AND SIGNIFICANCE OF
LOCALIZED STRESSES IN VARIOUS MEMBERS

112 Introduction. As discussed in the previous chapters, all the ordinary mathematical formulas for determining stresses in structural and machine members are based on the assumption that there is continuity of elastic action throughout the members and hence that the distribution of stress on any section of a member can be expressed by a mathematical law or equation, usually of relatively simple form. For example, in a tension member subjected to an axial load the stress is assumed to be distributed uniformly over each cross section; in a beam the stress on each cross section is assumed to increase directly with the distance from the neutral axis, etc.

As pointed out in Chapters 1 and 2, the assumption that the distribution of stress on a section of a member may be expressed mathematically by the relatively simple laws assumed in obtaining the stress formulas in ordinary mechanics of materials may be largely in error under some conditions of use of the member. The conditions which may cause the stress at the point considered in the member to be radically different from the value of σ, or of τ, calculated from the ordinary formulas, consist mainly of (a) abrupt changes in section such as occur at the roots of the threads of a bolt, at the bottom of a tooth on a gear, at a section of a plate or beam containing a rivet hole, at the corner of a keyway in a shaft; (b) pressure at the points of application of the external forces, as, for example, at bearing blocks near the ends of a beam, at the points of contact of the wheels of a locomotive and the rail, at points of contact of gear teeth or of ball bearings on the races; (c) discontinuities in the material itself, such as non-metallic inclusions in steel, air holes in concrete, pitch pockets and knots in timber, or variations in the strength and stiffness of the component elements of which the member is made, such as crystalline grains in steel, fibers in wood, ingredients in concrete; and (d) initial stresses in the member due, for example, to overstraining and cold working of metals during erection or fabrication, to heat treatment of metals, to shrinkage in castings and in concrete, or to residual stress resulting from welding operations.

The conditions that cause the stresses to be greater than those given by the ordinary stress equations of mechanics of materials are frequently called *discontinuities* and *stress raisers* since they destroy the assumed regularity of stress distribution by sudden increases in the stress at points near the stress raiser, frequently called *stress peaks*. The term *stress gradient* in the neighborhood of the stress raiser is used frequently to indicate the rate of increase of the stress with respect to the decreasing distance as the stress raiser is approached; the gradient is sometimes considered to have an influence on the damaging effect of the peak value of the stress.

The maximum stresses resulting from the foregoing conditions are developed, as a rule, in only a small portion of the member and hence are called *localized stresses* or *stress concentrations*. In many members, particularly in those in which the stress is highly localized, a mathematical analysis of the stresses developed is impossible or impracticable, and hence experimental or mechanical methods of stress analysis are used.

In Part III are given the values of localized stresses resulting from some of the conditions mentioned in the foregoing discussion, together with the engineering significance of such stresses in members used under various conditions for resisting loads. For photographs of many members that failed in service as a result of stress concentrations, see *Prevention of the Failure of Metals under Repeated Stress*, by the Metallurgical Staff of Battelle Memorial Institute, published by John Wiley & Sons, 1941. See also reference at the end of Art. 114.

113 Mathematical method of determining stress concentrations. Whether the significant stress (stress associated with structural damage) in a metal member under a given type of loading is the localized stress *at a point*, as found from the mathematical theory of elasticity (discussed in Appendix I), or a somewhat smaller value representing the average stress over a small area including the point, depends on the internal state of the metal such as grain type and size, state of stress, stress gradient, temperature, and rate of straining, which may influence the ability of the material to make local adjustments in reducing somewhat the damaging effect of the stress concentration at the point.

Furthermore, the solution for the values of stresses by the mathematical theory of elasticity, as applied to members having known discontinuities or stress raisers, leads in general to differential equations that are very difficult of solution. The mathematical method has been used with success to obtain the stress concentration in members containing rather simple types of abrupt changes of section such as that caused by a circular hole in a wide plate, but it cannot be regarded at present as an available method for determining the localized stresses in many important machine and structural members. It should be noted also that in the mathematical method the member is assumed to be made of an ideal homogeneous, isotropic, elastic material, and hence the value of the localized stress as found by this method should be thought of as being influenced only by the form or shape of the member since the effect of discontinuities in the material itself are not considered in this method. Nevertheless, the mathematical method is of great importance, not alone in obtaining directly useful results, but also in interpreting experimental methods of stress analysis.

114 Experimental methods. Experimental methods of determining stress concentrations are often of importance in helping to overcome the limitations of the purely mathematical method. For example, some of the experimental methods are primarily mechanical methods of solving the equation for stress obtained from the mathematical analysis. This statement applies to the first three of the list of methods given in the next paragraph. These three methods tend to give values comparable with the mathematical method. Likewise the elastic strain (strain gage) method, when a very short gage length is used over which the strain is measured with high precision, gives values of stress concentration closely approximating the theoretical mathematical value. In the other methods mentioned the properties of the materials used in the models usually influence the stress concentration obtained, causing values somewhat less than the theoretical values.

Each of the experimental methods, however, also has limitations, but at least one such method can usually be made to yield useful results in a given situation. The names of some of the more commonly used experimental methods are (1) photoelastic (polarized light), (2) elastic membrane (soap film, see Fig. 147), (3) electrical analogy, (4) elastic strain (strain gage), (5) brittle coating, (6) brittle material (plaster model), (7) ductile material (Lüders' line), (8) rubber model, and (9) repeated stress.

These and other methods are discussed in considerable detail in *Handbook on Experimental Stress Analysis*, by M. Hetényi and others, published by John Wiley & Sons, 1950.

§ 1   Theoretical Stress Concentration Factors

115 Theoretical stress concentration factor defined. The localized stress accompanying an abrupt change in section or any other type of discontinuity or stress raiser in a load-resisting member is usually obtained by multiplying the nominal stress given by an elementary stress formula (see Chapter 2) by a factor called a stress concentration factor.   In other words, the stress concentration factor for a given discontinuity is the ratio of the maximum (localized) stress to the stress as calculated from the elementary formula on the assumption that the abrupt change in section does not increase the stress.   For example, the localized stress or stress concentration σ_{max} at the edge of a relatively small hole at the center of a wide flat plate that resists an axial tensile load P is

$$\sigma_{max} = k(P/a) = k\sigma_0 \tag{475}$$

or
$$k = \sigma_{max}/\sigma_0 \tag{476}$$

in which k is the stress concentration factor and $\sigma_0 = P/a$ is the (nominal) stress that would occur at the same point if the bar did not contain the hole; that is, in this illustration the cross section a is the *gross* area including the area which is removed at the hole.   If the diameter of the hole is relatively large, or in other abrupt changes in section in which the reduction of area is considerable, the *net* area of cross section is frequently used in calculating the nominal stress σ_0, and hence the value of the stress concentration factor for a given discontinuity will depend on the method of calculating the nominal stress.

If σ_{max} (or τ_{max}) in a member is the theoretical value of the localized stress as found from the mathematical theory of elasticity, or the photoelasticity method, etc., k is given the subscript t, and k_t is called the *theoretical stress concentration factor;* it is also sometimes referred to as a *form factor.*   If, on the other hand, the value of k is found from tests of the actual material under the conditions of use, as for example under repeated stress by determining first the endurance limit from specimens that contain the abrupt change in section or notch, and then obtaining endurance limit from specimens free from the notch, k is given the subscript e, and k_e is called the *effective* or *significant stress concentration factor;* the term *strength reduction factor* is also used, especially in connection with repeated loads (fatigue).   Thus we may write

$$\sigma_{theo} = k_t\sigma_0 \quad \text{and} \quad \sigma_{eff} = k_e\sigma_0 \tag{477}$$

Values of k_e are discussed in § 2 of this chapter.

The values of theoretical stress concentrations given in the following articles are not meant to be exhaustive but rather to be illustrative of the effects of different discontinuities as shown by the various methods of determining theoretical stress concentrations or localized stresses.

The discontinuities that will be considered first are circular holes and grooves, since these discontinuities are rather common and have been treated both by the mathematical method and by several experimental methods.

116 Stress concentrations as found by mathematical theory of elasticity. (a) *Circular Hole in Plate Stressed in One Direction.* Let a plate with a small hole be subjected to a uniform tensile stress σ_0

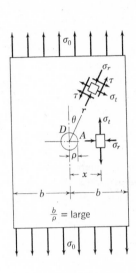

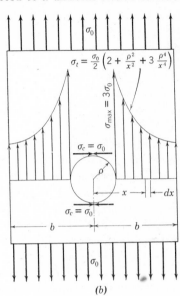

(a)   (b)

Fig. 193 Stress in plate containing hole.

at its ends, as indicated in Fig. 193. The stress distribution near the hole (assuming the plate to be infinite in width) has been obtained by Foppl, Inglis, and others from the mathematical theory of elasticity.

The normal and shearing stresses at any point whose coordinates are r and θ (Fig. 193a) are given by the following expressions:

$$\sigma_t = \frac{\sigma_0}{2}\left(1 + \frac{\rho^2}{r^2}\right) - \frac{\sigma_0}{2}\left(1 + 3\frac{\rho^4}{r^4}\right)\cos 2\theta \tag{478}$$

$$\sigma_r = \frac{\sigma_0}{2}\left(1 - \frac{\rho^2}{r^2}\right) + \frac{\sigma_0}{2}\left(1 - 4\frac{\rho^2}{r^2} + 3\frac{\rho^4}{r^4}\right)\cos 2\theta \tag{479}$$

$$\tau = \frac{\sigma_0}{2}\left(1 + 2\frac{\rho^2}{r^2} - 3\frac{\rho^4}{r^4}\right)\sin 2\theta \tag{480}$$

in which σ_t denotes the normal stress in a direction perpendicular to r,

σ_r denotes the normal stress parallel to r, and τ is the shearing stress in each of these directions as shown in Fig. 193a. σ_0 is the stress at the ends of the plate, and also the stress that would exist at the point if the plate had no hole, ρ is the radius of the hole, and θ is the angle between r and the axis parallel to the direction of σ_0. For any point on the section through A at the distance x from the center of the hole the tensile stress can be found from Eq. 478 by making $\theta = 90°$ and $r = x$; thus σ_t becomes

$$\sigma_t = \frac{\sigma_0}{2}\left(2 + \frac{\rho^2}{x^2} + 3\frac{\rho^4}{x^4}\right) \tag{481}$$

The distribution of the stress σ_t on the section through A according to this equation is shown in Fig. 193b. At the edge of the hole, $x = \rho$, and hence

$$\sigma_{\max} = 3\sigma_0 \tag{482}$$

which states that the stress at the edge of a small hole in a wide plate subjected to a uniform tensile stress in one direction is three times as large as the uniform tensile stress in the gross section, that is, three times as large as would occur at the same point if there were no hole in the plate. Similarly, at point D (Fig. 193a) the stress may be found from Eq. 478 by making $\theta = 0°$ and $r = \rho$; the stress is found to be a compressive stress and equal to σ_0 ($\sigma_c = \sigma_0$), as indicated in Fig. 193b.

The foregoing equations are based on the assumption that the plate is infinite in width. Howland modified the mathematical analysis to make it apply to plates of finite width. His results agree well with results obtained by the photoelastic method for plates of the same dimensions (see Fig. 199).

(b) *Circular Hole in Plate Subjected to Stresses in Two Perpendicular Directions.* EQUAL STRESSES OF SAME SIGN. If the plate containing the hole is acted on by equal tensile or compressive stresses σ_0 (Fig. 194a), the concentration of stress at the edge of the hole can be found by use of the principle of superposition. For example, the vertical pull on the edge of the plate (Fig. 194a), if acting alone, produces a tensile elastic stress at A equal to $3\sigma_0$ (Eq. 482) and a compressive stress at B equal to σ_0; similarly the horizontal pull, if acting alone, produces a tensile stress at B equal to $3\sigma_0$ and a compressive stress at A equal to σ_0. By the principle of superposition, therefore, the stress at A and at B is

$$\sigma_{\max} = 3\sigma_0 - \sigma_0 = 2\sigma_0 \tag{483}$$

This value may also be found by using Lamé's formula for thick-walled cylinders (see Chapter 10). Let a disk of diameter D be cut from the plate; if D is large relative to d, the stress on the circumference of the disk will be affected very little by the hole. Furthermore, the stress on the circumference of the disk will be normal to the circumference and equal to each of the two stresses σ_0, as indicated in Fig. 194b; this fact follows from Eq. 13 of Chapter 3, noting that $\sigma_1 = \sigma_2$.

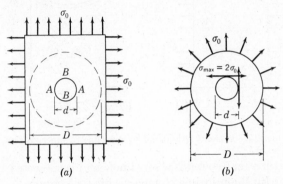

FIG. 194   Stress at hole in plate subjected to equal tensions in two directions.

According to Lamé's equation, the tensile stress in a tangential direction at all points on the edge of the hole in Fig. 194b is

$$\sigma_{\max} = 2\sigma_0 \frac{D^2}{D^2 - d^2} \tag{484}$$

and for a small hole in which d is small relative to D this becomes approximately

$$\sigma_{\max} = 2\sigma_0 \tag{485}$$

which agrees with Eq. 483.

UNEQUAL STRESSES. As already noted, when the plate is stressed in one direction only, the maximum stress is tangent to the edge of the hole and is in the direction of the applied stress; its value is $\sigma_{\max} = 3\sigma_0$. Furthermore, when the plate is stressed *equally* in two perpendicular directions the maximum stress is tangent to the hole at all points on the circumference of the hole and its value is $\sigma_{\max} = 2\sigma_0$. If now the plate is subjected to unequal stresses (σ_0 and p_0) in two perpendicular directions, as indicated in Fig. 195a, the principle of superposition leads to the conclusion that the tangential stress at point B is

$$\sigma_B = 3\sigma_0 - p_0 \tag{486}$$

and the stress at A is

$$\sigma_A = 3p_0 - \sigma_0 \tag{487}$$

EQUAL STRESSES OF OPPOSITE SIGN.   PURE SHEAR.   If in Fig. 195a p_0 is changed to a compressive stress and made equal in magnitude to σ_0, the state of stress is that of pure shear (see Art. 17) such as occurs in a

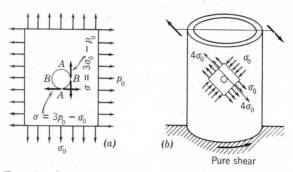

FIG. 195   Stress at hole found by principle of superposition.

thin hollow tube that contains a small hole and is subjected to twisting (Fig. 195b).   By the principle of superposition we obtain

$$\sigma_{\max} = 3\sigma_0 - (-\sigma_0) = 4\sigma_0 \tag{488}$$

That is, the maximum theoretical tensile stress at the edge of a small hole in a hollow cylinder subjected to torsion is four times the maximum tensile stress that would occur in the cylinder if the cylinder contained no hole.   This value may be used also for the approximate value of the theoretical elastic stress at the edge of a small radial hole in a *solid* shaft, such as an oil hole in a crankshaft.

(c) *Elliptical Holes.*   The theoretical stress at the edge of an elliptical hole in a plate subjected to a direct tensile stress has been obtained by

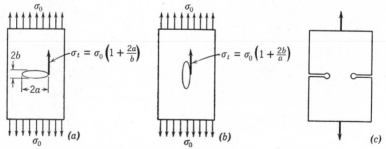

FIG. 196   Stress at edge of elliptical hole in plates.

Inglis.   If the major semi-axis is a and the minor semi-axis is b (Fig. 196a), and if the major axis is perpendicular to the direction of the applied tensile stress, the maximum elastic stress σ_t at the edge of the hole is

$$\sigma_t = \sigma_0[1 + (2a/b)] \tag{489}$$

If, then, a flaw or crack which extends nearly through the thickness of a plate can be considered to be an ellipse whose ratio of a to b is very large, we may obtain some idea of the localized stresses that would occur at the ends of such cracks if the material remained elastic. For example, if the long dimension of the crack is perpendicular to the direction of the pull as in Fig. 196a,

when $\qquad a/b = 3 \qquad \sigma_t = 7\sigma_0 \tag{490}$

when $\qquad a/b = 100 \qquad \sigma_t = 201\sigma_0 \tag{491}$

when $\qquad a/b = 1000 \qquad \sigma_t = 2001\sigma_0 \tag{492}$

These values must be considered to give only a general indication of the effects of cracks and similar defects because local yielding occurs before such high elastic stresses can develop. They suggest, however, the desirability of increasing the curvature at the edge of a crack or slit by drilling a hole at the edge of the slit, as indicated in Fig. 196c, and thus relieving somewhat the high theoretical localized stress at the edge of the slit.

(d) *Ellipsoidal Cavity.* In a member subjected to axial tension the theoretical stress at the edge of an internal cavity having the shape of an ellipsoid has been obtained by Sadowsky and Sternberg. The theoretical stress concentration factors for two special cases of such an internal discontinuity will be considered; namely for ellipsoids of revolution of the prolate spheroid type (football shape) and the oblate spheroid type (door-knob shape). The data for a prolate spheroid is given first. The semi-major axis a of the ellipsoid, which is the axis of revolution, is oriented so that it is perpendicular to the direction of the axial pull in the member, and the semi-minor axis b always lies in a plane parallel to the axial pull. If the nominal stress in the member is σ_0, the maximum theoretical stress occurs at the end of the semi-major axis a and has values for various ratios of b/a as given in Table 18. The ellipsoid

TABLE 18

THEORETICAL STRESS AT END OF SEMI-MAJOR AXIS a OF INTERNAL ELLIPSOIDAL CAVITY OF PROLATE SPHEROID SHAPE

Ratio b/a	1.0	0.8	0.6	0.4	0.2	0.1
Theoretical stress	$2.05\sigma_0$	$2.17\sigma_0$	$2.33\sigma_0$	$2.52\sigma_0$	$2.70\sigma_0$	$2.83\sigma_0$

of revolution having the shape of the oblate spheroid has its semi-minor axis b, which is the axis of revolution, oriented in the direction of the uniaxial pull in the member, and the semi-major axis a always lies in a plane perpendicular to the load. If the nominal stress in the member is σ_0 the maximum theoretical stress occurs at the end of a semi-major axis a and has values for various ratios b/a as given in Table 19. These

TABLE 19

THEORETICAL STRESS AT END OF SEMI-MAJOR AXIS a OF INTERNAL ELLIPSOIDAL
CAVITY OF OBLATE SPHEROID SHAPE

Ratio b/a	1.0	0.8	0.6	0.4	0.2	0.1
Theoretical stress	$2.05\sigma_0$	$2.50\sigma_0$	$3.3\sigma_0$	$4.0\sigma_0$	$7.2\sigma_0$	$13.5\sigma_0$

values of the theoretical maximum elastic stress show that an internal flaw or cavity of spherical shape such as a gas bubble (an ellipsoid for which $b/a = 1$) raises the theoretical stress from σ_0 to $2.05\sigma_0$; a long, narrow, stringlike internal flaw or cavity ($b/a = 0$) oriented in a direction perpendicular to the load raises the stress from σ_0 to $2.83\sigma_0$; and a very flat, round cavity oriented so that the flat plane is perpendicular to the load raises the stress from σ_0 to values as high or higher than $13.5\sigma_0$ if the material remains elastic; this value is comparable to the value for a narrow elliptical hole as given by Eq. 489.

(e) *Grooves.* The values of the theoretical stress concentration factors obtained by Neuber in his mathematical analysis of the stresses at grooves as shown in Figs. A to D of Table 20 may be obtained from the diagram given by Neuber and shown in Fig. 197.

For example, let it be assumed that a member contains the notch shown in Fig. A of Table 20 and is subjected to a bending moment M. Let it be assumed also that $\rho = 0.25$ in., $t = 1.5$ in., and $b = 9.5$ in. From these values are obtained $\sqrt{t/\rho} = 2.45$ and $\sqrt{b/\rho} = 6.16$. As indicated in Table 20, scale f applies for $\sqrt{t/\rho}$ and curve 2 for $\sqrt{b/\rho}$. Thus, to find the value of the theoretical stress concentration factor we enter Fig. 197 with $\sqrt{b/\rho} = 6.16$, proceed vertically upward to cut curve 2, then horizontally to the left to the axis of ordinates. We join this point to point $\sqrt{t/\rho} = 2.45$ on the left-hand axis of abscissas (on which scale f is applicable) by a straight line. This line is tangent to the circle corresponding to the appropriate theoretical stress concentration factor; thus $k_t = 4.25$.

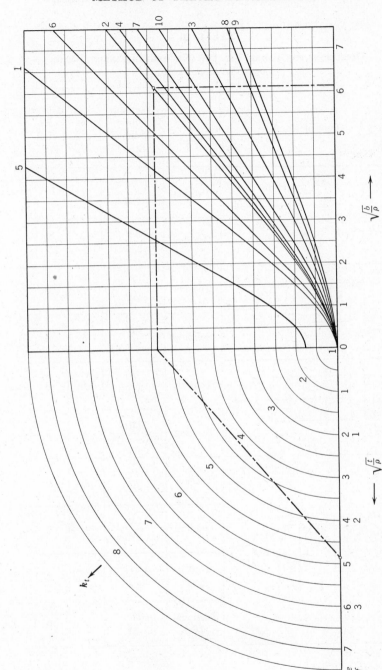

Fig. 197 Neuber's diagram (nomograph) for finding theoretical stress concentration factor at root of notch.

TABLE 20

DIRECTIONS FOR USE OF FIG. 197 (NEUBER) IN FINDING STRESS CONCENTRATION FACTOR k_t

Type of Notch	Type of Load	Formula for Nominal Stress	Scale for $\sqrt{\dfrac{t}{\rho}}$	Curve for Finding k_t
Fig. A	Tension	$\dfrac{P}{2bh}$	f	1
	Bending	$\dfrac{3M}{2b^2h}$	f	2
Fig. B	Tension	$\dfrac{P}{bh}$	f	3
	Bending	$\dfrac{6M}{b^2h}$	f	4
Fig. C	Tension	$\dfrac{P}{2bh}$	f	5
	Bending	$\dfrac{3Mt}{2h(c^3 - t^3)}$	e	5
Fig. D	Tension	$\dfrac{P}{\pi b^2}$	f	6
	Bending	$\dfrac{4M}{\pi b^3}$	f	7
	Direct shear	$\dfrac{1.23V}{\pi b^2}$	e	8
	Torsional shear	$\dfrac{2T}{\pi b^3}$	e	9

Some values of theoretical stress concentration factors for bending obtained from Neuber's diagram (Fig. 197) as found by Moore and Jordan are given in Fig. 198.

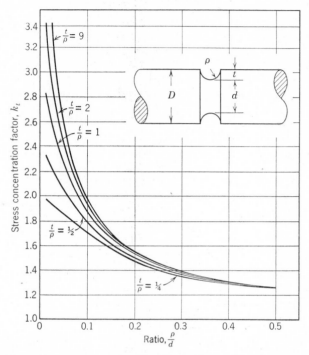

FIG. 198 Theoretical stress concentration factors for semicircular grooves in cylindrical member subjected to bending only as obtained from Neuber's diagram. (From Moore and Jordan.)

117 Stress concentration determined by photoelastic method. The values of stress concentrations found by the photoelastic method agree well with the results obtained from the mathematical theory of elasticity for those cases that can be analyzed mathematically. Thus the photoelastic method may be used to check mathematical methods, and it may be applied to some members in which the stress cannot be obtained mathematically; however, the technique of obtaining reliable results with the photoelastic method is acquired only after considerable experience. Special care must be exercised to obtain trustworthy results when the radius of the notch is very small.

Values of stress concentration factors obtained by the photoelastic method for three forms of abrupt changes in section in flat specimens are shown as reported by Frocht in Fig. 199. In each specimen the

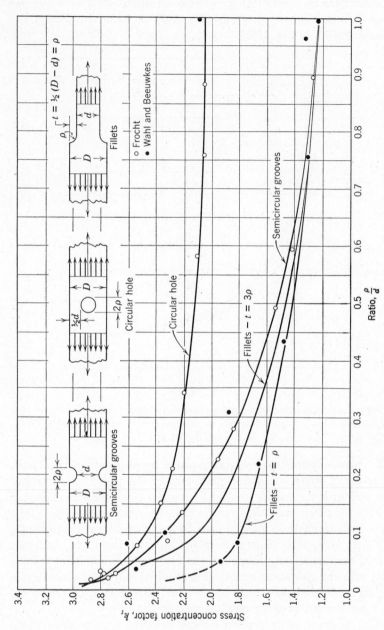

FIG. 199.   Theoretical stress concentration factors obtained by use of the photoelastic method.

stress distribution is uniform at sections on either side of the abrupt change in section; when the stress distribution is variable on either side of the abrupt change in section as in bending, the stress concentration factor is found to be somewhat smaller. These curves show that the value of k_t varies with the ratio ρ/d. However, k_t depends also on the ratio D/d. For the particular groove, hole, and fillet shown in Fig. 199 the values of ρ/d and D/d are related by the equation $D/d = 1 + 2\rho/d$.

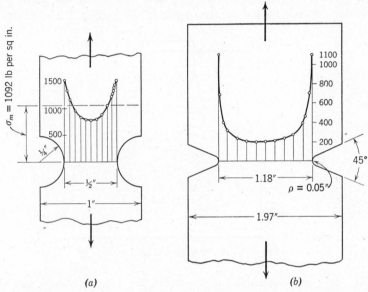

(a)   (b)

FIG. 200   Stress distribution at notches found by photoelastic method (from Coker).

The values of k_t for the hole and groove in Fig. 199 can be found also by Neuber's solution as obtained from Fig. 197 for various values of ρ/d. These values obtained from Neuber's nomograph agree satisfactorily with those found by the photoelastic method. But there is no mathematical solution for the theoretical stress concentration factor for the fillet, and hence the photoelastic method is of special value for this type of discontinuity. For the fillet in Fig. 199 for which $t = \rho$, the curve marked $t = \rho$ gives values of k_t. For members in which t is not equal to ρ the values of k_t will be different as shown, for example, by the curve marked $t = 3\rho$. For the influence of t/ρ on the values of k_t for a fillet subjected to axial tension and to bending, see "Photoelastic Studies in Stress Concentration," by M. M. Frocht, *Mechanical Engineering*, August 1936, p. 485.

The distribution of stress shown in Fig. 200 was obtained by Coker by the photoelastic method. The maximum stress at the edge of the groove in Fig. 200a is 1.37 times the average stress on the reduced section, that is $k_t = 1.37$, by the photoelastic method. The value as found by using Neuber's nomograph is $k_t = 1.45$. In Fig. 200b the groove has a much smaller radius and the plate is much wider. The photoelastic method gives a maximum stress of 1100 lb per sq in., whereas the nominal or average stress was 230 lb per sq in., that is, $k_t = 4.78$. The value as found by Neuber's nomograph is $k_t = 5.50$. The rather sharp notch gives a high concentration of stress. However, the stress concentration depends on the relative depth of the notch. For example, if

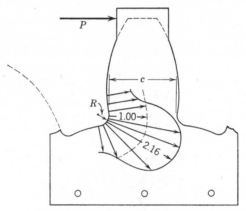

FIG. 201   Stress at root of gear tooth.

in Fig. 200b the dimensions of the notch are kept as shown and the outer width of the plate is reduced to 1.18 in. (the width of the root section is then 0.39 in.) the value of $k_t = 2.6$, from Neuber's solution.

Stress in Gear Teeth. Several investigators have obtained by the photoelastic method the stresses at the roots of gear teeth. Figure 201 shows the distribution of the bending stress at the fillet of one gear tooth; the direction of the stress at any point on the fillet is tangent to fillet. As indicated in the figure, the maximum stress at the fillet was found to be 2.16 times greater than that given by the ordinary flexure formula; that is, for this particular tooth the theoretical factor of stress concentration was 2.16. Table 21 gives values of the stress-concentration factors for other tooth proportions. These values should be considered as only approximately correct inasmuch as the tests indicate that the loading conditions influence the results, such as the height above the fillet at which the load is applied and its direction with respect to the axis of the gear tooth. In addition, the stress concentrations on the compressive side are somewhat different from those on the tension side. The localized stress at the point (or line) of contact of two gear teeth is discussed under the heading of contact stresses in Chapter 11.

TABLE 21

Fillet Radius, R (inches)	Ratio of Fillet Radius to Tooth Width, R/c	Factor of Stress Concentration, k_t
$\frac{5}{16}$	0.088	2.37
$\frac{3}{8}$	0.104	2.16
1	0.260	1.61
$1\frac{1}{2}$	0.375	1.46

Stress Due to Circular Hole in Beam. If a circular hole is made in a beam with the axis of the hole perpendicular to the plane of the loads, the stress distribution on the cross section containing the axis of the hole is very different from that in a solid beam. Coker determined, by the photoelastic method, the stress distribution on a section of a beam

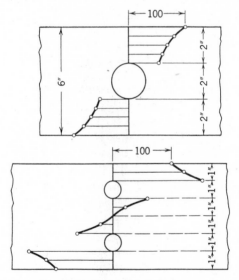

Fig. 202   Stress at hole in beam.

containing one hole at the center of the beam and also on a section containing two holes placed equidistant from the horizontal center line of the beam (Fig. 202). It will be noted that the stress at the outer edges of the holes in the beam with two holes is about 50 per cent larger than that at the outer fibers of the beam at this section.

The stress distribution shown in this beam will help explain the cause of the failure of a steel frame shown in Fig. 203a, the details of which were as follows: The steel frame (beam) had a rectangular cross section and had a hole drilled through it at the center of the depth in order to attach a small member. The axis of this hole was, therefore, the centroidal axis of the section, which was considered to be the neutral axis, and hence the stress at the edge of the hole was thought to be very small compared to the stress σ (Fig. 203b) at the outer fibers at this

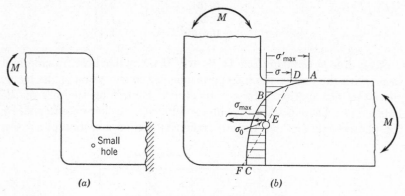

Fig. 203 Stress at hole in curved beam.

section; the stress distribution on the section was considered to be linear as in a straight beam, indicated by the line DEF. A number of such beams, however, fractured in service in which the member was subjected to repeated loads; the fracture in each case started as a crack at the edge of the hole. Since the hole is close to the curved portion of the member, the stress distribution on the section through the hole is approximately as shown by the curved line ABC in Fig. 203b (see Art. 48). Thus the stress is σ_0 at the point where the stress was thought to be practically zero; furthermore, the hole causes a stress concentration at this point which increases the theoretical stress from σ_0 to $\sigma_{max} = 3\sigma_0$, approximately. The stress σ_{max} proved to be the damaging stress since under the repeated loads a crack started at the edge of the hole and gradually spread across the section, resulting in the characteristic fatigue failure. By placing the hole in the neighborhood of the point B, the failures were prevented.

118 Stress concentration determined by elastic-strain method. By using a specially designed, highly sensitive and accurate mechanical strain gage which measured elastic strains in a 0.1-in. gage length, Peterson and Wahl obtained stress concentration factors for a shaft contain-

ing a transverse hole and subjected to bending loads. Their results are
shown in Fig. 204. With the same instrument they obtained the stress

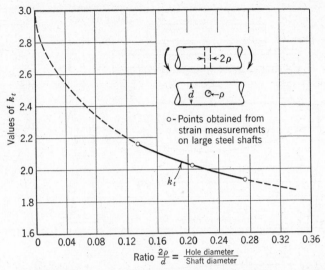

Fig. 204   Theoretical stress concentration factors for shaft in bending with transverse hole as found by elastic strain method. (From Peterson and Wahl.)

at a fillet in a large steel shaft tested as a beam. These values checked
closely with the values found by Frocht by the photoelastic method for
fillets of the same proportions.

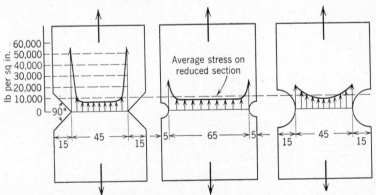

Fig. 205   Stress at notches found by lateral-strain method. (From Preuss.)

A number of different types of instruments have been devised for
obtaining strains in short gage lengths; the electrical resistance (SR-4)
gage is perhaps the most widely used at present. It has been demon-

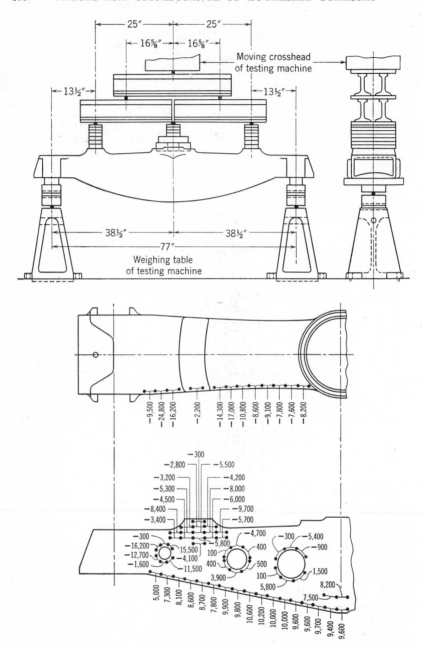

FIG. 206   Stresses in a car bolster found by strain gage method. (From L. E. Endsley.)

strated many times that such instruments give values of stress concentrations approaching the theoretical values if the strains remain in the elastic range. Preuss, by delicate measurement of the change in thickness and by means of Poisson's ratio, found the distribution of elastic stress at various reduced sections in tension members; some of his results are given in Fig. 205. As indicated in this figure, the maximum stress at the edges of the contractions in area varies from about 4.6 to 1.7 times the average stress on the reduced area.

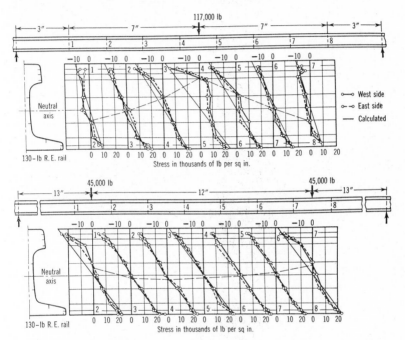

FIG. 207   Effect of bearing pressure of load at center of beam on longitudinal stresses in beam. (From A. N. Talbot, *Bull. A.R.E.A.*, Vol. 31.)

Stress Distribution in Car Bolster. L. E. Endsley has found the stress concentration at various locations in different types of car bolsters; in these members the stress concentration may be due both to abrupt changes of section and to localized surface pressures. Figure 206 shows the distribution of elastic stress in one type of bolster as found by use of a 2-in. strain gage.

The concentrations of stress at various regions in the bolster may be found by studying Fig. 206. It will be observed that the maximum stress (24,800 lb per sq in.) occurs on the top of the bolster at the juncture of the loading surface with the top surface of the beam. A strain gage having a gage length smaller than 2 in. would no doubt indicate concentration of stress somewhat greater than those given in Fig. 206.

Effect of Local Pressure of Load on Stresses in a Beam. The effect on the longitudinal bending stresses in a beam caused by the bearing pres-

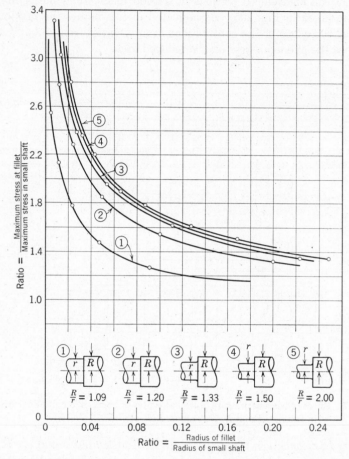

Fɪɢ. 208   Torsional shearing stress concentration at fillet in shaft of two diameters.

sure of a concentrated load applied at the mid-span section of a steel rail beam is shown in the upper part of Fig. 207. The load was applied approximately along a line across the top of the rail section. It will be observed that the effect of the bearing pressure on the longitudinal stress extends well below the middle of the depth of the rail. The point of zero longitudinal stress is about 1 in. above the calculated position of the neutral axis for the section beneath the load, and the stress on the cross section does not vary directly as the distance from the neutral axis, as is usually assumed for such a beam. The results for the section underneath the load, however, are approximate because relatively long gage lengths were used and the two dimensional aspect of the state of stress was neglected.

If, however, the same beam is loaded as shown in the lower part of Fig. 207, the stresses in the central portion, which is subjected to constant bending moment free from the influence of the bearing pressure of the loads, are in agreement with the usual assumptions for simple bending.

119 Torsional stress concentration at fillet in shaft obtained by electrical analogy method. If all cross sections of a shaft are circular but the shaft contains a rather abrupt change in diameter, a localized stress occurs at the abrupt change of section. Jacobsen has investigated the concentration of torsional shearing stress at a fillet where the diameter of a shaft changes more or less abruptly, depending on the radius of the fillet. The electrical analogy method was used.

The results of the investigation are given in Fig. 208. For example, if the radius of a circular shaft changes from 2 in. to 1.5 in. by means of a fillet having a radius of $\frac{1}{8}$ in., $R/r = 1.33$, and $\rho/r = \frac{1}{12} = 0.083$; the maximum elastic shearing stress at the fillet as given by Fig. 208 is approximately 1.7 times the maximum shearing stress in the small shaft as found by the equation $\tau = Tr/J$, where T is the twisting moment, and J is the polar moment of inertia of the cross section of the smaller shaft ($J = \pi r^4/2$).

120 Torsional stress concentration found by elastic-membrane method. Griffith and Taylor, by using a soap film as the elastic membrane (see Art. 86), found the torsional shearing stress in a hollow shaft at the filleted corner of a keyway and also at the center of the flat bottom of the keyway. The external and internal diameters were 10 in. and 5.8 in., respectively, and the keyway was 1.0 in. deep and 2.5 in. wide.

Figure 209 shows the value of the ratios of the maximum tor-

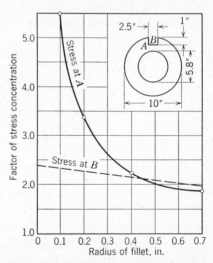

Fig. 209 Factors of torsional shearing stress concentration at keyway in hollow shaft.

sional shearing stress at the fillet for various radii of fillet to the maximum shearing stress that would be developed in the shaft if the shaft had no keyway. In other words, the ordinates to the curve give the theoretical stress concentration factors k_t due to the keyway.

Ordinates to the dotted line in Fig. 209 are the stress concentration factors for the shearing stress at the center of the bottom of the keyway; it will be noted that the stress at this point is approximately twice as great as would be the maximum shearing stress in the shaft if it had no keyway.

Torsional Stress at Fillet in Angle Section. The torsional shearing stress at a sharp internal corner of a bar would be infinite if the material did not yield when the stress becomes sufficiently high. If the corner is rounded off by means of a fillet, the stress is reduced; the amount of reduction corresponding to fillets of different radii in an angle section was found by Griffith and Taylor by use of the soap-film method. The section was 1 in. wide (Fig. 210), and the straight portions or arms of the section were long.

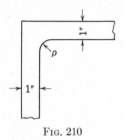

Fɪɢ. 210

The ratios of the maximum shearing stress at the fillet to the shearing stress in the straight portion or arm of the angle section for various radii of fillets are given in Table 22. These values show that a small fillet has a large influence in reducing the stress at the corner, and that practically no advantage is gained by making the radius of the fillet larger than $\frac{1}{4}$ in.

TABLE 22

Radius of Fillet, Inches (see Fig. 210)	Ratio: $\dfrac{\text{Maximum Stress}}{\text{Stress in Arm}}$
0.10	1.89
0.21	1.54
0.30	1.48
0.40	1.44
0.50	1.43
0.60	1.42
0.70	1.41

Note. The stress concentration factors given in the foregoing articles are theoretical values for the various forms of discontinuities. Values of theoretical stress concentration factors for many other forms of discontinuities are available in the technical literature.

Problems

226. A thin-walled cylindrical tank has a diameter D and a wall thickness t. It is subjected to an internal pressure p. The wall has a stress raiser consisting of a small circular hole. By making use of Eqs. 486 and 487, derive the expressions for the theoretical maximum stresses σ_A and σ_B at the hole on longitudinal and transverse cross sections, respectively, of the cylinder through the hole. It is assumed that the elastic strength of the material is not exceeded. If σ_A and σ_B are to be expressed in pounds per square inch, state the units in which p, D, and t must be expressed.

$Ans.$ $\sigma_A = 2.5pD/2t$; $\sigma_B = pD/4t$.

227. A cylindrical shaft has a circumferential groove. The depth of the groove is $t = 0.1$ in., and the radius at the root of the groove is $\rho = 0.05$ in. The radius of the cross section of the shaft at the root of the groove is $b = 1.0$ in. By making use of Neuber's nomograph (Fig. 197) find the value of k_t if the shaft is subjected to (a) an axial tensile load, (b) a bending moment, and (c) a torsional moment.

228. Let the shaft described in Prob. 227 be subjected to a combination of loads consisting of a pure bending moment $M = 25,000$ lb-in. and a torsional moment $T = 50,000$ lb-in. From the stress concentration factors found in Prob. 227, compute the values of the following theoretical stresses in the shaft at the root of the groove: (a) the maximum principal stress, (b) the maximum shearing stress, and (c) the maximum octahedral shearing stress.

229. In Fig. C of Table 20 is shown a flat bar with a slot whose ends are circular; let the dimensions have the following values: $b = 10t$, $c = 11t$, $\rho = t$. The fact that $\rho = t$ means that the slot is a circular hole. Show by means of Neuber's nomograph that, if the bar is loaded in tension, k_t is approximately 3 for the circular hole in this bar whose half-width c is large in comparison to the radius of the hole.

230. In Fig. C of Table 20 the flat bar has the following dimensions: $t = \rho = \frac{1}{2}$ in., $b = \frac{1}{2}$ in., $c = 1$ in. This means that the bar has a circular hole whose diameter is equal to half the width of the plate. If the bar is subjected to a tensile load P, find by the use of Neuber's nomograph (Fig. 197) the value of k_t for the maximum stress at the hole.

$Ans.$ $k_t = 2.3$.

§ 2   Significant Stress Concentration Factors

121   Significant or effective stress concentration factor defined. The values of stress concentration factors obtained by the methods discussed in the preceding articles of this chapter are primarily theoretical values; that is, they are values which apply mainly to ideal, elastic material and depend primarily on the geometry or form of the abrupt change in section; they are therefore sometimes called form factors.

Frequently, however, the damaging influence of a stress concentration at an abrupt change in section or at any other form of discontinuity in a member made of real material is not indicated satisfactorily by the full theoretical value of the stress concentration. In other words, the theoretical stress concentration or localized stress is not the significant or effective stress in indicating nearness to structural damage to the member; the damaging effect of the stress concentration depends on the characteristics of the material and on the type of loading as well as on the geometry or form of the member. Possible reasons for this fact are discussed in subsequent paragraphs.

The significant value of the stress concentration, therefore, is obtained by multiplying the nominal stress, as computed from an elementary stress equation (see Chapter 2), by a *significant or effective stress concentration factor,** denoted by k_e, the value of which for any discontinuity or stress raiser is usually less than the theoretical stress concentration factor k_t for the same discontinuity.

The value of k_e is obtained by testing at least two samples or specimens (or two sets of specimens) of the actual material. One specimen (or set of specimens) is prepared without the discontinuity or stress raiser so that the significant stress will also be the nominal stress as computed by an elementary stress formula. A second specimen (or set of specimens) is prepared with the stress raiser present and is given the same test; again the stress is computed by the same elementary stress formula.

It is assumed that the damage (failure) in the two specimens starts when the stresses in the specimens attain the same value, the loads causing these equal stresses, of course, being unequal; the damaging stress in the specimen containing the stress raiser is caused by the lesser load.

The significant stress concentration factor for any discontinuity or stress raiser, then, may be defined as the ratio of the stress calculated from the load at which structural damage starts in the specimen free from the stress raiser to the nominal stress calculated by the same stress formula from the load at which damage starts in the sample which contains the stress raiser.

122   Conditions influencing the value of k_e.   Notch sensitivity.
At abrupt changes of section, such as a hole, a fillet, or a groove, in a member, the significant value of the stress developed in the member may be assumed to be equal to the nominal value of stress given by the ordinary stress equations plus some proportion ($\frac{1}{4}$, $\frac{1}{2}$, $\frac{3}{4}$, say) of the increase in the theoretical stress caused by the abrupt change in section; this increase in stress will be the difference between the nominal value of stress and the value of the maximum localized stress obtained mathematically from the theory of elasticity or by the photoelastic, soap-film, elastic strain, and electrical analogy methods. This means that the nominal stress plus some proportion of the increase in stress

---

* The term *strength reduction factor* is also used. It should be made clear, however, that the strength of the *material* is not considered to be reduced by the stress raiser but the strength (load-carrying capacity) of the *member* is reduced.

caused by the abrupt change of section is considered to be effective in causing damage to the member. For example, if the abrupt change in section is caused by a small hole in the center of a plate subjected to an axial tensile load, and if one-half of the difference between the nominal stress $\sigma_0 = P/a$ and the maximum theoretical value of the localized stress $\sigma_{max} = 3P/a$ is used, then the significant stress concentration factor would be $k_e = 1 + \frac{1}{2}(3 - 1) = 2$. Thus the significant stress σ_e in the member would be considered, for this example, to be $\sigma_e = 2P/a$.

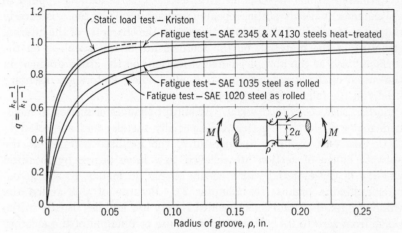

FIG. 211   Influence of radius of groove on notch sensitivity index.

The principle used in the foregoing example can be stated in a general form as follows: Let q represent the proportion of the increase in the theoretical localized stress σ_t above the nominal stress σ_0 to be used for determining the significant stress. The increase in stress at the point of concentration is $\sigma_t - \sigma_0 = k_t\sigma_0 - \sigma_0 = \sigma_0(k_t - 1)$ in which σ_0 is the nominal stress given by the elementary stress equation in which the effect of the given discontinuity is neglected. In accordance with the procedure in the foregoing example the value of the significant stress is

$$\sigma_e = k_e\sigma_0 = \sigma_0 + q\sigma_0(k_t - 1)$$

Thus
$$k_e = 1 + q(k_t - 1) \tag{493}$$

and hence
$$q = (k_e - 1)/(k_t - 1) \tag{494}$$

The name frequently given to q as defined in the foregoing equations is the *notch sensitivity index* of the material for the given form of discontinuity and for the given type of loading. For example, in Eq. 493, if $q = 0$, $k_e = 1$, and the material and member are said to be insensitive to the effects of the stress concentration; whereas if $q = 1$, $k_e = k_t$, and the member is said to be fully sensitive to the effects of the stress concentration. The values of k_e (and hence of q) must be determined from tests as described in Art. 121. It has been found from such tests (see Fig. 211) that the values of k_e and of q depend mainly upon the ability of the material and the member to make adjustments or accommodations, such as local yielding, which reduce the damaging effects of the localized stress. The ability of the material to make these adjustments or accommodations depends, in turn, on the type of loading applied to the member (whether static, repeated, impact, etc.); on the existence in the member of initial or residual stresses; on the character of the internal structure of the material; on the temperature of the member; on the surface finish at the abrupt change of section; on the stress gradient in the region of the stress concentration, etc. These factors are discussed briefly in the following paragraphs.

Static Loads; Ductile Material. At abrupt changes of section in members made of *ductile* * materials (especially metals) and subjected to static loads at ordinary temperatures, the localized stresses at the abrupt change of section are relieved to a large degree by localized yielding of the material which occurs largely, in metals, as slip across intercrystalline planes (see Chapter 2). Because of this action the value of q for the conditions specified is very low and lies usually in the range from zero to 0.1. However, if the use or function of the member is such that the amount of inelastic strain required for this relieving action must be restricted, the value of q may be as large as one-half. If the temperature of a metal member is very low when subjected to static loads, slip in the crystals seems to be reduced and is likely to be less effective in relieving the concentrated stress, and hence the value of q may be as much as one-half or even greater.

If the metal member is subjected to static load while at an elevated temperature, the mechanism (designated as creep, see Art. 4) by which localized yielding occurs may cause the value of q to vary from nearly zero to nearly unity. This situation arises from the fact that creep of metals may be the result of either one or both of two different inelastic mechanisms, depending on the temperature and stress imposed: (a) Creep may be caused mainly by intercrystalline slip, especially at the lower range of creep temperatures and at relatively high stresses; this type of creep relieves the stress concentration to a large degree ($q = 0$, nearly); or (b) creep may be due to the viscous flow of the unordered (so-called amorphous) grain boundary material, especially at the higher temperatures and lower stresses, and stress concen-

* See footnote in Chapter 1, p. 4.

tration is relieved very little by such inelastic deformation ($q = 1$, nearly).

Static Loads; Brittle Material. If the member containing an abrupt change in cross section is made of a relatively brittle material and is

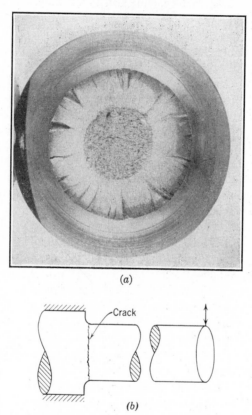

(a)

(b)

FIG. 212   Failure by progressive spreading of a crack which starts at region of stress concentration (fatigue fracture).

subjected to static loads, q will usually have a value in the range from one-half to one, except for certain materials which contain many internal stress raisers inherent in the internal structure of the material such as graphite flakes in gray cast iron; an external stress raiser in the form of an abrupt change in section in such a material has only a small additional influence on the strength of the member, and hence the value of q is relatively small.

Repeated Loads. Let a member having an abrupt change in section be subjected to a load which is repeated many times. Under these conditions the mode of failure is progressive localized fracture, even though the material is classed as ductile (see Art. 4), and the ability of the material to make adjustments or accommodations by localized yielding is greatly reduced as compared to its ability under static loads; this type of (fatigue) fracture, shown in Fig. 212, gives little or no evidence of yielding before complete fracture of the member occurs. Thus the value of q for loads repeated a large number of times is relatively large, usually being between one-half and one; the value of unity is approached in general for the harder (heat-treated) metals, and the lower value is approached for metals used in their softer condition. Furthermore, the internal structure of metals, especially of steel, has some influence on the value of q. If the pearlitic grain size in steel is very fine, q is likely to be nearly unity, but, if the grain size is very coarse, the value of q is decreased.

Residual Stresses. The presence of initial or residual stresses in the member at the abrupt change in section also may influence the value of q. If the member is subjected to static loads and the residual stress has the same direction as the nominal load stress, it combines with the concentrated load stress to increase the magnitude of the significant stress, and hence q is relatively large. If the residual stress has a direction opposite to the nominal load stress, it makes the significant stress smaller and hence a small value of q may be used. For example, if the significant stress at the abrupt change of section is a tensile stress, a compressive residual stress such as that caused by shot-peening the surface at the stress raiser will reduce the value of q and hence will reduce the damaging effect of the stress concentration. If, however, the member is subjected to repeated loads, especially completely reversed repeated loads, the influence of initial or residual stresses is uncertain. It appears that micro-residual stresses play a larger part in repeated loading than do the macro-residual stresses. And there is some evidence that the macro-residual stresses under repeatedly applied completely reversed load stresses are decreased by the repeated stressing.

Very Abrupt Changes in Section. Stress Gradient. Let the change in section of a member be very abrupt; that is, let the hole, fillet, or groove, etc., forming the abrupt change in section have a very small radius compared to the dimensions of the section, so that the theoretical stress gradient is steep in the region of stress concentration. The value of k_t for such a stress raiser is large, but the value of k_e found from tests of such members, under either static or repeated loads, is usually much smaller than k_t; that is, the value of q is smaller than would be found from tests of members of the same material with less abrupt changes of section. Figure 211 gives the results of tests of specimens having an abrupt change of section caused by a circumferential groove which show the foregoing facts. In this figure the value of q is plotted as ordinates, and the radius of the groove at the abrupt change of section is plotted as abscissas.

The results of these tests are represented by smooth curves drawn through points (not shown) representing the test data. The data used for each curve were obtained by testing specimens of the same material, the specimens being identical except for the size of the groove radius. The upper curve is for static load tests of specimens of Kriston (one of the plastics) which is a very brittle material. The other curves are for repeated bending-load tests of steels. In these tests, made by Moore, Jordan, and Morkovin, the values of a/ρ and t/ρ were kept constant, which means that the value of k_t was kept constant (see Neuber's nomograph, Fig. 197). However the groove radius ρ was varied and all these curves show that when the groove radius approaches very small values q is quite small, but when the groove radius is relatively large, the value of q approaches unity.

The results of these tests indicate that the damaging effects to a member from notches having small radii at the roots of the notches such as scratches, small holes, grooves, or fillets, or small inclusions, at a section of the member are considerably less than would be indicated by the large values of the theoretical stress at such stress raisers; in other words q (and hence k_e) is relatively small. Much of the available data for the value of k_e and of q have been obtained by conducting repeated load tests of specimens with cross sections of relatively small dimensions containing fillets, grooves, holes, etc., having small radii. These data furnish valuable information for computing significant stresses in a member having such discontinuities within the range of conditions used in the tests, but the values of q are probably unnecessarily small for use in computing k_e by Eq. 493 for holes, fillets, grooves, etc., whose radii are relatively large.

Significance of Stress Gradient. The question naturally arises as to why the value q for a given material under a given type of loading should depend upon the value of the root radius of the notch when it is small as indicated by the curves of Fig. 211. Much discussion of this question is found in the technical literature, but no completely satisfactory reason can be given. A possible explanation is as follows: At one or more points on the surface of the member at the root of the notch the stress concentration will have its highest value, but at nearby points in the member in any direction from the root of the notch the values of the stress diminish. For most notches the highest rate (stress gradient) at which the stress diminishes occurs at points in a cross section of the member at the notch root. Let S be the stress gradient at the root of the notch, that is, S is the slope of a line which is tangent at the root of the notch to the curve of stress distribution on the cross section at the root of the notch. This slope gives the rate at which the stress is diminishing at points just underneath the root of the notch. If S is large, the stress magnitude will diminish rapidly so that the stress at a point just underneath the root of the notch will be only very slightly larger than the value given at this point by the ordinary (nominal) stress equation.

In Part V it is shown that S for notches such as holes, fillets, and grooves, is given approximately by the following equation:

$$S = 2.5\sigma_{max}/\rho = 2.5k_t\sigma_0/\rho \qquad (495)$$

From Eq. 495 it is seen that, for a given value of nominal stress σ_0 and of k_t, if ρ becomes small, the value of S becomes very large. When ρ is small and S is large, the magnitude of the concentrated stress diminishes so rapidly that only a very thin layer of material at the root of the notch is subjected to the stress concentration. This means that the so-called adjustments or accommodations which take place in the material and which tend to relieve high stresses can take place easier since such a small amount of material is involved. Furthermore, the machining and polishing of a specimen at the root of the notch will frequently cause the material in this thin layer to become strengthened (by work hardening) in its ability to resist stress. The greater apparent ability of this thin layer of material to resist higher stress plus the fact that the unchanged material (parent material) underneath this layer is not required to resist the highly concentrated stress would also explain the reason why q becomes so much smaller as ρ becomes very small.

The foregoing discussion of stress gradient applies mainly to so-called mechanical notches such as holes and fillets rather than to so-called chemical notches such as corrosion pits (see Art. 123).

Impact or Energy Loading. If machine parts and structural members are subjected to impact or energy loading, that is, if a member is required to absorb energy delivered to it by a body having a relatively large velocity when it comes in contact with the member, localized stresses have, in general, a large influence in decreasing the load-carrying capacity of the member. As discussed in Chapter 3, the energy absorbed per unit volume by a material when stressed within the elastic strength is $\frac{1}{2}\sigma^2/E$; that is, the energy absorbed by a material is proportional to the square of the stress in the material. This means that the small portions of a member where the high localized stresses occur absorb an excessive amount of energy before the main portion of the member can be stressed appreciably, and hence before the main portion can be made to absorb an appreciable share of the energy delivered to the member. As a result, the small portion where the localized stress occurs is likely to be stressed above the yield point of the material, and the energy required to be absorbed may be great enough to cause rupture even if the material is relatively ductile; the reader may recall that a familiar method of breaking a bar of ductile metal is to file a V notch in one side of the bar and then to clamp one end of the bar in a vise with the notch close to the face of the vise and strike the bar near the other end a sharp blow with a hammer so that the bar is bent with the notch on the tension side of the bar.

The tests most widely used to measure the effects of a notch under impact loads are the Charpy and Izod impact tests. However, neither of these notched-bar single-blow impact tests gives a quantitative value of k_e. These tests are important primarily in determining whether or not a material of known history of manufacture and treatment is substantially the same as similar material which has proved to be satisfactory in service. There is no satisfactory test or method for determining a value of q for stress raisers in members subjected to impact loading.

123 Corrosion fatigue. The severe damaging effects that mechanical notches such as holes and fillets and so-called chemical notches such as corrosion pits are likely to have on the resistance of steel to repeated stress, particularly of alloy steels heat treated to give high strength, are shown in Fig. 213. It should be stated that the effect of corrosion that takes place while the material is being repeatedly stressed is much more damaging to the fatigue strength of steel than is corrosion that takes place prior to stressing (called stressless corrosion). The main reason for this fact seems to be that the products of the corrosion tend to form a protecting film which excludes the corroding agent from contacting the metal if the protecting film is not subjected to stress; if, however, the rather brittle film is repeatedly stressed in the presence of the corroding agent, the film cracks and allows the corroding agent to continue to attack the metal underneath the film. The effect of corrosion on the fatigue strength of steel is shown by the S-N diagrams in Fig. 213. For example, the quenched and tempered SAE 3140 steel tested indicated an endurance limit of approximately 90,000 lb per sq in. when tested in air (a very mild corrosive medium), and this was reduced to about 10,000 lb per sq in. when the specimens were tested in the presence of water; the presence of a small hole caused little further decrease in fatigue strength. Furthermore the shape of the S-N diagram for stresses above the endurance limit was influenced greatly by the corrosion.

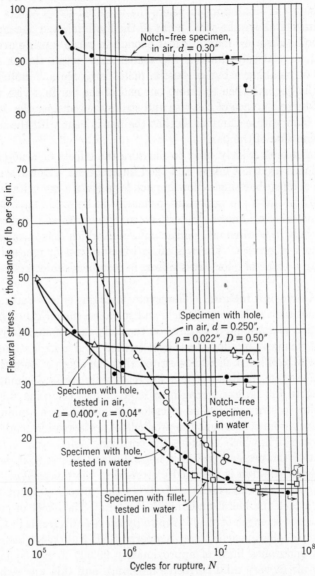

Fɪɢ. 213 *S—N* diagrams showing effect of abrupt changes in cross section and corrosion on resistance of steel to repeated cycles of completely reversed bending stress. The original material was the same for all tests. (From Bulletin 293, Engineering Experiment Station, Univ. of Illinois, by T. J. Dolan)

124 Effect of range of stress. In the preceding discussion it was assumed that the member or specimen was subjected to repeated cycles of completely reversed stress, that is, in each stress cycle the stress varied from a given tensile stress to an equal compressive stress. If a specimen in which the stress is concentrated is subjected to repeated cycles of stress in which the stress is not completely reversed it is convenient to consider the cycle or range of stress to be made up of a steady stress and a completely reversed (alternating) stress superimposed on the steady stress. There is considerable evidence indicating that the damaging effect of the stress concentration in such a repeated cycle of stress is associated only with the completely reversed (alternating) component of the stress cycle and not with the maximum stress in the cycle. Thus the stress concentration factor for the particular discontinuity is applied only to the alternating stress component and is the same as that found for completely reversed stress alone.

125 Methods of reducing harmful effects of stress concentrations. The problem that frequently arises in engineering is that of reducing the value of a stress concentration below the minimum value that will cause a fatigue fracture to occur or of raising the fatigue strength of the material so that fracture is avoided, rather than that of calculating the effective stress concentration. Some of the ways that have been employed in an attempt to reduce the damaging effects of localized stresses are listed as follows:

1. Reducing the value of the stress concentration by decreasing the abruptness of the change in cross section of the member by use of fillets, etc., either by adding or by removing small amounts of material.

2. Reducing the value of the stress concentration by making the portion of the member in the neighborhood of the stress concentration less

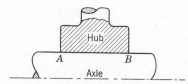

FIG. 214 Stress concentration occurs at A and B when wheel is shrunk on axle and axle is subjected to bending.

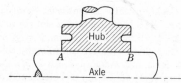

FIG. 215 Stress concentrations reduced by removing material so that hub at A and B will deflect more easily.

stiff; this may be done, for example, by removing material in various ways, as indicated in Figs. 214 and 215. It may sometimes be done by substituting a member made of material with a lower modulus of elasticity, such as replacing a steel nut on a steel bolt by a bronze nut for reducing the stress concentration at the threads of the steel bolt.

3. Increasing the fatigue strength of the material by cold working the portions of the members where the stress concentrations occur; for example, by the cold rolling of fillets and of bearing surfaces on axles, or by the shot blasting or shot peening of surfaces of machine parts. The increased fatigue strength of a member caused by local cold working of the metal at the region of stress concentration in some cases may be due primarily to residual compressive stresses set up in the cold worked metal by the surrounding elastic material as this elastic material attempts to return to its original position when the cold working tool is removed, especially if the repeated cycle of stress is not reversed. Likewise, over-straining of the outer fibers of a beam or of the inner fibers of a thick-walled pressure vessel or pipe may create favorable initial stresses.

4. Increasing the fatigue strength of the material by alloying and heat treating portions of steel members that resist the high stress, by case hardening, nitriding, flame hardening, etc. In such treatments, however, care must be taken to avoid tensile residual stresses.

5. Reducing the stress concentration by removing surface scratches, tool marks, small laps, and similar stress raisers by creating a smooth surface by polishing.

6. Reducing the stress concentration by the prevention of minute surface corrosion pits by protecting the surface from acid fumes or from moisture through the use of a corrosion-resisting covering, as for example by incasing the member in grease or spraying on a coating of lacquer.

Illustrative Problems

Problem 231. A cantilever beam is made of a flat bar of hot-rolled SAE 1020 steel. The beam contains a slot cut as shown in Figure C of Table 20 whose dimensions are $b = \frac{1}{2}$ in., $t = 2$ in., $\rho = \frac{1}{4}$ in., $h = 1$ in., and $c = 2.5$ in. (a) If the beam is subjected at its free end to many completely reversed cycles of bending moment, the maximum value of which is M, compute the significant value of the stress in terms of M at the top or bottom end of the slot (that is, at the root of the notch); make use of Fig. 211. (b) If the maximum utilizable stress for this material under completely reversed cycles of stress is 25,000 lb per sq in., compute the allowable moment M based on a factor of safety of 4.

Solution. (a) From Fig. 197 $k_t = 2.7$, and from Fig. 211 the value of q taken as an ordinate to the curve representing fatigue test data for SAE 1020 steel is $q = 0.93$. Therefore Eq. 493 gives

$$k_e = 1 + 0.93(2.7 - 1) = 2.58$$

The nominal stress σ_0 at the root of the notch on either end of the slot (see Table 20) is found from the flexure formula to be

$$\sigma_0 = \frac{3Mt}{2h(c^3 - t^3)} = \frac{3 \times M \times 2}{2 \times 1(2.5^3 - 2^3)} = 0.395M \text{ lb/in.}^2$$

Hence the significant value of the stress or effective stress σ_e is

$$\sigma_e = k_e\sigma_0 = 2.58 \times 0.395M = 1.02M \text{ lb/in.}^2$$

(b) The allowable or working stress σ_w is $0.25 \times 25,000 = 6250$ lb per sq in. Hence $6250 = 1.02M$; $M = 6100$ lb-in.

Problem 232. Let the cantilever beam in Prob. 231 be unchanged except that $\rho = 0.03$ in. This makes the slot approximately a long narrow crack in the bar. Compute the significant stress at the root of the notch.

Solution. (a) From Fig. 197 we find that $k_t = 6.3$. Figure 211 shows that, for fatigue tests of SAE 1020 steel, $q = 0.64$ when $\rho = 0.03$ in. Hence

$$k_e = 1 + 0.64(6.3 - 1) = 4.4$$

Therefore the significant stress is

$$\sigma_e = k_e\sigma_0 = 4.4 \times 0.395M = 1.74M \text{ lb/in.}^2$$

By comparing the solution of this problem with that in Prob. 231 it is seen that the theoretical value of k_t is 6.3 as compared to 2.7, that is, a 133 per cent increase. But the value of k_e is 4.4 as compared to 2.58, that is, a 70 per cent increase; the significant stress is increased by the latter percentage. These facts indicate that, as the value of k_t increases with a decrease in ρ, the value of k_e also increases, but to a lesser degree.

(b) The allowable stress is $\sigma_w = 6250$ lb per sq in. Therefore $6250 = 1.74M$; $M = 3600$ lb in.

Problems

233. A flat bar of a material which is relatively brittle has a fillet as shown in Fig. 199. The thickness of the bar is 1 in.; $\rho = \frac{1}{8}$ in., $d = 2$ in., and $D = 2\frac{1}{4}$ in. The bar is subjected to an axial static tensile load P. If the allowable (working) stress for the material under this condition of loading is $\sigma_w = 2000$ lb per sq in., compute the maximum allowable load P for the member. Assume that $q = 0.8$.

234. In Prob. 228 let the twisting moment T and the bending moment M be repeatedly applied through completely reversed cycles. Let it be assumed that for the material in the shaft under repeated loads the value of $q = 0.8$. Compute the significant value of the maximum principal stress in the shaft at a cross section through the root of the groove.

Selected References

1. Inglis, C. E., "Stresses in a Plate Due to the Presence of Cracks and Sharp Corners," *Transactions of the Institute of Naval Architects (British)*, Vol. LX, Pt. I, p. 219. Also *Engineering (London)*, Vol. 95, 1913, p. 413.

2. Neuber, H., *Kerbspannungslehre*, published by Julius Springer, Berlin, 1937. See Translation 24, David Taylor Model Basin, U. S. Navy, Washington, D. C., November 1945.
3. Timoshenko, S., "On Stresses in a Plate with a Circular Hole," *Journal of the Franklin Institute*, Vol. 197, 1924.
4. Sadowsky, M. A., and E. Sternberg, "Stress Concentration around a Tri-axial Ellipsoidal Cavity," *Journal of Applied Mechanics*, 1949, Vol. 71, p. 149.
5. Seely, F. B., and T. J. Dolan, "Stress Concentration at Fillets, Holes, and Keyways as Found by the Plaster-model Method," *Bulletin* 276, Engineering Experiment Station, University of Illinois, 1935.
6. de Forrest, A. V., and G. Ellis, "Brittle Lacquers as an Aid to Stress Analysis," *Journal of the Aeronautical Sciences*, Vol. 7, 1940, p. 205.
7. Peterson, R. E., and A. M. Wahl, "Two- and Three-dimensional Cases of Stress Concentration, and Comparison with Fatigue Tests," *Transactions of the American Society of Mechanical Engineers*, Vol. 47, 1925, p. 619, Vol. 58, 1936, p. A–15–22.
8. Peterson, R. E., "Application of Stress Concentration Factors in Design," *Proceedings of the Society for Experimental Stress Analysis*, Vol. 1, No. 1, 1943, p. 118.
9. Frocht, M. M., and D. Landsberg, "Factors of Stress Concentration in Bars with Deep Sharp Grooves and Fillets in Tension," *Proceedings of the Society for Experimental Stress Analysis*, Vol. 8, 1951, pp. 149–162.
10. Jacobsen, L. S., "Torsional-stress Concentrations in Shafts of Circular Cross-section and Variable Diameter," *Transactions of the American Society of Mechanical Engineers*, Vol. 47, 1925, p. 619.
11. Griffith, A. A., and G. I. Taylor, "The Use of Soap Films in Solving Torsion Problems," *Proceedings of the Institution of Mechanical Engineers, London*, October-December, 1917, p. 755.

PART FOUR

Energy Methods

Chapter 13

CONSIDERATIONS OF ENERGY PRINCIPLES FOR DETERMINING RELATIONS BETWEEN LOADS AND DEFLECTIONS

126 Importance of deflection. The need for a relationship between the loads acting on a member or a structure and the deformation or deflection of the member arises frequently as a result of either one of the two following general situations: (a) The maximum permissible loads or forces that can be applied to the member may be limited by the allowable deflection of the member; and (b) in dealing with statically indeterminate members or structures the relationships between the forces and deflections are needed to supplement the conditions of equilibrium for determining the forces acting on the statically indeterminate member or structure.

127 Two general approaches to the problem. Two general methods or theorems for determining the relationship between the forces (and couples) acting on a member or structure in equilibrium and the deflection at some point of the member will be considered. In the first method the desired relationship is involved in a theorem which expresses the force at some point on the member in terms of the strain energy stored in the member and the deflection of the point. In the second theorem the deflection of the point is expressed in terms of the force acting at the point and the so-called complementary energy; it is difficult to give a physical meaning to the expression for complementary energy, although it is associated with, or complementary to, the energy stored in the member and is expressed in the same units as is energy. Each theorem has advantages and disadvantages for each of the purposes stated in Art. 126, as will be shown in subsequent chapters where the techniques for using them will be developed. It is the primary objective of this chapter to derive and interpret the two theorems.

128 First theorem: Strain energy. The strain energy theorem will be derived for a rather simple structure, namely, one in which the members are subjected to axial forces and on which there is applied only one load that does work on the structure (the other external forces or loads are the reactions of the rigid supports which do no work). Other restrictions on the structure will be introduced in subsequent analysis.

In Fig. 216a let ABC represent a pin-connected, pin-loaded truss in equilibrium. The truss is attached to rigid supports at A and B and is subjected to a varying horizontal load H at C. The deflection of C in the direction of H is δ_H. The load H is resisted by the axial forces S_1 and S_2 in the two members as indicated in Fig. 216h. The original

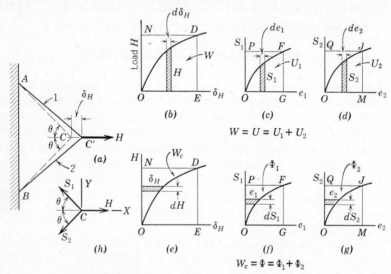

$$W = U = U_1 + U_2$$

$$W_c = \Phi = \Phi_1 + \Phi_2$$

Fig. 216 Relation between load and deflection.

lengths of the members are l_1 and l_2 (assumed for the present to be unequal), and the elongation of the members are e_1 and e_2. It is assumed that the relationship between S_1 and e_1 and that between S_2 and e_2 are known, but no restrictions are placed on these relationships except that they must be single valued, that is, for every value of S_1 there is only one value of e_1, etc.; otherwise there would not be a unique value for the strain energy. This restriction is of great importance primarily in dealing with inelastic deflections in which part of the deflection of a structure arises from inelastic strains in one or more members of the structure. This restriction means that after a member has been inelastically strained the force in this member cannot be allowed to decrease since the S-e relationship for unloading of such a member is different than that for loading.

Let the coordinates of the points on curve OD in Fig. 216b represent the unknown and desired pairs of corresponding values of the increasing magnitudes of H and δ_H as the truss in Fig. 216a is loaded. The problem is to obtain the energy theorem from which the relationship represented by the curve OD may be found.

By definition, the work W done by the force H as it increases to the value DE is

$$W = \int H \, d\delta_H \tag{496}$$

represented by the area under the curve OD in Fig. 216b.

Since the supports A and B are assumed to be rigid, the work W done by H is equal to the total energy transferred to the structure, and all the work W is expended in producing deformations in the structure. But, in accordance with the principle of conservation of energy, none of this energy is lost; it occurs in the structure as potential energy, usually designated as strain energy. If, then, U denotes the total strain energy in the structure, we may replace W by U, and hence Eq. 496 becomes

$$U = \int H \, d\delta_H \tag{497}$$

If now both sides of Eq. 497 are differentiated with respect to δ_H, the result is

$$H = dU/d\delta_H \tag{498}$$

If in addition to H there are other loads which do work on the structure such as a vertical force V (not shown) applied at C in Fig. 216a, the derivation of Eq. 498 would be substantially the same as the foregoing procedure except that partial differentiation would be used instead of total differentiation for the reason that each of the deflections δ_H and δ_V in the directions of H and V, respectively, would depend on both of the loads H and V. Therefore, the basic equation or theorem for obtaining the relation between any load and the deflection of its point of application in the direction of the load is

$$H = \partial U/\partial \delta_H \quad \text{or} \quad V = \partial U/\partial \delta_V \quad \text{etc.} \tag{499}$$

Note. A more detailed mathematical procedure for obtaining the results in Eq. 499 is as follows: Let two forces H and V be applied at C (Fig. 216), and let the resulting deflections of C in the direction of H and V be δ_H and δ_V. Each force will be a function of δ_H and δ_V. This fact will be emphasized by expressing the forces not as H and V alone but by the mathematical notation $H(\delta_H, \delta_V)$ and $V(\delta_H, \delta_V)$. Equations 496 and 497 for the two forces may then be written

$$W = \int_{(0,0)}^{(\delta_H, \delta_V)} [H(\delta_H, \delta_V) \, d\delta_H + V(\delta_H, \delta_V) \, d\delta_V] = U \tag{a}$$

The integral in Eq. a is a line integral because it represents the integral of the functions $H(\delta_H, \delta_V)$ and $V(\delta_H, \delta_V)$ along some path traveled by the point C in moving to its final position C'. Furthermore, in a conservative force system the value of the internal strain energy U does not depend upon the order in which the loads H and V are applied. Therefore, the line integral is said to be path independent and is an exact integral. The following equations are the necessary and sufficient conditions to insure that the integral of Eq. a shall be exact:

$$\partial U/\partial \delta_H = H \quad \text{and} \quad \partial U/\partial \delta_V = V$$

These are Eqs. 499. For a discussion of line integrals, see *Higher Mathematics for Engineers*, by I. S. and E. S. Sokolnikoff, published by the McGraw-Hill Book Co., 1941.

In the solution of many engineering problems it can be assumed that only elastic behavior of the members occurs, which implies that U is elastic strain energy and that the force system is conservative as required in the foregoing proof; this in turn implies that the force-deformation relationship is reversible and hence is single valued; this single-valued requirement is the essential or significant condition insured by specifying that the force system must be conservative. If, however, inelastic deformation occurs, the force system is not conservative, which means that the strain energy in the member is not recoverable and that the process is not reversible; but nevertheless the force-deformation relationship will be single valued provided that the inelastic deformation in any member is not accompanied by a decrease in the force in the member (no unloading of the member). This requirement therefore would permit the application of Eq. 499 to members subjected to inelastic deformation; such a member or structure would be analogous to a conservative system in that the force-deformation relationship would be single valued. The requirement that a member must not be permitted to unload will usually be satisfied in statically determinate members, but frequently in a statically indeterminate member unloading will occur as inelastic deformation is developed in the member, and in such cases Eq. 499 is not applicable.

The strain energy theorem expressed by Eqs. 498 and 499 may be stated in words as follows. As several loads are applied to a member or structure, let any one of the loads be denoted by P and its point of application by A; also let δ_{AP} denote the deflection of A in the direction of P. The value of the load P corresponding to any given value of δ_{AP} is equal to the partial derivative of the total internal strain energy U with respect to δ_{AP}.

The success in the use of Eq. 498 or 499 depends on the ease with which the energy U can be expressed in terms of δ_H, δ_V, etc., so that the differentiation of U with respect to δ_H, δ_V, etc., can be performed. The problem of expressing U in terms of the deflections is primarily a problem of geometry and involves considerable work, but the expressions are obtained in many problems without serious difficulties, provided that the deflections are relatively small so that the change in the original geometrical shape of the member or structure is negligible. This condition is usually satisfied since the deformations of the members, even if they are inelastic, are small relative to the dimensions of the structure.

Thus the expression for U for use in Eq. 499 can be found in terms of the forces (S) and deformations (e) in the members of the structure, provided that the relationship between S and e for each member is given, as is assumed in Figs. 216c and 216d. This relationship is usually known or can be obtained from experimental results for the material; but, as stated in the note in Art. 128, if the deformation involves inelastic behavior of the member, the relation between S and e must be obtained for increasing load S, and the member must not be allowed to unload as the inelastic deformation develops.

Thus, referring to Figs. 216c and 216d, we may write

$$U = U_1 + U_2 = \int S_1 \, de_1 + \int S_2 \, de_2 \qquad (500)$$

The theorem expressed by Eqs. 498 and 499 is explained further in the following illustrative problem.

Illustrative Problems

Problem 235. To illustrate the generality of the foregoing theorem or method, let the members AC and BC in Fig. 216a be made of a material whose stress-strain relationship in tension is $\sigma = E'(\epsilon)^n$. Then the relationship between the axial force S and the elongation e of each of the members AC and BC will be represented by the equation $S = (E'a/l^n)e^n$, in which a and l are the cross-sectional area and length of each member, E' is a constant whose dimensions are force per unit area, and n is a constant equal to, or less than, unity; the values of E' and n depend on the material. Let it be required to obtain, by use of the strain energy theorem, the relationship between H and δ_H. *Note*: A power law for expressing the relation between σ and ϵ or between S and e as suggested in this problem is sometimes useful. Observe that if $n = 1$ the relationship is a straight line which is a close approximation for most metal members subjected to elastic deformation. Also, when $n = 1$, E' becomes E, which is the modulus of elasticity of the material; if $n = \frac{1}{3}$, the relationship between S and e is a curve which approximates the behavior of certain polymers such as rubber, etc.

Solution. From Eq. 500 we compute the energy as follows:

$$U = 2\int_0^e S \, de = 2\frac{E'a}{l^n}\int_0^e e^n \, de = 2\frac{E'a}{(n+1)l^n}e^{n+1}$$

Equation 499 may now be written

$$H = \frac{\partial U}{\partial \delta_H} = 2\frac{E'a}{l^n}e^n\frac{de}{d\delta_H} \qquad (a)$$

It is evident that e must be expressed in terms of δ_H so that the derivative of e with respect to δ_H can be computed. If it is assumed in Fig. 216a that the change in the angle θ when C moves to C' can be neglected,[*] the elongation e in either member is found from geometry to be given by the expression $e = \delta_H \cos \theta$, and the differentiation of this equation gives $de/d\delta_H = \cos \theta$. Hence

$$H = 2E'a \cos \theta \left(\frac{\delta_H \cos \theta}{l} \right)^n$$

If $n = 1$
$$H = 2(Ea/l)\delta_H \cos^2 \theta$$

where E is the modulus of elasticity of the material. In the latter equation H and δ_H are related linearly, but, as already noted, this method is not restricted to problems in which the load and deflection are linearly related.

Problem 236. The truss shown in Fig. 217a has three steel members of equal length l and equal cross-sectional area a. The members are pin-connected at A, B,

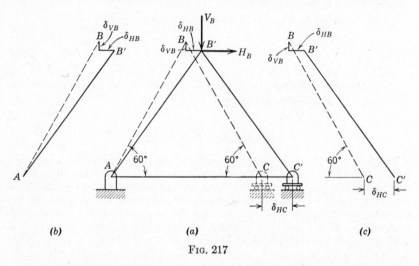

| (b) | (a) | (c) |

FIG. 217

and C by smooth pins so that AC is horizontal and AB and BC lie in a vertical plane. The truss is loaded at B by a vertical load V_B and a horizontal load H_B. If $l = 10$ ft, $a = 3$ sq in., $V_B = 4000$ lb, and $H_B = 10,000$ lb, compute the vertical and horizontal deflection δ_{VB} and δ_{HB}, respectively, at the point B by making use of the theorem expressed by Eq. 499.

[*] The exact expression relating e and δ_H as obtained from the geometry of Fig. 216a

is
$$e = \sqrt{(\delta_H + l \cos \theta)^2 + (l \sin \theta)^2} - l$$

This expression reduces to $e = \delta_H \cos \theta$ if δ_H is sufficiently small to justify neglecting the term δ_H^2. For relatively large deflections, however, such as might occur if members AC and BC were helical springs, the approximate solution might lead to appreciable error even though all members behaved elastically according to Hooke's law.

Solution. We must express U in terms of the elongations e_{AB}, e_{BC}, and e_{AC} of the members and various constants. Since the axial forces S resisted by the members produce stresses within the elastic range of the material, and the members are made of steel for which a linear relation exists between S and e, we can write

$$U = \tfrac{1}{2}S_{AB}\, e_{AB} + \tfrac{1}{2}S_{BC}\, e_{BC} + \tfrac{1}{2}S_{AC}\, e_{AC}$$

But, since the elongation of any member is $e = Sl/aE$, the foregoing expression may be written

$$U = \frac{1}{2}\frac{aE}{l} e^2{}_{AB} + \frac{1}{2}\frac{aE}{l} e^2{}_{BC} + \frac{1}{2}\frac{aE}{l} e^2{}_{AC} = \Sigma\, \frac{1}{2}\frac{aE}{l} e^2$$

In accordance with Eqs. 499 we must differentiate this equation with respect to δ_{HB} and δ_{VB}. Thus

$$H_B = \frac{\partial U}{\partial \delta_{HB}} = \frac{aE}{l} e_{AB}\frac{\partial e_{AB}}{\partial \delta_{HB}} + \frac{aE}{l} e_{BC}\frac{\partial e_{BC}}{\partial \delta_{HB}} + \frac{aE}{l} e_{AC}\frac{\partial e_{AC}}{\partial \delta_{HB}} = \Sigma\, \frac{aE}{l} e\frac{\partial e}{\partial \delta_{HB}} \quad (a)$$

$$V_B = \frac{\partial U}{\partial \delta_{VB}} = \frac{aE}{l} e_{AB}\frac{\partial e_{AB}}{\partial \delta_{VB}} + \frac{aE}{l} e_{BC}\frac{\partial e_{BC}}{\partial \delta_{VB}} + \frac{aE}{l} e_{AC}\frac{\partial e_{AC}}{\partial \delta_{VB}} = \Sigma\, \frac{aE}{l} e\frac{\partial e}{\partial \delta_{VB}} \quad (b)$$

The elongations e_{AB}, e_{BC}, and e_{AC} must be expressed in terms of δ_{VB} and δ_{HB} so that the indicated partial derivatives in these equations may be computed. For this purpose we refer to the geometry of Figs. 217b and 217c. From Fig. 217b it is seen that the deflection δ_{VB} tends to shorten AB by an amount $\delta_{VB}\cos 30°$, and δ_{HB} tends to lengthen AB by $\delta_{HB}\cos 60°$, if it is assumed that the change in slope of AB' from AB is negligibly small. Hence

$$e_{AB} = \delta_{HB}\cos 60° - \delta_{VB}\cos 30° = \tfrac{1}{2}\delta_{HB} - \tfrac{1}{2}\sqrt{3}\delta_{VB}$$

From Fig. 217c, in a similar manner, we see that δ_{VB} tends to shorten BC by $\delta_{VB}\cos 30°$, δ_{HB} to shorten BC by $\delta_{HB}\cos 60°$ and δ_{HC} to lengthen BC by $\delta_{HC}\cos 60°$. Therefore

$$e_{BC} = -\delta_{VB}\cos 30° - \delta_{HB}\cos 60° + \delta_{HC}\cos 60° = -\tfrac{1}{2}\sqrt{3}\delta_{VB} - \tfrac{1}{2}\delta_{HB} + \tfrac{1}{2}\delta_{HC}$$

and from Fig. 217a it is seen that $e_{AC} = \delta_{HC}$. When these values of elongations and the indicated partial derivatives are substituted in the foregoing equations for H_B and V_B and like terms collected, the result is

$$H_B = (aE/l)(\tfrac{1}{2}\delta_{HB} - \tfrac{1}{4}\delta_{HC})$$

$$V_B = (aE/l)(\tfrac{3}{2}\delta_{VB} - \tfrac{1}{4}\sqrt{3}\delta_{HC})$$

These two equations contain the deflection δ_{HC} in addition to the deflections δ_{HB} and δ_{VB}, which are the required quantities. Therefore we must write one additional equation before we can solve for the three unknown deflections. This is done by writing an equation like Eq. 499 for the horizontal force H_C at C (H_C is known to be zero, since the rollers at C are frictionless, and likewise, the vertical deflection at C is zero). This equation is

$$H_C = \frac{aE}{l} e_{AB}\frac{\partial e_{AB}}{\partial \delta_{HC}} + \frac{aE}{l} e_{BC}\frac{\partial e_{BC}}{\partial \delta_{HC}} + \frac{aE}{l} e_{AC}\frac{\partial e_{AC}}{\partial \delta_{HC}} = \Sigma\, \frac{aE}{l} e\frac{\partial e}{\partial \delta_{HC}} = 0$$

When the foregoing values of e_{AB}, e_{BC}, and e_{AC} and their partial derivatives with respect to δ_{HC} are substituted in this equation, it reduces to

$$H_C = (aE/l)(-\tfrac{1}{4}\sqrt{3}\ \delta_{VB} - \tfrac{1}{4}\delta_{HB} + \tfrac{5}{4}\delta_{HC}) = 0$$

The value of $aE/l = (3 \times 30 \times 10^6/120 = 750{,}000$ lb/in. is substituted in these equations, which reduce to

$$6\delta_{VB} - \sqrt{3}\ \delta_{HC} = \tfrac{16}{750}$$

$$2\delta_{HB} - \delta_{HC} = \tfrac{40}{750}$$

$$-\sqrt{3}\ \delta_{VB} - \delta_{HB} + 5\delta_{HC} = 0$$

The solution of these three simultaneous equations gives the following values for the deflections:

$$\delta_{VB} = 0.006 \text{ in.} \qquad \delta_{HB} = 0.031 \text{ in.} \qquad \delta_{HC} = 0.008 \text{ in.}$$

Note. Important conclusions should be drawn from the solution of this problem and of Prob. 235. In Prob. 235 only one joint of the truss was deflected and only one load caused the deflection (Fig. 216a), and therefore the computation of the deflection was simple. But in Prob. 236 two loads are applied and two joints are deflected, and it is important to observe that the solution resulted in three simultaneous equations which had to be solved to obtain any one or more of the desired values of the deflections. When only one deflection, such as δ_{VB} in Prob. 236 is needed, as is often the case, the strain energy method used in the foregoing problems requires considerably more labor than does the complementary energy method which is derived in the next article and used to solve both of the foregoing problems.

It should be observed, also, that the application of the strain energy method is not restricted to members in which the load-deformation relation is linear, and that a non-linear relationship may arise in two ways, namely, (a) as a result of deflections which change appreciably the geometry of the structure even though the deflections are relatively small and elastic, and (b) as a result of inelastic deformations of the members. However, as stated in the note in Art. 128, the force in the member must not decrease as the inelastic deformation in the member develops.

129   Second theorem: So-called complementary energy. The problem is the same as that stated in Art. 127, namely, to derive a relation between H and δ_H in Fig. 216a, but by this second method the result will be an equation expressing δ_H in terms of H and a function Φ which is expressed in the same units as is energy but which is not readily interpreted physically as energy. In Fig. 216e the curve OD is the same as in Fig. 216b; that is, coordinates of points on the curve represent the desired values of δ_H and H. In deriving this second theorem the area ODN above curve OD in Fig. 216e has special significance because it can be used for the purpose of deriving the desired equation. This area represents a quantity expressed in the same units as is work and will be called complementary work W_c. The value of the complementary work is given by the expression

$$W_c = \int \delta_H\, dH \tag{501}$$

The next step in the derivation of the theorem is similar to that taken in deriving the first theorem (Art. 128), namely, to replace W_c in Eq. 501 by a so-called complementary energy expression denoted by Φ which is equal to W_c and which is expressed in terms of the resisting force S and the deformation e in each member as was done in Art. 128 in replacing W in Eq. 496 by the stored energy U.

The expression for Φ for each member is obtained as follows. In Figs. 216f and 216g the curves OF and OJ are identical with those in Figs. 216c and 216d, respectively; that is, these curves represent the known relationship between the axial force S and the elongation e of each member. In Fig. 216f the area OFP represents the so-called complementary energy Φ_1. Thus Φ_1 is represented by the area OFP which is complementary to the area which represents the stored energy in member AC. Thus the expression for Φ_1 is

$$\Phi_1 = \int e_1 \, dS_1 \tag{502}$$

Similarly the complementary energy Φ_2 for BC is equal to the area OJQ which is given by the expression

$$\Phi_2 = \int e_2 \, dS_2 \tag{503}$$

The total complementary energy Φ is given by the sum of Eqs. 502 and 503:

$$\Phi = \Phi_1 + \Phi_2 = \int e_1 \, dS_1 + \int e_2 \, dS_2 \tag{504}$$

But for small deflections the complementary work W_c is equal * to the complementary energy Φ, and this equality of W_c and Φ corresponds to

---

* This fact is proved for one load, only, as follows. From the principle of conservation of energy, if we assume in Figs. 216c and 216d that the relationship between S_1 and e_1 is given by OPF instead of curve OF, and for S_2 and e_2 by OQJ instead of curve OJ, we can say that the area of rectangle $ONDE$ in Fig. 216b is equal to the sum of the rectangular areas $OPFG$ and $OQJM$ in Figs. 216c and 216d; that is,

$$H \, \delta_H = S_1 e_1 + S_2 e_2 \tag{a}$$

The truth of this statement is established by making use of the fact that the application of the principle of conservation of energy is not restricted by the shape of the curves OF and OJ representing the relationship between S_1 and e_1 and S_2 and e_2, except that they must be single valued. It follows then that under the stated conditions OND will represent the relation between δ_H and H, provided that the deformations of the members are small. If the deformation were not small, relatively large changes in the angle θ would occur and hence H could not remain constant as assumed, while S_1 and S_2 remain constant. Therefore with this restriction Eq. a is

the equality of W and U which was used in Art. 128 to derive Eqs. 498 and 499. Thus Eq. 501 may be written

$$\Phi = \int \delta_H \, dH \qquad (505)$$

If both sides of Eq. 505 are differentiated with respect to H, the result is

$$\delta_H = d\Phi/dH \qquad (506)$$

If in addition to H other loads are applied to the structure such as a vertical load V acting at C in Fig. 216a, the derivation of Eq. 506 could be presented in a manner similar to the foregoing procedure, but partial differentiation would be required instead of total differentiation for the reason that each of the deflections δ_H and δ_V depend on both of the loads H and V. Therefore, the basic equation or theorem for obtaining the relation between the deflection in the direction of the load at any point of the structure and the load acting at the point is

$$\delta_H = \partial\Phi/\partial H \qquad \text{or} \qquad \delta_V = \partial\Phi/\partial V \qquad \text{etc.} \qquad (507)$$

Each of these equations expresses the theorem of so-called complementary energy.

The facility with which Eqs. 507 can be used depends upon the ease with which Φ can be expressed in terms of the loads. For statically determinate members or structures this can usually be done without difficulties by making use of the equations of equilibrium, provided that the deflections are small so that the changes which occur in the angles between the members of the structure may be neglected.

true. By noting in Figs. 216b through 216g that $W + W_c = H\delta_H$, $U_1 + \Phi_1 = S_1 e_1$, and $U_2 + \Phi_2 = S_2 e_2$, respectively, Eq. a may be written in the form

$$W + W_c = U_1 + U_2 + \Phi_1 + \Phi_2 = U + \Phi$$

or

$$W - U = \Phi - W_c$$

and, since W is equal to U by the principle of conservation of energy, we have $\Phi = W_c$. It appears, therefore, that the complementary energy method is not restricted to members in which the load-deflection relationship is linear. However, the nonlinear relationship between any load and its deflection must be the result of nonlinear relations between S and e, such as occur for small plastic deformations, and not the result of large elastic deflections which cause a marked change in the geometry of the structure.

Illustrative Problems

Problem 237. Solve Prob. 235 by means of the complementary energy method or theorem.

Solution. First the expression for Φ will be found from Eq. 504, namely, $\Phi = 2\int e\,dS$. But e in this equation must be expressed in terms of S in order to evaluate the integral. The equation relating S and e is $e = l(S/aE')^{1/n}$. Therefore

$$\Phi = 2\int l\left(\frac{S}{aE'}\right)^{1/n} dS = 2\,\frac{n}{n+1}\,\frac{l}{(aE')^{1/n}}\,S^{(n+1)/n}$$

The theorem expressed by Eq. 506 may now be written

$$\delta_H = \frac{d\Phi}{dH} = 2l\left(\frac{S}{aE'}\right)^{1/n}\frac{dS}{dH}$$

But we note that S must be expressed in terms of H so that the derivative of S with respect to H can be computed. This is done by applying the equations of equilibrium to the forces acting on the pin C as shown in the free-body diagram of the pin. Thus in Fig. 216h

$$S = \frac{H}{2\cos\theta} \qquad \text{and hence} \qquad \frac{dS}{dH} = \frac{1}{2\cos\theta}$$

The substitution of these expressions in the foregoing equations gives the desired relation between δ_H and H which is

$$\delta_H = \frac{l}{\cos\theta}\left(\frac{H}{2aE'\cos\theta}\right)^{1/n}$$

This equation is the same as that found in Prob. 235, as will be seen if the equation in Prob. 496 is solved for δ_H. If in the foregoing equation $n = 1$, the result is

$$\delta_H = \frac{Hl}{2Ea\cos^2\theta}$$

where E is the modulus of elasticity of the material. In the latter equation H and δ_H are linearly related, but this theorem (and also the first theorem as noted in Prob. 496) is not restricted to problems in which the load and deflections are linearly related.

Problem 238. Solve for the vertical deflection δ_{VB} of the point B in Fig. 217a as described in Prob. 236 by making use of the complementary energy theorem.

Solution. We compute Φ by making use of Eq. 504 which for the truss in Fig. 216a is

$$\Phi = \int_0^{S_{AB}} e_{AB}\,dS_{AB} + \int_0^{S_{BC}} e_{BC}\,dS_{BC} + \int_0^{S_{AC}} e_{AC}\,dS_{AC}$$

in which the upper limits are the maximum or final values of S_{AB}, S_{BC}, etc.

From Prob. 236 we have $e_{AB} = S_{AB}l/aE$, etc. If these values of the elongation are substituted in the foregoing equation, the result is

$$\Phi = \frac{1}{2}\frac{S^2_{AB}\,l}{aE} + \frac{1}{2}\frac{S^2_{BC}\,l}{aE} + \frac{1}{2}\frac{S^2_{AC}\,l}{aE} = \Sigma\,\frac{1}{2}\frac{S^2 l}{aE}$$

We now differentiate both sides of this equation partially with respect to V_B as indicated by Eq. 507 which gives

$$\frac{\partial \Phi}{\partial V_B} = \delta_{VB} = \frac{S_{AB}\, l}{aE} \frac{\partial S_{AB}}{\partial V_B} + \frac{S_{BC}\, l}{aE} \frac{\partial S_{BC}}{\partial V_B} + \frac{S_{AC}\, l}{aE} \frac{\partial S_{AC}}{\partial V_B} = \Sigma \frac{Sl}{aE} \frac{\partial S}{\partial V_B}$$

But we note that the axial forces S in the members must be expressed in terms of the loads H_B and V_B so that the partial derivatives can be computed. This is done by making use of the equations of equilibrium. For this purpose free-body diagrams of joints B and C are drawn, and from the application of the equations of equilibrium to the forces on these joints the following equations for the axial forces in the members are obtained. It should be noted that the signs used are in accordance with the convention that the force S in any member is considered to be a tensile force if positive and a compressive force if negative. Thus

$$S_{AB} = H_B - \frac{1}{\sqrt{3}} V_B \qquad S_{BC} = -\frac{1}{\sqrt{3}} V_B - H_B \qquad S_{AC} = \frac{1}{2\sqrt{3}} V_B + \frac{1}{2} H_B$$

The partial differentiation of these equations with respect to V_B gives

$$\frac{\partial S_{AB}}{\partial V_B} = -\frac{1}{\sqrt{3}} \qquad \frac{\partial S_{BC}}{\partial V_B} = -\frac{1}{\sqrt{3}} \qquad \frac{\partial S_{AC}}{\partial V_B} = \frac{1}{2\sqrt{3}}$$

The foregoing values of S_{AB}, S_{BC}, and S_{AC} and their partial derivatives are substituted in the equation for δ_{VB} with the result that

$$\delta_{VB} = \frac{l}{aE} \left(\frac{3}{4} V_B + \frac{1}{4\sqrt{3}} H_B \right) =$$

$$\frac{120}{3 \times 30 \times 10^6} \left[\frac{3}{4} (4000) + \frac{1}{4\sqrt{3}} 10,000 \right] = 0.006 \text{ in.}$$

Problem 239. Compute the horizontal deflection δ_{HC} of the point C in the frame described in Prob. 236 and in Fig. 217a by means of the complementary energy theorem as expressed by Eq. 507.

Solution. The expression for the complementary energy Φ is the same as given in Prob. 238. We must differentiate Φ partially with respect to a horizontal load H_C at C to get the deflection δ_{HC}, and since there is no such load it is necessary to introduce a fictitious load H_C at C until the partial differentiation is completed, after which the value of H_C is set equal to zero. In other words we solve the problem as if an actual load H_C were applied and then substitute the particular value of H_C which in this problem is $H_C = 0$. By differentiating the expression for Φ in Prob. 238 we get

$$\frac{\partial \Phi}{\partial H_C} = \delta_{HC} = \frac{S_{AB}\, l}{aE} \frac{\partial S_{AB}}{\partial H_C} + \frac{S_{BC}\, l}{aE} \frac{\partial S_{BC}}{\partial H_C} + \frac{S_{AC}\, l}{aE} \frac{\partial S_{AC}}{\partial H_C} = \Sigma \frac{Sl}{aE} \frac{\partial S}{\partial H_C}$$

By drawing free-body diagrams of joints B and C showing the forces acting on these joints, including the fictitious load H_C at C, and applying the equations of equilibrium to these forces, we find the axial forces in the members to be

$$S_{AB} = H_B - \frac{1}{\sqrt{3}} V_B \qquad S_{BC} = -\frac{1}{\sqrt{3}} V_B - H_B \qquad S_{AC} = \frac{1}{2\sqrt{3}} V_B + \frac{1}{2} H_B + H_C$$

The partial derivatives with respect to H_C are

$$\partial S_{AB}/\partial H_C = 0 \qquad \partial S_{BC}/\partial H_C = 0 \qquad \partial S_{AC}/\partial H_C = 1$$

These values are substituted in the foregoing equation for δ_{HC} with the result that

$$\delta_{HC} = \frac{l}{aE}\left(\frac{1}{2\sqrt{3}}V_B + \frac{1}{2}H_B + H_C\right)$$

From this equation we can find the deflection δ_{HC} caused by any set of values of the loads V_B, H_B, and H_C (within the elastic range of the material). Since in this problem $V_B = 4000$ lb, $H_B = 10,000$ lb, and $H_C = 0$, we obtain

$$\delta_{HC} = \frac{120}{3 \times 30 \times 10^6}\left(\frac{1}{2\sqrt{3}}\,4000 + \frac{1}{2}\,(10,000) + 0\right) = 0.008 \text{ in.}$$

Problem

240. By means of the complementary energy method compute the elastic deflection of the joint at C in the direction of the load P in the truss in Fig. 218. The cross-sectional area of each member is $a = 5$ sq in., and the load $P = 10,000$ lb. Each member is made of steel.

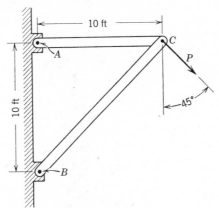

Fig. 218

130   Comparison of the two theorems. *Common Characteristics.* Both of the methods or theorems discussed in the preceding articles of this chapter for determining the load-deflection relationship for a member or structure which is in equilibrium make use of scalar quantities, namely, the strain energy U and the so-called complementary energy Φ. Likewise in both theorems a partial derivative of a scalar quantity is involved; in the strain energy theorem U is differentiated partially with respect to the deflection, and in the complementary energy theorem Φ is differentiated partially with respect to the load. These two scalar quantities are frequently called potentials or potential functions.

Both theorems are applicable to a member or a structure for which the load-deflection relationship is non-linear as well as linear, although the labor and difficulties encountered are usually much greater in the solution of a problem in which a non-linear relationship exists between a load and the deflection of its point of application than in the solution that involves a linear load-deflection relationship. If the non-linear relationship between loads and deflection is due to inelastic deformation, both theorems may be employed if a restriction is placed upon the forces in the member where the inelastic deformation occurs which states that these forces are not allowed to decrease and further that the inelastic deformation does not continue to increase with time (creep) if these forces are held constant.

In deriving both theorems it was assumed that certain ideal conditions existed, namely, that the joints of the pin-loaded structure made perfect fits, so that the structure was free from loose joints and also from initial internal forces, and that the supports were perfectly rigid so that no work was done by the reactions. Likewise it was assumed that no member was sufficiently slender to buckle when subjected to axial compressive loads.

These two theorems were derived by making use of a simple pin-connected, pin-loaded truss. However, it is shown in the next chapter that both theorems apply also to load-deflection relationships for the bending of beams subjected to either concentrated or distributed loads. Likewise it is shown that they apply to relationships between moments (couples) and angle changes at a section of a member subjected to bending or to torsion.

Essential Difference. The essential difference between the two methods or theorems can be stated briefly as follows: In the strain energy method U must first be expressed in terms of the deformations of the elements of a member or of the members of a structure, and finally in terms of the deflection of the member or structure. This procedure requires the use of the geometry of the deformations and deflections, and although the structure is in equilibrium the equations of equilibrium are not needed in this theorem. In the complementary energy theorem the quantity Φ must be expressed in terms of the forces in the members and finally in terms of the external loads. This procedure requires the use of the equations of equilibrium for determining the forces and no use is made of the geometry of the deformations. Thus the complementary energy theory may become cumbersome if the force systems involved are highly statically indeterminate. The strain energy method is not restricted in this way, which is of special importance in certain highly redundant members or structures as will be discussed briefly in Art. 159 (Chapter 16).

Ease in Application. The strain energy method usually requires more labor in its application for determining deflections than does the complementary energy method because, as was noted in the solution of Prob. 236, the strain energy method leads to the solution of a set of simultaneous equations for the deflection, and usually these equations contain more deflections than are required to be found in the problem. However, the strain energy method is especially useful in problems in which known deflections must be given to certain points of the member or structure, and the loads required to produce these deflections must be calculated. This method is also especially useful in dealing with highly redundant members, as will be shown in Chapter 16.

The complementary energy method is very useful in the solution of problems dealing with deflections of a wide range of members, machines, and structures, especially when the load-deflection relationships are linear. When the load and its deflection are linearly related, the complementary energy is equal to the strain energy, and this method leads to a theorem which was first formulated by Castigliano in 1879 and which has become widely known.

131 Castigliano's theorem. Castigliano's theorem states that, if external forces act on a member or structure which is subjected to deflections that are small and linearly related to the loads (as they occur in most load-resisting members stressed within the elastic limit of the material), the deflection, in the direction of any one of the forces, of the point of application of the force is equal to the partial derivative with respect to the force of the total internal strain energy in the member. Thus Castigliano's theorem is given by the expression

$$\partial U / \partial H = \delta_H \tag{508}$$

The truth of Eq. 508 is demonstrated by showing that it is a special case of Eq. 507. For the conditions stated in this theorem the relationships in Figs. 216c, 216d, 216f, and 216g between S_1 and e_1 and between S_2 and e_2 would be linear and hence the curves OF and OJ would be straight lines; for these conditions U_1 will be equal to Φ_1, and U_2 will be equal to Φ_2, and therefore U (the sum of U_1 and U_2) will be equal to Φ (the sum of Φ_1 and Φ_2). Hence Eqs. 507 can be rewritten as follows:

$$\partial U / \partial H = \delta_H \quad \text{and} \quad \partial U / \partial V = \delta_V \tag{509}$$

The use of Castigliano's theorem is illustrated in Chapter 14.

Another method of making use of the complementary energy theorem for conditions somewhat less restricted than those required by Castigliano's theorem is called the dummy load method. It is considered in Chapter 15.

132 Other methods. In addition to the two methods discussed in the foregoing articles there are two other general methods of considering the equilibrium of deformable bodies based on the principle of conservation of energy. These methods are frequently referred to in the literature on this subject as the method of minimum potential energy and the method of virtual displacements (or of virtual work); the two methods are related to each other. However, they are not used directly in this book.

Minimum Energy. In order to give, very briefly, the basic principle for this method, let it be assumed that a mechanical system consists of a member or structure and certain other bodies which are capable of exerting forces P_1, P_2, etc., on the structure. Let it be assumed that this system is isolated so that no energy is transferred into or out of the system as changes in the energy within the isolated system take place, thereby giving rise to the application of the forces P_1, P_2, etc., to the structure. This condition for an isolated mechanical system is satisfied approximately if the contacts with bodies outside the system considered consist of so-called rigid supports.

The principle of conservation of energy for such a system states that the potential energy in the system must remain constant. But the energy in the system may be considered to consist of two main parts, namely, the strain energy U in the member itself and the energy E that is available in the remaining part of the system associated with the external loads P_1, P_2, etc.; the energy E is sometimes called the potential energy of the loads. Thus the principle of conservation of energy of the isolated system is expressed by the equation

$$U + E = \text{Constant} \tag{510}$$

This statement means that, if part of the energy E is used in deforming the member or structure, the energy stored in the structure will increase so that the total energy will remain constant. Furthermore, the process is reversible, which means that if the structure is unloaded the energy U is transferred back to E.

Let δ_1, δ_2, etc., be the deflections of the member at the points of application and in the direction of the loads P_1, P_2, etc., respectively. If now U and E are each expressed in terms of these deflections, we can differentiate both sides of Eq. 510 partially with respect to the deflection as follows:

$$\partial(U + E)/\partial\delta_1 = 0, \text{ etc.} \tag{511}$$

Equation 511 has special significance because the zero value of the partial derivative indicates that the quantity $(U + E)$ is either a maximum or a minimum. From physical considerations it can be shown from Eqs. 510 and 511 that when the system is in a state of stable equilibrium the total energy $(U + E)$ is a minimum. It is important to note that the total energy in the system is a minimum and not the energy in the member alone; furthermore the minimum value of the total energy must be consistent with the conditions of equilibrium and continuity for the structure.

The connection between Eq. 511 and the condition of equilibrium may be seen by writing Eq. 511 in the form

$$(\partial U/\partial \delta_1) + (\partial E/\partial \delta_1) = 0 \tag{512}$$

But from Eq. 499 we obtain $\partial U/\partial \delta_1 = P_1$. It follows, therefore, from Eq. 512 that $\partial E/\partial \delta_1 = -P_1$, which makes Eq. 512 express a condition of equilibrium.

Virtual Displacements. The principle of virtual displacements is in effect a statement of Eq. 510 in terms of infinitesimal changes in the quantities U and E. We have seen that U increases at the expense of E (or vice versa). Thus in Eq. 510 if a small change ΔU occurs in U and a small change ΔE occurs in E we may write Eq. 510 in the following manner:

$$U + \Delta U + E - \Delta E = \text{Constant} \tag{513}$$

But, since $U + E = \text{constant}$, this equation may be written

$$\Delta U - \Delta E = 0 \qquad \text{or} \qquad \Delta U = \Delta E \tag{514}$$

which states that in an isolated system in equilibrium a small change in the strain energy U in the member or structure is accompanied by a change of equal magnitude in E.

The procedure or technique of using so-called virtual displacements in applying the foregoing idea is not discussed in this book.

Chapter 14

DEFLECTION OF MEMBERS AND SIMPLE STRUCTURES BY CASTIGLIANO'S THEOREM

133 Introduction. As noted in the preceding chapter, the deformation and deflections of load-resisting members of machines and structures are important in themselves and also in determining the forces and moments in statically indeterminate members and structures.

In this chapter the deflection of statically determinate members will first be found by Castigliano's theorem, and hence, as noted in Art. 131, we can consider only relatively small deformations and deflections that are linearly related to the forces acting on the members. But such deflections are of great importance in engineering problems involving load-resisting members.

The application of Castigliano's theorem for determining deflections will be considered in several steps. First the relation between deflection and loads will be found for a simple truss whose members are subjected only to axial forces. The load-deflection relationship will then be found for a member subjected to bending and shearing forces. Next, Castigliano's theorem will be modified for determining the relation between loads and angular deflection or rotation, which will be used for determining the rotation of a member in a truss, the change of slope at a section of a beam, and the angle of twist of a bar or shaft. Finally, the load-deflection and load-rotation relationships will be found for a member which is loaded in such a manner that each cross section is subjected to a combination of an axial force, a bending moment, a twisting moment, and a direct shearing force.

Applications of Castigliano's Theorem

134 Members subjected to axial forces. Let Fig. 219 represent a structure in which each member is subjected to an axial force at each end of the member. The external forces or loads acting on the structure are P_1, P_2, P_3, and Q, and the reactions of the supports at A and

438

G; it will be noted that the conventions used in Fig. 219 indicate that these reactions do no work on the structure. Let it be required to find by Castigliano's theorem the vertical deflection of the panel point C; it is assumed that the members are subjected only to linear elastic deformations and that no member buckles when subjected to compressive axial forces.

Castigliano's theorem (Art. 131, Chapter 13) states that if external forces (loads) act on a member or structure and cause small elastic deflections, the deflection of the point of application of the force

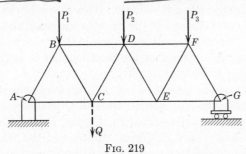

Fig. 219

in the direction of the force is equal to the partial derivative of the total internal strain energy U with respect to the force. That is,

$$\delta_Q = \partial U / \partial Q \tag{515}$$

where δ_Q is the deflection in the direction of Q of the point of application of Q. This furnishes a method of finding the elastic displacement of any point in a structure, although it would appear that only the deflection of points at which the loads are applied could be found. However, the deflection of any point due to any system of loads may be found by introducing a fictitious load at the point in question and writing the expression for the derivative of the strain energy with respect to the fictitious load at this point; such an expression will be valid for any magnitude of the fictitious force which will produce elastic deformation of the member and can, therefore, be made equal to zero after the differentiation.

The method of Castigliano as applied to the truss in Fig. 219 requires that the internal strain energy U be expressed in terms of the axial forces in each of the members and the constants a, E, and l for the member. The internal strain energy of any one member of the truss in Fig. 219 is $U_1 = \frac{1}{2}S_1 e_1$, but $e_1 = S_1 l_1 / a_1 E_1$, and hence $U_1 = \frac{1}{2}(S_1{}^2 l_1 / a_1 E_1)$. Therefore the total strain energy in all members is

$$U = \Sigma \frac{1}{2} \frac{S^2 l}{aE} \tag{516}$$

If both sides of Eq. 516 are differentiated partially with respect to Q and used with Eq. 515, the result is

$$\frac{\partial U}{\partial Q} = \Sigma \frac{Sl}{aE} \frac{\partial S}{\partial Q} = \delta_Q \qquad (517)$$

Physical Meaning of Terms. In Eq. 517 it should be noted that the quantity Sl/aE is the elongation of any member of the structure due to the actual external forces acting on the structure. The partial derivative $\partial S/\partial Q$ is interpreted physically as the rate at which the axial force in a member changes when Q changes. This rate is always linear if the deflections and angle changes of the member are small and hence it may be found as the change in S per unit change in Q; or as used in the dummy (unit) load method discussed in the next chapter it is the value of S caused by a value of Q equal to unity.

If in a truss, such as shown in Fig. 219, no load acts at the point C whose deflection is desired, a fictitious load Q is assumed to act at C. When this is done, the actual loads P_1, P_2, and P_3 and the reactions at A and G will usually have numerical values, and the axial forces S in the members are found in terms of Q and the numerical values of the actual loads by making use of the equations of equilibrium. However, in order to compute the partial derivative $\partial S/\partial Q$ in Eq. 517 for each member, the actual loads may or may not be given their numerical values, but the fictitious load Q (which finally will be made equal to zero) must be represented by the symbol Q, and the forces S are expressed in terms of Q and the values of the actual loads; the partial differentiation is then performed after which the actual value $Q = 0$ is introduced. This method is used in the following illustrative problem.

Illustrative Problem

Problem 241. A pin-connected truss, in which all members have the same length $l = 10$ ft and modulus of elasticity $E = 30,000,000$ lb per sq in., is loaded as shown in Fig. 220. Find the deflection of the panel point D: (a) in the horizontal direction, (b) in the vertical direction. The cross-sectional area a of each member is given in the table accompanying the solution of the problem.

Solution. (a) *Horizontal Deflection.* Since l_1 and E are the same for all members, Eq. 517 may be written as follows to obtain the horizontal deflection:

$$\delta_{P_1} = \frac{l}{E} \Sigma \frac{S}{a} \frac{\partial S}{\partial P_1}$$

The loads and reactions are shown in Fig. 220a. The axial forces S in the members as found by applying the equations of equilibrium (by either the method of joints or the method of sections) are tabulated in column 2 of the accompanying table, in which the computations are made for use in Eq. 517 or the foregoing equation. In

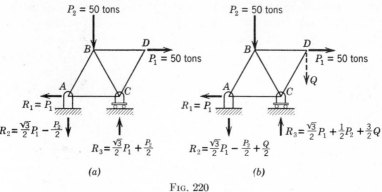

Fig. 220

this table the values of the loads P_1, P_2 are always positive, and the signs of the terms are taken so that when the actual values of P_1 and P_2 are substituted a positive force is tensile and a negative force is compressive.

COMPUTATIONS FOR HORIZONTAL MOVEMENT OF PANEL POINT OF TRUSS

Member	Axial Force S in Each Member Due to Loads	$\dfrac{\partial S}{\partial P_1}$	Cross Section a, in.^{2}	Product $\dfrac{S}{a}\dfrac{\partial S}{\partial P_1}$ When Values of Loads Are Substituted
AB	$P_1 - \dfrac{1}{\sqrt{3}}P_2$	1	2.5	$17{,}000$
AC	$\dfrac{1}{2}P_1 + \dfrac{1}{2\sqrt{3}}P_2$	$\dfrac{1}{2}$	4.5	$8{,}750$
BC	$-P_1 - \dfrac{1}{\sqrt{3}}P_2$	-1	12.0	$13{,}100$
BD	P_1	1	6.0	$16{,}670$
CD	0	0	6.0	0

$$\Sigma\frac{S}{a}\frac{\partial S}{\partial P_1} = 55{,}520$$

Therefore the horizontal deflection is

$$\delta_{P_1} = \frac{l}{E}\Sigma\frac{S}{a}\frac{\partial S}{\partial P_1} = \frac{120 \times 55{,}520}{30{,}000{,}000} = 0.22 \text{ in.}$$

(b) *Vertical Deflection.* Since there is no vertical force at D, we must introduce a fictitious load Q at this point as shown in Fig. 220b. The vertical deflection δ_Q of the point D, as given by Eq. 517, is

$$\delta_Q = \frac{l}{E} \Sigma \frac{S}{a} \frac{\partial S}{\partial Q}$$

The computations necessary for applying this equation are given in the accompanying table.

COMPUTATIONS FOR VERTICAL MOVEMENT OF PANEL POINT OF TRUSS

Member	Axial Force S in Each Member Due to All Loads, Including Q	$\dfrac{\partial S}{\partial Q}$	Cross Section a, in.^{2}	Product $\dfrac{S}{a}\dfrac{\partial S}{\partial Q}$ When Values of All Loads, Including $Q = 0$, Are Substituted
AB	$P_1 - \dfrac{1}{\sqrt{3}}P_2 + \dfrac{1}{\sqrt{3}}Q$	$\dfrac{1}{\sqrt{3}}$	2.5	9800
AC	$\dfrac{1}{2}P_1 + \dfrac{1}{2\sqrt{3}}P_2 - \dfrac{1}{2\sqrt{3}}Q$	$-\dfrac{1}{2\sqrt{3}}$	4.5	-5050
BC	$-P_1 - \dfrac{1}{\sqrt{3}}P_2 - \dfrac{1}{\sqrt{3}}Q$	$-\dfrac{1}{\sqrt{3}}$	12.0	7600
BD	$P_1 + \dfrac{1}{\sqrt{3}}Q$	$\dfrac{1}{\sqrt{3}}$	6.0	9600
CD	$\dfrac{2}{\sqrt{3}}Q$	$\dfrac{2}{\sqrt{3}}$	6.0	0

$$\Sigma \frac{S}{a} \frac{\partial S}{\partial Q} = 21,950$$

Therefore the vertical deflection is

$$\delta_Q = \frac{l}{E} \Sigma \frac{S}{a} \frac{\partial S}{\partial Q} = \frac{120 \times 21,950}{30,000,000} = 0.09 \text{ in.}$$

With the conventions used for signs, it is apparent that the plus sign of each of these values of deflection indicates a movement having the same direction and sense as the applied forces P_1 and Q, respectively. A negative sign would mean that the deflection is in the same direction as the force but is opposite in sense.

135 Elastic deflection of beam. Let Fig. 221 represent a simply supported straight beam resting on rigid supports and subjected to loads P_1, P_2, and P_3. Let it be required to find the vertical elastic (small) deflection of the point C by means of Castigliano's theorem. At point C let a fictitious load Q be applied in the direction of the desired deflection δ_Q of point C. From Castigliano's theorem

$$\delta_Q = \partial U / \partial Q \tag{518}$$

in which U is equal to the total elastic strain energy in the beam due to the work done by the loads P_1, P_2, P_3 and Q (the reactions do no work).

The strain energy U in Eq. 518 is obtained by considering the beam

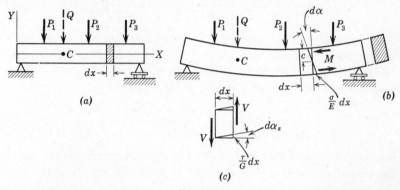

(a)

(b)

(c)

Fig. 221

to be made of elements or differential portions of length dx, as indicated in Fig. 221a, and obtaining the sum of the energies in the elements. The internal moment or couple at any section of the element dx due to all the loads, including Q, is M, as shown in Fig. 221b. This moment causes one face of the element dx to rotate through an angle $d\alpha$ with respect to the other face, and hence the internal work or strain energy U_{dx} done by M is $\frac{1}{2}M\,d\alpha$. Since the angular deformation $d\alpha$ is considered to be small, we may write

$$d\alpha = \tan d\alpha = \frac{(\sigma/E)\,dx}{c}$$

where σ is the stress in the fiber at the distance c from the neutral axis, caused by the actual loads. But $\sigma = Mc/I$; hence

$$d\alpha = (M/EI)\,dx \tag{519}$$

It should be noted that in Eq. 519 the quantity M/EI is the rotation of one face relative to the other of an elemental block one unit in length. This quantity is sometimes called the angle change per unit length of the beam. From Eq. 519 the strain energy in an element of the length dx is found to be

$$U_{dx} = \frac{1}{2} M \, d\alpha = \frac{1}{2} \frac{M^2 \, dx}{EI} \qquad (520)$$

If now the element beginning at the left support is designated as dx_1, the next as dx_2, etc., for the full length of the beam, the total strain energy U in the beam as a result of all the loads, including Q, is given by the expression

$$U = \frac{1}{2} \frac{M_1{}^2}{EI} \, dx_1 + \frac{1}{2} \frac{M_2{}^2}{EI} \, dx_2 + \cdots = \frac{1}{2} \int \frac{M^2}{EI} \, dx \qquad (521)$$

The summation is represented by the integral because there are an infinite number of elements. The deflection δ_Q is obtained by partial differentiation of both sides of Eq. 521 with respect to the fictitious load Q which results, from Eq. 518, in the equation

$$\delta_Q = \frac{\partial U}{\partial Q} = \frac{M_1}{EI} \frac{\partial M_1}{\partial Q} \, dx_1 + \frac{M_2}{EI} \frac{\partial M_2}{\partial Q} \, dx_2 + \cdots = \int \frac{M}{EI} \frac{\partial M}{\partial Q} \, dx \quad (522)$$

It should be noted that in Eq. 522 the integral represents the sum of the partial derivatives of the energy in each element dx of the beam and that, since the differentiation is with respect to Q instead of x, the differentiation does not remove the integral sign.

It should also be noted that in Eq. 522 if the expression for M or if the value of E or I changes for different portions of the beam the integral has to be replaced by several integrals, each of which applies to a different portion of the beam. For such a beam Eq. 522 is written in the form

$$\delta_Q = \frac{\partial U}{\partial Q} = \int \frac{M_1}{E_1 I_1} \frac{\partial M_1}{\partial Q} \, dx + \int \frac{M_2}{E_2 I_2} \frac{\partial M_2}{\partial Q} \, dx + \cdots \qquad \text{etc.} \quad (522a)$$

In Eqs. 522 and 522a the term M/EI is the angle change per unit length of beam at any section, and the partial derivative is the rate at which the bending moment at the section changes with changes in Q.

Equations 522 and 522a apply to straight, flexural members whose lengths are large relative to their depths so that bending is the primary cause of the deflection. If the beam is relatively short and deep, the deflection due to vertical shearing forces acting on each element dx, which have been neglected in Eqs. 522 and 522a, may produce an additional deflection at C which is not negligible.

Deflection of Beam Due to Shear. The deflection of the beam at the point C resulting from vertical shearing forces V on the elements dx, as shown in Fig. 221c, is found by Castigliano's theorem in a manner similar to the method used in deriving Eqs. 522 and 522a. An approximate expression for the energy U due to direct shear is

$$U_s = \int \frac{1}{2} \frac{V^2}{Ga} \, dx \qquad (523)$$

Hence

$$\delta_Q = \frac{\partial U_s}{\partial Q} = \int \frac{V}{Ga} \frac{\partial V}{\partial Q} \, dx \qquad (523a)$$

in which G is the shearing modulus of elasticity and a is the cross-sectional area of the beam. The shearing stress τ on any vertical section of the element dx is taken as the average value over the depth of the beam, that is, $\tau = V/a$ in the derivation of Eq. 523. If the value of V, G, or a changes for different portions of the beam, Eq. 523a becomes

$$\delta_Q = \int \frac{V_1}{G_1 a_1} \frac{\partial V_1}{\partial Q} \, dx + \int \frac{V_2}{G_2 a_2} \frac{\partial V_2}{\partial Q} \, dx + \cdots \qquad \text{etc.} \qquad (523b)$$

The deflection obtained by Eq. 523 or 523a is added to the deflection from Eq. 522 or 522a to obtain the total deflection of the beam at the point. Usually, except for relatively short, deep beams, the deflection caused by shear may be neglected without introducing serious error. However, in some beams it is of importance.

Illustrative Problems

Problem 242. Find by Castigliano's theorem the maximum deflection δ_P of a simple beam of span l and constant cross section subjected to a concentrated load P at the center of the span.

Solution. As indicated in Fig. 222, let the origin of axes be taken at the left support. Then the expressions for M are

$$M = \frac{P}{2} x, \text{ for } x = 0 \text{ to } x = \frac{l}{2}$$

$$M = \frac{P}{2} x - P\left(x - \frac{l}{2}\right), \text{ for } x = \frac{l}{2} \text{ to } x = l$$

$R_1 = \dfrac{P}{2}$ Fig. 222

$$U = \frac{1}{2} \int \frac{M^2 \, dx}{EI} = \frac{1}{2EI} \int_0^{l/2} \left(\frac{Px}{2}\right)^2 dx + \frac{1}{2EI} \int_{l/2}^{l} \left[\frac{P}{2}(l - x)\right]^2 dx$$

But since both halves of the beam are in the same state of stress, U is expressed more simply as follows:

$$U = 2\left(\frac{1}{2EI}\right) \int_0^{l/2} \left(\frac{Px}{2}\right)^2 dx = \frac{1}{96} \frac{P^2 l^3}{EI}$$

Therefore

$$\delta_P = \frac{\partial U}{\partial P} = \frac{1}{96} \frac{2Pl^3}{EI} = \frac{1}{48} \frac{Pl^3}{EI}$$

Problem 243. Find the vertical deflection of the free end of a cantilever beam of length l subjected to a single concentrated load at the distance l_1 from the free end (Fig. 223). Use Castigliano's theorem.

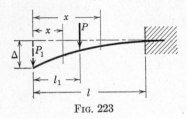

FIG. 223

Solution. No load is acting at the free end; hence a fictitious vertical load P_1 is assumed to act. Let Δ represent the deflection of the free end. Then we have by Eq. 522

$$\Delta = \int \frac{M}{EI} \frac{\partial M}{\partial P_1} dx$$

Expressions for M are

$M = P_1 x$, for $x = 0$ to $x = l_1$, and hence $\partial M/\partial P_1 = x$

$M = P_1 x + P(x - l_1)$, for $x = l_1$ to $x = l$, and hence $\partial M/\partial P_1 = x$

Thus the above expression for Δ becomes

$$\Delta = \int_0^{l_1} \frac{P_1 x}{EI} x \, dx + \int_{l_1}^l \frac{1}{EI} [P_1 x + P(x - l_1)x] \, dx$$

Now let P_1 be made equal to zero; then all terms containing P_1 will vanish, and hence

$$\Delta = \frac{1}{EI} \int_{l_1}^l P(x - l_1)x \, dx = \frac{1}{EI} \left[\frac{1}{3} P(l^3 - l_1^3) - \frac{Pl_1}{2}(l^2 - l_1^2) \right]$$

Problem 244. A half-ring is fixed at one end and loaded by a force P at the other end as shown in Fig. 224. The ring has a constant cross section, and the depth of the ring is small compared to the radius R. Find the horizontal deflection δ_P of the free end of the beam by Castigliano's theorem.

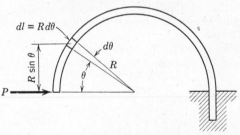

FIG. 224

Solution. The expressions for M, $\partial M/\partial P$, and dx to be used in Eq. 522 are

$$M = PR \sin \theta \qquad \partial M/\partial P = R \sin \theta \qquad dx = R \, d\theta$$

$$\delta_P = \int \frac{M}{EI} \frac{\partial M}{\partial P} dx = \frac{1}{EI} \int_0^\pi PR^3 \sin^2 \theta \, d\theta = \frac{PR^3}{EI} \left[\frac{\theta}{2} - \frac{1}{4} \sin 2\theta \right]_0^\pi = \frac{PR^3}{EI} \cdot \frac{\pi}{2}$$

136 Rotation at a section in a member or structure. In Chapter 13 the strain energy theorem and the complementary energy theorem were derived for finding the deflection of the joint of a pin-connected truss. Similar theorems involving the moments of forces can be derived for finding the rotation of any member of a truss and for finding the change in slope at any section in a beam, or for finding the angle of twist of a member subjected to a torsional moment, etc.

Rotation of Member of Truss. Let Fig. 225a represent a truss loaded as shown by a couple whose moment is C which consists of the forces C/l applied at joints F and G. Figure 225b shows the rotation θ_C of the

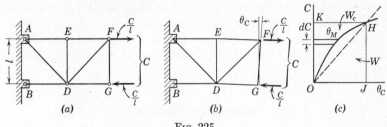

Fig. 225

member FG caused by the couple C. Let it be assumed that the rotation θ_C is small and that the relationship between C and θ_C up to the final value of C is represented by a curve (unknown) shown by OH in Fig. 225c. The complementary work of the couple C is represented by the area OKH in Fig. 225c and is given by the equation

$$W_c = \int \theta_C \, dC \qquad (524)$$

But the complementary energy Φ of the truss is equal to W_c, and hence

$$\Phi = \int \theta_C \, dC \qquad (525)$$

By differentiating both sides of Eq. 525 we have

$$d\Phi/dC = \theta_C \qquad (526)$$

If additional loads are applied at other joints of the truss in Fig. 225a, the rotation θ_C of member FG due to all the loads, including C, is given by Eq. 526, but since there are loads besides C the differentiation of Φ is partial so that Eq. 526 becomes

$$\theta_C = \partial\Phi/\partial C \qquad (527)$$

If in Fig. 225c the relationship between C and θ_C is linear, as indicated by the straight line OH, the complementary work W_c is equal to the work W, and consequently $\Phi = U$ and Eq. 527 is written

$$\theta_C = \frac{\partial U}{\partial C} \qquad (528)$$

Equation 528 is Castigliano's theorem for determining rotations. It can be used for any member or structure loaded by forces and couples that produce small rotations that are linearly related to the forces as is true in general for elastic strains in the member or structure. Its use is characterized by the fact that a couple must be applied at the section of the member or truss at which the rotation is desired. If no couple is located at the section, a fictitious couple C is applied and, after the differentiation with respect to C, as indicated in Eq. 528, the value of C is set equal to zero.

Illustrative Problem

Problem 245. The pin-connected truss shown in Fig. 226 has 5-ton vertical loads at joints E and F. Find the rotation of the member DF by using Castigliano's theorem. The cross-sectional area $a = 2$ sq in. for each member and is large enough

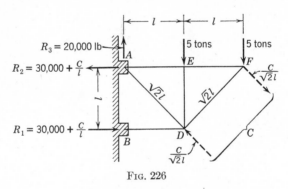

Fig. 226

to insure that the stress is below the elastic limit of the material. The length l and the least radius of gyration of the cross-sectional area are such that the members subjected to axial compression will not buckle. $E = 30,000,000$ lb per sq in.

Solution. A fictitious couple C is applied to the truss by placing a load $C/\sqrt{2}\,l$ perpendicular to DF at D and an equal load at F as shown in Fig. 226. The value of the strain energy U in the members is given by the equation

$$U = \Sigma \frac{1}{2}\frac{S^2}{aE}$$

and hence, by Eq. 528,

$$\theta_C = \frac{\partial U}{\partial C} = \Sigma \frac{Sl}{aE}\frac{\partial S}{\partial C} = \frac{1}{aE}\Sigma Sl \frac{\partial S}{\partial C}$$

The quantity $1/aE$ is factored out since a and E are constants for all the members. The values of S are the axial forces in all the members caused by all the external forces acting on the structure and are found from the equations of equilibrium. The results of these computations are given in the accompanying table. The partial derivatives of S with respect to C are also given. The products of S, l, and $\partial S/\partial C$ after C is set equal to zero are given in the last column of the table.

COMPUTATION OF ANGLE THROUGH WHICH MEMBER OF TRUSS ROTATES

Member	Axial Force S in Each Member Due to All Loads, Including Couple C	$\dfrac{\partial S}{\partial C}$	Product $Sl\dfrac{\partial S}{\partial C}$ with $C = 0$
AE	$10{,}000 + C/l$	$1/l$	$+10{,}000$
AD	$28{,}300$	0	0
BD	$-30{,}000 - C/l$	$-1/l$	$+30{,}000$
DE	$-10{,}000$	0	0
EF	$10{,}000 + C/l$	$1/l$	$+10{,}000$
DF	$-14{,}140 - 0.707\,C/l$	$-0.707/l$	$+14{,}140$

$$\Sigma\, Sl\,\frac{\partial S}{\partial C} = 64{,}140 \text{ lb}$$

$$\theta_C = \frac{1}{aE}\,\Sigma\, Sl\,\frac{\partial S}{\partial C} = \frac{64{,}140}{2 \times 30 \times 10^6} = 0.00107 \text{ radian}$$

137 Rotation of section of beam. Change in slope. In Fig. 227 let it be required to find the change in slope of section AA of the

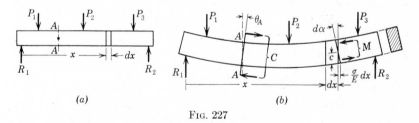

(a)   (b)

FIG. 227

beam caused by all the external forces acting on the beam. The section AA rotates through an angle θ_A as shown in Fig. 227b, and this angle is also the change in slope to the elastic curve of the beam at the section of the beam. A fictitious couple C is applied at section AA in addition to the loads P_1, P_2, and P_3 and reactions R_1 and R_2. The strain energy U in the beam when subjected to all the external forces, including C, is found by obtaining the sum of strain energy U_{dx} for all the elements dx, just as was done in Art. 135. The resulting equation is

$$U = \int \frac{1}{2} \frac{M^2}{EI} dx \tag{529}$$

By making use of Eq. 528 the change of slope θ_A is found by partial differentiation of both sides of Eq. 529 with respect to the couple C. Thus

$$\theta_A = \frac{\partial U}{\partial C} = \int \frac{M}{EI} \frac{\partial M}{\partial C} dx \tag{530}$$

In Eq. 530 if M, E, or I changes for different portions of the beam, the expression for θ_A becomes

$$\theta_A = \int \frac{M_1}{E_1 I_1} \frac{\partial M_1}{\partial C} dx + \int \frac{M_2}{E_2 I_2} \frac{\partial M_2}{\partial C} dx + \cdots \qquad \text{etc.} \quad (530a)$$

Illustrative Problems

Problem 246. Find the slope at the free end of a cantilever beam that carries a concentrated load P at the free end (Fig. 228).

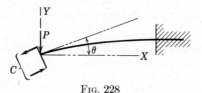

Fɪɢ. 228

Solution. According to Eq. 530 the change of slope θ at any section is the partial derivative of the total strain energy U with respect to the couple applied at the section. Since no couple acts at the end section, one must be introduced. Let it be denoted by C (Fig. 228). Then

$$\theta = \frac{\partial U}{\partial C} = \frac{\partial}{\partial C} \int \frac{1}{2} \frac{M^2 \, dx}{EI} = \int_0^l \frac{M}{EI} \frac{\partial M}{\partial C} dx$$

$$M = C + Px \qquad \text{and} \qquad \partial M / \partial C = 1$$

Hence

$$\theta = \int_0^l \frac{(C + Px)}{EI} \cdot 1 \cdot dx = \frac{Cl + (Pl^2/2)}{EI}$$

Now, making $C = 0$, we have

$$\theta = \tfrac{1}{2} \, (Pl^2/EI)$$

Problem 247. Find the change of slope of the section over the right support of the beam shown in Fig. 229 which rests on rigid supports at A and B and carries a uniformly distributed load of w per unit length. The reactions R_1 and R_2 of the supports are caused by the distributed load.

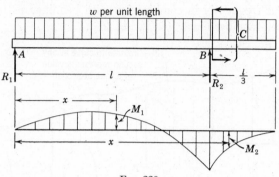

FIG. 229

Solution. We introduce a fictitious couple C at the section over the right support. The change in slope θ at this section is found by use of Eq. 530a. As applied to this beam it gives

$$\theta = \int_0^l \frac{M_1}{EI} \frac{\partial M_1}{\partial C} dx + \int_l^{4l/3} \frac{M_2}{EI} \frac{\partial M_2}{\partial C} dx$$

where M_1 is the moment at any section between supports, and M_2 is the moment at sections in the overhanging part as shown in Fig. 229. The expressions for M_1 and M_2 are

$$M_1 = \left(R_1 + \frac{C}{l} \right) x - \frac{wx^2}{2}$$

$$M_2 = \left(R_1 + \frac{C}{l} \right) x - \frac{wx^2}{2} + \left(R_2 - \frac{C}{l} \right)(x - l) - C$$

Thus $\partial M_1/\partial C = + x/l$ and $\partial M_2/\partial C = 0$

Therefore $\theta = \dfrac{1}{EI} \displaystyle\int_0^l \left[\left(R_1 + \frac{C}{l} \right) x - \frac{wx^2}{2} \right] \frac{x}{l} dx = \dfrac{1}{EI} \left[\dfrac{(R_1 + C)l^2}{3} - \dfrac{wl^3}{8} \right]$

But since the couple C is actually equal to zero, the change in slope is

$$\theta = \frac{1}{EI} \left(\frac{R_1 l^2}{3} - \frac{wl^3}{8} \right)$$

138 Angle of twist of cylindrical bar subjected to torsion. The angle of twist of a circular shaft caused by a torsional moment may be found by the same procedure as that used in Art. 137 in obtaining the change in slope at a section of a beam provided that the conditions

of small, elastic strains are imposed. Thus, in Fig. 230 let it be required
to find the angle of twist θ_A at section A due to a varying torsional
moment T as indicated by the ordinates to the curve above the shaft.
A variable torque or twisting moment is seldom encountered alone, but
it does occur frequently in combination with bending, as, for example,
in the curved member illustrated in Fig. 233.

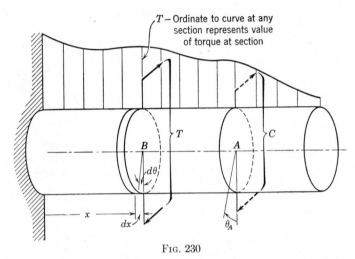

T – Ordinate to curve at any
section represents value
of torque at section

FIG. 230

According to Castigliano's theorem (Eq. 528) the angle of twist at
section A is given by the equation

$$\theta_A = \partial U / \partial C \qquad (531)$$

in which C is a fictitious torsional couple applied at section A, and U is
the strain energy in the shaft as a result of the application of all the
external forces, including C, to the member.

We must now derive the expression for the strain energy U. For this
purpose let the shaft be thought of as being made up of thin circular
disks of length dx as shown at section B, whose distance from the fixed
end is x. The twisting moment T in the element or disk causes the
right face of the disk at B to rotate through a small angle $d\theta$ relative to
the left face. Let the strain energy in the disk be represented by U_{dx}.
Then, since $d\theta$ is directly proportional to T within the elastic limit of
the material,

$$U_{dx} = \tfrac{1}{2} T \, d\theta \qquad (532)$$

But from elementary theory it is known that the angle of twist of a
cylindrical bar of length l subjected to a constant twisting moment T is

$\theta = Tl/JG$. Since T may be considered as constant over the length dx, it follows that

$$d\theta = \frac{T\,dx}{JG} \tag{533}$$

The substitution of this value of $d\theta$ in Eq. 532 gives

$$U_{dx} = \frac{1}{2}\frac{T^2\,dx}{JG} \tag{534}$$

The total strain energy U is equal to the sum of the values of U_{dx} for all differential lengths dx, and hence

$$U = \int \frac{1}{2}\frac{T^2\,dx}{JG} \tag{535}$$

By differentiating both sides of Eq. 535 with respect to the fictitious couple C and making use of Eq. 531, we have

$$\theta_A = \int \frac{T}{JG}\frac{\partial T}{\partial C}\,dx \tag{536}$$

In Eq. 536 if T, J, or G changes for different portions of the shaft, the expression for θ_A becomes

$$\theta_A = \int \frac{T_1}{J_1 G_1}\frac{\partial T_1}{\partial C}\,dx + \int \frac{T_2}{J_2 G_2}\frac{\partial T_2}{\partial C}\,dx + \cdots \qquad \text{etc.} \tag{537}$$

Illustrative Problems

Problem 248. As indicated in Fig. 231, a cylindrical bar of length $\pi/2$ ft is rigidly fixed at one end and subjected to a variable twisting moment as indicated by the ordinates to the curve $T = T_0 \cos x$. Find the angle of twist θ of the free end of the shaft.

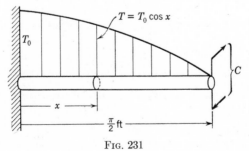

FIG. 231

Solution. We introduce a fictitious twisting couple C at the free end which has the same sense as the torque T. The twisting moment at any section is

$$T = T_0 \cos x + C$$

and hence

$$\partial T / \partial C = 1$$

Therefore from Eq. 536

$$\theta = \int_0^{\pi/2} \frac{T}{JG} \frac{\partial T}{\partial C} dx = \frac{1}{JG} \int_0^{\pi/2} (T_0 \cos x + C) \, dx = \frac{1}{JG} \left(T_0 + \frac{\pi}{2} C \right)$$

But $C = 0$. Therefore

$$\theta = T_0 / JG$$

Problem 249. The radius of a shaft of circular cross section changes gradually in accordance with a taper as shown in Fig. 232. The shaft tapers from its fixed end to a cross section of radius r_1 at its free end. If it were extended with the same taper a distance b from its free end, the radius r_1 would then be zero. The shaft is subjected to a single twisting moment T_0 at its free end. Find the angle of twist θ at the free end.

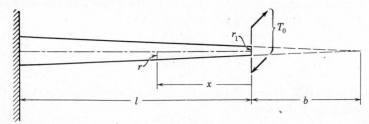

FIG. 232

Solution. The twisting moment T at any section a distance x from the free end is $T = T_0$. Since there is already a twisting couple at the free end, there is no need to introduce a fictitious couple C; that is, in using Eq. 536 we differentiate with respect to T_0. Hence $\partial T / \partial T_0 = 1$, and the value of θ is

$$\theta = \int_0^l \frac{T}{JG} \frac{\partial T}{\partial T_0} dx = \int_0^l \frac{T_0}{JG} dx$$

But J is not constant, since the radius r depends upon the distance x. The value of r is found from similar triangles to be $r = r_1(b + x)/b$ and therefore

$$J = \frac{\pi r^4}{2} = \frac{\pi r_1^4}{2b^4} (b + x)^4$$

Thus $\quad \theta = \frac{2b^4 T_0}{\pi r_1^4 G} \int_0^l \frac{dx}{(b + x)^4} = -\frac{2}{3} \frac{b^4 T_0}{\pi r_1^4 G} \left[\frac{1}{(b + x)^3} \right]_0^l = \frac{2}{3} \frac{b^4 T_0}{\pi r_1^4 G} \left[\frac{1}{b^3} - \frac{1}{(b + l)^3} \right]$

139 Deflection and angle of twist of member subjected to bending and twisting loads. Frequently a member is subjected to loads which produce at any cross section a bending moment and a twisting moment. Sometimes, also, a direct axial load and a direct shearing load may occur on the same section with the bending and twisting moments. The method of finding the deflection and angle of twist or change of slope will be the same, regardless of what combinations of loads are applied to the member, and hence only deflection is discussed here. However, the use of the method for finding angle changes is demonstrated in an illustrative problem.

Deflection. For the purpose of illustrating the method, let it be required to find the deflection of the free end of a cylindrical rod bent into a quarter circle of radius R as shown in Fig. 233a. The rod is fixed at

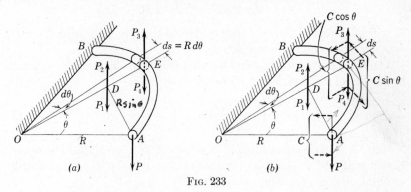

(a)   (b)

Fig. 233

one end B and is loaded at the free end A by a concentrated force P that is perpendicular to the plane AOB of the quarter circular arc.

The deflection is found by Castigliano's theorem from the equation

$$\delta_A = \partial U/\partial P \tag{538}$$

We must therefore find the expression for the total strain energy U in the member. In Fig. 233a let E be any cross section of the rod, let θ be the angle subtended by the arc AE, and let a differential length ds of the rod at section E subtend the angle $d\theta$. In order to obtain the bending moment and twisting moment for the section E, a perpendicular AD is drawn to OE and the load P is transformed, for convenience, into a force $P_1 = P$ at D and the couple PP_2, which is the bending moment at section E. Likewise the force P_1 at D is transformed into the force $P_4 = P_1$ at E and the couple P_1P_3, which is the twisting moment at section E. Now the moment arm of the bending couple PP_2 is $AD = R$ sin θ, and the moment arm of the twisting couple P_1P_3 is $DE = R(1 - \cos\theta)$. Hence, at any section,

$$\text{Bending moment} = M = PR \sin \theta$$
$$\text{Twisting moment} = T = PR(1 - \cos \theta) \tag{539}$$

From Eqs. 520 and 534 the strain energy U_{ds} absorbed by the element
of length ds, which is here considered as a straight cylindrical element
because the radius r of its cross section is small in comparison with R, is

$$U_{ds} = \frac{1}{2} \frac{M^2}{EI} ds + \frac{1}{2} \frac{T^2}{JG} ds \tag{540}$$

and the total strain energy for the whole rod is

$$U = \int_0^l \frac{1}{2} \frac{M^2}{EI} ds + \int_0^l \frac{1}{2} \frac{T^2}{JG} ds \tag{541}$$

It will be observed that the energy due to the direct shearing force P_4
$= P$ on any section E is neglected.

The deflection of the free end is found from Eq. 538 by differentiating
both sides of Eq. 541, which gives

$$\delta_P = \int_0^l \frac{M}{EI} \frac{\partial M}{\partial P} ds + \int_0^l \frac{T}{JG} \frac{\partial T}{\partial P} ds \tag{542}$$

If in Eq. 542 we substitute for ds a value $R\, d\theta$, use Eq. 539 for expressions for M and T, and take the partial derivatives $\partial M/\partial P$ and $\partial T/\partial P$
as obtained from Eq. 539, the result is

$$\delta_P = \int_0^{\pi/2} \frac{PR^3}{EI} \sin^2 \theta\, d\theta + \int_0^{\pi/2} \frac{PR^3}{JG} (1 - \cos \theta)^2\, d\theta$$

$$= \frac{\pi}{4} \frac{PR^3}{EI} + \frac{PR^3}{JG} \cdot \frac{3\pi - 8}{4} \tag{543}$$

Illustrative Problems

Problem 250. Find the angle of twist Ω_A of the free end A of the curved rod in
Fig. 233a.

Solution. We must introduce a fictitious twisting couple C in the plane of the
cross section at A, as shown in Fig. 233b, and obtain Ω_A by partial differentiation of
U, the total strain energy in the curved rod, with respect to C. U is given by Eq. 541,
but we must write the expressions for M and T at any cross section in terms of the
loads P and C and the angle θ. From Fig. 233b these expressions are

$$M = PR \sin \theta - C \sin \theta = \sin \theta (PR - C)$$

$$T = PR(1 - \cos \theta) + C \cos \theta$$

The substitution of these quantities in Eq. 541 and also $ds = R\, d\theta$ gives

$$U = \frac{R}{2EI} \int_0^{\pi/2} (PR - C)^2 \sin^2 \theta\, d\theta + \frac{R}{2JG} \int_0^{\pi/2} [PR(1 - \cos \theta) + C \cos \theta]^2\, d\theta$$

The differentiation of U partially with respect to C gives

$$\Omega_A = \frac{\partial U}{\partial C} = -\frac{R}{EI} \int_0^{\pi/2} (PR - C) \sin^2 \theta \, d\theta + \frac{R}{JG} \int_0^{\pi/2} [PR(1 - \cos\theta) + C \cos\theta]$$

$$\cos\theta \, d\theta = -\frac{R}{EI}\left[(PR - C)\left(\frac{\theta}{2} - \frac{1}{4}\sin 2\theta\right)\right]_0^{\pi/2} + \frac{R}{JG}\left[PR \sin\theta \right.$$

$$\left. + (C - PR)\left(\frac{\theta}{2} + \frac{1}{4}\sin 2\theta\right)\right]_0^{\pi/2} = -\frac{\pi}{4}\frac{PR^2 - RC}{EI} + \frac{R}{JG}\left[PR + (C - PR)\frac{\pi}{4}\right]$$

But since $C = 0$ we obtain

$$\Omega_A = \frac{PR^2}{JG}\left(1 - \frac{\pi}{4}\right) - \frac{\pi}{4}\frac{PR^2}{EI}; \qquad J = 2I = \frac{2\pi r^4}{4}$$

$$\Omega_A = \frac{PR^2}{r^4}\left[\left(\frac{2}{\pi} - \frac{1}{2}\right)\frac{1}{G} - \frac{1}{E}\right]$$

Problem 251. In Fig. 234 is shown a relatively short circular bar rigidly fixed at one end and attached to a rigid disk at its free end. If the bar is loaded through point A on the outer surface of the disk by the forces F, P, and W, find the vertical deflection of the point A.

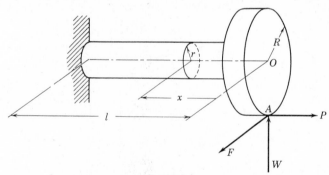

Fig. 234

Solution. The total elastic strain energy U in the bar is determined by adding the terms giving the energy accompanying the work done by an axial force, bending moments, direct shear, and torsional moment. These are given by Eqs. 516, 521, 523, and 535. It will be observed from Fig. 234 that at any section of the bar P produces an axial force $S = P$; F causes a bending moment $M_V = Fx$ about a vertical axis through the section; W and P cause a bending moment $M_H = PR + Wx$ about a horizontal axis; W causes a direct shear $V_V = W$; F causes a direct shear $V_H = F$; and F causes a torque $T = FR$. Hence

$$U = \frac{1}{2}\frac{S^2 l}{aE} + \int_0^l \frac{1}{2}\frac{M_V^2}{EI}\,dx + \int_0^l \frac{1}{2}\frac{M_H^2}{EI}\,dx + \int_0^l \frac{1}{2}\frac{V_V^2}{aG}\,dx + \int_0^l \frac{1}{2}\frac{V_H^2}{aG}\,dx + \int_0^l \frac{1}{2}\frac{T^2}{JG}\,dx$$

Differentiation with respect to W gives

$$\delta_W = \frac{Sl}{aE}\frac{\partial S}{\partial W} + \int_0^l \frac{M_V}{EI}\frac{\partial M_V}{\partial W}\,dx + \int_0^l \frac{M_H}{EI}\frac{\partial M_H}{\partial W}\,dx + \int_0^l \frac{V_V}{aG}\frac{\partial V_V}{\partial W}\,dx$$

$$+ \int_0^l \frac{V_H}{aG}\frac{\partial V_H}{\partial W}\,dx + \int_0^l \frac{T}{JG}\frac{\partial T}{\partial W}\,dx$$

By taking the partial derivatives with respect to W of the foregoing expressions for S, M_H, etc., we obtain

$$\frac{\partial S}{\partial W} = 0 \qquad \frac{\partial M_V}{\partial W} = 0 \qquad \frac{\partial M_H}{\partial W} = x \qquad \frac{\partial V_V}{\partial W} = 1 \qquad \frac{\partial V_H}{\partial W} = 0 \qquad \frac{\partial T}{\partial W} = 0$$

By substituting these quantities in the integrals and noting that the definite integral of zero is zero, we obtain the following expression for the vertical deflection at W.

$$\delta_W = \frac{1}{EI}\int_0^l (PR + Wx)x\,dx + \frac{1}{aG}\int_0^l W\,dx = \frac{1}{EI}\left[\frac{PRl^2}{2} + \frac{Wl^3}{3}\right] + \frac{Wl}{aG}$$

Problems

252. Find the vertical deflection of the point C in the truss shown in Fig. 235, assuming that all members have the same cross section and are made of the same material.

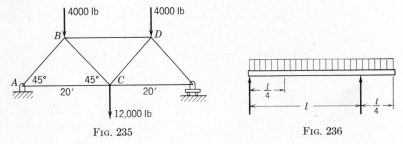

Fig. 235

Fig. 236

253. Find from Eq. 530 the slope of the elastic curve at the left support of the beam shown in Fig. 236.

$$Ans. \quad \theta = -\frac{7}{192}\frac{wl^3}{EI}.$$

254. A cylindrical steel bar 2 in. in diameter has a semicircular shape having an inner radius R of 9 in. (Fig. 237). A load P of 400 lb is applied as shown. Find (a) the vertical deflection of the free end, (b) the horizontal deflection of the free end, (c) the change in slope of the section at which the load is applied.

$$Ans. \quad (a)\ 0.030\ \text{in.} \qquad (b)\ 0.0085\ \text{in.}$$

255. Show that the maximum deflection of the beam represented in Fig. 238, in which the moment of inertia I_c of the central half is twice that of the end quarters, is

$$\Delta = \frac{3}{128}\frac{Pl^3}{EI_c}$$

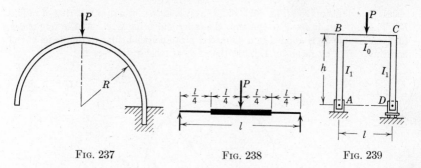

FIG. 237   FIG. 238   FIG. 239

256. Find the deflection of the point D of the two-legged frame shown in Fig. 239.

$$Ans. \quad \Delta = Pl^2h/8EI_0.$$

257. In Prob. 250 (see Fig. 233) let the force P be applied at A horizontally to the right along the direction of OA, all the other conditions in Prob. 250 being unchanged, and find the deflection of the free end. *Note:* The deflection consists of two components, δ_x in the direction of P, and δ_y perpendicular to P.

$$Ans. \quad \delta = \sqrt{\delta^2_x + \delta^2_y} = \frac{1}{2}\frac{PR^3}{EI}\sqrt{(\pi^2/4) + 1}.$$

258. Find the deflection, in the direction of P, of the point A of the free end of the cylindrical bar shown in Fig. 240. The loads PP are perpendicular to the plane of the bar. The radius of the bar is r.

$$Ans. \quad \Delta_A = \frac{2Ph^2}{\pi r^4}\left(\frac{2h}{3E} + \frac{l}{G}\right).$$

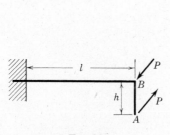

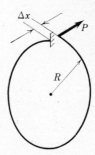

FIG. 240   FIG. 241

259. In Prob. 250, let the bar form a full circular ring as shown in Fig. 241, and find the deflection Δ_x of the free end.

$$Ans. \quad \Delta_x = \frac{2PR^3}{r^4}\left(\frac{2}{E} + \frac{3}{G}\right).$$

260. In Prob. 258 (Fig. 240), assume that only the force P at A acts on the bar, the force P at B not being applied, and find the deflection of A in the direction of P.

$$Ans. \quad \Delta_x = P\left(\frac{h^3}{3EI} + \frac{l^3}{3EI} + \frac{h^2l}{GJ}\right).$$

261. A cylindrical rod (Fig. 242), of radius r, is in the form of a half-ring of radius R. The half-ring is fixed at one end, the other end being free. At the free end a torsional couple T_0 is applied in a diametral plane perpendicular to the plane of the half-ring. Find by means of Eq. 541 the angle of twist of the free end.

$$Ans. \quad \theta = \frac{T_0 R}{Gr^4} + \frac{2T_0 R}{Er^4}.$$

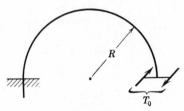

Fig. 242

262. In Prob. 251 find the deflections δ_F and δ_P of point A in the direction of each of the forces F and P, respectively. *Note:* The total deflection of A is equal to the vector sum of these deflections δ_F and δ_P and of δ_W as found in Prob. 251.

Chapter 15

DEFLECTION OF MEMBERS AND SIMPLE STRUCTURES BY UNIT LOAD OR DUMMY LOAD METHOD

140 Introduction. In Chapter 14 the deflection of statically determinate members and structures in which the loads and deflections (assumed to be small) were linearly related were found by Castigliano's theorem. It is shown in Art. 131 that Castigliano's theorem is a special case of the more general theorem of complementary energy in which the so-called complementary energy Φ is equal to the strain energy U in the member or structure. Hence the use of Castigliano's theorem is limited to linear relationships between loads and deflections, since only under these conditions is it true that $\Phi = U$.

The unit load or dummy load method derived in this chapter is also a method of applying the complementary energy theorem, but it is not restricted to a linear relationship between load and deflection as is Castigliano's theorem. However, the deflections must be relatively small. The dummy load method will be derived first for a structure in which only axial forces are resisted by the members, but the method is also applicable in dealing with deflections of beams, torsion members, etc.

141 Members subjected to axial forces. In Fig. 243a is represented a pin-connected structure in which each member is subjected to an axial force at each end of the member. The external loads P and Q are applied at joint B vertically and horizontally, respectively; the support at A is assumed to be rigid, and the support at C can move without friction in a horizontal direction but cannot deflect vertically. Let it be required to find the deflection δ in the horizontal direction of the joint at B, if the relationship between the axial force S and elongation e of each member of the structure is represented by a curve such as OF in Fig. 243b. From Eq. 507 the deflection δ is

$$\delta = \partial\Phi/\partial Q \qquad (544)$$

in which Φ is a function expressed in terms of S and e and, as already noted, is called the complementary energy for the structure, and Q is the load applied horizontally at B in the direction of the desired deflection δ of this point. Let the expression for the function Φ for this structure be written by using Eq. 504, Chapter 13, and then be substituted

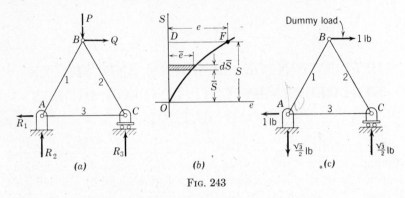

FIG. 243

in Eq. 544. If now the partial differentiation of Φ with respect to Q is performed, we obtain *

$$\delta = e_1 \frac{\partial S_1}{\partial Q} + e_2 \frac{\partial S_2}{\partial Q} + e_3 \frac{\partial S_3}{\partial Q} = \Sigma e \frac{\partial S}{\partial Q} \qquad (545)$$

in which e_1, e_2, e_3 are the final values of the elongations of the members marked 1, 2, 3, respectively, in Fig. 243a, and S_1, S_2, S_3 are the final values of the axial forces, respectively, in these members, corresponding

* The formal proof of this statement requires careful consideration as follows: The expression for Φ is found by adding the areas ODF (Fig. 243b) for all the members. Thus

$$\Phi = \int \bar{e}_1 \, d\bar{S}_1 + \int \bar{e}_2 \, d\bar{S}_2 + \int \bar{e}_3 \, d\bar{S}_3 \qquad (a)$$

where the subscripts refer to the members having the corresponding numbers in Fig. 243a. $\bar{e}$ and $\bar{S}$ represent any value of elongation and axial force, respectively, during the application of the loads. The e and S without the bar, as in Eq. 545, indicate final values corresponding to the actual loads P and Q. The value of $\bar{e}$ in each member can be expressed as a function of $\bar{S}$ in the member because the shape of the curve OF for each member is known. Let this fact be expressed by the following notation

$$\bar{e}_1 = f_1(\bar{S}_1) \qquad \bar{e}_2 = f_2(\bar{S}_2) \qquad \bar{e}_3 = f_3(\bar{S}_3) \qquad (b)$$

By substituting the values of $\bar{e}_1$, $\bar{e}_2$, and $\bar{e}_3$ from Eq. b in Eq. a, we obtain

$$\Phi = \int_0^{S_1} f_1(\bar{S}_1) \, d\bar{S}_1 + \int_0^{S_2} f_2(\bar{S}_2) \, d\bar{S}_2 + \int_0^{S_3} f_3(\bar{S}_3) \, d\bar{S}_3 \qquad (c)$$

From Eq. c it will be noted that the integrands of these definite integrals will be functions of the upper limits, and hence Φ is a function of S_1, S_2, and S_3, the values of to the actual loads P and Q. Each of the quantities $\partial S_1/\partial Q$, $\partial S_2/\partial Q$, $\partial S_3/\partial Q$ in Eq. 545 is the rate at which the axial force S in the member increases with respect to the load Q as it is applied. Let u denote this rate; that is, let

$$u \equiv \partial S/\partial Q \qquad\qquad (546)$$

A Special Interpretation of u. From the foregoing definition of u for any member in the structure, it is evident that u may be interpreted as the change in the internal force S in the member per unit (1 lb) change in the load Q, where Q is the load acting at the point whose deflection is desired. The other loads on the structure are not involved in the rate of change of S for the reason that S is differentiated *partially* with respect to Q.

This interpretation of u means that the values of u for all members of the structure may be found by applying to the structure a fictitious or dummy load Q equal to unity and then calculating the internal force in each member caused by the dummy load and the reactions it produces by applying the equations of equilibrium in the usual manner. Thus the dummy load or unit load method changes the problem of determining the value of $u \equiv \partial S/\partial Q$ from one of differentiation (after determining S from the equations of equilibrium) to one of equilibrium only, that is, both S and u for each member are found from the equations of equilibrium.

A thorough understanding of this interpretation of u and its implications is of sufficient importance to justify further discussion. In Fig. 243a let it be required to obtain the value of u_1 for member AB, by both the axial forces that correspond to the actual loads. Let this fact be indicated by the notation

$$\Phi \equiv \Phi(S_1, S_2, S_3) \qquad\qquad (d)$$

This is the function Φ in Eq. 544 that is differentiated partially with respect to Q. The values of S_1, S_2, and S_3 each depend upon Q. Thus, by definition, the partial derivative of the function Φ for this structure with respect to Q is

$$\frac{\partial \Phi}{\partial Q} = \frac{\partial \Phi}{\partial S_1}\frac{\partial S_1}{\partial Q} + \frac{\partial \Phi}{\partial S_2}\frac{\partial S_2}{\partial Q} + \frac{\partial \Phi}{\partial S_3}\frac{\partial S_3}{\partial Q} \qquad\qquad (e)$$

But the values of $\partial \Phi/\partial S_1$, $\partial \Phi/\partial S_2$, $\partial \Phi/\partial S_3$ in this equation may be shown to be equal to e_1, e_2, e_3, respectively, and therefore the right side of Eq. e is the same as that of Eq. 545. This fact is established by partial differentiation of both sides of Eq. c with respect to S_1, S_2, and S_3, respectively, which results in the following three expressions:

$$\partial \Phi/\partial S_1 = f_1(S_1) \qquad \partial \Phi/\partial S_2 = f_2(S_2) \qquad \partial \Phi/\partial S_3 = f_3(S_3) \qquad (f)$$

But from Eq. b the right sides of Eq. f are equal to e_1, e_2, and e_3, respectively. Hence, when these values are substituted in Eq. e, and it is noted from Eq. 544 that $\delta = \partial \Phi/\partial Q$, Eq. 545 is obtained.

methods. By use of the equations of equilibrium, the axial force S_1 in AB caused by the actual loads is found to be

$$S_1 = \tfrac{1}{2}Q \csc 30° - \tfrac{1}{2}P \sec 30° \qquad (547)$$

and hence
$$u_1 = \partial S_1/\partial Q = \tfrac{1}{2} \csc 30° \qquad (548)$$

Before the dummy load method is used for obtaining u_1, it should be noted that Eq. 548 shows that u_1 is a constant. This means that the deflections of the structure must be relatively small so that the change in the geometry of the structure will not influence the values of S as calculated by use of the equations of equilibrium based on the original geometry of the structure.

By the dummy (unit) load method u_1 is found as follows: In Fig. 243c let a load $Q = 1$ lb be applied horizontally at B. This load causes the reactions shown at A and C. From the equations of equilibrium this system of loads causes a force u_1 in AB equal to $\frac{1}{2} \csc 30°$, which is the same as given by Eq. 548.

By making use of the foregoing interpretation of the terms in Eq. 545 the following equation for the deflection of a panel point of a structure of the type shown in Fig. 243a may be written

$$\delta = \Sigma eu \qquad (549)$$

in which e is the elongation of each member, and u is the axial force in each member of the structure caused by a dummy load of unity (1 lb) applied at the panel point and in the direction in which the deflection of the point is desired. Although u may be thought of as a force, it really is a dimensionless * quantity, as is evident from the expression $u = \partial S/\partial Q$.

It should be noted that the deformation e in Eq. 549 may be produced in any manner such as by changing the temperature of the member, as well as by applying external forces to the structure, and furthermore the deformations may be inelastic as well as elastic deformations, provided that, as previously noted, the deformations are not so large that the geometry of the structure is changed appreciably, thereby introducing serious errors in the values of the internal forces S calculated by use of the equations of equilibrium based on the original undeformed shape of the structure. Furthermore, when inelastic strains occur in the mem-

---

* In some textbooks where a method frequently called virtual work is used to derive Eq. 549, the expression is written

$$1 \text{ lb} \times \delta = \Sigma eu$$

and in this expression u will have the units of force.

ber, the forces in the member must not be allowed to decrease (see Chapter 13).

Elastic Deflections. If it is assumed that the deformations e in the members of a pin-connected structure are linear elastic deformations and are caused by loads applied to the structure, the value of e in any member is given by the expression $e = Sl/aE$, and hence for small elastic deflections

$$\delta = \Sigma \frac{Sul}{aE} \qquad (550)$$

in which δ = deflection of any panel point of the structure in the desired direction caused by the loads acting on the structure.

$\quad\quad S$ = axial force in each member caused by the loads acting on the structure.

$\quad\quad u$ = same meaning as in Eq. 549.

$\quad l, a, E$ = length, cross-sectional area, and modulus of elasticity of each member, respectively.

Illustrative Problem

Problem 263. A pin-connected truss, in which all members have the same length $l = 10$ ft and the modulus of elasticity $E = 30,000,000$ lb per sq in., is loaded as shown in Fig. 244a (see Prob. 241, Chapter 14). If it is assumed that all members are strained elastically, find the horizontal deflection of the point D by making use of the dummy (unit) load method expressed by Eq. 550.

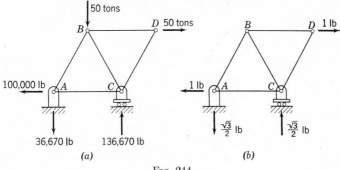

(a) $\qquad\qquad\qquad\qquad (b)$

Fɪɢ. 244

Solution. Eq. 550 for the conditions stated may be written

$$\delta = \frac{l}{E} \Sigma \frac{Su}{a}$$

Figure 244a shows the structure with the actual loads and reactions, and Fig. 244b shows the dummy load of 1 lb and the reactions it produces. The dummy unit load is applied horizontally at D since the horizontal deflection of D is desired. By referring to Fig. 244a and using the equations of equilibrium we may find the value of the axial force S due to the actual loads for each member; the results are tabulated in the accompanying table. In a similar procedure, with Fig. 244b, the value of the axial force u in each member is found and listed in the accompanying table. If the forces are tension they are tabulated as positive, and if compression they are given a negative sign.

COMPUTATIONS FOR HORIZONTAL MOVEMENT OF PANEL POINT OF TRUSS

Member	Axial Force S in Member Due to Actual Loads, lb	Axial Force u in Member Due to Dummy Load, lb	Cross Section a, in.^{2}	Product $\dfrac{Su}{a}$, lb/in.^{2}
AB	+42,400	+1	2.5	17,000
AC	+78,800	$+\frac{1}{2}$	4.5	8,750
BC	−157,500	−1	12.0	13,100
BD	+100,000	+1	6.0	16,670
CD	0	0	6.0	0

$$\Sigma \frac{Su}{a} = 55{,}520 \text{ lb/in.}^2$$

Therefore the horizontal deflection at D is

$$\delta = \frac{l}{E} \Sigma \frac{Su}{a} = \frac{120 \times 55{,}520}{30{,}000{,}000} = 0.22 \text{ in.}$$

This is the same as the result obtained in part a of Prob. 241 (Chapter 14).

142 Deflection of beam. Let Fig. 245a represent a horizontal beam of length l simply supported on rigid supports and subjected to concentrated loads P_1, P_2. Let it be required to find the vertical deflection at some point A of the beam by means of the dummy load method. The expression for the deflection is obtained by proceeding exactly as in Art. 141 for the truss and is found to be the same form as that of Eq. 549 in which the angle $d\alpha$ replaces e and the bending moment $m \equiv \partial M/\partial Q$ replaces $u \equiv \partial S/\partial Q$. In the expression $\partial M/\partial Q$, M is the bending moment at any section of the beam, and hence $\partial M/\partial Q \equiv m$ is the change in the bending moment per unit change in Q, or the moment caused by a 1-lb load. It should be noted, however, that although m may be considered to be a moment (caused by a 1-lb load) it is evident from the expression $m = \partial M/\partial Q$ that the dimension of m is a length. In accordance with Eq. 549, the expression for the deflection of A, if the effect of vertical shear is neglected, becomes

$$\delta_A = \int m \, d\alpha \tag{551}$$

in which m is the bending moment at any section of the beam caused by a dummy load of unity acting at the point whose deflection is to be found, and in the direction of the desired deflection, as shown in Fig. 245b, and $d\alpha$ is the rotation in radians of one face relative to the other of an element of length dx of the beam.

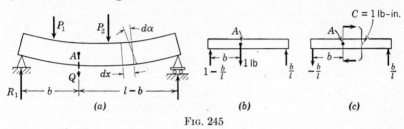

Fig. 245

There is no restriction on the manner of producing the angular deformation $d\alpha$; it could be caused, for example, by temperature changes as well as by applying loads to the beam. Furthermore, the angular deformation may be inelastic as well as elastic, provided that the deformations in the elements of the beam are not sufficiently large to cause an appreciable change in the geometry of the beam and thereby cause an error in the bending moments (and other results of the equations of equilibrium) as calculated on the basis of the geometry of the undeformed member. In fact this method is used in Chapter 17 for computing the deflection of simply supported beams that are subjected to loads which cause small amounts of inelastic strain at the extreme fibers of the beam, but it must be assumed that the bending moments in the beam do not decrease when the inelastic strains occur, that is, no unloading of the member occurs.

Elastic Deflections. If it is assumed that the angular deformations $d\alpha$ in the elements of the beam are elastic deformations and are the result of the bending moments M in the elements caused by the external loads applied to the beam, the expression for $d\alpha$ in any element is $d\alpha = (M/EI) \, dx$ (Art. 135, Chapter 14), provided that the beam is essentially a straight beam and that the effect of vertical shear may be neglected.

The expression for the deflection at any point of the beam may then be written

$$\delta = \int \frac{Mm \, dx}{EI} \tag{552}$$

in which M is the bending moment at any section caused by the actual loads (and reactions) acting on the beam, and m has the same meaning as in Eq. 551.

Illustrative Problem

Problem 264. Find the elastic vertical deflection of the point A (Fig. 246a) of a simply supported beam subjected to a uniformly distributed load of w lb per ft of span.

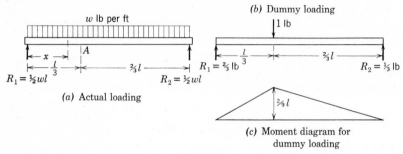

(a) Actual loading

(b) Dummy loading

(c) Moment diagram for dummy loading

FIG. 246

Solution. The actual loading is shown in Fig. 246a. The moment at a section at the distance x from the left support is

$$M = (wlx/2) - (wx^2/2)$$

The corresponding dummy loads and moments are shown in Figs. 246b and 246c. According to Eq. 552 the deflection is

$$\delta = \int_0^{l/3} \frac{Mm_1\,dx}{EI} + \int_{l/3}^l \frac{Mm_2\,dx}{EI}$$

in which $m_1 = 2x/3$, for the length $l/3$, and $m_2 = 2x/3 - [x - (l/3)]$, for the length $2l/3$.

$$\delta = \frac{1}{EI}\int_0^{l/3}\left(\frac{wlx}{2} - \frac{wx^2}{2}\right)\frac{2x}{3}\,dx + \frac{1}{EI}\int_{l/3}^l\left(\frac{wlx}{2} - \frac{wx^2}{2}\right)\left[\frac{2x}{3} - \left(x - \frac{l}{3}\right)\right]dx$$

$$\delta = \frac{1}{EI}\left(\frac{wl^4}{324} + \frac{2wl^4}{243}\right) = \frac{11}{972}\frac{wl^4}{EI}$$

143 Rotation of a section of a beam. Change of slope. Let it be required to find the change in slope θ_A of the section at A of the beam of length l in Fig. 245a caused by the external forces acting on the beam. By using the procedure in Art. 141 it is found that Eq. 549 may be used to find θ_A if e is replaced by the angle $d\alpha$ and u by the bending moment $m' \equiv \partial M/\partial C$. In the expression $\partial M/\partial C$, M is the bending moment at any section of the beam, and C is a couple applied at the section where θ_A is desired. Hence m' is the change in bending moment per unit of

C, that is, the moment caused by a couple of 1 lb-in. as shown in Fig. 245c. Thus,

$$\theta_A = \int m' \, d\alpha \qquad (553)$$

in which $d\alpha$ is the rotation of one face of an element of length dx with respect to the other face, and m' is the bending moment at any section of the beam caused by a dummy couple of unity (1 lb-in.) applied at the section where the change in slope is desired (Fig. 245c). Although m' may be thought of as a bending moment, it is evident from the expression $m' \equiv \partial M / \partial C$ that it is actually dimensionless.

Elastic Deflections. If the beam acts elastically in resisting the loads applied to it, the value of $d\alpha$ in Eq. 553 is $M \, dx/EI$, and hence the expression for the change in slope is

$$\theta_A = \int \frac{M m' \, dx}{EI} \qquad (554)$$

in which m' has the same meaning as previously in Eq. 553, and M the bending moment at any section of the beam due to the actual external forces acting on the beam.

Illustrative Problem

Problem 265. Find the change of slope of the section over the right support of the beam shown in Fig. 247.

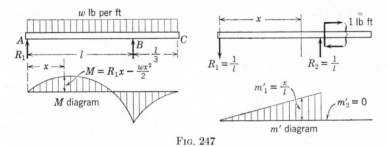

FIG. 247

Solution. According to Eq. 554, referring to Fig. 247, we have

$$\theta_B = \int \frac{M m' \, dx}{EI} = \int_0^l \frac{M_1 m'_1 \, dx}{EI} + \int_l^{4l/3} \frac{M_2 m'_2 \, dx}{EI}$$

$$M_1 = R_1 x - (wx^2/2) \qquad M_2 = R_1 x - (wx^2/2) + R_2(x - l)$$

$$m'_1 = -x/l \qquad m'_2 = 0$$

Hence
$$\theta_B = \int_0^l \frac{R_1 x - (wx^2/2)}{EI} \frac{x}{l} \, dx = \frac{1}{EI}\left(\frac{R_1 l^2}{3} - \frac{wl^3}{8}\right)$$

144 Angle of twist of bar subjected to torsion. Let it be required to find the angle of twist θ_A at section A of the cylindrical bar of circular cross section shown in Fig. 248. The bar is subjected to a twisting moment T at any section, the value of which varies as the ordinate to the curve shown above the bar. By using the procedure in Art. 141

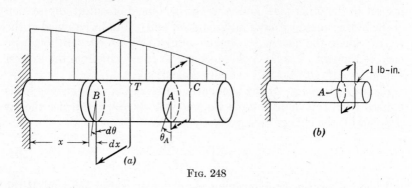

FIG. 248

it is found that Eq. 549 may be used to find θ_A if e is replaced by the angle $d\theta$ and u by the twisting moment $t = \partial T/\partial C$, and hence

$$\theta_A = \int t\, d\theta \tag{555}$$

where $d\theta$ is the angle of twist of one face of an element of length dx of the bar with respect to the other face, as shown by section B, Fig. 248a, and t is the twisting moment at any section of the beam caused by a dummy couple of unity (1 lb-in.) applied at the section of the bar where the angle of twist θ is desired (Fig. 248b). Although t may be thought of as a twisting moment, it is evident from the expression $t = \partial T/\partial C$ that it is actually dimensionless.

Elastic Deflections. If the bar in Fig. 248a acts elastically in resisting the twisting moment T at every section, the expression for the angle $d\theta$ is $T\,dx/GJ$ (Eq. 533, Chapter 14), and the expression for the angle of twist is

$$\theta_A = \int (Tt/GJ)dx \tag{556}$$

in which G is the shearing modulus of elasticity, and J is the polar moment of inertia.

Illustrative Problems

Problem 266. As indicated in Fig. 249a, a cylindrical bar of length $l = \pi/2$ ft is rigidly fixed at one end and is subjected to a variable twisting moment indicated by the ordinates to the curve $T = T_0 \cos x$, where T_0 is the twisting moment at the fixed end. Find the angle of twist of the free end of the shaft by use of Eq. 556.

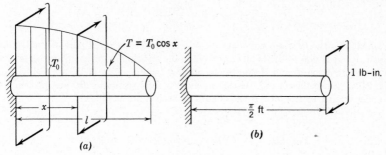

FIG. 249

Solution. The value of t at any section is the twisting moment caused by the dummy twisting couple of 1 lb-in. in Fig. 249b and is $t = 1$. Hence, Eq. 556 gives

$$\theta = \int_0^{\pi/2} \frac{T_0 \cos x\, dx}{GJ} = \frac{T_0}{GJ} \sin x \Big]_0^{\pi/2} = \frac{T_0}{GJ}$$

Compare this solution with that of Prob. 248 (Chapter 14) which was solved by Castigliano's theorem.

Problem 267. As shown in Fig. 250a, a metal rod of circular cross section of radius r has the shape of a semicircle AB of radius R, whose value is large compared

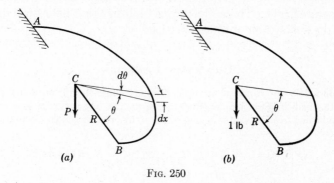

FIG. 250

to that of r. The rod is bent sharply at B and extends along a radius to the center C of the semicircle. The bent rod is fixed at A and is loaded at its free end C by a force P that acts perpendicularly to the plane of the semicircle. By making use of the dummy load method, find the expression for the deflection at the load P in the direction of the load.

Solution. The deflection of C is made up of two parts: the deflection δ_1, resulting from the bending of BC, which by Eq. 552 is

$$\delta_1 = \int_0^R \frac{Mm\,dx}{EI}$$

and the deflection δ_2, resulting from the twisting of the semicircular bar AB, given in the expression

$$\delta_2 = \int_0^\pi \frac{Tm_T\,dx}{GJ}$$

in which T is the twisting moment at any section of the curved part of the bar between A and B due to the load P, and m_T is the twisting moment at any section on the curve between A and B due to the dummy load of unity (1 lb) applied at C in Fig. 250b. Since there is no twisting moment on any section of BC and no bending moment on any section of AB the quantities needed are as follows:

$$\text{For } BC\colon \quad M = Px \qquad m = x$$

$$\text{For } AB\colon \quad T = PR \qquad m_T = R \qquad dx = R\,d\theta$$

Therefore

$$\delta = \delta_1 + \delta_2 = \int_0^R \frac{Mm\,dx}{EI} + \int_0^\pi \frac{Tm_T\,dx}{GJ} = \int_0^R \frac{Px^2\,dx}{EI} + \int_0^\pi \frac{PR^3\,d\theta}{GJ}$$

$$\delta = \frac{PR^3}{3EI} + \frac{\pi PR^3}{GJ}$$

145 Deflection and angle of twist of member subjected to combined loads.

When a load or loads produce at any cross section of a member a combination of an axial force, a bending moment, and a twisting moment, the deflection or angle of twist may be found by Eqs. 549 through 556 which give the deflection or angle of twist for each of the separate loads. Three illustrative problems that follow will demonstrate the application of these equations.

Illustrative Problems

Problem 268. A cylindrical bar (Fig. 251a) of radius r has the form of a quarter-ring with a radius R which is large relative to r. The ring is fixed at one end, the other end being free. A load P is applied at the free end perpendicular to the plane

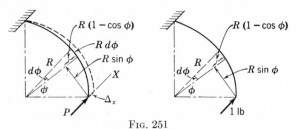

FIG. 251

of the quarter-ring. Find the elastic deflection Δ_x of the free end of the quarter-ring in the direction of P.

Solution. A part of the deflection is due to bending moment on each section, and a part is due to a torsional moment on each section. Therefore,

$$\Delta_x = \int \frac{Mm\,ds}{EI} + \int \frac{Tm_T\,ds}{GJ}$$

From Fig. 251 we find

$$M = PR \sin\phi \qquad T = PR(1 - \cos\phi)$$

$$m = R \sin\phi \qquad m_T = R(1 - \cos\phi)$$

$$ds = R\,d\phi$$

Therefore

$$\Delta_x = \int_0^{\pi/2} \frac{PR^2 \sin^2\phi R\,d\phi}{EI} + \int_0^{\pi/2} \frac{PR^2(1 - \cos\phi)^2 R\,d\phi}{GJ}$$

$$= \frac{PR^3}{EI} \int_0^{\pi/2} \sin^2\phi\,d\phi + \frac{PR^3}{GJ} \int_0^{\pi/2} (1 - \cos\phi)^2\,d\phi$$

$$= \frac{PR^3}{EI} \left[\frac{\phi}{2} - \frac{\sin 2\phi}{4}\right]_0^{\pi/2} + \frac{PR^3}{GJ} \left[\phi - 2\sin\phi + \frac{\phi}{2} + \frac{\sin 2\phi}{4}\right]_0^{\pi/2}$$

$$= \frac{PR^3}{EI} \frac{\pi}{4} + \frac{PR^3}{GJ} \frac{3\pi - 8}{4}; \quad J = 2I = 2\frac{\pi r^4}{4}$$

$$= \frac{PR^3}{r^4} \left(\frac{1}{E} + \frac{3\pi - 8}{2\pi G}\right) = \frac{PR^3}{r^4} \left(\frac{1}{E} + \frac{0.226}{G}\right)$$

Problem 269. Figure 252a represents a pipe that carries steam. The straight and curved parts of the pipe lie in one plane so that it is said to be a two-dimensional pipe line. Both ends of such a pipe line are usually fixed, and when temperature

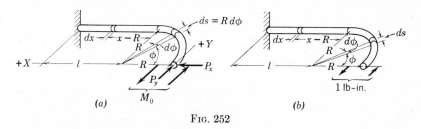

(a)   (b)

Fig. 252

changes occur two forces and a bending moment are necessary to hold the pipe to its fixture at the ends. In Fig. 252a one end is shown free of its fixture, and the forces P_x, P_y and bending moment M_0 required to hold it fixed are shown. If it is assumed that the end where the forces and moments are applied is free, find the rotation θ of this end in the plane of the bending moment M_0. It is assumed that the pipe acts elastically.

Solution. The rotation θ is given by the equation

$$\theta = \int_0^{\pi/2} \frac{Mm'\,ds}{EI} + \int_R^{R+l} \frac{Mm'\,dx}{EI}$$

in which $ds = R\,d\phi$. The expressions for M obtained from Fig. 252a are

For $\phi = 0$ to $\pi/2$: $M = -M_0 + P_x R \sin \phi - P_y R(1 - \cos \phi)$

For $x = 0$ to l: $M = -M_0 + P_x R - P_y x$

The expressions for m' obtained from Fig. 252b are

For $\phi = 0$ to $\pi/2$: $m' = -1$ For $x = 0$ to l: $m' = -1$

Therefore

$$\theta = -\frac{1}{EI} \int_0^{\pi/2} [-M_0 + P_x R \sin \phi - P_y R(1 - \cos \phi)]R\,d\phi$$

$$- \frac{1}{EI} \int_R^{R+l} (-M_0 + P_x R - P_y x)\,dx$$

$$= \frac{1}{EI} \left[+M_0 \left(\frac{\pi}{2} R + l \right) - P_x(R^2 + Rl) + P_y \left(-R^2 + \frac{\pi}{2} R^2 + Rl + \frac{1}{2} l^2 \right) \right]$$

Problem 270. Figure 253a represents a three-dimensional pipe line of three lengths l_1, l_2, and l_3. Both ends of such a pipe are usually fixed. However, one end is shown here free of its connection, but the moments and forces which are necessary

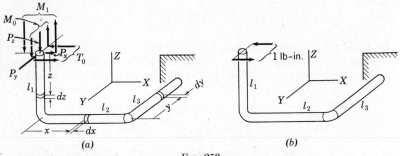

(a)   (b)

FIG. 253

to keep it in a fixed position when temperature changes occur are shown. Find the rotation θ in the plane of the twisting moment T_0 due to these forces. It is assumed that the pipe acts elastically, and as a simplifying approximation it is assumed that the radii of the quarter bends may be neglected.

Solution. In Fig. 253a at any section of the pipe there will be moments with respect to each of the three axes X, Y, Z; one of these will be a twisting moment, and two will be bending moments. Also at every section there is an axial force and two shearing forces, each force being parallel to a coordinate axis, but the direct effects produced by these forces on the deformation of the pipe are neglected here. For l_1 let T_z represent the twisting moment and M_x and M_y the two bending moments.

For l_2 these quantities are T_x, M_y, and M_z, and for l_3 they are T_y, M_x, and M_z, respectively. In Fig. 253b let the twisting moment at each section due to the dummy unit twisting couple be represented by t, and the bending moments by m'. These quantities for l_1 are t_z, m'_x, m'_y, respectively; for l_2 they are t_x, m'_y, m'_z; and for l_3 they are t_y, m'_x and m'_z, respectively.

Note that the unit couple is in the same plane and has the same sense as T_0. The rotation θ in the plane of T_0 is given by the equation

$$\theta = \int_0^{l_1} \frac{M_x m'_x \, dz}{EI} + \int_0^{l_1} \frac{M_y m'_y \, dz}{EI} + \int_0^{l_1} \frac{T_z t_z \, dz}{GJ} + \int_0^{l_2} \frac{M_y m'_y \, dx}{EI} + \int_0^{l_2} \frac{M_z m'_z \, dx}{EI}$$

$$+ \int_0^{l_2} \frac{T_x t_x \, dx}{GJ} + \int_0^{l_3} \frac{M_x m'_x \, dy}{EI} + \int_0^{l_3} \frac{M_z m'_z \, dy}{EI} + \int_0^{l_3} \frac{T_y t_y \, dy}{GJ}$$

The expressions for the bending moments and twisting moments are given in the accompanying table.

0 to l_1		0 to l_2		0 to l_3	
Actual Moments	Dummy Moments	Actual Moments	Dummy Moments	Actual Moments	Dummy Moments
$M_x = M_0 - zP_y$	$m'_x = 0$	$M_y = M_1 - l_1 P_x$ $\quad + xP_z$	$m'_y = 0$	$M_x = M_0 - l_1 P_y + yP_z$	$m'_x = 0$
$M_y = M_1 - zP_x$	$m'_y = 0$	$M_z = T_0 - xP_y$	$m'_z = 1$	$M_z = T_0 - l_1 P_y + yP_x$	$m'_z = 1$
$T_z = T_0$	$t_z = 1$	$T_x = M_0 - l_1 P_y$	$t_x = 0$	$T_y = M_1 + l_2 P_z - l_1 P_x$	$t_y = 0$

When the expressions from the table are substituted in the integrals for obtaining θ, the result is

$$\theta = \int_0^{l_1} \frac{T_0 \, dz}{GJ} + \int_0^{l_2} \frac{(T_0 - xP_y) \, dx}{EI} + \int_0^{l_3} \frac{(T_0 - l_2 P_y + yP_x) \, dy}{EI}$$

$$= \frac{T_0 l_1}{GJ} + \frac{T_0(l_2 + l_3) + \frac{1}{2}P_x l_3{}^2 - P_y(\frac{1}{2}l_2{}^2 + l_2 l_3)}{EI}$$

Problems

271. A cantilever beam (Fig. 254) has, for half of its length, a moment of inertia I and for the other half a moment of inertia of nI. The beam is subjected to a concentrated load P at the free end. Find the elastic deflection of the free end.

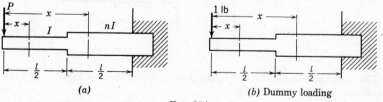

(a) (b) Dummy loading

FIG. 254

272. A half-ring is fixed at one end and loaded with a force P at the other end, as shown in Fig. 255. The ring has a constant cross section, and the depth of the ring is small compared to the radius R. Find the horizontal elastic deflection Δ of the free end of the beam.

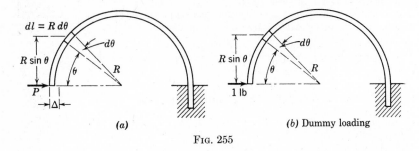

(a)

(b) Dummy loading

Fig. 255

273. Find the horizontal elastic deflection δ_D of the point D of the frame shown in Fig. 256.

$$Ans. \quad \delta_D = \frac{1}{8}\frac{Phl^2}{EI_0}.$$

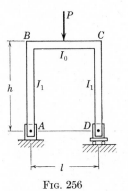

Fig. 256

274. Find the vertical elastic deflection of the panel point D of Fig. 244a.

275. Find the elastic deflection of the point A in the beam shown in Fig. 257.

$$Ans. \quad \delta = \frac{P}{EI}\left(\frac{l^3}{3} - \frac{l^2 l_1}{2} + \frac{l_1^3}{6}\right).$$

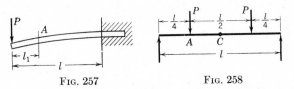

Fig. 257

Fig. 258

276. Find the elastic deflection of the point A of the beam of Fig. 258. Also find the deflection of the center point C.

$$Ans. \quad \delta_A = \frac{1}{48}\frac{Pl^3}{EI}.$$

277. A steel rod having a square cross section 2 in. on a side is in the form of a semicircle having a mean radius of 12 in. One end of the rod is fixed and the other end is free, as shown in Fig. 259. The free end is subjected to a load P of 2000 lb, as shown in Fig. 259. The proportional limit of the material is 40,000 lb per sq in. Find the horizontal deflection of the free end.   *Ans.* $\delta = 3PR^3\pi/2EI = 0.407$ in.

278. Find the elastic deflection of the free end of the pipe in Fig. 253a in the direction of the force P_y.

Note: For additional problems see those at the end of Chapter 14.

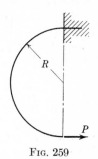

Fig. 259

146 Special method for beam loaded only at its ends. Some beams are subjected to forces or loads which act only at the ends of the beam as indicated in Figs. 260 and 261. The deflection and the change of slope at the ends of the beam caused by the loads can be expressed in terms of the loads, the quantities E and I, and certain properties of a line L representing the length of the centerline of the beam.

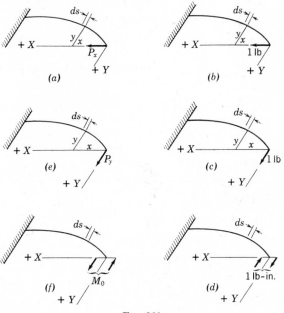

Fig. 260

These properties of the line are its length L, the first and second moments of L with respect to a set of axes X, Y, and the product of inertia of L with respect to these axes. The fact that these properties of the line L can be used in determining the deflection of the beam is of considerable importance in solving special types of statically indeterminate problems, especially in solving for the reactions at the ends of steam pipe lines due to the expansion caused by the heat, as will be shown in Art. 154 of Chapter 16. The importance of the method to be discussed in this article arises from the fact that, by choosing the axes through the centroid of the line L, the first moments of L are equal to zero, and this condition reduces the number of unknowns in the set of simultaneous

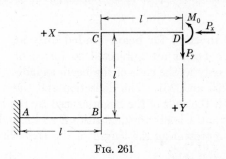

FIG. 261

linear equations involved in the analysis of statically indeterminate pipe lines and certain other structural members such as arches, etc., as will be shown later.

Let Fig. 260a represent a cylindrical rod that is fixed at one end and loaded by a concentrated force P_x at its free end. The beam is curved in the xy plane, but the radius of curvature at any cross section is large in comparison to the radius r of the cross section.

Deflection δ_{xx} Due to P_x. Let it be required to find by the dummy load method the expression for the deflection δ_{xx} at the free end of the beam in the direction of the force P_x. The effects of the direct axial force and of transverse shear in the beam are considered to be negligible. From Eq. 552 we obtain

$$\delta_{xx} = \int_0^L \frac{Mm\,ds}{EI}$$

From Figs. 260a and 260b $M = yP_x$ and $m = y$; ds is a differential element of the length L of the beam. Therefore

$$\delta_{xx} = \int_0^L \frac{P_x y^2\,ds}{EI} = \frac{P_x}{EI}\int_0^L y^2\,ds \qquad (557)$$

But the integral in Eq. 557 is, by definition, the moment of inertia of the length L of the beam with respect to the X axis. Let it be denoted by I_{Lx}. Hence

$$\delta_{xx} = P_x \cdot I_{Lx}/EI \qquad (558)$$

It is of interest to note that this equation states that the deflection of the end of the beam in the x direction caused by P_x is equal to P_x times the deflection caused by a load of unity applied at the end in the x direction. For this reason the quantity I_{Lx}/EI is sometimes referred to as the coefficient for determining the deflection. This method of obtaining deflections is used in several subsequent equations.

Deflection δ_{xy} Due to P_x. Let δ_{xy} represent the deflection at the free end of the beam in Fig. 260a in the y direction caused by the load P_x. Then, from Eq. 552,

$$\delta_{xy} = \int_0^L \frac{Mm\,ds}{EI}$$

From Figs. 260a and 260c $M = yP_x$, and $m = x$. Thus

$$\delta_{xy} = \int_0^L \frac{P_x xy\,ds}{EI} = \frac{P_x}{EI} \int_0^L xy\,ds \qquad (559)$$

But the integral in Eq. 559 is the product of inertia I_{Lxy} of the length L of the beam with respect to the X and Y axes. Thus, making this substitution in Eq. 559, we have

$$\delta_{xy} = P_x(I_{Lxy}/EI) \qquad (560)$$

Change of Slope θ_x Due to P_x. Let θ_x represent the change in slope at the free end of the beam in Fig. 260a due to the force P_x. From Eq. 554

$$\theta_x = \int_0^L \frac{Mm'\,ds}{EI}$$

From Figs. 260a and 260d $M = yP_x$, and $m' = 1$. Therefore

$$\theta_x = \int_0^L \frac{P_x y\,ds}{EI} = \frac{P_x}{EI} \int_0^L y\,ds \qquad (561)$$

The integral in Eq. 561 represents the first moment M_{Lx} of the line L with respect to the X axis. By the substitution of M_{Lx} in Eq. 561 for the integral we have

$$\theta_x = P_x(M_{Lx}/EI) \qquad (562)$$

Deflections δ_{yy}, δ_{yx} and Change of Slope θ_y Due to P_y. In the same way that Eqs. 558, 560, and 562 were derived, we may find the indicated quantities for the force P_y shown in Fig. 260e. They are, respectively,

$$\delta_{yy} = P_y(I_{Ly}/EI) \qquad (563)$$

$$\delta_{yx} = P_y(I_{Lxy}/EI) \qquad (564)$$

$$\theta_y = P_y(M_{Ly}/EI) \qquad (565)$$

in which I_{Lxy} is the product of inertia of L as in Eq. 560, I_{Ly} is the moment of inertia of L with respect to the Y axis, and M_{Ly} is the first moment of L with respect to the Y axis.

Deflections δ_x, δ_y and Change of Slope θ Due to Moment M_0. Let the beam of Fig. 260a be loaded by a bending moment M_0 at the free end as shown in Fig. 260f, and let δ_x be the deflection of the free end in the x direction, δ_y the deflection in the y direction, and θ_{M_0} the change in slope at the free end, all caused by M_0. The expressions for these values are as follows:

$$\delta_x = M_0(M_{Lx}/EI) \tag{566}$$

$$\delta_y = M_0(M_{Ly}/EI) \tag{567}$$

$$\theta_{M_0} = M_0(L/EI) \tag{568}$$

It was assumed in deriving Eqs. 560 through 568 that the centerline of the beam lies entirely in a single plane. However, if this is not the case, these equations can be derived for so-called space systems, and they hold true with regard to projections of the centerline of the beam on the axes or coordinate planes concerned.

Deflection Due to Combination of P_x, P_y, and M_0. Let it be assumed that the forces P_x, P_y and the moment M_0 are applied simultaneously at the free end of the beam in Fig. 260. Let Δ_x, Δ_y, and θ be the resulting deflections in the x and y directions and the change in slope, respectively, at the free end. By applying the foregoing Eqs. 562 through 568 we can compute the separate effects of each force and moment and combine them to obtain the following expressions:

$$\Delta_x = P_x(I_{Lx}/EI) - P_y(I_{Lxy}/EI) + M_0(M_{Lx}/EI) \tag{569}$$

$$\Delta_y = -P_x(I_{Lxy}/EI) + P_y(I_{Ly}/EI) - M_0(M_{Ly}/EI) \tag{570}$$

$$\theta = P_x(M_{Lx}/EI) - P_y(M_{Ly}/EI) + M_0(L/EI) \tag{571}$$

The explanation of the signs in Eqs. 569, 570, and 571 is as follows: Δ_x and Δ_y are positive and P_x and P_y are positive when in the positive direction of the X and Y axes, respectively; θ and M_0 are positive when each tends to increase the slope, that is, to move from the positive end of the X axis toward the positive end of the Y axis; I_{Lx} and I_{Ly} and L are always positive; and M_{Lx}, M_{Ly}, and I_{Lxy} may be either positive or negative, depending on the choice of position of the X and Y axes and upon the shape of the centerline of the length L of the beam. However, the signs in these equations are arranged so that when all these quantities are substituted with their proper sign the values of Δ_x, Δ_y, and θ will have the correct sign.

The following illustrative problem shows how the foregoing expressions can be used to solve for the deflection when P_x, P_y, and M_0 act simultaneously on the beam.

Illustrative Problem

Problem 279. Figure 261 shows a cylindrical rod of total length $3l$ that is bent sharply at its third points to make right angles as shown at B and C. All three lengths l lie in the same plane (xy plane) after the rod is bent. The end at A is fixed, and the free end is subjected to loads P_x, P_y and a moment M_0 that lies in the xy plane. At the free end find the deflections in the x and y directions and the rotation in the xy plane by means of Eqs. 569, 570, and 571.

Solution. The forces P_x and P_y are positive since they act in the directions of the positive ends of the axes; also M_0 is positive. We compute the properties of the line L as follows:

$$M_{Lx} = l \cdot l + \tfrac{1}{2}l \cdot l = \tfrac{3}{2}l^2 \qquad M_{Ly} = l \cdot l + \tfrac{3}{2}l \cdot l + \tfrac{1}{2}l \cdot l = 3l^2$$

$$I_{Lx} = I_{xAB} + I_{xBC} = l^3 + (l^3/3) = \tfrac{4}{3}l^3$$

$$I_{Ly} = I_{yAB} + I_{yBC} + I_{yCD} = [(l^3/12) + l(\tfrac{3}{2}l)^2] + l^3 + (l^3/3) = \tfrac{11}{3}l^3$$

$$I_{Lxy} = I_{xyAB} + I_{xyBC} + I_{xyCD} = l \cdot \tfrac{3}{2}l \cdot l + l \cdot l \cdot \tfrac{1}{2}l + l \cdot \tfrac{1}{2}l \cdot 0 = 2l^3$$

The substitution of these quantities and $L = 3l$ into Eqs. 569, 570, and 571, respectively, gives

$$\Delta_x = \frac{1}{EI}\left(\frac{4}{3}l^3 P_x - 2l^3 P_y + \frac{3}{2}l^2 M_0\right)$$

$$\Delta_y = \frac{1}{EI}\left(-2l^3 P_x + \frac{11}{3}l^3 P_y - 3l^2 M_0\right)$$

$$\theta = \frac{1}{EI}\left(\frac{3}{2}l^2 P_x - 3l^2 P_y + 3lM_0\right)$$

Problems

280. Solve Prob. 269 by making use of Eqs. 569, 570, and 571.

281. In Prob. 269 solve for the deflection Δ_x in the direction of the X axis.

Chapter 16

FORCES AND MOMENTS IN STATICALLY INDETERMINATE MEMBERS AND STRUCTURES

147 Introduction. Even though a member is in equilibrium under the action of a known type of force system, it may not be possible to determine all the unknown forces and moments (couples) acting on a member in a machine or structure from the conditions of equilibrium alone, for the reason that the number of unknowns may be greater than the number of conditions of equilibrium for the force system involved. Hence additional conditions or equations must be found, to be used in conjunction with the equilibrium conditions, in order to determine the unknown forces and moments. Such members are said to be statically indeterminate. The additional conditions will usually involve the deformational behavior of the member or structure, and this chapter discusses methods of expressing and using these additional conditions for obtaining the forces and moments in statically indeterminate members or structures.

A member may be said to be statically indeterminate externally or internally, according as the unknown quantities are, respectively, external forces (reactions, etc.) or internal forces; this distinction is merely a matter of convenience, for any force may be considered to be external to a part of a member.

The more common types of statically indeterminate members or structures are those that may be assumed to be in a single plane such as a beam, and a truss or similar framework of members. For such members or structures the conditions of equilibrium expressed algebraically furnish three equations, one set of three being

$$\Sigma F_x = 0 \qquad \Sigma F_y = 0 \qquad \Sigma M = 0$$

and the same conditions expressed graphically require that the force and funicular (or string) polygons shall close. For a non-coplanar force system six equations of equilibrium may be written.

Physical Significance. Redundant Element. The physical meaning of statical indeterminateness is seen in the condition that there are more supports or more members present in the machine or structure than are necessary to maintain equilibrium of the structure; that is, the structure will still resist the loads if one or more supports or members are

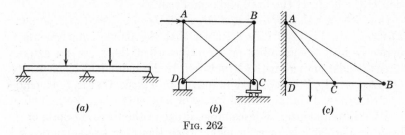

FIG. 262

omitted. Supports or members that may be removed without destroying the equilibrium of the member or structure are said to be redundant supports or redundant members.

For example, the beam in Fig. 262a is statically indeterminate externally. The middle support could be removed, and the beam would still be in equilibrium; the beam has one redundant support. The structures represented in Figs. 262b and 262c may be considered to be statically indeterminate internally. One member (*AC*, for example) could be removed in each structure, and the remaining structure would resist the loads; each structure has one redundant element.

Importance of Deformation. The forces or moments in a statically indeterminate member or structure not only must satisfy the conditions of equilibrium but also must be consistent with the deformations imposed by the geometry of the deformed member or structure and by the nature of the restraints. This fact is frequently stated by saying that the forces and moments must satisfy the law of consistent deformations. The additional equations needed to supplement the equations of

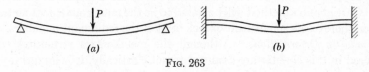

FIG. 263

equilibrium are obtained by expressing, in various ways, this so-called law of consistent deformations. For example, let Figs. 263a and 263b represent two beams of the same material and dimensions, and let each beam be subjected to a load *P* at its mid-point. The beams differ only in the restraints at the ends; in Fig. 263a the ends are simply supported, and in Fig. 263b the ends are supported and clamped, that is, fixed. The difference in the shape of the elastically deflected beams caused by the difference in restraints at the ends is shown, and the additional equation necessary for solving for the moments at the ends of the beam of Fig. 263b is found by expressing the fact that no rotation of the section of the beam at the fixed ends can occur.

Initial or Residual Forces and Moments Due to Misfit of Redundant Element. In Fig. 262 it is assumed that the redundant elements fit perfectly into the member or structure when there are no external forces (loads) acting on the structure. If the redundant element does not fit perfectly, it is necessary to force it into place, that is, the member or structure will contain initial forces or moments when the redundant is fitted into its place. For example, if one of the three supports of the beam in Fig. 262a is lower or higher than the other two supports, it is necessary to bend the beam to bring it into contact with all three supports. Also, if in Fig. 262b one of the members AC or BD is too long or too short to fit into the joints at its ends, it will be necessary to deform the structure or the member to force it into place. Under these conditions the beam (Fig. 262a) would contain initial bending moments, and the members of the truss (Fig. 262b) would contain initial axial forces before any loads are applied. The values of the initial moments or forces will depend upon the amount of deformation of the member or structure that is necessary to make the redundant element fit into place.

In the examples considered in this chapter it will first be assumed that no initial forces or moments are present in the member or structure and also that only small elastic deformations occur. Later in the chapter (Art. 156) the influence of lack of fit on the elastic forces in statically indeterminate structures will be considered. Furthermore, both the dummy load methods and Castigliano's method will be used in introducing the elastic deformational behavior of the structure; the dummy load method will be used primarily for a structure in which the members fit perfectly, and Castigliano's method will be found to be the more convenient method when there exists some misfit or lack of fit of the redundant members.

Inelastic Deformations. Although the members or structures considered in this chapter are assumed to act elastically, it is important to note that in many machines or structures the various members or supports of the structure may deform partly inelastically without destroying the proper load-resisting function of the structure. Thus the condition which limits the maximum utilizable loads that may be applied to the structure may not be the *beginning* of inelastic deformation in the elastically most-stressed member as is assumed in the design for elasticity.   The influence of small inelastic deformations on the load-carrying capacity of a member is discussed in Chapter 17.   Furthermore, if the safe loads for a structure are determined as some part of the ultimate (maximum) loads which the structure can resist without total destruction or collapse (so-called ultimate-load design, see Chapter 19), the distribution of forces to the members of the structure based on elastic behavior of the structure would be of secondary importance. In ultimate-load design, however, special attention must be given to the buckling action of slender compression members.

Degree of Statical Indeterminateness.   The degree of statical indeterminateness of a structure may be defined algebraically as the number

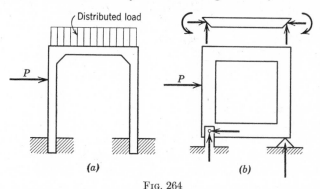

(a)   (b)

FIG. 264

of unknown forces or moments in excess of the number of equations of equilibrium that may be written.   Consider that, for any given (plane) structure, each component member may be taken out and treated as a free body (see Fig. 264).   Then at each end of the member there may exist a moment, a thrust, and a shear, or six unknown quantities for each member, the loads on the members being assumed to be known. For each member the three equations of equilibrium, $\Sigma F_x = 0$, $\Sigma F_y = 0$, and $\Sigma M = 0$, may be written.   Hence, if there are n members in the structure, $3n$ independent equations of equilibrium may be written. If b is the number of unknown quantities (forces, moments, etc.) that may exist at the ends of the member and at the connection of the structure with the ground or foundation, we may write the following equation for a statically indeterminate member or structure

$$b - 3n = m \qquad (572)$$

where m indicates the degree of indeterminateness of the structure.

It must not be assumed, however, that the degree of indeterminateness alone indicates the difficulty or work involved in solving for the unknown forces and moments in a structure, for the solution may be greatly simplified by the conditions of symmetry of the loads or of the structure or of both.

Procedure. The procedure for determining the elastic forces and couples exerted by redundant supports and members varies somewhat with the type of problem, but it is helpful to have in mind a general method in attacking any problem. The main steps in the procedure may be stated as follows:

Remove redundant supports or redundant members (or both), making the member, structure, or machine statically determinate, and by use of the principles discussed in the preceding chapters of Part IV write an expression for the elastic deformation or deflection in the direction of the forces and couples exerted by these redundant supports and members. Then, in place of the redundant supports and members removed, introduce the forces and couples which they exert on the other members, and, from the same principles, write an expression for the elastic deformation which these forces or couples produce; if the redundant element removed is a member that exerts two equal and opposite forces on the remaining structure, the deformation found is the deformation of the application point of one force with respect to the other. By this general procedure two expressions are found for the same deformation or deflection, one expression involving the known forces of a statically determinate member, the other involving the unknown forces exerted by the redundant members. This procedure will be illustrated in the following articles, in which the deformations are assumed to be elastic.

Application of Dummy Load Method

148   Beam fixed at one end, simply supported at other end. *Load Uniformly Distributed.* The elastic beam is represented in Fig. 265a and is one degree or onefold statically indeterminate. Let the reaction R_1 be taken as the redundant element. If, then, R_1 is removed, the end will deflect an amount δ_1 (Fig. 265b). The value of δ_1 may be found, by the dummy load method, to be

$$\delta_1 = \int \frac{Mm\, dx}{EI} = \int_0^l \frac{wx^3\, dx}{2EI} = \frac{wl^4}{8EI}$$

The deflection δ_2 produced by R_1 must be equal and opposite to δ_1. The deflection caused by R_1 will be R_1 times the deflection δ' caused by

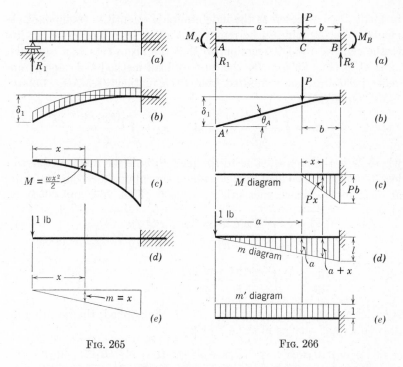

FIG. 265   FIG. 266

a 1-lb load at the end. By the dummy load method we may write

$$\delta' = \int \frac{m^2 \, dx}{EI} = \int_0^l \frac{x^2 \, dx}{EI} = \frac{l^3}{3EI}$$

But, since the point does not move, δ_2 must be equal in magnitude to δ_1, and hence

$$R_1 l^3 / 3EI = w l^4 / 8EI$$

Therefore $R_1 = \frac{3}{8} w l$

All other reactions, moments, etc., may now be found by the equations of equilibrium.

Problem

282. In the beam considered in the foregoing article, let the redundant element be the couple M_0 at the wall, and find its value by use of Eq. 554 of Art. 143, Chapter 15.

149 Beam fixed at both ends. *Single Concentrated Load.* The elastic beam in Fig. 266a is twofold statically indeterminate, since there are four reactions (a moment or couple and a shear force at each end) and only two equations of equilibrium. Let the reaction R_1 and the moment M_A be chosen as the indeterminate quantities (redundant elements). Let R_1 and M_A be removed; that is, let a section be cut just to the right of the left reaction, so that the beam acts as a cantilever fixed at B (Fig. 266b). By the dummy load method the slope θ_A and deflection δ_1 may be computed from the equations (see Arts. 142 and 143, Chapter 15):

$$\delta_1 = \int \frac{Mm \, dx}{EI} \quad \text{and} \quad \theta_A = \int \frac{Mm' \, dx}{EI}$$

where M is the moment due to the load P, m is the moment due to a load of unity applied at A, and m' is the moment due to a couple of unity applied at A. Hence, measuring x from C (Figs. 266c and 266d), we obtain

$$\delta_1 = \int_0^b \frac{Px(a + x) \, dx}{EI} = \frac{Pb^2}{EI}\left(\frac{a}{2} + \frac{b}{3}\right)$$

$$\theta_A = \int_0^b \frac{Px \, dx}{EI} = \frac{Pb^2}{2EI}$$

Now let the reaction R_1 and moment M_A be applied; the resulting deflection δ'_1 and change in slope θ'_A are

$$\delta'_1 = \int \frac{Mm \, dx}{EI} = \int_0^l \frac{(R_1 x - M_A)x \, dx}{EI} = \frac{1}{EI}\left(\frac{R_1 l^3}{3} - \frac{M_A l^2}{2}\right)$$

$$\theta'_A = \int \frac{Mm' \, dx}{EI} = \int_0^l \frac{(R_1 x - M_A) \, dx}{EI} = \frac{1}{EI}\left(\frac{R_1 l^2}{2} - M_A l\right)$$

Since there is no deflection and no change of slope at A, $\delta_1 = \delta'_1$, and $\theta_A = \theta'_A$. Hence we may write

$$\frac{Pb^2}{EI}\left(\frac{a}{2} + \frac{b}{3}\right) = \frac{1}{EI}\left(\frac{R_1 l^3}{3} - \frac{M_A l^2}{2}\right)$$

and

$$\frac{Pb^2}{2EI} = -\frac{M_A l}{EI} + \frac{R_1 l^2}{2EI}$$

Solving these equations, we obtain

$$R_1 = (Pb^2/l^3)(3a + b) \quad \text{and} \quad M_A = Pab^2/l^2$$

150 Semicircular beam fixed at both ends. In Fig. 267a, let ABC represent a cylindrical bar in the form of a semicircular beam fixed at both ends and subjected to a concentrated load P at the midpoint B. The radius of the bar is r, and the radius of the beam is R;

it is assumed that R is large compared to r. Let it be required to find the reactions at the ends of the beam.

At each end of the beam there are three reactive elements, namely a shear V_0, a bending moment M_0, and a twisting moment T_0 as shown at the end A in Fig. 267b. From the conditions of symmetry it is known that the same values exist at the other end C. Furthermore, the problem is simplified if one-half the beam is removed by cutting it at B. A shearing force of $P/2$ and an unknown bending moment M_1 in the plane perpendicular to ABC must be placed at B to replace the effects at this section caused by the part that is removed. The twisting moment at section B is zero owing to symmetry.

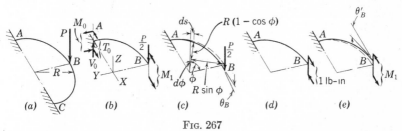

$$(a) \qquad (b) \qquad (c) \qquad (d) \qquad (e)$$

Fig. 267

The system of forces and couples, including the reactions at A, in Fig. 267b is equivalent to a system of parallel forces in space, and hence there are three equations of equilibrium. Thus, by use of the condition of symmetry the number of unknowns is reduced from six to four, namely, V_0, M_0, T_0, and M_1, and there is only one redundant element. From the equations of equilibrium we obtain the following relationships for the forces shown in Fig. 267b:

$$\Sigma F_z = V_0 - (P/2) = 0 \qquad\qquad V_0 = P/2$$

$$\Sigma M_x = M_0 - (PR/2) = 0 \qquad\qquad M_0 = PR/2$$

$$\Sigma M_y = T_0 + M_1 - (PR/2) = 0 \qquad T_0 = (PR/2) - M_1$$

From the last equation it is noted that we must determine the moment M_1 at section B before T_0 can be found. To find M_1 it is regarded as the redundant element and is removed from the member which would then be loaded as shown in Fig. 267c. The load $P/2$ causes at B a change of slope θ_B of the beam in the plane of M_1 which is given by the equation (see Art. 145, Chapter 15)

$$\theta_B = \int_0^{\pi/2} \frac{Mm'\,ds}{EI} + \int_0^{\pi/2} \frac{Tt\,ds}{GJ}$$

From Figs. 267c and 267d, we obtain

$$M = (PR/2) \sin \phi \qquad m' = 1 \times \cos \phi \qquad ds = R \, d\phi$$

$$T = (PR/2)(1 - \cos \phi) \qquad t = 1 \times \sin \phi$$

Thus the expression for θ_B becomes

$$\theta_B = \frac{PR^2}{2EI} \int_0^{\pi/2} \sin \phi \cos \phi \, d\phi + \frac{PR^2}{2GJ} \int_0^{\pi/2} (\sin \phi - \sin \phi \cos \phi) \, d\phi$$

$$= \frac{PR^2}{4EI} \left[\sin^2 \phi \right]_0^{\pi/2} + \frac{PR^2}{2GJ} \left[-\cos \phi - \frac{1}{2} \sin^2 \phi \right]_0^{\pi/2}$$

$$= \frac{PR^2}{4} \left[\frac{1}{EI} + \frac{1}{GJ} \right]$$

But the value of M_1 must be such that the actual change in slope of the beam at B is zero. This means that the change in slope θ'_B due to M_1 (and the reactions), as shown in Fig. 267e, must be equal and opposite to θ_B caused by the load $P/2$ (and the reactions) in Fig. 267c. The angle θ'_B is given by the equation

$$\theta'_B = \int_0^{\pi/2} \frac{Mm' \, ds}{EI} + \int_0^{\pi/2} \frac{Tt \, ds}{GJ}$$

From Figs. 267d and 267e the quantities M, T, m', and t for this equation are

$$M = M_1 \cos \phi \qquad m' = 1 \times \cos \phi \qquad ds = R \, d\phi$$

$$T = M_1 \sin \phi \qquad t = 1 \times \sin \phi$$

Thus the expression for θ'_B becomes

$$\theta'_B = \frac{M_1 R}{EI} \int_0^{\pi/2} \cos^2 \phi \, d\phi + \frac{M_1 R}{GJ} \int_0^{\pi/2} \sin^2 \phi \, d\phi$$

$$= \frac{M_1 R}{EI} \left[\frac{\phi}{2} + \frac{1}{4} \sin^2 \phi \right]_0^{\pi/2} + \frac{M_1 R}{GJ} \left[\frac{\phi}{2} - \frac{1}{4} \sin^2 \phi \right]_0^{\pi/2}$$

$$= \frac{\pi M_1 R}{4} \left[\frac{1}{EI} + \frac{1}{GJ} \right]$$

From the fact that $\theta_B = \theta'_B$ we have

$$\frac{PR^2}{4} \left[\frac{1}{EI} + \frac{1}{GJ} \right] = \frac{\pi M_1 R}{4} \left[\frac{1}{EI} + \frac{1}{GJ} \right]$$

Hence $M_1 = PR/\pi$

The substitution of this value of M_1 in the last one of the equation of equilibrium gives

$$T_0 = \frac{PR}{2} - \frac{PR}{\pi} = PR\left(\frac{\pi - 2}{2\pi}\right)$$

151 Two-hinged frame. *Concentrated Load at Mid-span.* Let Fig. 268 represent a two-hinged frame having the dimensions and moments of inertia indicated in the figure. Let the horizontal reaction H be selected as the redundant quantity. If then H is removed and

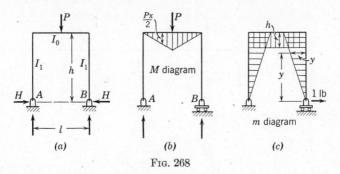

FIG. 268

the base B of the right-hand column is placed on rollers so that it is free to move outward, it will move a distance

$$\delta_1 = \int (Mm/EI)\, dx$$

in which M is the moment at any point due to the given loading with the redundant quantity removed, and m is the moment at any point due to the load of unity at the point where the deflection is to be found.

If, now, an inward horizontal force H is applied at B, the deflection δ_2 it produces will be opposite to, and H times, the deflection caused by a 1-lb outward force at B (Fig. 268c). Hence

$$\delta_2 = -H \int (m^2/EI)\, dx$$

Since the point B does not move, $\delta_1 + \delta_2 = 0$, and hence

$$\int (Mm/EI)\, dx - H \int (m^2/EI)\, dx = 0$$

or

$$H = \frac{\int (Mm/EI)\, dx}{\int (m^2/EI)\, dx} \tag{573}$$

This is a standard form of expression for the solution of a onefold statically indeterminate structure. The values of M and m are indicated in the moment diagrams in Figs. 268b and 268c. The values of M are seen to be zero for the columns of the bent, and the moment diagram for the top girder is the same as that for a simple beam similarly loaded. The value of m for a section of the column is seen to be equal to the distance of the section from the base, or $m = y$, and the value of m for the top girder is constant and equal to h. Hence

$$H = \frac{2\int_0^{l/2} \dfrac{Ph}{2EI_0}}{2\int_0^h \dfrac{y^2\,dy}{EI_1} + \int_0^l \dfrac{h^2\,dx}{EI_0}} = \frac{\dfrac{Pl^2h}{8I_0}}{\dfrac{2h^3}{3I_1} + \dfrac{lh^2}{I_0}}$$

Letting $I_0 h / I_1 l = n$, we have

$$H = \frac{Pl}{8h}\frac{3}{2n+3}$$

All other reactions, moments, and forces may now be found by the usual equations of equilibrium.

152   Continuous truss on three supports. Let it be required to determine the magnitude of the reactions and the axial forces in the

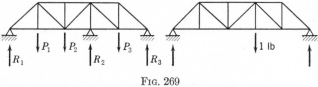

Fig. 269

pin-connected truss shown in Fig. 269. Let the reaction R_2 be the redundant quantity. Let the central support be removed, and let S denote the axial force in any member of the resulting statically determinate truss due to the given loads P_1, P_2, etc. Let a unit load be applied to the truss at the central support (Fig. 269), and let u denote the axial force in any member due to this unit load.

As discussed in Art. 141, the deflection δ_1 of the truss of Fig. 269, with the central support removed, is $\delta_1 = \Sigma(Sul/aE)$. If now an upward force R_2 be applied to the truss just sufficient to lift the panel point R_2 to its original position, the deflection δ_3 due to this force R_2

would be equal and opposite to δ_1, and would be R_2 times the deflection δ_2 caused by a 1-lb load. Hence

$$\delta_3 = -R_2\delta_2 = -R_2\,\Sigma(u^2l/aE)$$

But $\qquad \delta_1 + \delta_3 = 0 = \Sigma(Sul/aE) - R_2\,\Sigma(u^2l/aE)$

Hence $\qquad\qquad R_2 = \dfrac{\Sigma(Sul/aE)}{\Sigma(u^2l/aE)}$ (574)

The similarity of this expression, for members resisting axial forces, to the expression found for H in the preceding example which involved

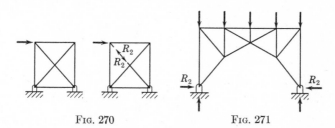

FIG. 270 FIG. 271

bending moments should be noted. The expression is encountered in problems where a single indeterminate reaction or redundant member is present. For example, in the redundant frame of Fig. 270 one member may be selected as the redundant member and cut in two; if R_2 denotes the indeterminate force in this member, its value may be found from Eq. 574. Again, in the two-hinged spandrel braced arch of Fig. 271 the horizontal reaction R_2 at the supports may be taken as the indeterminate quantity and Eq. 574 then applied.

153 King post truss. In a king post truss (Fig. 272), part of the load P is carried by beam action, and part by truss action. The procedure in determining moments and forces, however, is the same as

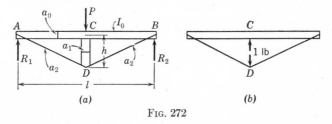

FIG. 272

that applied in the preceding articles and outlined in Art. 147. In Fig. 272, let CD be the redundant member. Let CD, then, be removed, and let the deflection δ_1 of C in the direction of CD be found; or, rather, let the relative deflection of the application points of the two forces exerted by CD be found. The expression of δ_1 would be, in general,

$$\delta_1 = \Sigma(Sul/aE) + \int (Mm/EI)\, dx \qquad (575)$$

but in this case, since no force would occur in AD and BD, we have

$$\delta_1 = \int (Mm/EI)\, dx \qquad (576)$$

Now, if the forces S_{CD} exerted by CD were acting alone (Fig. 272b), the relative deformation δ_2 of their points of application would be S_{CD} times the relative deflection caused by 1-lb forces. Hence

$$\delta_2 = S_{CD}[\Sigma(u^2l/aE) + \int (m^2/EI)\, dx] \qquad (577)$$

in which $\Sigma(u^2l/aE)$ involves all members, including CD, and, since δ_1 must be equal to δ_2, we have

$$S_{CD} = \frac{\displaystyle \int (Mm/EI)\, dx}{\displaystyle \Sigma(u^2l/aE) + \int (m^2/EI)\, dx} \qquad (578)$$

After the force in CD is found, the forces and moments in other members may be found from the equations of equilibrium.

154 Forces and moments in pipe line due to temperature change. In Fig. 273a the outline $ABCDE$ represents a typical two-dimensional (all lengths in the same plane) steam pipe line. The pipe

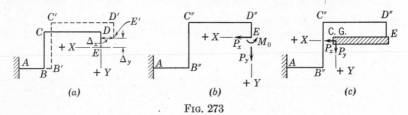

(a)   (b)   (c)

Fig. 273

is usually fixed at the ends A and E so that it can be assumed that the deflection and rotation of the ends are negligible. Such pipes are fastened into place * at ordinary (room) temperature, but the steam or

---

* It is customary to make such pipes with dimensions that are shorter than the actual distance between the fixed ends A and E and to force the pipe into place by so-called cold stretching. Thus, when installed at room temperature the pipe has

other fluid that moves through the pipe is usually at a somewhat higher (or lower) temperature than room temperature. The pipe tends to take the temperature of the fluid, and in doing so it expands or contracts, thereby causing forces and moments throughout the length of the pipe because the fixed ends cannot translate or rotate.

Expansion Due to Temperature Rise. When the pipe, whose centerline lies in one plane only, tends to expand in length as a result of an increase in temperature, two forces and a bending moment are necessary at each end of the pipe to hold it to its fixtures, that is, there are a total of six unknown forces and moments to be determined. To explain this fact, let it be assumed that the pipe is unfastened at E before the temperature rises. When the rise in temperature occurs, each length of pipe expands, B moving to B', C to C', D to D', and E to E'. The distances Δ_x and Δ_y moved through by the free end E are easily computed from a knowledge of the coefficient of expansion of the material and the change in temperature of the pipe. It is important to note that such an expansion as described here always causes a translation of elemental lengths of the pipe with no bending rotation (or change of slope) involved. Hence there is no rotation at the point E as it moves to E', which means that the change in slope θ is zero.

Forces and Moment Necessary To Restore Free End to Fixture. In Fig. 273b are shown the forces P_x, P_y and the moment M_0 at the end E that are necessary to deflect the end through the known distances Δ_x and Δ_y and at the same time prevent any change in slope θ at the end. Equations 569, 570, and 571 of Chapter 15 are the equations from which P_x, P_y, and M may be found. Thus we may write

$$P_x(I_{Lx}/EI) - P_y(I_{Lxy}/EI) + M_0(M_{Lx}/EI) = \Delta_x \qquad (579)$$

$$-P_x(I_{Lxy}/EI) + P_y(I_{Ly}/EI) - M_0(M_{Ly}/EI) = \Delta_y \qquad (580)$$

$$P_x(M_{Lx}/EI) - P_y(M_{Ly}/EI) + M_0(L/EI) = 0 \qquad (581)$$

The quantities in the coefficients of P_x, P_y, and M_0 in Eqs. 579, 580, and 581 have been defined in Art. 146 of Chapter 15. Equations 579, 580, and 581 are three linear simultaneous equations in P_x, P_y, and M_0 and can be solved when the values of the coefficients are substituted.

residual forces and moments in it, but when it reaches the operating temperature these residual forces and moments are partly or wholly removed, depending upon how much cold stretching is applied. However, in the analysis considered here, no cold stretching is assumed. It should be noted that if the pipe line is operated at a temperature at which creep takes place these forces and moments are no longer determined by assuming an elastic material.

The forces and the moments at any section of the pipe can then be computed.

Use of Centroid of Pipe Line. The number of simultaneous linear equations that must be solved, such as Eqs. 579, 580, and 581, can be reduced from 3 to 2 by selecting the origin of the axes X and Y at the centroid of the pipe system (Fig. 273c) rather than at the end (Fig. 273b). This fact becomes evident from Eqs. 579, 580, and 581 by noting that the values of the first moments M_{Lx} and M_{Ly} are each equal to zero if X and Y are centroidal axes. Under these conditions Eqs. 579, 580, and 581 reduce to

$$P_x(\bar{I}_{Lx}/EI) - P_y(\bar{I}_{Lxy}/EI) = \Delta_x \qquad (582)$$

$$-P_x(\bar{I}_{Lxy}/EI) + P_y(\bar{I}_{Ly}/EI) = \Delta_y \qquad (583)$$

The cross-hatched bar in Fig. 273c extending from E to the centroid of the pipe system represents a fictitious rigid connection through which the forces P_x, P_y applied at the centroid exert the forces P_x, P_y and the moment M_0 on the end of the pipe. It should be noted from Eq. 581 that the moment M_0 which must be applied at the centroid is equal to zero when the axes are chosen with the origin at the centroid, since all other terms in Eq. 581 are zero. Thus the application of P_x and P_y at the centroid is equivalent to applying the same forces and the moment M_0 at the end.

Three-dimensional Pipe Systems. If the pipe in Fig. 273 has lengths that are not all in the same plane, it is called a three-dimensional pipe system. Under these conditions there exist at each end of the pipe two transverse forces, one axial force, two bending moments, and one twisting moment when a change in temperature of the pipe occurs. Thus, since there are twelve unknowns and six equations of equilibrium, such a pipe line has six redundants. Thus, six equations similar to Eqs. 579, 580, and 581 are needed, but these equations can be reduced to three by making use of the centroid as in Eqs. 582 and 583; see reference 7 at the end of this chapter.

Illustrative Problem

Problem 283. In Fig. 274a is represented a pipe line in which three equal lengths of $l = 20$ ft lie in one plane. The ends A and D are rigidly fastened when the temperature is 70° F and there are no fixed end moments or forces at this temperature. The pipe is of steel of nominal outside diameter of 12 in. and wall thickness $t = 0.687$ in. so that $I = 475$ in.[4]. The pipe carries steam at 500° F, and at this temperature $E = 26{,}400{,}000$ lb per sq in. and the coefficient of expansion is such that as the temperature rises from 70° F to 500° F 100 ft of this pipe will expand in length 3.75 in. Calculate the forces and moment at the end of the pipe when the temperature is 500° F.

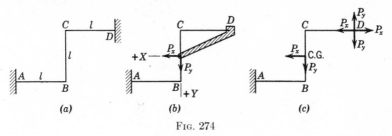

FIG. 274

Solution. We first assume the end at D to be free (detached from its fastening), and the deflections Δ_x and Δ_y of the free end caused by the expansion are calculated as follows:

$$\Delta_x = \text{Expansion of } AB + \text{Expansion of } CD$$

$$= (20 \times 3.75)/100 + (20 \times 3.75)/100 = 1.5 \text{ in.}$$

$$\Delta_y = \text{Expansion of } BC = (20 \times 3.75)/100 = 0.75 \text{ in.}$$

By selecting the X and Y axes at the centroid, we need to find only forces P_x and P_y acting at the centroid to restore the end at D to its fixed or fastened position. We compute for use in Eqs. 582 and 583 the following:

$$\bar{I}_{Lx} = 2[l \cdot (l/2)^2] + \tfrac{1}{12}l^3 = \tfrac{7}{12}l^3 = \tfrac{7}{12}(240)^3 = 8.05 \times 10^6 \text{ in.}^3$$

$$\bar{I}_{Ly} = 2(\tfrac{1}{3}l^3) = \tfrac{2}{3}(240)^3 = 9.23 \times 10^6 \text{ in.}^3$$

$$\bar{I}_{Lxy} = l(\tfrac{1}{2}l)(\tfrac{1}{2}l) + l(-\tfrac{1}{2}l)(-\tfrac{1}{2}l) = \tfrac{1}{2}l^3 = \tfrac{1}{2}(240)^3 = 6.9 \times 10^6 \text{ in.}^3$$

We substitute the foregoing quantities in Eq. 582 and 583 and obtain

$$\frac{8.05 \times 10^6}{26.4 \times 10^6 \times 475} P_x - \frac{6.9 \times 10^6}{26.4 \times 10^6 \times 475} P_y = 1.5$$

$$-\frac{6.9 \times 10^6}{26.4 \times 10^6 \times 475} P_x + \frac{9.23 \times 10^6}{26.4 \times 10^6 \times 475} P_y = 0.75$$

These equations reduce to

$$1.818 P_x - 1.558 P_y = 4250$$

$$-1.360 P_x + 1.818 P_y = 1852$$

from which $P_x = 8950$ lb and $P_y = 7700$ lb. To get the moment at end D it is necessary only to transform the forces P_x and P_y at the centroid into equivalent forces and couples at the point D as shown in Fig. 274c. The total moment at D is the algebraic sum of the clockwise couple $P_x l/2$ and the counterclockwise couple $P_y l$. Hence, $M_0 = 7700 \times 240 - 8950 \times 120 = 775{,}000$ lb-in., counterclockwise.

From the equations of equilibrium it is found that the forces and moment at A are equal, respectively, to the corresponding values at D. However, the maximum bending moment occurs at C, its value being $M_c = 1{,}072{,}000$ lb-in.

Problems

284. Find, by the dummy load method, the reaction R_2 of the central support of the truss shown in Fig. 275. Assume E and a are the same for all members.

Ans. $R_2 = 3280$ lb upward.

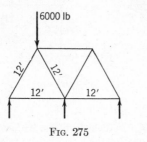

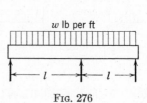

FIG. 275   FIG. 276

285. Find, by the dummy load method, the reaction R_2 of the central support in the continuous beam of Fig. 276, in which the left span length is $l = 12$ ft and the right is $l = 9$ ft.

286. A beam is fixed at one end and supported at the other; it is subjected to a concentrated load P at the mid-span section. Find, by the dummy load method, the reaction of the support in terms of P. *Ans.* $R = \frac{5}{16}P$.

287. In Fig. 277 is shown a cylindrical shaft of circular cross section that is fixed at both ends. If the shaft is subjected to a twisting moment T as shown, find the resisting twisting moment at each end.

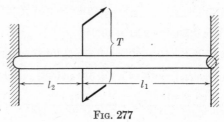

FIG. 277

288. In Prob. 286 let the moment at the wall be assumed to be the redundant quantity, and find the value of this moment by using the dummy load method.

Ans. $M = -\frac{3}{16}Pl$.

289. Figure 278 represents a steam pipe whose ends are fixed into place at 70° F with no moments or forces at the ends at this temperature. The pipe is to carry

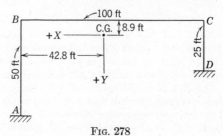

FIG. 278

steam at a temperature of 700° F. If the pipe has an inside diameter of 11.626 in.
and an outside diameter of 12.75 in. (this gives $I = 400$ in.[4]) and expands 5.75 in.
per 100 ft with the given change in temperature, compute the forces P_x and P_y and
moments at the ends of the pipe due to the temperature change. Assume that
$E = 25,000,000$ lb per sq in. at 700° F.

$Ans.$ $P_x = 1220$ lb; $P_y = 199$ lb.

$M_D = 372,000$ lb-in.; $M_A = 500,000$ lb-in.

290. Figure 279 represents a rigid beam (one in which the deflections are negligible)
supported on three identical elastic posts. Compute the reactions in the three posts
due to the load P. $Ans.$ $R_1 = 7P/12$; $R_2 = 4P/12$, $R_3 = P/12$.

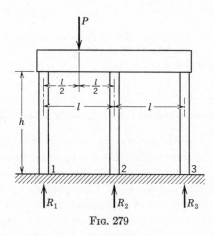

FIG. 279

291. A beam loaded at mid-span by P (Fig. 280) is fixed at one end and supported
at the other by a coil spring that resists deflection at that end with a force proportional to the deflection; that is, if δ is the deflection at the spring, the force (or reaction) is $R = K\delta$, where K is the spring constant. Compute the reaction at each end
of the beam and the moment at the fixed end in terms of P, E, I, and K.

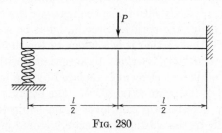

FIG. 280

292. Solve Prob. 283 if the length $l = 40$ ft and all other data are the same.

293. In Fig. 272, the following data are given: $P = 1000$ lb, $a_0 = 10$ sq in., $a_1 = 4$
sq in., $a_2 = 2$ sq in., $I_0 = 220$ in.[4], $l = 16$ ft, $h = 6$ ft. Find the forces in CD and
AD, and the maximum bending moment in AB. Assume the E is the same for all
members. $Ans.$ $S_{CD} = 870$ lb; $S_{AD} = 725$ lb; $M = 520$ lb-ft.

294. In Fig. 281 find the bending moment M_A at the fixed end of the member in terms of the known quantities P, h, and l.   *Ans.* $M = \frac{1}{2}Ph$.

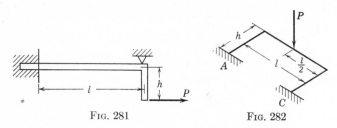

FIG. 281   FIG. 282

295. In Fig. 282 find the twisting moment T_0 at the fixed ends A and C of the bar in terms of the known quantities P, h, and l. The bar is a cylindrical rod whose radius r is small compared to h and l.

$$Ans. \quad T = \frac{Pl^2}{8E[(h/G) + (l/E)]}.$$

Application of Castigliano's Theorem

155 Advantage of theorem. In carrying out the procedure out-lined in Art. 147 for determining the forces and moments in statically indeterminate elastic structures, Castigliano's theorem may be used instead of the dummy load method. Castigliano's method is especially convenient when the number of redundants in the statically indetermi-nate structure is small and when there is a misfit in one or more of the redundant members, as will be illustrated in the following articles.

156 Beam fixed at one end, supported by spring at other end. *Load Uniformly Distributed.* Let Fig. 283 represent the beam and spring (the structure), and let the force in the coil spring be the redundant element. Two problems will be considered. First, let it be assumed that before the uniformly distributed load is applied the redundant ele-ment (spring) fits perfectly into the space between the end of the beam and the support below the spring. Second, let it be assumed that the spring does not fit, that is, that it is too long or too short by a length λ.

Redundant Element Fits Perfectly. In accordance with the procedure of Art. 147, the redundant element is replaced by the force R_1 which it exerts on the end of the beam (Fig. 283b). The beam is now considered to be a statically determinate cantilever beam subjected to the loads w and R_1. Let U_b be the elastic strain energy stored in the beam after these loads are applied. By Castigliano's theorem (Chapter 14) the deflection at the load R_1 is

$$\delta_1 = -\partial U_b/\partial R_1 \tag{584}$$

The negative sign in Eq. 584 means that δ_1 is opposite in sense to R_1.

In Fig. 283b it is shown that the force R_1 also deflects the top end of the spring a distance δ_2. If U_s represents the elastic strain energy stored in the spring, then by Castigliano's theorem the deflection δ_2 of the spring is

$$\delta_2 = \partial U_s/\partial R_1 \tag{585}$$

The positive sign is used in Eq. 585 since in Fig. 283c δ_2 and R_1 have the same sense.

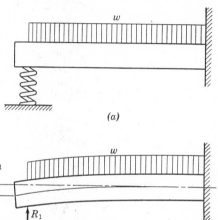

Fig. 283

Because the redundant element (spring) fits perfectly in the structure, its deflection δ_2 is equal to the deflection δ_1 of the beam. Therefore, if Eq. 584 is subtracted from Eq. 585, the resulting equation is

$$(\partial U_s/\partial R_1) + (\partial U_b/\partial R_1) = 0 \quad \text{or} \quad \partial(U_s + U_b)/\partial R_1 = 0 \tag{586}$$

In Eq. 586 the sum $U_s + U_b$ represents the total elastic strain energy stored in the structure (spring and beam). If we let U represent this total elastic strain energy, Eq. 586 becomes

$$\partial U/\partial R_1 = 0 \tag{587}$$

This equation in which R_1 in general represents the force or moment in any redundant member may be used in the solution of any statically indeterminate problem, provided that the redundant member fits perfectly in the structure before any external forces are applied to the structure. Its use will be illustrated in the problems which follow this article.

Lack of Fit of Redundant Member. In Fig. 283 let it be assumed that the redundant member or element (spring) is slightly too long to fit into place between the beam and the support before the distributed load w is applied. Let λ represent this excess length, called lack of fit, of the spring. When the spring is inserted by forcing it into place, the beam is deflected upward and the spring is compressed, that is, some elastic strain energy is stored in the beam and spring before the external load w is applied.

The procedure in solving this problem of finding the force R_1 and the moments in the beam is the same as in the preceding problem, and hence Eqs. 584 and 585 are applicable; in this case, however, the deflection δ_2 is not equal to δ_1, but $\delta_2 - \delta_1 = \lambda$, in which λ is the lack of fit of the spring. Thus, when Eq. 584 is subtracted from Eq. 585 the resulting equation is

$$(\partial U_s/\partial R_1) + (\partial U_b/\partial R_1) = \lambda \quad \text{or} \quad \partial(U_s + U_b)/\partial R_1 = \lambda \quad (588)$$

If we again let $U = U_s + U_b$, Eq. 588 becomes

$$\partial U/\partial R_1 = \lambda \qquad (589)$$

If we had assumed that the spring was too short, this fact would have given the expression $\delta_2 - \delta_1 = -\lambda$, and hence the right side of Eq. 589 would have been negative.

157 Interpretation of the equation $\partial U/\partial R_1 = 0$. The form of the equation $\partial U/\partial R_1 = 0$ obtained in the preceding article suggests that R_1 has such a value that U is a minimum. The equation therefore has sometimes been interpreted (erroneously) to mean that the forces in the members of a statically indeterminate structure are such that the total elastic strain energy stored in the structure as the result of the loads applied to the structure will have the least values consistent with the requirements of the conditions of equilibrium of the forces in the structure. In other words, of the various values of the forces and moments in the members, which will satisfy the conditions of equilibrium, the values that occur are the ones that will cause the total strain energy in the structure to be a minimum.

But it has been pointed out (Art. 132) that the minimum energy principle is an outgrowth of the principle of conservation of energy which involves the total potential energy of the whole (isolated) system and not merely the strain energy in one member or part of the system. To distinguish between the two ideas, Eq. 587 is frequently referred to as the principle of least work.

It is important to note, however, that Eq. 587 is the result of assuming that all members of the structure fit perfectly before loads are applied to the structure so that all the strain energy in the structure results from the application of the loads on the structure; its derivation had no direct connection with minimum energy. The meaning of Eq. 587 as a special case of Eq. 589 may be shown as follows: In Eq. 589 the total elastic strain energy U consists of two parts, namely, U_r which is due to the initial or residual forces and moments, and U_L which is contributed by the external loads. In Fig. 284 let the total elastic strain energy U be represented by ordinates and the magnitude of the redundant force R_1

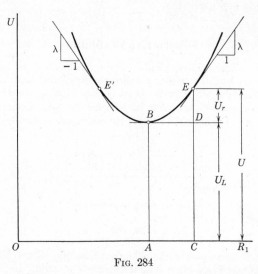

Fig. 284

by abscissas. The abscissa OA represents the value of R_1 when the redundant element fits perfectly, and the ordinate AB to the curve represents the value of U_L. If the redundant element is too long (does not fit perfectly), the force R_1 for a given external load may be increased as indicated by the abscissa OC, and the strain energy U increased by the amount U_r as shown by DE. If the redundant element is too short for a perfect fit the point E would be at E' on the opposite side of B, but the strain energy U_r due to the residual forces and moments is still positive so that the ordinate to E' is greater than AB.

Attention is now called to the left sides of Eqs. 587 and 589. It is noted that the partial derivative of U with respect to R_1 represents the slope of the tangent line drawn at any point to the curve such as those shown at E, E', and B (Fig. 284). At E this slope is λ, at E' it is $-\lambda$ and at B it is zero. Thus, if the redundant element fits perfectly, we may interpret Eq. 587 as expressing the fact that there is a minimum of strain energy stored in the member or structure considered. As already noted this fact is often referred to as Castigliano's theorem of least work, but it should be observed that Eq. 589 is a more general theorem, and the idea of a minimum of elastic strain energy can be associated with the physical behavior of the structure only when $\lambda = 0$, that is, when all redundant elements fit perfectly before the loads are applied to the structure. This means that the total elastic strain energy U in the statically indeterminate structure is the result of applying loads to the structure, and hence no initial energy can be stored in the structure before the loads are applied.

Illustrative Problems

Problem 296. Figure 285 represents a beam, fixed at one end and simply supported at the other end, that resists a uniformly distributed load. Both supports are assumed to be rigid, but when the beam is placed into position it is found that the end over the simple support has to be deflected upward a distance λ in order to rest on the support. Compute the value of the reaction R at the simple support.

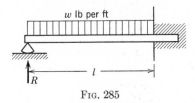

w lb per ft

l

R

FIG. 285

Solution. R will be selected as the redundant quantity. The total strain energy U is the strain energy in the beam since the supports are rigid. Hence

$$U = \int \tfrac{1}{2}(M^2/EI)\, dx$$

From Eq. 589 we obtain

$$\partial U/\partial R = \lambda = \int (M/EI)(\partial M/\partial R)\, dx$$

$M = Rx - (wx^2/2)$; therefore $\partial M/\partial R = x$. Hence

$$\lambda = \int_0^l \frac{Rx - (wx^2/2)}{EI}\, x\, dx$$

Therefore $R = (3EI\lambda/l^3) + \tfrac{3}{8}wl$

If the beam fits perfectly in place, that is, if $\lambda = 0$, the value of R is $\tfrac{3}{8}wl$ which checks the result obtained in Art. 148.

Problem 297. Find the axial forces in the members of the pin-connected steel truss shown in Fig. 286 if $P = 100,000$ lb and the cross-sectional area of each member is $a = 3$ sq in. The modulus of elasticity of steel is $E = 30,000,000$ lb per sq in. Assume that the redundant member BD fits perfectly and that the elastic limit of the material is not exceeded.

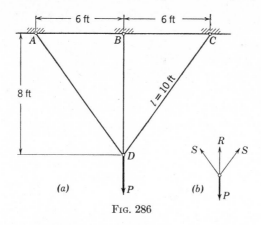

Fɪɢ. 286

Solution. From symmetry it is seen that the forces in AD and CD are each equal to S as indicated in Fig. 286b. Let R represent the force in the redundant BD. The elastic strain energy U is expressed as follows:

$$U = 2\left(\frac{1}{2}\frac{S^2 l}{aE}\right) + \frac{1}{2}\frac{R^2(0.8l)}{aE}$$

In order to differentiate U partially with respect to R in accordance with the equation $\partial U/\partial R = 0$, S must be expressed in terms of R and the load P. This is done by making use of Fig. 286b and the equations of equilibrium. Thus, $S = \frac{5}{8}(P - R)$. Therefore

$$U = \frac{25}{64aE}(P - R)^2 l + \frac{1}{2}\frac{R^2(0.8l)}{aE}$$

$$\frac{\partial U}{\partial R} = 0 = -\frac{50}{64aE}(P - R)l + \frac{R(0.8l)}{aE}$$

Hence $R = 0.494P = 49,400$ lb.; $S = 0.316P = 31,600$ lb.

Problem 298. Solve Prob. 297 if the redundant member BD is 0.05 in. too short and has to be forced into place before the load P is applied.

Solution. From Eq. 589 we obtain

$$\partial U/\partial R = \lambda = 0.05$$

The positive sign is used for λ; the redundant BD is stretched to make it fit, and hence λ agrees in sense with the deformation in BD caused by the load P. The expression for U is the same as in Prob. 297, and hence

$$\frac{\partial U}{\partial R} = -\frac{50}{64aE}(P - R)l + \frac{0.8lR}{aE} = 0.05$$

Hence $R = \frac{64 \times 0.05}{101.2}\frac{aE}{l} + \frac{50}{101.2}P = 0.0316\frac{aE}{l} + 0.494P$

$$= 23,700 + 49,400 = 73,100 \text{ lb}$$

and $S = \frac{5}{8}(P - R) = 16,800$ lb

A comparison of these results with those of Prob. 297 shows that a relatively small amount of lack of fit in the redundant element BD makes a substantial difference in the elastic forces in the members caused by the external loads. Furthermore, if the load P were gradually increased until the most highly stressed member reached its yield point, the forces in other (understressed) members would immediately increase and bring about a more advantageous distribution of forces in the member without causing serious damage to the structure. This fact raises the question as to whether design on the basis of elasticity is always desirable. See Part V for further discussion.

Problem 299. A circular ring (Fig. 287) is subjected to equal opposite loads P. Derive the expression for the bending moment at any section of the ring. (This problem was considered in Art. 56.)

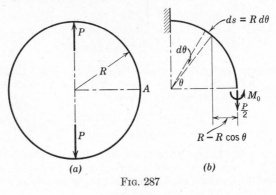

(a)   (b)

FIG. 287

Solution. The conditions of symmetry make it necessary to consider only one quadrant. The force $P/2$ and the bending moment M_0 acting at section A are shown in Fig. 287b.

If the ring is cut through section A as assumed in applying the procedure of Art. 147, there will be no rotation of the section under the condition assumed, and hence

$$\partial U/\partial M_0 = \theta_A = 0$$

in which
$$U = \int_0^{\pi/2} \frac{M^2 R\, d\theta}{2EI}.$$

The condition assumed is that no residual moment exists in the ring at section A owing to misfit either in assembling the ring in place in the structure when it is used or in the original manufacture of the ring. Otherwise, when the section at A is cut, the residual moment at the section would be released and there would be a rotation of the section and hence θ_A would not be equal to zero. The foregoing equations give

$$\frac{\partial U}{\partial M_0} = \int_0^{\pi/2} \frac{M}{EI} \frac{\partial M}{\partial M_0} R\, d\theta = 0$$

At any section the bending moment is

$$M = M_0 - \frac{P}{2} R(1 - \cos\theta) \quad \text{and} \quad \frac{\partial M}{\partial M_0} = 1$$

Therefore $\int_0^{\pi/2} \dfrac{M}{EI} \dfrac{\partial M}{\partial M_0} R\, d\theta = \dfrac{R}{EI} \int_0^{\pi/2} \left[M_0 - \dfrac{P}{2} R(1 - \cos\theta) \right] d\theta = 0$

Hence $\qquad\qquad M_0 = \dfrac{PR}{2}\left(1 - \dfrac{2}{\pi}\right) = 0.182PR$

Thus the bending moment at any section is

$$M = 0.182PR - (PR/2)(1 - \cos\theta) = -0.318PR + (PR/2)\cos\theta$$

From this expression it is seen that the maximum bending moment occurs when $\theta = 90°$, that is, at the sections where the loads P act the maximum moment has the value of

$$M_{max} = -0.318\, PR$$

The decrease in the diameter of the ring may now be found by the methods of Chapter 14 or 15.

Problems

300. In Prob. 296 assume that the beam has a length $l = 12$ ft and a square cross section 2 in. by 2 in. Assume also that w is such that for a perfect fit ($\lambda = 0$) the maximum calculated stress is 20,000 lb per sq in. What will be the value of R if $\lambda = \frac{1}{8}$ in.?

301. Find, by the method of Castigliano, the twisting moment T_0 at the fixed ends A and C of the bar in Prob. 295 (Fig. 282).

302. Find, by the method of Castigliano, the reaction at the central support of the beam in Prob. 285.

303. A quarter part of an elastic circular ring is fixed at each end as shown in Fig. 288. It supports a load P which acts along a radius of the circle making a 45° angle with the radii to fixed ends A and B. By the method of Castigliano compute the bending moments at the fixed ends.

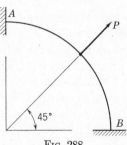

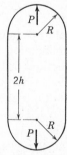

FIG. 288   FIG. 289

304. Find, by the method of Castigliano, the maximum moment in the link shown in Fig. 289, taking into consideration the strain energy due to bending only, and assuming that the cross-sectional dimensions are small compared to the radius R.

$$Ans.\quad M_{max} = \frac{PR^2(\pi - 2)}{4h + 2\pi R}.$$

305. Find, by the method of Castigliano, the bending moment in a circular ring (similar to that shown in Fig. 287) subjected over the upper half and lower half to a vertical distributed load of w per horizontal unit of length (see Art. 57).

$$Ans.\quad M_0 = wR^2/4.$$

158   Alternate strain energy method. In Art. 128, Chapter 13, it was shown that the partial derivative of the strain energy of a member or structure with respect to the deflection of a point in a given direction is equal to the force or load on the member or structure at that point in the given direction $(Q = \partial U/\partial \delta_Q)$. Under certain conditions this relationship can be used to great advantage in solving statically indeterminate problems, especially if many redundants are involved. The next article will illustrate this fact.

159   Weight supported by many rods. In Fig. 290 is shown a known weight W supported by many rods, each of which is pin-connected at its ends. Let it be required to find the deflection of the joint

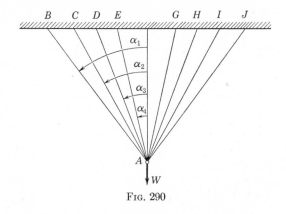

Fig. 290

A and the axial force in each of the rods. If there are n rods the problem is indeterminate to the $n - 2$ degree, and if it is solved by the dummy load method or by the least work method the solution may be tedious because of a large number of simultaneous equations that must be solved. As was suggested in Art. 130 of Chapter 13, this problem is more easily solved by expressing the strain energy U in terms of the deflections of the joint at A and then differentiating U with respect to deflection. The strain energy U as found in Prob. 235, Chapter 13, is

$$U = \Sigma \frac{1}{2} \frac{aEe^2}{l} \tag{590}$$

in which a is the cross-sectional area, E is the modulus of elasticity, l is the length of each rod, and e is the elongation of each rod. Let δ be the deflection of the joint A in the direction of the load W. The elongation e of any member is

$$e = \delta \cos \alpha \tag{591}$$

where α is the angle the member makes with the vertical line through A. The substitution of Eq. 591 in Eq. 590 gives

$$U = \Sigma \frac{1}{2} \frac{aE\delta^2 \cos^2 \alpha}{l} \tag{592}$$

From Eq. 500 (Chapter 13) we have

$$W = \frac{\partial U}{\partial \delta} = \Sigma \frac{aE\delta \cos^2 \alpha}{l} = \delta\Sigma \frac{aE \cos^2 \alpha}{l} \tag{593}$$

Hence

$$\delta = \frac{W}{\Sigma[(aE \cos^2 \alpha)/l]} \tag{594}$$

The elongation of any member, say the nth member, is found by the substitution of Eq. 594 in Eq. 591 which gives

$$e_n = \frac{W \cos \alpha_n}{\Sigma[(aE \cos^2 \alpha)/l]} \tag{595}$$

The axial force in the nth member is

$$S_n = a_n E_n e_n / l_n \tag{596}$$

and the substitution of e from Eq. 595 gives

$$S_n = \frac{a_n E_n W \cos \alpha_n}{l_n \Sigma[(aE \cos^2 \alpha)/l]} \tag{597}$$

Thus by making use of Eq. 597 the axial force can be found in each member of the structure in Fig. 290 without the necessity of solving a set of simultaneous linear equations.

Selected References for Part IV

1. Williams, D., "The Relations between Energy Theorems Applicable in Structural Theory," *Philosophical Magazine*, Ser. 7, Vol. 26, 1938, pp. 617–635. A comparison of the various energy theorems is given in this article.
2. Westergaard, H. M., "On the Method of Complementary Energy and Its Application to Structures Stressed beyond the Proportional Limit, etc.," *Transactions of the American Society of Civil Engineers*, Vol. 107, 1942, pp. 765–772. A rather general derivation of the complementary energy theorem is given in this paper.
3. Southwell, R. V., *Introduction to the Theory of Elasticity*, Oxford Engineering Science Series, Clarendon Press, 1936. The first three chapters present a discussion of various strain energy theorems as applied to deformable bodies that obey Hooke's law.

4. Pippard, A. J. S., *Strain Energy Methods of Stress Analysis*, Longmans, Green and Co., 1928. Chapter II presents a discussion of the energy theorems attributed to Castigliano. A discussion of lack of fit of a redundant member in a statically indeterminate machine or structure is given on pp. 29–32, and on pp. 33–35 a discussion of temperature stresses will be found.

5. Southwell, R. V., "Current Trends in Structural Research." This is one paper of a symposium called the Colston Papers. These have been published in a book called *Engineering Structures*, Academic Press, Inc., New York, 1949. In this paper the author has discussed what he calls "ill-conditioned equations." Such equations may occur if Castigliano's theorem is used to solve statically indeterminate problems. A set of so-called ill-conditioned equations is a set of simultaneous linear equations in which small changes in the coefficients in the equations will produce large changes in the unknown quantities when the equations are solved.

6. Niles, Alfred S., "The Energy Method, Which One?" *Journal of Engineering Education*, Vol. 33, May 1943, pp. 698–706. This paper gives a discussion of the state of confusion that exists in the literature as to the names attached to the various energy methods and suggests more appropriate names for these methods.

7. Spielvogel, S. W., *Piping Stress Calculations Simplified*, McGraw-Hill Book Co., 1943. This book gives a detailed description of the method employed in Art. 154, including a discussion of three-dimensional pipe lines. Many illustrative problems are given.

PART FIVE

Influence of Small Inelastic Strains on the
Load-carrying Capacity of Members

160 Introduction. In the design of a member for strength it is usually assumed, especially if the member is subjected to uniaxial stress, that the maximum utilizable load-carrying capacity of the member is reached when the loads cause a stress or a strain in the most-stressed fibers equal to that which occurs at the elastic limit of the material as found from a tensile (or compressive) test.

In many uses of load-resisting members, however, the strain in the most-stressed fibers may exceed somewhat the strain corresponding to the elastic limit without causing structural damage to the member especially if the inelastic part of the strain is of the same order of magnitude as the elastic part. To state the idea differently, in many engineering applications a member functions satisfactorily in resisting loads until a small amount of inelastic (plastic) deformation has occurred in the most stressed fibers, and hence the loads that may be applied to the member before structural failure by yielding occurs are greater than those which first cause a maximum stress equal to the elastic limit. This condition is met especially in a member that is made of ductile material and is subjected at ordinary temperatures to static loads which cause a non-uniformly distributed uniaxial stress because such a stress distribution permits the inelastic strains to cause a redistribution of the stresses, thereby giving a more favorable distribution of stress for resisting further increase in the loads. Common illustrations of such members are: a tension member having an abrupt change in section caused by a hole, a groove, a fillet, etc.; and a beam (even a straight beam with constant cross section), especially a curved beam. The analysis of axially loaded compression members, especially the inelastic buckling of columns, is considered in Part VI.

511

The maximum load that can be applied to a member without causing it to cease to function properly as a load-resisting member will frequently be referred to as the maximum utilizable load or limiting resistance load (see Art. 2). The working load will be less than the maximum utilizable load, depending on the factor of safety. It should be recalled also (see Art. 2) that when inelastic strains occur the factor of safety cannot be applied to stresses but must be applied to loads.

It is the purpose of Part V to determine how much the load-carrying capacities of such members are increased by permitting the strain in the most-stressed fibers to exceed the strain ϵ_e at the elastic limit by amounts of the same order of magnitude as ϵ_e. Only members in which the stress is predominately uniaxial will be considered because in such members a very simple and satisfactory assumption can be made as to the manner in which the stresses are redistributed when inelastic strains occur at the point or region of peak stress. For members in which biaxial stresses occur such as in torsion members, or for members in which the stresses are triaxial such as in a thick-walled cylinder having closed ends, the manner in which the stresses are redistributed when inelastic strains occur is more difficult to determine; for solving these problems relationships involving the principal stresses and strains occurring in the inelastically strained part of the member must be found, and such relationships are more difficult to obtain. These problems are discussed briefly in Chapter 10.

It was noted previously that structural damage to a member may be caused by general yielding which usually starts as a localized yielding at some point or small region where a stress peak occurs and then gradually spreads as the load is increased. The term general yielding is not susceptible of quantitative definition since it depends on service conditions as well as on the stress distribution and properties of the material. General yielding, however, usually will have occurred when the yielding (inelastic strains) in any region of a member has become unrestricted; that is, the yielding is no longer retarded to an important degree by surrounding material which is acting elastically.

In some members, before structural damage has been caused by spreading of yielding through a section of the member, the strains in the most-stressed fibers may be several times the elastic limit strain ϵ_e, depending on the steepness of the slope of the curve of elastic stress distribution near the stress peak, that is, on the stress gradient S at the point. If the stress gradient is large, indicating that the stress changes rapidly over small distances from the point of peak stress, the initial yielding will be highly localized and substantial increases in the load will be required to cause the yielding to spread, even over a short distance. Under this condition a large increase in load may be required to cause yielding to extend over a portion of the member sufficient to cause failure by too great a change in shape of the member, that is, by general yielding. If the stress gradient is small, indicating that the stress changes very gradually over small distances from the peak, the initial yielding, though at first localized, may spread quickly with small increases in the load and cause failure by general yielding without much increase in the value of the load that starts the yielding.

In the chapters that follow, a rational method is given for computing the stress gradient in various members and of using it in determining the rate at which the load-carrying capacity of a member increases as yielding occurs in the most-stressed fibers. A quantitative knowledge of the influence of small inelastic deformations on the strength of members is of great importance in many load-resisting members, and there is great need for rational methods of obtaining this knowledge and thereby of making less use of empirical methods.

The reader should understand that it is not proposed that the working loads will cause an appreciable amount of inelastic deformations. The working load is to be taken as some fractional part of the maximum utilizable load. For example, if the maximum utilizable load P_u is considered to be the load which corresponds to the resistance of the member after a specified small inelastic strain occurs, then the working load P_w is taken as $P_w = P_u/N$, where N is a factor of safety, and P_w will in general cause stresses less than the elastic limit of the material; therefore the so-called elastic stress formulas are applicable in the design of the member. Also the reader is reminded that it is assumed here that there is sufficient ductility in the member to permit the assumed inelastic strains to occur.

Chapter 17

EFFECT OF SMALL INELASTIC STRAINS IN AXIALLY LOADED MEMBERS AND IN STRAIGHT BEAMS

161 Preliminary considerations. The load P_e or bending moment M_e at which the highest stressed fiber of a tension member or of a beam will just begin to strain inelastically is calculated by using the ordinary formulas relating loads and uniaxial stresses, that is, $P_e = \sigma_e a$ or $M_e = \sigma_e I/c$, respectively, in which σ_e is the elastic (proportional) limit of the material as obtained from a direct tension or compression test. If the member contains a stress raiser such as a hole, a fillet, or a groove, the corresponding formulas are $P_e = \sigma_e a/K_t$ and $M_e = \sigma_e I/K_t c$, in which K_t is the theoretical stress concentration factor, values of which are given in Chapter 12. It is known that the load P (or the bending moment M) required to cause inelastic strains to spread to a point a short distance from the point of stress peak at which initial yielding occurs is somewhat larger than the load P_e (or M_e).

The main problem considered in this chapter is to determine the magnitude of P (or of M) after inelastic strains have spread to a point in a cross section of the member a small distance away from the point of stress peak. In the subsequent articles in this chapter a rational method giving approximate results will be discussed for solving this problem for several types of members subjected to direct tensile or compressive loads or to bending loads, in which the stresses are primarily uniaxial. This method gives results which have been shown to be reliable because of their rather close agreement with experimental values.

Inception and Progress of Yielding. Fully Plastic Condition. Before discussing the proposed method it is important to consider the manner in which yielding may take place at a cross section of a member and how the spread of yielding may affect the maximum utilizable load. The general mechanism of yielding is described in Chapter 1, but attention should here be called to the fact that, in a member made of material which has a yield point, yielding (inelastic strain) starts when the

514

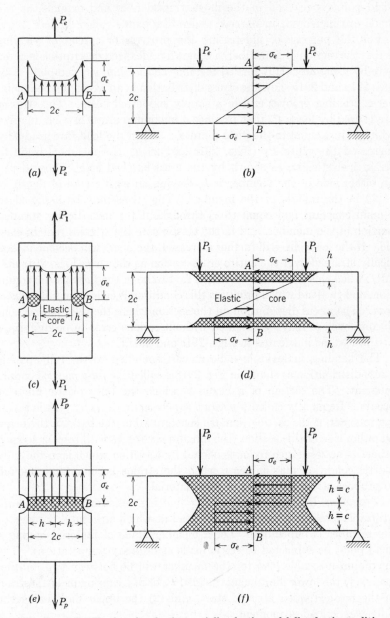

FIG. 291 Stress distributions for elastic, partially plastic, and fully plastic conditions.

yield point is reached in the most-stressed fiber and extends, as the loads are increased, in narrow wedge-like bands called Lüders' lines.

For the purpose of illustrating the progress or spread of yielding across the section of a member, a somewhat idealized description is given here by using an axially loaded member and a beam as examples. Figures 291a and 291b show the stress distribution in an axially loaded member containing grooves and in a simply supported beam. The stresses are caused by loads P_e that produce a maximum stress in each member which is just equal to the yield point σ_e. When the loads are gradually increased to values P_1 (Figs. 291c and 291d), the members begin to strain inelastically, as shown by the cross-hatched areas whose depth on either side of the member is h, leaving an elastic core of depth $2c - 2h$ in the middle of the member. The stress may be assumed to remain constant and equal to σ_e throughout the inelastically strained portion of the member, and in the elastic core the stresses remain elastic. If the loads are still further increased, the fibers will become inelastically strained over the entire cross section as shown in Figs. 291e and 291f; when this occurs the section is said to be in the *fully plastic* condition, and the load which produces this condition is called the *fully plastic load*. The stress distribution on the section where the fully plastic condition develops may be assumed without serious error to be uniformly distributed, as illustrated in Figs. 291e and 291f.

The bending moment in a beam corresponding to the fully plastic stress distribution as shown in Fig. 291f is called the *fully plastic* bending moment. The section of a beam at which the fully plastic moment occurs is frequently called a *plastic hinge* because the fully plastic resisting moment at the section remains constant while the parts of the beam on either side of this section (the hinge) may rotate with respect to each other. The resistance to loads offered by a section which is in the fully plastic condition may increase when the strains become large enough to produce strain hardening of this material.

Maximum Utilizable Load. The limiting resistance or maximum utilizable load for a member is the load at which structural damage to the member is impending. Let a member made of material having a yield point be subjected to static loads at ordinary temperatures. The maximum utilizable load for the member will lie between two limiting loads: (1) the lower limit being the load P_e or M_e, causing inelastic strain in the most stressed fiber to start, and (2) the upper limit being the fully plastic load or moment.

It is not easy to state quantitatively the extent to which inelastic strains must spread in a member before structural damage (general yielding) is said to be impending. If the inelastic strains are confined to a particular section of the member, as would be the case in Fig. 291c if the radii of the grooves were small, structural damage is not considered to occur until the fully plastic condition is reached, but if inelastic strains occur simultaneously on parts of many sections, as shown in Fig. 291d, structural damage (general yielding) may occur before any particular cross section reaches the fully plastic condition and hence before the fully plastic load is reached. It is, therefore, necessary to determine the manner in which a member resists loads in the range between the beginning of inelastic strains and the development of the fully plastic condition. One way of doing this is to derive a relationship between the load and the depth h to which inelastic strains have spread or penetrated in the most strained cross section or sections. This method is used in the succeeding articles.

162 Circular hole in plate stressed in one direction. In Fig. 292a is shown a plate containing a hole whose radius ρ is small in comparison to the half-width b of the plate. Let the plate be subjected to an axial load P_e which causes a uniform stress σ_0 at any section some distance from the hole. The maximum stress in the plate will occur at the edge of the hole. Let this maximum stress be just equal to the elastic limit σ_e of the material as obtained from a tensile test; the distribution of stress on the section through the hole is shown in Fig. 292a. Since the theoretical stress concentration factor is $K_t = 3$ (Art. 116), $\sigma_e = 3\sigma_0$, and hence

$$P_e = \tfrac{1}{3}\sigma_e a \tag{598}$$

where a is the cross-sectional area of the (solid) plate. Let it be assumed that the tensile stress-strain curve for the material is as illustrated by Fig. 292b, and hence the material has a yield point, the value of which is equal to the elastic limit σ_e. If the load on the plate is increased to a magnitude P somewhat greater than P_e (but not great enough to cause fully plastic yielding), the longitudinal strains near the hole will exceed the value ϵ_e which occurs at the elastic limit, but the stress will remain equal to σ_e. Inelastic strains will occur over a part of the plate on either side of the hole to some distance x_1. The stress distribution may be assumed to be approximately as shown in Fig. 292c by the ordinates to ABC and $A'B'C'$. AB and $A'B'$ represent a uniform distribution of stress which exists on that part of the cross section of the plate which has been inelastically strained. The curves BC and $B'C'$ represent the distribution of stress on the section over the part of the plate which remains elastic.

The equation representing the curves DBC and $D'B'C'$ may be assumed with only small error to have the same form as Eq. 481, namely,

$$\sigma = \frac{\sigma_0}{2}\left(2 + \frac{\rho^2}{x^2} + 3\frac{\rho^4}{x^4}\right) \tag{599}$$

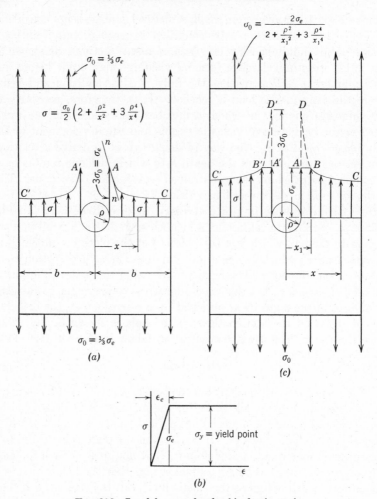

FIG. 292   Load for any depth of inelastic strain.

This curve must pass through the point B whose coordinates are $x = x_1$ and $\sigma = \sigma_e$. The substitution of these values in Eq. 599 gives

$$\sigma_0 = \frac{2\sigma_e}{2 + (\rho^2/x_1{}^2) + 3(\rho^4/x_1{}^4)} \tag{600}$$

in which σ_0 represents the nominal or average stress in the plate on a section at some distance from the hole based on the assumption (erroneous) that the stresses on the inelastically strained portion of the section at the hole are represented by ordinates to the curve DB (or $D'B'$) instead of being constant as shown by ordinates to the line AB (or $A'B'$). But the error in this value of σ_0 is always small in a relatively wide plate because the area under the curve ABC, which is directly proportional to one-half the load P, is very large in comparison to the area ABD. In fact, for small depths x_1, which are of primary interest in this chapter, the area ABD is very small so that the error in σ_0 is negligible. Therefore, the load P corresponding to a depth x_1 of penetration of inelastic strain is

$$P = \sigma_0 a = \frac{2\sigma_e a}{2 + (\rho^2/x_1{}^2) + 3(\rho^4/x_1{}^4)} \tag{601}$$

Ratio P/P_e. It is important to note that in Eq. 601 the value of the load-carrying capacity P of the member increases rather rapidly as the depth x_1 of inelastic strain increases. This phenomenon is best demonstrated, however, by making use of the dimensionless ratio P/P_e. This ratio is obtained by the division of Eq. 601 by Eq. 598, which gives

$$\frac{P}{P_e} = \frac{6}{2 + (\rho^2/x_1{}^2) + 3(\rho^4/x_1{}^4)} \tag{602}$$

In Fig. 293 is shown an enlarged view of one-half of the plate of Fig. 292. The distance x_1 to which inelastic strains have penetrated are shown as abscissas, and the values of P/P_e as ordinates. The ordinates to points on the curve OC represent values of P/P_e which have been obtained from Eq. 602 by the substitution of the corresponding values of x_1 which are expressed as multiples of the radius ρ. The curve rises quickly from the value $P/P_e = 1$, corresponding to the load at which inelastic strains are just on the verge of occurring; for example, when $x_1 = 1.5\rho$ the depth of penetration of inelastic strain is one-half the radius of the hole and the ratio P/P_e is about 2. The curve lies so close to a tangent line OA drawn to it at the initial point O that it is helpful to investigate the slope of this tangent line and show its relationship to the stress gradient S which is the slope of the stress distribution curve at the same point.

The dimensional units of the slope of line OA are in.$^{-1}$. The dimensions of the stress gradient S (see tangent line nn in Fig. 292a) are pounds per cubic inch. These quantities are thus not directly related. However, if the stress gradient S is divided by the maximum stress σ_{max} which occurs at the point of peak stress, the dimension of the ratio S/σ_{max} thus obtained is in.$^{-1}$. It will now be shown that the slope of OA is exactly equal in magnitude to the ratio S/σ_{max}. This fact is important because, as will be shown later, it is usually easy to determine the value of S and of σ_{max}, whereas it is usually difficult (and in many instances impossible) to derive the equation of the P/P_e curve and hence in such cases the slope cannot be found directly.

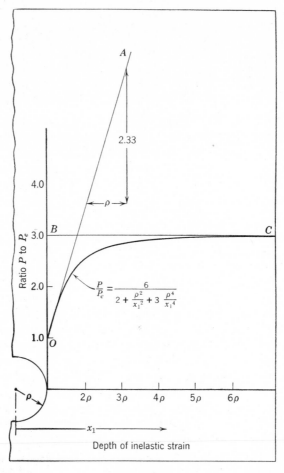

Fig. 293

Slope of P/P_e Curve. In order to find the slope of the P/P_e curve in Fig. 293 at any point x_1, both sides of Eq. 602 are differentiated with respect to x_1 which gives

$$\frac{d(P/P_e)}{dx_1} = \frac{12[(\rho^2/x_1^3) + 6(\rho^4/x_1^5)]}{2 + (\rho^2/x_1^2) + 3(\rho^4/x_1^4)} \tag{603}$$

The substitution of the value $x_1 = \rho$ in Eq. 603 gives the value of the slope of the tangent line OA to the P/P_e curve at O. Thus the slope at O is

$$\frac{d(P/P_e)}{dx_1} = \frac{2.33}{\rho} \tag{604}$$

Ratio $S/\sigma_{\max}$. Let it now be required to determine the ratio $S/\sigma_{\max}$ at the edge of the hole and to show that this ratio is equal to the right-hand side of Eq. 604. The derivative with respect to x of the right-hand side of Eq. 599 will represent the slope of a tangent line to the stress distribution curve at any point on the cross section passing through the hole. This derivative is

$$\frac{d\sigma}{dx} = \frac{\sigma_0}{2}\left(-2\frac{\rho^2}{x^3} - 12\frac{\rho^4}{x^5}\right) \tag{605}$$

The slope of the curve at the edge of the hole, that is, the slope of the line nn in Fig. 292a, is the stress gradient S desired, and is found by the substitution of $x = \rho$ in Eq. 605. Thus

$$S = d\sigma/dx = -7\sigma_0/\rho \tag{606}$$

But $\sigma_0 = \frac{1}{3}\sigma_{\max}$ (Art. 116), and hence

$$S/\sigma_{\max} = -2.33/\rho \tag{607}$$

Therefore, the numerical value $S/\sigma_{\max}$ at the edge of the hole is equal to the slope of the P/P_e curve at the same point (origin) where inelastic strain first occurs. Although the foregoing proof is restricted to a plate containing a hole, it can be shown that the proof is applicable to any member in which the stresses are unidirectional. The importance of the principle will be demonstrated in subsequent articles by applying it in obtaining the P/P_e curve for several other types of members. Before doing this, however, one further comment concerning the P/P_e curve in Fig. 293 is needed. It is noted that the curve becomes nearly tangent to a horizontal line BC at the larger values of x_1, that is, when the inelastic strains have spread to points whose distances from the hole are five or six times the radius of the hole. Moreover, the location of the line BC has special significance in that it corresponds to fully plastic yielding at the section; its position is at a value represented by the ratio of the fully plastic load P_p to the load P_e. This ratio is

$$\frac{P}{P_e} = \frac{P_p}{P_e} = \frac{\sigma_e a}{\sigma_e a/K_t} = K_t = 3$$

which is the theoretical stress concentration factor for the hole. Thus we are able to draw two tangent lines to the P/P_e curve, one at the point O corresponding to the beginning of yielding having the slope $S/\sigma_{\max}$, and the other a horizontal line which passes through a point on the vertical axis at $P/P_e = K_t$. These two tangents to the P/P_e curve are very helpful in constructing an approximate P/P_e curve for many types of members because the equation for the P/P_e curve (or M/M_e curve for bending members) is usually very complex and in many instances cannot be derived.

163 Filleted bar loaded in direct tension. As an illustration of the method suggested in the preceding article for determining the load P corresponding to a small amount of plastic deformation, let the member be an axially loaded tension member in which the cross section is reduced in width by a fillet whose radius is ρ, as shown in Fig. 294a. The wider section is twelve times the fillet radius and the narrower section is six times the fillet radius. These dimensions are chosen for illustrative purposes in order that quantitative values of the stress gradient and stress concentration factor can be used. The bar is made of a ductile material having a yield point as shown by Fig. 292b. Let it be required to construct for this member a curve giving the approximate value of the load P when inelastic strain has progressed to any depth x_1 from the fillet as illustrated in Fig. 294a.

The value of the load P_e at which inelastic strain will start at the fillet is

$$P_e = \sigma_e a/K_t = \sigma_e a/1.9 \qquad (608)$$

in which the value $K_t = 1.9$ is obtained from the curve marked $t = 3\rho$ in Fig. 199. The elastic stress distribution across the section at the fillet accompanying the load P_e is about as illustrated by the dashed curve from A to D in Fig. 294a, but the equation of this curve is not known. When a load P greater than P_e is applied, inelastic strains occur to some depth x_1 and the stress distribution is illustrated by ordinates to the curve $ABCD$, but the location of the curve BC is not known. Thus the derivation of an equation for determining the load P cannot be given. Therefore, use is made of the two tangent lines described in the previous article to construct a curve which will give approximate values of P.

The ratio $S/\sigma_{\max}$ for a filleted bar loaded in tension has been found by A. M. Wahl from photoelastic analysis to be

$$S/\sigma_{\max} = 2.6/\rho \qquad (609)$$

Therefore, the slope of the tangent to the P/P_e curve at the fillet where the first inelastic strain occurs is given by Eq. 609. In Fig. 294b is shown the left half of the bar of Fig. 294a. Values of the ratio P/P_e are represented as ordinates on a vertical axis, and the depth of yielding x_1 is denoted by abscissas in multiples of the radius ρ of the fillet. The tangent OA to the curve is constructed by passing a line through

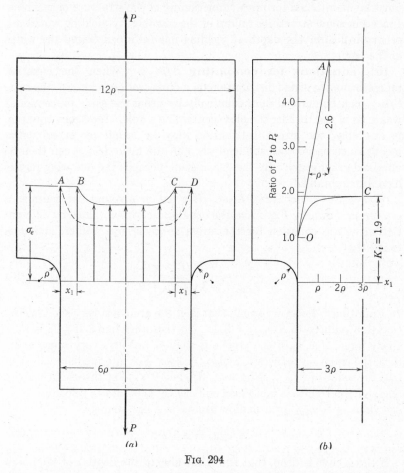

Fig. 294

the point O and having a slope $2.6/\rho$. The horizontal line passes through C at a distance $K_t = 1.9$ above the x_1 axis. The P/P_e curve is tangent to these two lines and should lie relatively close to both tangents for short distances away from each point of tangency. Therefore, it is possible to draw a curve such as OC in Fig. 294b which shows the manner in which the ratio P/P_e increases with the depth x_1 of yielding. For example, the curve OC as shown in Fig. 294b (or any other curve that the reader may choose to draw which is tangent to both lines) shows that the load P is from 50 to 75 per cent greater than P_e after inelastic strains have penetrated only to a depth $x_1 = \rho$. This relatively small amount of yielding would not cause structural damage to the member unless a very close tolerance in dimensions of the member must be maintained for proper functioning of the structure or machine. Indeed in some structures failure of the member by yielding would not occur until after the depth of yielding has fully penetrated the width of the bar.

164 Equations for computing $S/\sigma_{\max}$. When the equation representing the stress distribution on a cross section is known, the ratio $S/\sigma_{\max}$ can be derived mathematically by using the same procedure as was used in Art. 162 for the plate containing a hole. If no such equation is available, the stress distribution may be found by experimental means, such as photoelastic analysis, and the ratio $S/\sigma_{\max}$ can then be obtained graphically. By the use of such methods the following results have been obtained:

Grooved Bar under Axial Load. If a flat or a round bar contains a groove as shown by Fig. 295a, the equation for S is obtained by differentiation of the equation for the stress as given by Neuber, and it is found that

$$\frac{S}{\sigma_{\max}} = \frac{6}{\rho} \frac{\sqrt{t/2\rho} + 1}{3\sqrt{t/2\rho} + 2} \tag{610}$$

In Eq. 610 if $t/2\rho$ is very small, that is, if the groove is very shallow, the equation reduces to $S/\sigma_{\max} = 3/\rho$. On the other hand, if $t/2\rho$ is relatively large, that is, if the groove is shallow but also very sharp at its root, the equation reduces to $S/\sigma_{\max} = 2/\rho$. For intermediate values of $t/2\rho$ the value of $S/\sigma_{\max}$ is between $3/\rho$ and $2/\rho$. For the use here to be made of the results it is deemed sufficiently accurate to select an average value of $S/\sigma_{\max}$ for a shallow groove in a bar, namely,

$$S/\sigma_{\max} = 2.5/\rho \tag{611}$$

If the groove is deep, that is, if the value of the depth t of the notch is more than about one-fourth the width or diameter of the bar, an equation similar to Eq. 610 is found from which is obtained the average value

$$S/\sigma_{\max} = 1.9/\rho \tag{612}$$

Member under Axial Load: Any Notch. It has been shown that for axially loaded members containing a circular hole, a fillet, or a shallow or deep groove, the value of $S/\sigma_{\max}$ is equal to $2.3/\rho$, $2.6/\rho$, $2.5/\rho$, and $1.9/\rho$, respectively. It may be assumed that, if the notch has some other form, such as, for example, an elliptical hole in a plate as illustrated in Fig. 295b, the value of the ratio may be expressed as

$$S/\sigma_{max} = \text{Constant}/\rho \qquad (613)$$

The choice of value of the constant in Eq. 613 depends on how closely

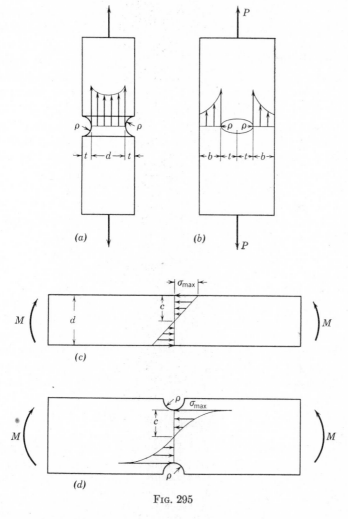

Fig. 295

the notch resembles one of those discussed previously. For example, for the elliptical hole in Fig. 295b the value of 2.3 may be chosen for the constant.

Straight Beam without Notch. In a beam a non-uniform stress distribution occurs on each cross section even for a beam that is straight and is free from a notch. From Fig. 295c, which shows a straight beam of constant cross section subjected to bending moments M at each end, it may be observed that the stress gradient is $S = \sigma_{max}/c$ in which c is the distance of the outermost fiber from the centroidal axis. Thus for a straight beam without a notch

$$S/\sigma_{max} = 1/c \qquad (614)$$

Curved Beam without Notch. In a cross section of a curved beam of radius of curvature R the stress at any point at any distance y from the centroidal axis is given by Eq. 158, in which M is the bending moment at the section. In order to obtain the value of S this equation is differentiated with respect to y. When this is done and the value $y = -c$ is substituted to give S at the point of maximum bending stress on the section, the result is

$$S = \frac{\dfrac{1}{c^2} \cdot M}{aZ \left(\dfrac{R}{c} - 1\right)^2} \qquad (615)$$

When Eq. 615 is divided by the expression for the maximum bending stress σ_{max} as given by Eq. 158 for a curved beam, the result is

$$\frac{S}{\sigma_{max}} = \frac{\dfrac{1}{c} \cdot \dfrac{R}{c}}{Z \left(\dfrac{R}{c} - 1\right)^2 - \left(\dfrac{R}{c} - 1\right)} \qquad (616)$$

Straight Beam with Notch. Neuber has given an equation for the stresses at a groove in a beam as shown in Fig. 295d. By the procedures previously discussed the values of S/σ_{max} have been found. The result for a shallow groove in a beam is

$$S/\sigma_{max} = 2.5/\rho \qquad \qquad \bullet \quad (617)$$

which is the same as for direct tension-compression (Eq. 611). However, if the groove is not shallow, that is, if the depth of the groove is more than about one-fourth of the diameter or depth of the section, the result is

$$S/\sigma_{max} = (1.9/\rho) + (1/c) \qquad (618)$$

Equation 618 shows that the ratio S/σ_{max} for the groove in direct tension-compression as given by Eq. 612 is superposed on the value S/σ_{max} for an unnotched straight beam as given by Eq. 614. It will be assumed that the effect of any other notch on the value of S/σ_{max} in bending of a straight beam can be obtained in the same way.

Problems

306. A member made of mild steel having a yield point $\sigma_e = 35,000$ lb per sq in. is a flat bar containing a centrally located elliptical hole as shown by Fig. 295b. The bar has a thickness of 1 in., and the other dimensions are $b = 4$ in., $t = 1$ in., and $\rho = \frac{1}{2}$ in. The bar is subjected to an axial load P. Compute the load P which will (a) cause inelastic strain to be on the verge of occurring at the edges of the hole where the radius is ρ; (b) cause inelastic strain to spread to a depth of $\frac{1}{2}$ in. from the edges of the hole.

307. A cylindrical bar has a circumferential groove as shown in Fig. 295a. The material in the bar has a yield point $\sigma_e = 60,000$ lb per sq in. The dimensions of the bar at the root of the groove are $d = 2$ in., $t = \frac{1}{4}$ in. and $\rho = \frac{1}{4}$ in. Compute an approximate value of the axial load P which will cause inelastic strains to spread to a depth of $\frac{1}{10}$ in. from the root of the groove.

165 Ratio M/M_e for straight beam having rectangular cross section. The foregoing method of obtaining an approximate value of the increased load-carrying capacity resulting from small plastic strains of the most-stressed fibers of axially loaded members will now be applied to members subjected to bending loads. Let it be assumed that a straight beam has a rectangular cross section and is made of a material having a stress-strain curve as shown in Fig. 292b, that is, the material has a yield point σ_e. Furthermore, let the compression stress-strain curve be identical with the curve found in the tension test. If M is the bending moment corresponding to any given depth h of inelastic yielding in the fibers of the beam, and M_e is the bending moment causing inelastic deformation in the outermost fiber to start $(M_e = \sigma_e I/c)$, let it be required to determine a relationship between the ratio M/M_e and the depth h from the outer fibers to which inelastic strains have penetrated into the beam.

Dimensionless Moment-Depth of Plastic Strain Equation. In deriving such a relationship the procedure discussed in Art. 8 is used. In Fig. 296 is shown a portion of the beam subjected to a bending moment M which causes inelastic strains in the outer fibers. The conditions of equilibrium for a portion of the beam, such as that between sections AA and DD, require that the internal ($\sigma\,da$) forces on section AA must hold the bending moment in equilibrium. The equations of equilibrium are

$$\int \sigma\,da = 0 \tag{619}$$

$$\int y\,\sigma\,da = M \tag{620}$$

The integrals in Eqs. 619 and 620, however, cannot be solved until the law of distribution of stress over the cross section is determined.

This may be done as follows: It is found experimentally that if the sections AA and DD are not too close * to each other the distribution of strains in these fibers of a beam of usual dimensions is linear for inelastic strain as well as for elastic strains. Thus the strains ϵ of the fibers between the sections AA and DD are represented by the abscissas from the line DD to the line D_1D_1. It is assumed that the stresses in the fibers at any section are determined by the strains in the fibers in accordance with the tensile (and compressive) stress-strain diagram as shown in Fig. 292b. Thus if the fibers are strained inelastically to a depth h it is

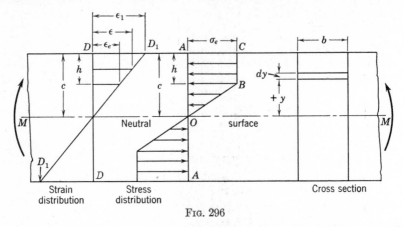

Fig. 296

assumed that the strain in the fibers at this depth is equal to ϵ_e and these fibers are just on the verge of yielding. Furthermore, the stress may be assumed to be constant over the depth h and equal to the yield point σ_e. This distribution is represented by BC. From B to O the stress decreases linearly from σ_e at B to zero at the neutral surface at O in accordance with the equation

$$\sigma = \frac{y}{c-h}\,\sigma_e \qquad (621)$$

Since the tensile stress-strain curve has been assumed to be identical with that in compression, the stress distribution in the lower half is the same as in the upper half of the beam.

Equations 619 and 620 can now be integrated. From Eq. 619 the location of the neutral axis is found to be at the centroidal axis; this

* If the gage length of the fibers is small, that is, if the distance between DD and AA in Fig. 296 is less than ¼ in., say, the un-isotropic effect of Lüders' bands will be noted and plane sections will not remain plane. When longer gage lengths are used, a statistical or average value of strain is obtained which makes it appear that plane sections remain plane.

would not be true if the tensile and compressive properties were not the same. The integration of Eq. 620 is

$$M = 2 \int_0^c \sigma y \, da = 2 \int_0^{c-h} \frac{y}{c-h} \sigma_e y b \, dy + 2 \int_{c-h}^c \sigma_e y b \, dy$$

$$= \tfrac{2}{3} b \sigma_e (c-h)^2 + \sigma_e b c^2 - \sigma_e b (c-h)^2 \qquad (622)$$

$$M = \tfrac{2}{3} \sigma_e b c^2 + \tfrac{2}{3} \sigma_e b c h - \tfrac{1}{3} \sigma_e b h^2$$

Furthermore, $M_e = \sigma_e I/c = \tfrac{2}{3} \sigma_e b c^2$. If Eq. 622 is divided by this value of M_e, the following dimensionless equation is obtained:

$$M/M_e = 1 + (h/c) - \tfrac{1}{2}(h^2/c^2) \qquad (623)$$

In Fig. 297 a portion of the beam of Fig. 296 is shown (rotated 90° for convenience) for the purpose of plotting a curve representing Eq.

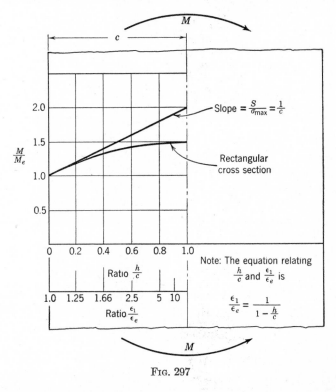

FIG. 297

623. Ordinates in Fig. 297 are values of the ratio M/M_e, and abscissas are values of h/c. The value $h/c = 0$ represents the condition in which the outer fibers are on the verge of straining inelastically, and a value

of $h/c = 1$ represents the fully plastic condition in which the fibers of the beam have strained inelastically throughout the entire depth of the beam. The substitution of the value of $h/c = 1$ into Eq. 623 gives a value $M/M_e = 1.5$ which is called the "fully plastic" value of this ratio. The factor 1.5 is sometimes also called the "form factor" or "shape factor" for the beam of rectangular cross section and is not to be confused with stress concentration factors, which are sometimes referred to as form factors.

The slope at any point of the curve showing the relation between M/M_e and h/c is obtained by differentiation of Eq. 623 with respect to h, which gives

$$\frac{d(M/M_e)}{dh} = \frac{1}{c} - \frac{h}{c^2} \tag{624}$$

The slope corresponding to the point where inelastic strains start ($M/M_e = 1$) is obtained from Eq. 624 by substituting $h/c = 0$. This slope is

$$\frac{d(M/M_e)}{dh} = -\frac{1}{c} \tag{625}$$

But it has already been shown by Eq. 614 that the right side of Eq. 625 is the value of $S/\sigma_{\max}$ for the beam. Furthermore, if a value of $h/c = 1$ is substituted in Eq. 624, the resulting value of the slope of the curve is zero. Therefore, the same two tangent lines to the M/M_e curve are found as were found for the P/P_e curve (Fig. 293) in direct tension. It is necessary only to obtain the value of $S/\sigma_{\max} = 1/c$ and the fully plastic value of M/M_e for a beam in order to construct these two tangents. This procedure is applied in Art. 166 and Prob. 310; but before discussing the application the moment-strain equation will be obtained.

Dimensionless Moment-strain Equation. Equation 623 gives the relationship between the bending moment and the depth h to which inelastic strains have penetrated. Frequently it is desirable to have the relationship between the bending moment and the magnitude of the strain ϵ_1 at the outermost fibers in order to obtain the maximum deflection of the beam. This relationship is obtained from Eq. 623 and from Fig. 296 by noting, from the similar triangles in the left-hand part of Fig. 296, that

$$\epsilon_1/\epsilon_e = c/(c - h) \tag{626}$$

The ratio h/c is obtained in Eq. 626 by dividing the numerator and denominator of the right-hand side by c so that this equation becomes

$$\frac{\epsilon_1}{\epsilon_e} = \frac{1}{1 - (h/c)} \tag{627}$$

Equation 627 is solved for h/c in terms of ϵ_1/ϵ_e, and the result is substituted in Eq. 623, which then becomes

$$\frac{M}{M_e} = \frac{3}{2} - \frac{1}{2(\epsilon_1/\epsilon_e)^2} \tag{628}$$

In Fig. 297 the lower scale of abscissas represent values of the dimensionless ratio ϵ_1/ϵ_e. For example, when the ratio $\epsilon_1/\epsilon_e = 1.25$, the value of $M/M_e = 1.2$ approximately and the depth of penetration of inelastic strains is $h = 0.2c$, as indicated by the upper abscissa scale.

In obtaining from Eq. 623 or Eq. 628 the maximum bending moment that can be applied to the beam without causing structural damage, some arbitrary value of the inelastic strain must be selected which represents the maximum inelastic strain which can occur in the outer fibers without causing the beam to cease to function satisfactorily because of excessive yielding. An inelastic strain corresponding to 0.1 and 0.2 per cent offset from the straight-line portion of the stress-strain curve will be selected for illustrative purposes. For most metals the offset is equal to the inelastic strain (or set). Values of offset up to 0.2 per cent have been used rather widely in obtaining the yield strength of a material not having a yield point in the tension test. The following problem will illustrate the use of the foregoing equations.

Illustrative Problem

Problem 308. A beam has a rectangular cross section 2 in. wide and 3 in. deep. The beam is made of mild steel whose stress-strain diagram is shown in Fig. 292b. The horizontal beam is simply supported and carries a concentrated load P at the center of the span as shown in Fig. 298a. Determine the bending moment that will cause this beam to fail if it is assumed that failure occurs by yielding when the inelastic part of the total strain in the outer fibers of the beam is 0.1 per cent. Compare this value with the bending moment that causes inelastic strain just to start (accompanying a stress equal to the elastic limit σ_e of the material). Assume that $\sigma_e = 30,000$ lb per sq in. Draw a sketch of the beam showing approximately the extent of the inelastically strained portion of the beam. Also solve this problem on the assumption that a 0.2 per cent, instead of the 0.1 per cent, is the inelastic strain which causes failure by yielding.

Solution. The strain corresponding to σ_e is

$$\epsilon_e = \sigma_e/E = 30,000/30,000,000 = 0.001$$

The maximum permissible strain, therefore, is

$$\epsilon_1 = \epsilon_e + 0.001 = 0.002$$

The substitution of these values in Eq. 628 gives

$$\frac{M}{M_e} = \frac{3}{2} - \frac{1}{2(0.002/0.001)^2} = 1.37$$

$$M_e = \frac{\sigma_e I}{c} = \frac{30,000 \times 2 \times 27 \times 2}{12 \times 3} = 90,000 \text{ lb-in.}$$

Therefore $M = 1.37 \times 90,000 = 123,000$ lb-in. at the mid-span section. The substitution of the values of ϵ_1 and ϵ_e in Eq. 627 gives a value of the depth of yielding $h = 0.50c$ at the mid-span section of the beam. In Fig. 298a is shown a sketch

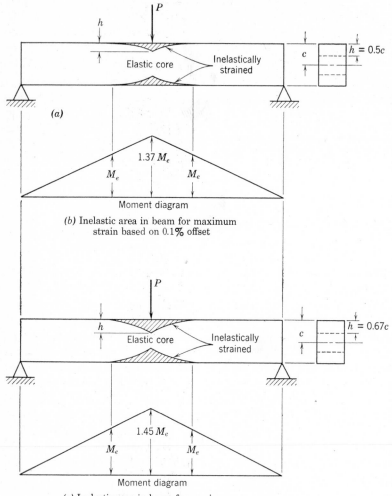

FIG. 298   Inelastic strain in beam.

of the beam below which is the bending moment diagram. The bending moment diminishes on either side of the mid-point from the value $M = 1.37M_e$ to a value M_e at the locations shown. The outer fibers in all sections between those at which the moments are M_e have strained inelastically (yielded), the penetration of yielding being the deepest at the mid-point, namely $h = 0.50c$. The cross-hatched areas show the extent of the inelastically strained portion of the beam. At the deepest penetration of inelastic strain one-half the depth of the beam remains as an elastic core. The equation of the curve bounding the cross-hatched area can be obtained from Eq. 623.

Solution Based on an Inelastic Strain of 0.20 Per Cent. The solution for the problem for an inelastic strain of 0.2 per cent is obtained in a similar manner and is shown in Fig. 298c; the greatest depth of inelastic strain is $h = 0.67c$. The elastic core which remains is then only one-third the depth of the beam.

The significance of the results of the two solutions of the foregoing problem can be stated as follows. First, Fig. 298b shows that a substantial increase in resisting moment (37 per cent in this instance) can be expected if only a relatively small portion of the beam is allowed to strain inelastically. Second, Fig. 298c shows that the applied bending moment can be increased only from $1.37M_e$ to $1.45M_e$, if the inelastic strain in the outer fiber is allowed to increase from a value equal to 0.1 per cent to that of 0.2 per cent. Thus the major portion of the increase in bending moment takes place before the inelastically strained portion of the beam becomes large enough to cause the beam to cease to function satisfactorily as a load-resisting member in many engineering structures and machines.

Problem

309. Solve Prob. 308 if the beam is made of a steel having a yield point of $\sigma_e = 60,000$ lb per sq in.   *Ans.* For $\epsilon_1 = 0.1\%$: $M = 1.28M_e$; $h = 0.33c$.
For $\epsilon_1 = 0.2\%$: $M = 1.37M_e$; $h = 0.50c$.

166 Influence of shape of cross section on the ratio M/M_e.
The shape of the cross section of a beam, whether circular, tubular, diamond, I section, etc., has a marked influence on the magnitude of the ratio M/M_e for a given depth of inelastic strain. The procedure applied in the derivation of Eqs. 623 and 628 for a beam of rectangular section may be used to derive equations for beams having other cross sections, but these equations are usually more complex and are not suitable for practical use. Instead of obtaining these equations it is much easier to construct curves by using the method described in Art. 165, that is, by making use of the tangent lines at the ends of the curve.

A beam whose cross section has an I shape of relative dimensions shown in Fig. 299 illustrates the construction of the M/M_e curve. The coordinate axes shown in Fig. 299 are the same as those in Fig. 297. Also shown in Fig. 299 is the line whose slope is $S/\sigma_{\max} = 1/c$, to which the curve is tangent at the start of inelastic strain where $M/M_e = 1$. At the other end of the curve where inelastic strain has fully penetrated the depth of the beam a horizontal line is tangent to the curve. In order to draw this line the value of M/M_e for the beam must be found for a depth of inelastic strain of $h = c$. If the material in the beam is assumed to have a stress-strain curve as shown in Fig. 292b, it can be assumed that when $h = c$ the stress distribution is uniform tension below the neutral axis and uniform compression above the neutral axis as shown in Fig. 299 next to the I section. The resisting moment resulting from this distribution is the sum of the moments of the $\sigma\, da$ forces acting on the cross section of flange and web and is found to be $M =$

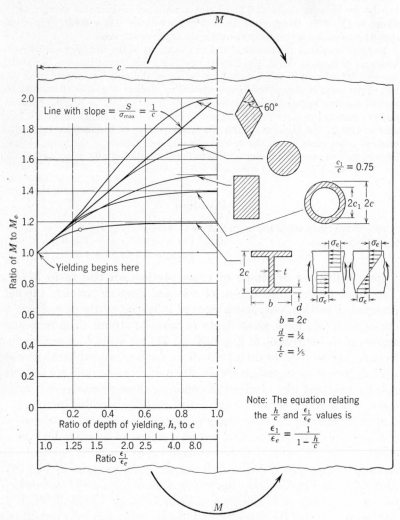

FIG. 299 Effect of shape of cross section on bending moment for any depth of inelastic strain.

$0.99\sigma_e c^3$. The value of M_e is calculated by use of the flexure formula $M_e = \sigma_e I/c$ and is found to be $M_e = 0.83\sigma_e c^3$ for this I section. Therefore, when $h = c$ it is found that $M/M_e = 0.99\sigma_e c^3/0.83\sigma_e c^3 = 1.19$. This is the ordinate to the horizontal tangent at the right end of the curve. The location of one additional point on the curve, together with these two tangents to the curve, will provide sufficient information for quite accurate construction of the curve. For this additional point let a value of $h = d = c/4$ be chosen; that is, let inelastic strain penetrate just through the flanges. The stress distribution corresponding to $h = c/4$ is shown at the right-hand side of the I section in Fig. 299. The value of M corresponding to this stress distribution is easily computed; $M = 0.95\sigma_e c^3$. The point desired is located at an abscissa of $h/c = 0.25$ and an ordinate of $M/M_e = 0.95\sigma_e c^3/0.83\sigma_e c^3 = 1.14$ as indicated by the open circle in Fig. 299. The curve for M/M_e for the I section is constructed by passing a smooth curve through this point and making the curve tangent to the aforementioned tangent lines at the ends of the curve.

In a manner similar to that used for the beam having an I section, the curves representing values of M/M_e for beams having cross sections which are rectangular, tubular or annular, circular, and diamond shaped have been constructed as shown in Fig. 299. These curves illustrate the very marked effect that the shape of cross section has on the value of M/M_e. It should be noted in Fig. 299 that the curve for a beam having a diamond cross section is highest and is tangent on the upper side of the line whose slope is $1/c$. The values of M/M_e which correspond to the fully plastic condition are sometimes called form factors since their values depend on the shape (form) of the cross section. Values of these form factors are designated here by the symbol k and are given for some typical cross sections in Table 23.

TABLE 23

FORM FACTOR k FOR BEAMS OF VARIOUS CROSS SECTIONS
$k = M/M_e$ FOR THE FULLY PLASTIC CONDITION

Type of Cross Section

	Rectangle	Circle	Diamond Shape (see Fig. 299)	Circular Tube (see Fig. 299) $c_1/c = 0.75$	Standard I Beams
Value of k	1.5	1.7	2.0	1.39	1.06–1.18

Illustrative Problems

Problem 310. A horizontal simply supported beam has an I shaped cross section whose relative dimensions are shown in Fig. 299 with the value of $c = 3$ in. The beam is made of mild steel for which the yield point is $\sigma_e = 37,500$ lb per sq in.; it is loaded at its mid-point by a concentrated load P. The beam has a span length of $l = 10$ ft and is supported so that lateral buckling of the upper (compression) flange is prevented. Compute the load P which will cause inelastic strain to penetrate just through the flanges of the beam. (This load will be nearly equal to the ultimate load the beam will support since the web offers very little additional resistance to bending.)

Solution. Since $h/c = \frac{1}{4}$, $M/M_e = 1.14$ as was found in the construction of the curve in Fig. 299.

$$M_e = \sigma_e I/c = 0.83\sigma_e c^3 = 841{,}000 \text{ lb-in.}$$

Therefore $M = 1.14 M_e = 958{,}000$ lb-in.

The maximum bending moment in the beam is $M = Pl/4 = 958{,}000$ lb-in.

Therefore $P = 31{,}700$ lb is the load that will cause inelastic deformation to penetrate to a depth equal to the thickness of the flanges at the mid-span section of the beam.

Problem 311. A roller chain which is used to raise and lower the gates on a dam has the dimensions shown in Fig. 300a. The outer side bars, the inner side bars, the pins, and the rollers in the chain are made of a chrome molybdenum steel whose tensile properties are as follows: Yield point $\sigma_e = 120{,}000$ lb per sq in., ultimate strength $\sigma_u = 145{,}000$ lb per sq in., elongation in 2-in. gage length = 14 per cent. It may be assumed that the maximum load that may be applied is limited by general yielding of the chain. Thus the maximum load will occur when a pin or side bar is in a fully plastic condition. Compute the working load P_w for this chain based on a factor of safety of 5. *Note:* The clearance between the pin and the holes in the side bars and roller is small (less than 0.01 in.).

Solution. General yielding may occur in one or more of the parts of the chain. Thus the side bars may yield in tension or the pin may yield as a result of the bearing stress. The pin may also yield in bending or in direct shear. Figure 300b is a sketch showing the pin and side bars after general yielding has occurred. The load P required to cause general yielding of each part will be found and divided by the factor of safety of 5 to find the working load. The least value so found will be the solution.

Tension in Side Bars. Yielding of the side bars will occur at the sections through the holes. The load that will cause general yielding of the chain will be assumed to be the load that causes the fully plastic condition on the section through the hole in the side bar. This load is

$$P_t = \sigma_e a_t = 120{,}000(4.5 - 2.375)0.875 \times 2 = 447{,}000 \text{ lb}$$

$$P_w = 447{,}000/5 = 90{,}000 \text{ lb}$$

Bearing on Side Bars or on Pin. It is known that the bearing stress as usually calculated will be at least equal to $\sigma_e = 120{,}000$ lb per sq in. before yielding takes place on the bearing area of such contact surfaces. The fully plastic bearing load is

$$P_b = \sigma_e a_b = 120{,}000 \times 0.875 \times 2.375 \times 2 = 500{,}000 \text{ lb}$$

$$P_w = 500{,}000/5 = 100{,}000 \text{ lb}$$

Direct Shear in Pin. The shearing yield point τ_e of the material is about $0.6\sigma_e$ or about 72,000 lb per sq in. Therefore the fully plastic shearing load on the pin is

$$P_s = \tau_e a_s = 72{,}000 \times (\overline{\pi 2.375^2}/4) \times 2 = 640{,}000 \text{ lb}$$

$$P_w = 128{,}000 \text{ lb}$$

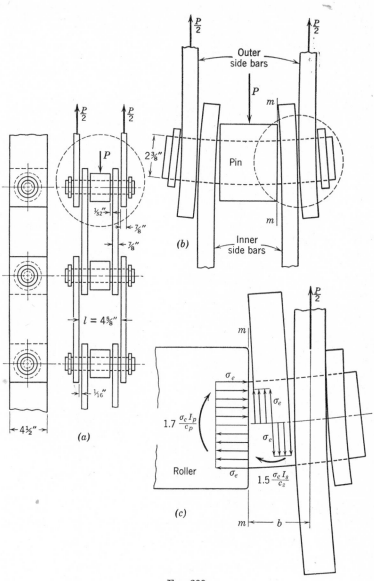

Fig. 300

Bending of the Pin. The load P that would cause inelastic bending of the pins and hence would cause general yielding of the chain may be found as follows: First, it will be assumed that the maximum bending moment in the pin occurs at the section at the right (or left) end of the roller, such as section mm in Fig. 300b; the small tolerance stated justifies the assumption.

The forces acting on the portion of the pin to the right of section mm are shown in Fig. 300c. It is assumed that the maximum value of P is reached when the fully plastic moment in the pin occurs, resulting in the stress distribution shown in section mm which causes a resisting moment of $1.7M_e$ (see Table 23). Furthermore, it is assumed that as this moment is being developed the inner side bar offers a restraining moment to the bending of the pin and in so doing develops its fully plastic moment $1.5M_e$ on the section through the hole, as shown in Fig. 300c.

Since the forces acting on the portion of the pin shown in Fig. 300c are in equilibrium, the algebraic sum of their moments must be equal to zero, or the same idea is expressed by equating the bending moment for section mm to the resisting moment on the section. Thus

$$\tfrac{1}{2}Pb - 1.5M_{es} = 1.7M_{ep}$$

in which s refers to the side bar and p to the pin. The value of b as shown in Fig. 300c is

$$b = \tfrac{1}{32} + \tfrac{7}{8} + \tfrac{1}{16} + \tfrac{1}{2} \times \tfrac{7}{8} = 1.40 \text{ in.}$$

Therefore
$$P = \sigma_e\left(2.43\frac{I_p}{c_p} + 2.14\frac{I_s}{c_s}\right)$$

For the pin:
$$\frac{I_p}{c_p} = \frac{\pi d^4/64}{d/2} = \frac{\pi d^3}{32} = 1.31 \text{ in.}^3$$

For the side bar:
$$\frac{I_s}{c_s} = \frac{\tfrac{1}{12}(4.5 - 2.375)\overline{0.875^3}}{0.5 \times 0.875} = 0.27 \text{ in.}^3$$

Therefore
$$P = 120,000(2.43 \times 1.31 + 2.14 \times 0.27) = 452,000 \text{ lb}$$

$$P_w = 458,000/5 = 90,400 \text{ lb}$$

A tensile test of the chain considered in this problem showed a yield point, by the drop of the beam, of 460,000 lb, which is in satisfactory agreement with the loads computed for bending of the pin and for tension in the side bars.

It is of interest to determine the value of P_w if it is assumed that the maximum load is governed by the elastic bending of the pin as given by the flexure formula in which the value of the stress is considered to be $\sigma_e = 120,000$ lb per sq in. Thus

$$\sigma_e = 120,000 = Mc_p/I_p$$

in which $M = \tfrac{1}{2}Pb$; it is assumed that the side bar does not offer any resistance to bending of the pin within the elastic behavior of the pin. From the foregoing equation

$$P = \frac{120,000I_p}{\tfrac{1}{2}bc_p} = 225,000 \text{ lb}$$

The corresponding working load is $P_w = 45,000$ lb. It is evident, therefore, that about one-half of the utilizable strength of the chain is the result of small, inelastic deformations.

However, an empirical method is often used in such problems to take advantage of the influence of yielding which experience and tests show is permissible. In this problem an empirical method consists in assuming that the bending moment M in the elastic stress flexural formula $\sigma_w = Mc/I$ is a fictitious moment equal to $Pl/14$ in which l is the distance between the inner edges of the outer side bars (see Fig. 300a). If this latter value of $M = P4.625/14 = 0.33P$ is used in the formula $\sigma_w = Mc/I$, we have

$$120,000 = 0.33P(c/I) = 0.33P/1.31$$

hence

$$P = 475,000 \text{ lb}$$

$$P_w = 475,000/5 = 95,000 \text{ lb}$$

These values of P and P_w are in satisfactory agreement with the values of $P = 452,000$ lb and $P_w = 90,400$ lb found previously for bending in the pin. It is hoped, however, that as more rational methods involving inelastic behavior of members are evolved, similar to the method used in the solution of this problem, empirical methods may become less prevalent.

Problems

312. Construct the curve showing the relation between M/M_e and h/c for a beam having an I section similar to that shown in Fig. 299 except that $b = c$, $d/c = \frac{1}{10}$, and $t/c = \frac{1}{15}$. Assume that the material in the beam has a stress-strain diagram in tension or compression as shown in Fig. 292b.

313. A simply supported beam has a length of 5 ft between supports. The cross section of the beam has a T shape composed of two rectangles. The bar of the T is 4 in. by $\frac{1}{2}$ in. and serves as the flange of the beam, and the stem is 4 in. by $\frac{1}{2}$ in. The beam is made of structural grade steel having a yield point of $\sigma_e = 35,000$ lb per sq in. and supports a concentrated load P acting at the mid-point and lying in the plane of symmetry. Compute the load P which will cause yielding at the section of maximum bending moment to become fully plastic.   *Ans.*   10,500 lb

167 The ratio M/M_e for beams made of material not having a yield point.

The question now arises as to the influence of small inelastic strains in the most-stressed fibers of a beam on the load-carrying capacity of the beam if the stress-strain diagrams in tension and compression for the material are as shown in Fig. 301a. Such stress-strain diagrams, which are not the same for tension and compression and do not have yield points, are typical of cast iron and of a number of nonferrous metals, especially of aluminum alloys.

The problem is to compute the value of the bending moment M corresponding to some value of the maximum strain ϵ_1 in the beam at a section where the strain has been permitted to become inelastic, or corresponding to some depth of yielding h. For this purpose it has been found that the use of the following simple approximation of the stress-strain curves gives satisfactory results.

First, as shown in Fig. 301a, a curve is drawn through points which represent the average numerical values of the compressive and tensile

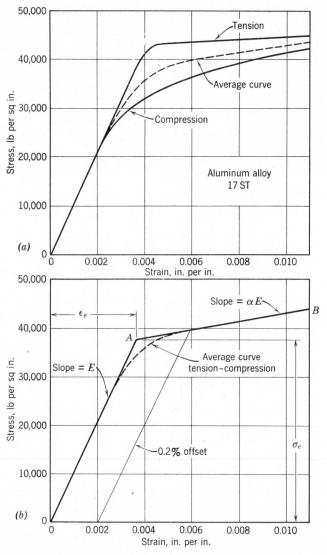

FIG. 301 Approximate stress-strain curve for a material not having a yield point.

stresses corresponding to each value of the strain. Second, as shown in Fig. 301b the average curve is replaced by two straight line segments OA and AB. The segment OA has a slope E representing the modulus of elasticity, segment AB has a slope αE, and the coordinates of point A are assumed to represent approximately the elastic limit strain ϵ_e and the elastic limit stress σ_e, respectively. The lines OA and AB are assumed to represent approximately the stress-strain relationship in either tension or compression. For OA the relationship between the stress and strain is

$$\sigma = E\epsilon \tag{629}$$

and for AB $$\sigma = \sigma_e + \alpha E(\epsilon - \epsilon_e) \tag{630}$$

To illustrate the foregoing approximations let it be required to derive an equation giving a relation between M and ϵ_1 or between M and h

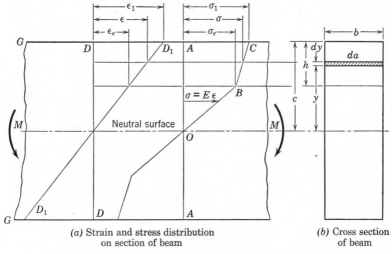

(a) Strain and stress distribution
on section of beam

(b) Cross section
of beam

Fig. 302   Beam loaded above elastic limit of material.

for a beam which has a rectangular cross section and which is made of a material having tensile and compressive stress-strain curves as shown in Fig. 301a.

This may be done by the same procedure as was used in Art. 165. Thus let Fig. 302a represent a segment of the beam which is subjected to a pure bending moment M at each end. The conditions of equilibrium for a portion of the beam between the sections GG and AA require that the internal $(\sigma\, da)$ forces on the section AA must hold the bending moment M in equilibrium. The equations of equilibrium are expressed by Eqs. 619 and 620. The first of the equilibrium equations gives the location of the neutral axis at the centroid of the section, a result which is of course slightly erroneous due to the approximations used in representing the stress-strain curves. The second equation of equilibrium is

$$M = 2\int_0^{c-h} \sigma y b \, dy + 2\int_{c-h}^{c} \sigma y b \, dy \tag{631}$$

In Eq. 631 it is required that the expressions giving the stress σ in each integral be expressed in terms of y, h, α, and c and σ_e rather than in terms of the strains as given by Eqs. 629 and 630. Such expressions may be obtained from Eqs. 629 and 630, respectively, if in Fig. 302a the similar triangles are used to eliminate the strain terms from these equations. When this is done these equations become

$$\sigma = \sigma_e y/(c - h) \tag{632}$$

$$\sigma = \sigma_e \left(1 - \alpha + \frac{\alpha y}{c - h}\right) \tag{633}$$

Equation 632 represents values of σ in the elastic or inner portion of the beam from O to B, and Eq. 633 in the inelastic portion from B to C as shown in Fig. 302a. When these expressions for σ are substituted in their respective places in Eq. 631 and the integrations are completed, the equation becomes

$$M = 2\sigma_e b c^2 \left\{ \left(\frac{1}{3} + \frac{1}{3}\frac{h}{c} - \frac{1}{6}\frac{h^2}{c^2}\right) + \alpha \left[\frac{1}{3\left(1 - \dfrac{h}{c}\right)} - \left(\frac{1}{3} + \frac{1}{3}\frac{h}{c} - \frac{1}{6}\frac{h^2}{c^2}\right) \right] \right\} \tag{634}$$

For the simplified stress-strain diagram $M_e = \sigma_e I/c = \frac{2}{3}\sigma_e b c^2$, and if Eq. 634 is divided by M_e the result is

$$\frac{M}{M_e} = \left(1 + \frac{h}{c} - \frac{1}{2}\frac{h^2}{c^2}\right) + \alpha \left[\frac{1}{1 - (h/c)} - \left(1 + \frac{h}{c} - \frac{1}{2}\frac{h^2}{c^2}\right) \right] \tag{635}$$

The term α in Eq. 635 is defined in Fig. 301b as the relation between the slope of the inelastic part AB of the approximate stress-strain curve and the slope E of the elastic part OA. Consequently if $\alpha = 0$ the slope of AB is zero, and this condition represents a material which has a yield point. This case was considered in Art. 165, and if $\alpha = 0$ is substituted in Eq. 635 this equation reduces to Eq. 623 which gives the ratio M/M_e for a material with a yield point as shown by Fig. 292b.

An important fact about Eq. 635 is that on the right-hand side the terms in each group of parentheses represent the value of M/M_e for $\alpha = 0$ for a beam having a rectangular cross section for any depth of yielding h. By making use of this fact Eq. 635 may be rewritten in the form

$$\left.\frac{M}{M_e}\right]_\alpha = \left.\frac{M}{M_e}\right]_{\alpha=0} + \alpha\left(\frac{1}{1-(h/c)} - \left.\frac{M}{M_e}\right]_{\alpha=0}\right) \qquad (636)$$

The importance of Eq. 636 is twofold. First, it can be proved that this equation is true not only for a beam of rectangular cross section but also for all other types of symmetrically loaded beams having cross sections with two axes of symmetry. Second, it makes possible the use of the curves of Figs. 297 and 299 which represent values of M/M_e corresponding to values of h/c, for a material for which $\alpha = 0$.

For finding the deflection of a beam and for finding the value of M/M_e corresponding to some value of ϵ_1/ϵ_e, it is desirable to have an equation relating M/M_e and ϵ_1/ϵ_e. This equation is obtained directly from Eq. 636 by substitution of the value of ϵ_1/ϵ_e from Eq. 627, which gives

$$\left.\frac{M}{M_e}\right]_\alpha = \left.\frac{M}{M_e}\right]_{\alpha=0} + \alpha\left(\frac{\epsilon_1}{\epsilon_e} - \left.\frac{M}{M_e}\right]_{\alpha=0}\right) \qquad (637)$$

The foregoing equations are used in determining the value of the ratio M/M_e corresponding to a value of h/c or of ϵ_1/ϵ_e. These equations have been obtained by the use of a stress-strain curve which is an approximation of the actual tensile and compressive stress-strain curves. However, there have been many tests carried out on beams made of materials not having a yield point, and the results of these tests show that the foregoing equations give reliable values of M/M_e when the approximate curve is used to determine the values of α, σ_e, and ϵ_e.

Fully Plastic Value of M/M_e When α Is Not Zero. When α is not zero there is no so-called fully plastic value of M/M_e, that is, no plastic hinge occurs until the full ultimate resistance to bending occurs. For this reason the ultimate bending resistance of beams made of materials such as alloys of aluminum, magnesium, and brass is sometimes set equal to the bending moment which will produce a certain predetermined amount of inelastic strain at the extreme fiber of the beam. This procedure is illustrated in one of the following illustrative problems.

Illustrative Problems

Problem 314. Solve Prob. 310 for an I beam made of aluminum alloy whose stress-strain diagrams in tension and compression are as shown by Fig. 301a.

Solution. The tension and compression stress-strain curves are averaged as shown in Figs. 301a and 301b, and the lines OA and AB are used to represent (approximately) the stress-strain relationship. From Fig. 301b the following values are found:

$$\sigma_e = 37,500 \text{ lb/in.}^2 \qquad \alpha = 0.07$$

The value of $h/c = \frac{1}{4}$, and hence from the curve in Fig. 299 $M/M_e = 1.14$ for $\alpha = 0$. From Eq. 636 we obtain

$$\frac{M}{M_e}\bigg]_{\alpha=0.07} = 1.14 + 0.07 \left(\frac{1}{1-\frac{1}{4}} - 1.14\right) = 1.15$$

But $$M_e = \sigma_e I/c = 0.83\sigma_e c^3 = 841{,}000 \text{ lb-in.}$$

Therefore $M = 1.15M_e = 967{,}000$ lb-in. The maximum bending moment is $M = Pl/4$. Therefore $P = 32{,}200$ lb.

Problem 315. A beam has a circular cross section whose diameter is 3 in. and is made of a material whose stress-strain curves in tension and compression are as shown in Fig. 301a. Determine the bending moment required to cause the inelastic part of the strain in the outer fibers of the beam to be 0.2 per cent.

Solution. As shown by the 0.2 per cent offset line in Fig. 301b, when a maximum strain of $\epsilon_1 = 0.0059$ is reached and the load is then released, the stress-strain relation on unloading will follow (approximately) the offset line down to an inelastic strain of 0.2 per cent. The values of $\sigma_e = 37{,}500$ lb per sq in. and $\epsilon_e = 0.0035$ are taken as the coordinates of point A. Therefore $\epsilon_1/\epsilon_e = 1.68$, and hence from the curve for a beam of circular section in Fig. 299 we find for a material with a value of $\alpha = 0$ that $M/M_e = 1.40$. Since $\alpha = 0.07$, we find from Eq. 637 that

$$\frac{M}{M_e}\bigg]_{\alpha=0.07} = 1.40 + 0.07(1.68 - 1.40) = 1.42$$

But $$M_e = \sigma_e I/c = 100{,}000 \text{ lb-in.}$$

Therefore $$M = 1.42M_e = 142{,}000 \text{ lb-in.}$$

From Eq. 627 we find that the depth of yielding is $h = 0.40c = 0.60$ in.

168 Residual stresses. In the foregoing articles methods have been given for computing the resistance of members subjected to axial or bending loads which cause a relatively small amount of inelastic strain. The release of such loads introduces residual stresses in the member at sections where inelastic strains occur. Two types of residual stresses may occur: namely, macroresidual stresses and microresidual stresses (see Art. 7, chap. 2). Approximate values of the macroresidual stresses may be computed by means of the following principle: When a load which has produced inelastic strains is released, the material in the member acts elastically, except for small inelastic strains (sometimes referred to as Bauschinger effect) caused by microstresses, as the load is released, and hence the stresses and the strains associated with the unloading cycle may be computed by using the usual elastic stress formulas, such as $\sigma = P/a$ or $\sigma = Mc/I$, and $\sigma = E\epsilon$ in which P for an axially loaded member or M for a beam is the magnitude of the load which is released. When the values of these stresses, which are assumed to occur during the load release cycle, are superposed algebraically on the stresses which exist in the member just before the load is released, the macroresidual stresses are determined. The application of this principle is limited to problems in which the residual stresses are not large enough to cause yielding of the fibers in a direction opposite to the initial yielding. Furthermore, the results may be in error due to the effect of microstresses.

Second and Subsequent Applications of Load. If the load P or M which has been released after producing inelastic strain is reapplied in the same direction, the stresses and strains occurring during the second and subsequent applications may be considered to be elastic, provided that the residual stresses occurring during the first release of the load do not cause inelastic strains in the opposite direction from that produced by the first application of the load.

Reversal of Direction of Load. If after the release of a load P or M which has produced inelastic strains the load is applied in the opposite direction, it will be found that inelastic strains in this opposite direction will occur at a load which is somewhat smaller than that originally applied. Some idea as to the magnitude of this reverse load which causes inelastic strains to start can be had by noting that the residual stresses at the most-stressed fibers remaining after the release of the first load are of the same direction as those produced by the reversed load.

Effect of Residual Stresses on Fully Plastic Strength. In many members there are (unknown) residual stresses present in the member before the application of the first load to the member. If they have the same direction as those produced by the first load, these residual stresses may cause inelastic strains to start at a smaller load than expected. However, the fully plastic strength of the member is affected very little by such initial residual stresses, particularly if the material has ample ductility.

169 Deflection of beam in which strains in outer fibers are inelastic. In many uses of beams the deflection of the beam rather than the strain or stress in the outer fibers may limit the maximum load that can be permitted to be applied to the beam. If the beam is inelastically strained, the deflections may be computed by the dummy load method as described in Chapter 15 provided that after inelastic strains have started at any cross section the bending moment at that section is not permitted to decrease. Thus by Eq. 551 (Chapter 15) the deflection at any section of the beam is

$$\delta = \int m \, d\alpha \qquad (638)$$

in which m and $d\alpha$ are quantities as described in Chapter 15. The angle $d\alpha$ is the rotation of a section of the beam with respect to another section at a distance dx from the first. If the strains in all the fibers at these two sections are elastic, the angle $d\alpha$ is given by the equation

$$d\alpha = (M/EI) \, dx \qquad (639)$$

But if the strains in the outer fibers have become inelastic, the expression for $d\alpha$ is found from the moment-strain equation. For a beam of rectangular cross section $d\alpha$ is found as follows (Eq. 628):

$$\frac{M}{M_e} = \frac{3}{2} - \frac{1}{2}\left(\frac{\epsilon_e}{\epsilon_1}\right)^2 = \frac{3}{2} - \frac{1}{2}\frac{(\epsilon_e \, dx/c)^2}{(\epsilon_1 \, dx/c)^2} = k - n\frac{d\alpha_e^2}{d\alpha^2} \qquad (640)$$

In Eq. 640 the constants k and n are substituted for $\frac{3}{2}$ and $\frac{1}{2}$, respectively, because this equation may be used with different values for k and n to give an approximate relationship for $d\alpha$ for beams having cross sections other than rectangular. From Eq. 640

$$d\alpha = \frac{n^{\frac{1}{2}}(M_e/EI) \, dx}{\sqrt{k - (M/M_e)}} \qquad (641)$$

in which $d\alpha_e = (M_e/EI) \, dx$ has been substituted from Eq. 639. Values of k and n for three types of cross sections are shown in Table 24. It should be noted that the value of k is equal to the fully plastic moment M divided by M_e and that $n = k - 1$.

TABLE 24

Type of Cross Section

	Rectangular	Circular	Standard I Beam
k	1.5	1.7	1.06–1.18
$n = k - 1$	0.5	0.7	0.06–0.18

Deflection of Simply Supported Beam: Concentrated Load at Mid-span. Let Fig. 303a represent the beam, and let the load P be such that the extreme fibers of the beam in the central portion of length $l - 2b$ have begun to yield. The deflection at the load P is given by the equation

$$\delta_P = 2\left[\int_0^b m \, d\alpha + \int_b^{l/2} m \, d\alpha\right] \qquad (642)$$

in which m is the bending moment at any section of the beam caused by a dummy load of unity as shown in Fig. 303b, and the angle $d\alpha$ in the interval $x = 0$ to $x = b$ is given by Eq. 639 and from $x = b$ to $x = l/2$ by Eq. 641. Hence,

$$\delta_P = 2\left[\int_0^b \frac{Mm}{EI}\,dx + n^{1/2}\frac{M_e}{EI}\int_b^{l/2}\frac{m\,dx}{\sqrt{k - (M/M_e)}}\right] \quad (643)$$

The expressions for M and m are $\frac{1}{2}Px$ and $\frac{1}{2}x$, respectively, in both integrals of Eq. 643. Therefore

$$\delta_P = 2\left[\frac{P}{4EI}\int_0^{2M_e/P} x^2\,dx + \frac{1}{2}n^{1/2}\frac{M_e}{EI}\int_{2M_e/P}^{l/2}\frac{x\,dx}{\sqrt{k - \frac{1}{2}(Px/M_e)}}\right] \quad (644)$$

where the limit b has been replaced by its equivalent $b = 2M_e/P$, since

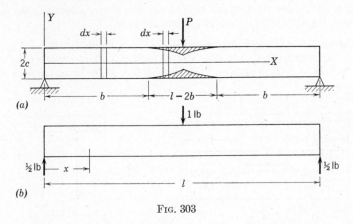

(a)

(b)

Fig. 303

at the distance b from each end of the beam the bending moment is $M_e = Pb/2$. When the integrals in Eq. 644 are evaluated, the result is

$$\delta_P = \frac{4M_e{}^3}{3P^2EI}\left[1 + 2n^{1/2}(2k + 1)(k - 1)^{1/2}\right.$$
$$\left. - 2n^{1/2}\left(2k + \frac{Pl}{4M_e}\right)\left(k - \frac{Pl}{4M_e}\right)^{1/2}\right] \quad (645)$$

In Eq. 645 if we let P have its value at the elastic limit of the beam, that is, $P = P_e = 4M_e/l$, the deflection is

$$\delta_{P_e} = \tfrac{1}{12}(M_e l^2/EI) = \tfrac{1}{48}(P_e l^3/EI) \quad (646)$$

The value of δ_{P_e} is the deflection of the beam just as the maximum extreme fiber stress in the beam reaches the yield point of the material.

Illustrative Problems

Problem 316. Let the beam of Fig. 303 have a rectangular cross section, and let the load P be such that the depth of penetration of yielding below the extreme fibers is $h = c/2$ at the section of maximum bending moment. From Eq. 645 derive the expression for the deflection at the load P.

Solution. For the conditions stated, $M = 1.37M_e$ (see Fig. 299), and the load is

$$P = \frac{4M}{l} = 4 \times 1.37 \frac{M_e}{l} = 5.48 \frac{M_e}{l}$$

The constants are $k = 1.5$ and $n = 0.5$. The substitution of these values in Eq. 645 gives

$$\delta_P = M_e l^2 / 8.1 EI$$

This result, when compared with Eq. 646, shows that, when the load on this beam having a rectangular cross section is increased 37 per cent above P_e, the elastic limit load, the deflection increases 50 per cent above δ_{P_e}.

Problem 317. A simply supported beam of span length $l = 46$ in. (Fig. 304) is loaded symmetrically by two concentrated loads P, each of which acts at a distance $l_1 = 19$ in. from a support. The cross section of the beam has an I shape

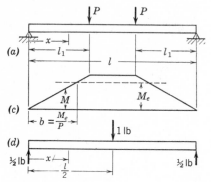
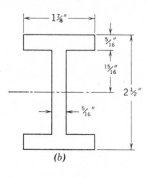

Fig. 304

whose dimensions are given in Fig. 304b. The beam is made of a low-carbon steel whose yield point $\sigma_e = 27,000$ lb per sq in. Compute the deflection at the center of the span for the following loads: (a) when the loads are such as to cause inelastic strains to be impending; (b) when the loads will cause inelastic strains to just penetrate the flanges, that is, when $h/c = 0.25$.

Solution. The deflection is given by the equation

$$\delta = 2 \left[\int_0^{M_e/P} m \, d\alpha + \int_{M_e/P}^{l_1} m \, d\alpha + \int_{l_1}^{l/2} m \, d\alpha \right]$$

From $x = 0$ to M_e/P: $m = \frac{1}{2}x$;

$$d\alpha = (M/EI) \, dx \qquad \text{where } M = Px$$

From $x = M_e/P$ to l_1: $m = \frac{1}{2}x$;

$$d\alpha = \frac{n^{\frac{1}{2}}(M_e/EI)\,dx}{\sqrt{k - (M/M_e)}} \qquad \text{where } M = Px$$

From $x = l_1$ to $l/2$: $m = \frac{1}{2}x$; $d\alpha$ is the same as for the interval $x = M_e/P$ to l_1, but $M = Pl_1$. The substitution of these values in the foregoing equation gives

$$\delta = 2\left[\frac{1P}{2EI}\int_0^{M_e/P} x^2\,dx + \frac{1}{2}n^{\frac{1}{2}}\frac{M_e}{EI}\int_{M_e/P}^{l_1}\frac{x\,dx}{\sqrt{k - (Px/M_e)}}\right.$$

$$\left. + \frac{1}{2}\frac{n^{\frac{1}{2}}(M_e/EI)}{\sqrt{k - (Pl_1/M_e)}}\int_{l_1}^{l/2} x\,dx\right]$$

$$= \frac{P}{EI}\frac{x^3}{3}\Big]_0^{M_e/P} + n^{\frac{1}{2}}\frac{M_e}{EI}\left[-\frac{2M_e x}{P}\left(k - \frac{Px}{M_e}\right)^{\frac{1}{2}} - \frac{4}{3}\frac{M_e^2}{P^2}\left(k - \frac{Px}{M_e}\right)^{\frac{3}{2}}\right]_{M_e/P}^{l_1}$$

$$+ \frac{n^{\frac{1}{2}}(M_e/EI)}{\sqrt{k - (Pl_1/M_e)}}\frac{x^2}{2}\Big]_{l_1}^{l/2}$$

$$= \frac{M_e^3}{3EIP^2} + n^{\frac{1}{2}}\frac{M_e^3}{EIP^2}\left[-\frac{2}{3}\left(k - \frac{Pl_1}{M_e}\right)^{\frac{1}{2}}\left(2k + \frac{Pl_1}{M_e}\right) + \frac{2}{3}(k - 1)^{\frac{1}{2}}(2k + 1)\right]$$

$$+ n^{\frac{1}{2}}\frac{M_e}{EI}\left(k - \frac{Pl_1}{M_e}\right)^{-\frac{1}{2}}\left(\frac{l^2}{8} - \frac{l_1^2}{2}\right) \qquad (a)$$

(a) *Yielding Impending.* For this case $P = P_e = M_e/l_1$. When this value of P is substituted in Eq. a, we obtain

$$\delta = \frac{1}{3}\frac{P_e l_1^3}{EI} + \frac{P_e l_1}{EI}\frac{n^{\frac{1}{2}}}{(k - 1)^{\frac{1}{2}}}\left(\frac{l^2}{8} - \frac{l_1^2}{2}\right)$$

If it is noted that $k - 1 = n$, this equation reduces to

$$\delta = \frac{1}{6}\frac{P_e l_1}{EI}\left(\frac{3}{4}l^2 - l_1^2\right)$$

which is the equation for the deflection of the beam when the loads do not cause inelastic strain. For this beam

$$P_e = M_e/l_1 = \sigma_e I/cl_1$$

Therefore

$$\delta = \frac{1}{6}\frac{\sigma_e}{Ec}\left(\frac{3}{4}l^2 - l_1^2\right) = \frac{1}{6}\frac{27{,}000}{30 \times 10^6 \times 1.25}\left(\frac{3}{4}\overline{46}^2 - \overline{19}^2\right) = 0.147 \text{ in.}$$

The actual deflection of this beam when tested under these loads was 0.153 in. Most of the difference between this computed value and the value obtained in the test is due to the effect of vertical shear which is neglected here.

(b) *Flanges Yielded; Yielding in Web Impending.* For a beam having the cross section in Fig. 304b, $M_e = 1.26\sigma_e$, and the theoretical fully plastic moment is $M_P = 1.55\sigma_e$. The ratio $M_P/M_e = 1.23$. Therefore $k = 1.23$ and $n = 0.23$ for the foregoing equations. The value of P which will cause inelastic strains to penetrate just through the flanges is found by using the fact that the bending moment which would cause a fully plastic stress σ_e in the flanges and elastic stresses in the web is $M = 1.46\sigma_e$. Since the maximum bending moment is $M = Pl_1$, we have $P = 1.46\sigma_e/l_1 = 2070$ lb. If the foregoing values are substituted into Eq. a, the result is $\delta = 0.217$ in. The actual deflection of the beam when tested under loads $P = 2070$ lb was $\delta = 0.21$ in. The test was conducted in a screw power machine, and the loads were not maintained for more than a few minutes. If the loads had been maintained for several hours, the deflection might have been somewhat greater owing to additional yielding which may take place with time under sustained loads when yielding is heterogeneous (Lueder's lines).

Problems

318. A horizontal beam of steel with a yield point $\sigma_e = 40,000$ lb per sq in. is simply supported at its ends and has a cross section of rectangular area 1.875 in. wide by 2.5 in. deep. Compute the deflection of the beam when inelastic strains at the section of maximum moment penetrate one-half the distance from the extreme fiber to the neutral axis. The length $l = 40$ in., and $E = 30,000,000$ lb per sq in.

319. A simply supported beam having a rectangular cross section 2 in. wide and 3 in. deep is loaded with a concentrated load at mid-span. The beam is made of steel whose stress-strain diagram is given in Fig. 292b in which $\sigma_e = 100,000$ lb per sq in. If the span length of the beam is 40 in. and the most stressed fibers are strained to a value of $\epsilon_1 = 0.007$ in. per in., determine the maximum deflection of the beam. Assume that $E = 30,000,000$ lb per sq in.   *Ans.*   0.45 in.

Chapter 18

EFFECT OF SMALL INELASTIC STRAINS FOR COMBINED BENDING AND AXIAL LOADS

170 Interaction curves. In Fig. 305a is shown a straight member of constant cross section subjected simultaneously to direct tension and bending. It is assumed that the stress-strain diagram for the material is represented by Fig. 292b of Chapter 17. It is assumed also that the deflection of the beam is negligible; each cross section of the member is subjected to an axial load P and a bending moment M. For each cross section in the central portion of the beam $M = Wl$.

Let it be required to find the combinations of P and M that cause the strain in the most-stressed fibers of the beam to just start to become inelastic; this condition is frequently described by stating that inelastic strain is impending. In Fig. 305b is shown a portion of the beam severed from the remaining portion. The load P and bending moment M cause on the severed section the stress distribution shown, the stress at any point of the section being the algebraic sum of the stresses σ_1 and σ_2 caused individually by P and M. When $\sigma_1 + \sigma_2$ just reaches the yield point σ_e of the material, inelastic strain is impending on the bottom fibers of the member. This condition is expressed by the equation

$$(P/a) + (Mc/I) = \sigma_e \qquad (647)$$

By dividing both sides of Eq. 647 by σ_e and noting that $P_e = \sigma_e a$ and $M_e = \sigma_e I/c$ Eq. 647 is transformed into

$$(P/P_e) + (M/M_e) = 1 \qquad (648)$$

which involves only dimensionless ratios. Equation 648 represents all combinations of P and M which will cause inelastic yielding to impend in the most-stressed fiber and is represented graphically by the straight line AB in Fig. 306, in which the ordinates are values of M/M_e and the abscissas are values of P/P_e. Such a line as AB is called an *interaction line* or *curve* relating values of P and M, and Eq. 648 is called an interaction equation. However, this interaction line represents the combination of loads which cause inelastic strains (yielding) to start. It is desirable to find also the interaction curve for loads that cause the in-

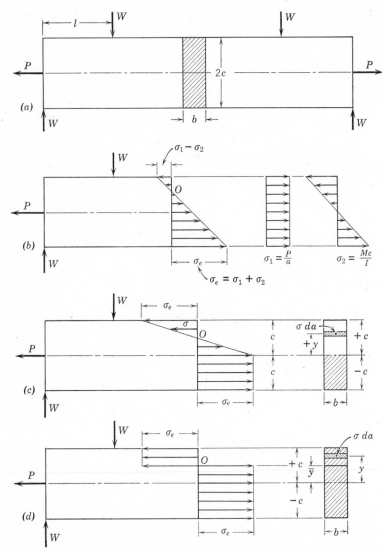

Fig. 305   Inelastic stresses in bar subjected to bending and axial tension.

elastic strains to penetrate to a small depth in the member, since such strains make it possible to increase the loads on many members without destroying the proper functioning of the member (without causing structural damage).

Interaction Curve for Loads Causing Arbitrary Depth of Yielding. For illustrative purposes it will be assumed that the cross section of the beam is rectangular and that the depth of yielding is one-half the depth

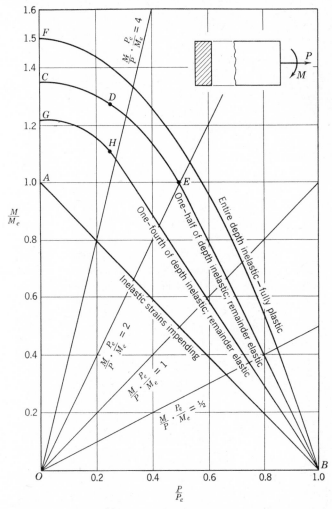

Fig. 306 Interaction curves for combined bending and axial tensile loads on member with rectangular cross section.

of the beam. This means that an elastic core remains whose depth is one-half the depth of the beam. The reason for maintaining an elastic core is to restrict the deformation so as to prevent general yielding, as discussed later in this article. One point on this interaction curve is at the point C in Fig. 306, which represents the value of M/M_e when $P = 0$. This value is $M/M_e = 1.37$ for pure bending as found in Fig. 297 (Chapter 17) for a depth of yielding on both sides of the beam of $h = 0.50c$. Another point on the interaction curve is at B, which represents the value of P/P_e when $M = 0$; for this condition inelastic strains require that $P = P_e$ or $P/P_e = 1$.

The mathematical expression for the interaction curve between B and C can be derived by making use of the equations of equilibrium, but this expression always requires two different equations, both of which are unwieldy and unsuitable; one equation which represents a straight line applies when P and M cause yielding only on one side of the member, and the other equation which represents a curved line applies when yielding is caused on both sides of the member by P and M. The interaction curve, however, can be drawn with sufficient accuracy by computing the coordinates of only one or two points, such as the point E at which the aforementioned straight line and curved line meet. The particular combination of loads P and M that correspond to this point is that which produces the distribution of stresses shown in Fig. 305c, in which the bottom fibers have strained inelastically to a depth c and the top fibers are on the verge of yielding in compression. The values of P and M corresponding to this stress distribution are obtained by applying the equations of equilibrium to the forces on the beam in Fig. 305c which give

$$P = \int_{-c}^{+c} \sigma \, da = bc\sigma_e \tag{649}$$

and
$$M = \int_{-c}^{+c} y\sigma \, da = \tfrac{2}{3}bc^2\sigma_e \tag{650}$$

The division of the value of P in Eq. 649 by $P_e = 2bc\sigma_e$ gives P/P_e $= \tfrac{1}{2}$, and the division of M in Eq. 650 by $M_e = \tfrac{2}{3}bc^2\sigma_e$ gives M/M_e $= 1.0$. These values are the coordinates which are sought and are represented by the point E in Fig. 306. The coordinates of points on the straight line between E and B represent combinations of values of P and M which cause a depth of yielding $h = c$ on the lower side of the bar and a stress at the upper side less than σ_e, that is, no yielding on the upper fibers occurs. The curve from C to E is drawn through points whose coordinates represent combinations of values of P and M that cause depths of yielding on the upper and lower portions of the member such that between the loads W the depth of the elastic core of material is one-half the depth of the member.

CHOICE OF DEPTH OF INELASTIC STRAIN. If this core is the minimum elastic core that is considered to be safe for the member to possess for its proper functioning as a load-resisting member, the curve $CDEB$ gives the maximum utilizable combination values of P and M. In other words, the member would be considered to be structurally damaged by loads greater than those given by the curve. If a smaller or larger elastic core is considered to be permissible, a curve may be constructed to give loads that will leave the elastic core specified. For example, in Fig. 306 the curves GHB, $CDEB$, and FB represent combinations of M and P which correspond, respectively, to one-fourth, one-half, and full-depth of yielding. The depth to be chosen as corresponding to structural failure will depend on the type of material and the use of the member.

A limiting amount of inelastic strain (yielding) could be imposed either by specifying a maximum permissible strain in the most-stressed fibers or by specifying a maximum permissible depth of yielding (the two are, of course, related), but it will be found that the construction of interaction curves is less difficult when a depth of yielding is specified.

Furthermore, since the material considered here is assumed to have a yield point, another reason for maintaining an elastic core of considerable size in contrast to permitting the fully plastic condition to be impending, especially in statically determinate members, lies in the fact that the yielding in such material is highly heterogeneous and slip or glide planes are likely to form across the elastic core at one or more sections. This action may produce a fully plastic condition at those sections, which in many uses of the member would be disastrous to its proper load-resisting function.

The loads corresponding with the fully plastic condition are of special interest because these loads are frequently considered to be the upper limit of the maximum utilizable values for members made of a material having a yield point.

Interaction Curve for Fully Plastic Stress Distribution. If P and M have such values that no part of the cross section remains elastic, the stress distribution accompanying this fully plastic condition is illustrated by Fig. 305d in which $\bar{y}$ is the distance from the centroid of the rectangular cross section to the neutral axis at O. If $P = 0$, the value of $\bar{y} = 0$ and $M = bc^2\sigma_e$, which is its fully plastic value for pure bending. Thus, when $P = 0$, the ratio $M/M_e = 1.5$, and this combination of P and M is represented by the coordinates of the point F in Fig. 306. On the other hand, when $M = 0$, the value of $\bar{y} = c$ and $P = 2bc\sigma_e$, which is its fully plastic value P_e, and this combination of P and M is represented by the point B in Fig. 306. The equation of the curve connecting F and B is derived by using the equations of equilibrium as follows:

$$\sigma_e \int_{-c}^{+\bar{y}} da - \sigma_e \int_{+\bar{y}}^{+c} da = P \tag{651}$$

$$-\sigma_e \int_{-c}^{+\bar{y}} y\, da + \sigma_e \int_{+\bar{y}}^{+c} y\, da = M \tag{652}$$

The integrals in Eqs. 651 and 652 are the areas and moments of areas, respectively, of the parts of the section below and above the neutral axis. Equation 651 reduces to

$$\sigma_e b(\bar{y} + c) - \sigma_e b(c - \bar{y}) = P \tag{653}$$

From Eq. 653 we find

$$\bar{y} = P/2\sigma_e b \tag{654}$$

Equation 652 reduces to

$$M = (c^2 - \bar{y}^2)\sigma_e b \tag{655}$$

By the substitution of $\bar{y}$ from Eq. 654 into Eq. 655 the value of M is found to be

$$M = \sigma_e b c^2 - (P^2/4\sigma_e b) \tag{656}$$

By dividing both sides of Eq. 656 by $\sigma_e b c^2$ this equation is transformed into the dimensionless equation

$$(M/\sigma_e b c^2) + (P^2/4\sigma_e^2 b^2 c^2) = 1 \tag{657}$$

The substitution of $\sigma_e b c^2 = 1.5 M_e$ and $4\sigma_e^2 b^2 c^2 = P_e^2$ in Eq. 657 gives

$$\tfrac{2}{3}(M/M_e) + (P^2/P_e^2) = 1 \tag{658}$$

which is represented by the curve from F to B in Fig. 306. This curve should be regarded as an upper limit to the values of P and M. In other words the line AB represents the start of inelastic action, and the curve FB represents its completion of penetration across the section, if yielding is homogeneous. For heterogeneous yielding (Lueder's lines) the curve $CDEB$ represents an intermediate condition which, from experience, seems to indicate the maximum utilizable loads.

Ratio of M to P. The combination of bending and direct axial loads M and P on most members is such that the ratio of M to P is constant as each of the loads increases. In Fig. 306 each of the radial lines through the origin represents combinations of M and P on a given member such that the ratio $(M/P)(P_e/M_e)$ is constant. For a member of given dimensions, P_e/M_e is constant (for a rectangular cross section $P_e/M_e = 3/c$). Therefore, these radial lines represent combinations of M and

P in which the ratio M/P is constant. The use of these lines with the curves in Fig. 306 is illustrated in the following problems.

Illustrative Problem

Problem 320. A link shown in Fig. 307a resists a tensile load P. The link has its middle portion offset so that the base of its rectangular cross section coincides with the action line of P. The link is made of a steel which has a yield point $\sigma_e = 45,000$ lb per sq in. Compute the values of the load P which will (a) cause inelastic strain

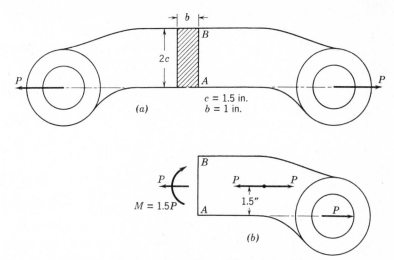

Fig. 307 Member subjected to axial tension and bending.

to be impending at the outermost fiber; (b) produce inelastic strains that will penetrate to a depth which is, respectively, one-fourth, one-half, and entirely across the section at AB.

Solution. (a) In Fig. 307b is shown a free-body diagram of part of the link on one side of section AB. The load P is shown resolved into a force P acting through the centroid of section AB and a couple whose moment is 1.5P. This force and couple are resisted at section AB by an equal and opposite force and couple, respectively. For section AB we have $P_e = 2bc\sigma_e$ and $M_e = \frac{2}{3}bc^2\sigma_e$. Therefore

$$\frac{M}{P} \cdot \frac{P_e}{M_e} = \frac{1.5P}{P} \cdot \frac{2bc\sigma_e}{\frac{2}{3}bc^2\sigma_e} = \frac{4.5}{c} = \frac{4.5}{1.5} = 3$$

We now select in Fig. 306 the radial line whose slope is 3. This radial line intersects the line AB at a point whose coordinates are

$$P/P_e = 0.25 \quad \text{and} \quad M/M_e = 0.75$$

and therefore for inelastic strain to impend $P = 0.25P_e = 0.25(2bc\sigma_e) = 0.25 \times 2 \times 1 \times 1.5 \times 45,000 = 33,800$ lb.

(b) The aforementioned radial line intersects the curves representing depths of penetration of one-fourth, one-half, and entirely across the section at values of $P/P_e = 0.33$, 0.38, and 0.41, respectively. But

$$P_e = 2bc\sigma_e = 2 \times 1 \times 1.5 \times 45{,}000 = 135{,}000 \text{ lb}$$

Therefore

$P = 0.33 \times 135{,}000 = 44{,}500$ lb for penetration of inelastic strain to one-fourth of the depth of the link

$P = 0.38 \times 135{,}000 = 51{,}300$ lb for one-half depth

$P = 0.41 \times 135{,}000 = 55{,}300$ lb for full depth (the fully plastic load)

These values of P represent increases in percentage of 26, 46, and 58, respectively, above the load at which yielding is impending on section AB. It should be noted that the lateral deflection of section AB has been neglected here. If this deflection is taken into account, the ratio M/P will decrease as the load is applied. This means that the radial line whose slope is represented by M/P is curved downward and that the intercepts with the curves of Fig. 306 are larger than those used in this problem, and hence the values of P as given here are conservative.

Problems

321. A bar of mild steel is 3 ft long and has a cross section 2 in. by 4 in. A tensile load P is applied to the ends of the bar such that its action line lies in a plane of symmetry half-way between the longitudinal axis and a 2-in. base. Compute the maximum utilizable load P on the bar, assuming that this load will cause penetration of inelastic yielding such that one-half the section is inelastically strained. Let $\sigma_e = 35{,}000$ lb per sq in.

322. A small clamp has dimensions as shown in Fig. 308. The clamp is made of steel whose tensile and compressive yield point is 40,000 lb per sq in. Compute the load P which will cause inelastic strains to occur in section AB so that one-half the section is inelastically strained. *Ans.* 340 lb

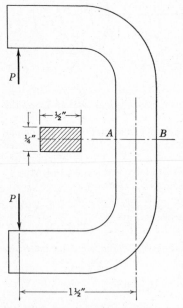

FIG. 308   Member subjected to axial tension and bending.

171 Influence of shape of cross section on interaction curves. By the procedure in the preceding article, curves representing combinations of values of P and M which cause specified depths of inelastic strains can be found for members having various shapes of cross sections. Figures 309 to 312 show curves for circular, I, T, and trapezoi-

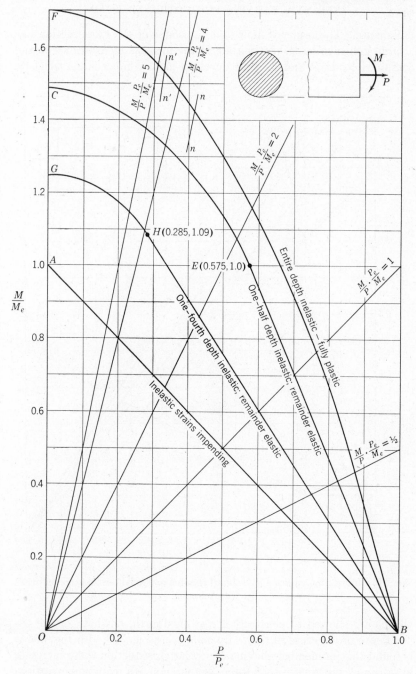

FIG. 309 Interaction curves for combined bending and axial tensile loads on member with circular cross section.

559

dal shapes. These curves show that the shape of the cross section has a large influence on the magnitude of the increase in resistance to the combined loads P and M that develops in a member when inelastic

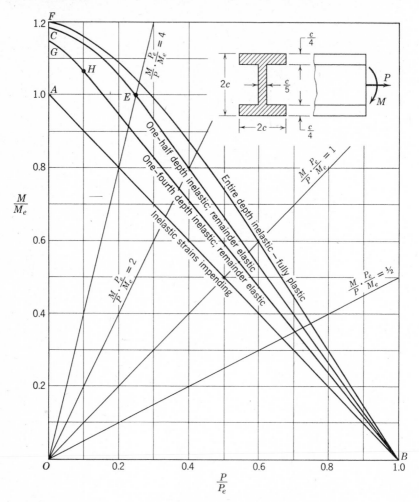

FIG. 310   Interaction curves for combined bending and axial tensile loads on member with I section.

strains are allowed to penetrate across one-fourth, one-half, or the entire depth of the cross section. By comparing Fig. 309 with Fig. 306 it is found that in members having a circular cross section these increases in resistance are greater than for a member having a rectangular section. From Fig. 310 it is seen that for a member having an I-shaped cross

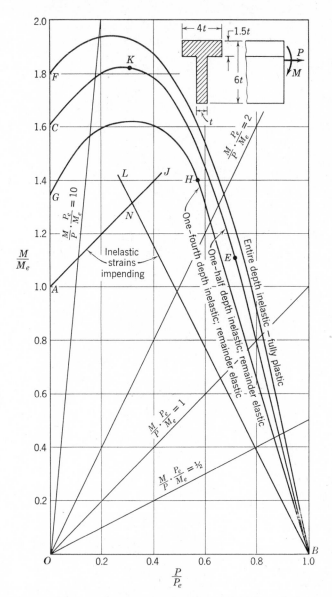

FIG. 311   Interaction curves for combined bending and axial tensile loads on member with T section.

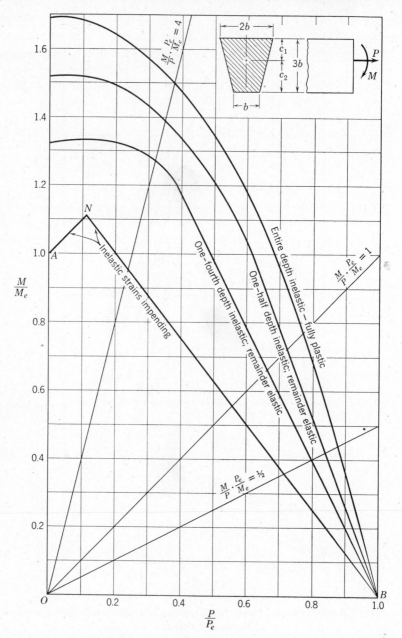

FIG. 312 Interaction curves for combined bending and axial tensile loads on member with trapezoidal section.

section these increases in resistance to loads are very much smaller than for the rectangular or the circular cross section.

The curves in Figs. 311 and 312 for members having T- and trapezoidal-shaped sections need further explanation because of the tendency for the resistance to bending to increase as the axial load P is increased.

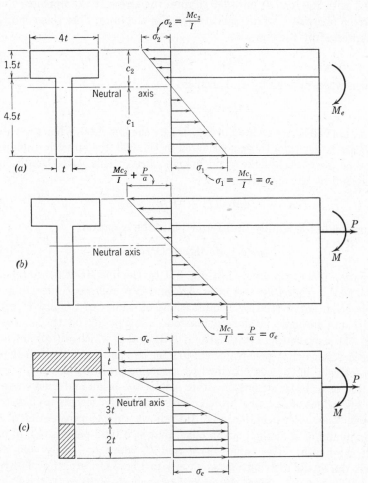

FIG. 313   Inelastic stresses in T beam.

T and Trapezoidal Sections. In Fig. 313a is shown a beam having a T section resisting the bending moment M_e which produces a maximum compressive bending stress $\sigma_1 = \sigma_e$ at the lower edge of the beam while the maximum tensile bending stress σ_2 at the upper edge is much less than σ_e. Figure 313b shows the same T beam which now resists an axial load P in addition to a bending moment M. The load P increases the tensile stress at the upper edge and decreases the compressive stress at the lower edge. For certain small values of P combined with the moment M_e the stresses at the upper and lower extreme fibers are each less than σ_e. Hence a bending moment M larger than M_e must be combined with the load P in order to raise the stress at the upper or lower extreme fibers to a value equal to σ_e. For the lower fiber this condition is expressed by the equation

$$(Mc_1/I) - (P/a) = \sigma_e \qquad (659)$$

which, when divided by σ_e, becomes

$$(M/M_e) - (P/P_e) = 1 \qquad (660)$$

Equation 660 is represented in Fig. 311 by the line AJ. When the values of P are larger than those considered in Eq. 660, the stress in the upper extreme fiber reaches the yield point σ_e first. This latter condition is expressed by the equation

$$(Mc_2/I) + (P/a) = \sigma_e \qquad (661)$$

Equation 661 is readily transformed into the equation

$$(c_2/c_1)(M/M_e) + (P/P_e) = 1 \qquad (662)$$

Equation 662 is represented in Fig. 311 by the line BL which intersects AJ at N. Therefore the lines AN and NB represent the complete interaction curve relating combinations of values of M and P which will cause inelastic strains to impend. The points on the curves in Fig. 311 representing combinations of M and P which will produce inelastic strains that penetrate one-fourth, one-half, and the full depth, respectively, have been obtained by assuming arbitrary depths of penetration of inelastic strains on either side of the beam and then computing the values of M and P which correspond to the accompanying stress distribution. For example, Fig. 313c shows a depth penetration of t at the top and of $2t$ at the bottom edge, that is, a total penetration of one-half the depth. The values of M and P, which are easily computed from the stress distribution as shown in Fig. 313c, are $M = 14.81\sigma_e t^3$ and $P = 3.25\sigma_e t^2$. Since $M_e = 8.05\sigma_e t^3$ and $P_e = 10.5\sigma_e t^2$, the following values are found: $M/M_e = 1.81$ and $P/P_e = 0.31$. The point K on the curve $CKEB$ represents these coordinates. The foregoing method is used because it is rather difficult to compute a value of M corresponding to an assumed value of P, or vice versa, since the depths of penetration of inelastic yielding must first be determined. The following problems illustrate the use of the curves in Fig. 311.

Illustrative Problem

Problem 323. Let the cross section of the link of Prob. 320 (see Fig. 307) have a T cross section as shown in Fig. 314, and let $t = 0.53$ in.; this value is chosen so that the area of the T cross section is approximately equal to the area of the rectangular cross section of the link in Prob. 320. Compute the values of the load P corresponding to each of the following conditions, and compare these values with the corresponding values as found from Prob. 320: (a) to cause impending inelastic strains in the extreme fibers; (b) to cause inelastic strains to penetrate to one-fourth the total depth, (c) one-half the depth, and (d) the entire depth, respectively.

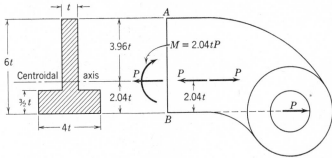

Fig. 314

Solution. Figure 314 shows the forces and moments which hold in equilibrium that part of the link to the right of section AB. The resisting forces on section AB are an axial force P and a moment $M = 2.04tP$. For this cross section

$$P_e = \sigma_e a = 10.5t^2\sigma_e \quad \text{and} \quad M_e = \frac{\sigma_e I}{c} = \frac{\sigma_e 31.8t^4}{3.96t} = 8.05t^3\sigma_e$$

Therefore

$$\frac{M}{P} \cdot \frac{P_e}{M_e} = 2.04t \cdot \frac{10.5t^2\sigma_e}{8.05t^3\sigma_e} = 2.66$$

In Fig. 311 we select the radial line whose slope is 2.66. This radial line intersects the line BN at an abscissa $P/P_e = 0.42$, the curve GHB at $P/P_e = 0.54$, the curve $CKEB$ at $P/P_e = 0.57$, and the curve FB at $P/P_e = 0.58$. Therefore since $P_e = 10.5t^2\sigma_e = 10.5(0.53)^2 \times 45,000 = 135,000$ lb, the required values of P are as follows:
  For inelastic strain to impend:

$$P = 0.42 \times 135,000 = 56,700 \text{ lb}$$

For inelastic strain to penetrate to one-fourth depth:

$$P = 0.54 \times 135,000 = 72,900 \text{ lb}$$

For inelastic strain to penetrate to one-half depth:

$$P = 0.57 \times 135,000 = 77,000 \text{ lb}$$

For inelastic strain to penetrate the full depth:

$$P = 0.58 \times 135,000 = 78,300 \text{ lb}$$

These values of P are greater in percentage by 67, 64, 50, and 42, respectively, than the corresponding values for the link of Prob. 320 which has a rectangular cross section of the same area as the T section in this problem. These facts show that the use of an unsymmetrical section such as the T or trapezoid for members subjected to combined bending and axial loads represents a more efficient use of material, no matter which of the conditions illustrated here is used as the measure of the maximum utilizable strength of the member. As in Prob. 320, the effect of the deflection, which lowers the value of M/P, is neglected here. The values of P as given are therefore somewhat smaller than would be found if the deflection were taken into account.

Problems

324. Solve Prob. 321 if the bar has a circular cross section whose radius is 2 in. and if the action line of the load is parallel to the long axis and is at a distance of 1 in. from it.

325. Solve Prob. 322, assuming that the cross section is a trapezoid whose shape is that shown in Fig. 312. Let the value of the short base b of the trapezoid be equal to 1 in.   *Ans.* $P = 68000$ lb

172   Interaction relationship of P and M for curved members. In relatively sharply curved members subjected to bending there is usually an axial load which must also be resisted by the section at which the maximum bending moment occurs. For most curved members, however, the ratio of M/P is relatively large so that the radial lines whose slope is represented by M/P intersect the interaction curves at values of P/P_e between 0 and 0.2. However, the interaction curves for straight beams (see Figs. 306, 309, 311, and 312) show very little reduction in the value of M/M_e until P/P_e becomes greater than about 0.2, a fact which indicates that for most curved members the effect of the axial load can be neglected when computing the maximum bending moment; if more accurate computations are desired, interaction relationships between M and P may be constructed for curved members in the same way as for straight members.

173   Interaction relationship of direct shear and bending moment. The loads on most beams produce a bending moment and a direct shearing force on each section of the beam. For example, Fig. 315a represents a simply supported beam which resists a concentrated load. Figure 315b represents a part of this beam and the forces acting in the part; the forces acting on the cross section consist of the bending moment M and the shearing force V. The value $V = V_e$ represents the direct shearing force required to produce a maximum shearing stress in the section equal to the shearing yield point τ_e corresponding to the stress distribution as shown in Fig. 315d. This shearing force is $V_e = \tau_e It/Q$, in which I is the moment of inertia of the cross section about the neutral axis, t is the thickness of the cross section at the neutral axis, and Q is the first moment of the area of the section lying on either side of the neutral axis. It is important to recall, as shown in Fig. 315d, that the maximum vertical shearing stress on the section for which the total shearing force is V occurs at the neutral axis where the bending stress is zero, and conversely the maximum bending stress occurs at the outermost fibers where the vertical shearing stress is zero. There are also shearing stresses on planes making 45° angles with the cross section; these are due to the bending stresses. If the bending

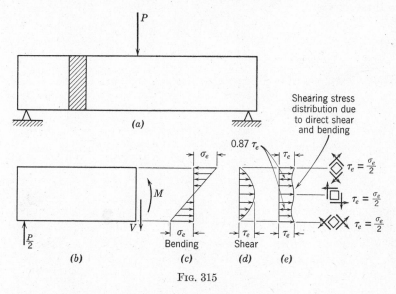

FIG. 315

stress at each point of the cross section is combined with the vertical shearing stress, at that point the maximum combined shearing stress at each point of the cross section is given by the distribution shown in Fig. 315e. This distribution of shearing stress, which is for a beam having a rectangular cross section, shows that both M_e and V_e can be applied to a section of this beam simultaneously without causing inelastic strain. If the beam in Fig. 315a had a standard I beam cross section, the effect of direct shearing stress in the web would be somewhat greater, but a direct shearing force as great as about $0.6V_e$ could be applied simultaneously with the bending moment M_e without causing inelastic strain.

From the foregoing articles and from this discussion it can be concluded that most members are much more efficient in resisting a combination of bending and direct shear than they are in resisting a combination of bending and axial loads. In fact, if the ratio V/V_e is relatively small, the effect of the direct shear V upon the resistance of the beam to bending loads which produce small inelastic strains is negligible. Thus, if V/V_e is small, the bending moment required to cause the fully plastic condition is approximately equal to the fully plastic value $k(\sigma_e I/c)$ (see Table 23, Chapter 17). If V/V_e is not small, a conservative relationship between M/M_e and V/V_e may be had by using the interaction curves for relating M/M_e and P/P_e given in foregoing articles. This is accomplished by the substitution of V/V_e in place of P/P_e as abscissas to these curves.

Chapter 19

INTRODUCTION TO ULTIMATE LOAD ANALYSIS
OF STATICALLY INDETERMINATE MEMBERS

174 Introduction. In Part IV the analysis of the so-called elastic stresses in statically indeterminate structures was considered by methods involving elastic strain energy. In the design of some statically indeterminate members much advantage can be taken of the increased resistance to static loads accompanying the inelastic strains which occur without impairing the usefulness of the member to carry the loads, even if the fully plastic condition is allowed to develop at one or more sections. The increased resistance obtained in statically indeterminate members by allowing some inelastic strains is usually considerably more than in the corresponding member that is statically determinate. This fact is illustrated in the articles which follow. However, a warning should here be given that in compression members the fully plastic condition may lead to buckling and hence plastic strains in compression members should be considered with special care.

Let P_e or M_e be the load or moment on a statically indeterminate tension member or beam, respectively, which will cause inelastic strains to be impending at the most stressed fibers of the member. The magnitude of P_e or M_e can be found with the elastic strain energy methods of Part IV. The material in the member is assumed to have a stress-strain diagram as shown in Fig. 292b, Chapter 17. Let P_p or M_p be the load on the member which will cause the fully plastic condition in the member; that is, P_p or M_p is the load corresponding to the impending total destruction of the elastic core of material in the member which is followed immediately by unrestricted yielding of the member.

The articles which follow are concerned with the computation of the load P_p which is considered to be the ultimate load that can be applied to a member made of ductile material. The method employed consists in using, in addition to the equations of equilibrium, the fact that the resisting forces or moments at a fully plastic section or sections of a member (see Art. 160, Chapter 17) are equal to their fully plastic values and remain constant while the member continues to deform at the section. The method is described best by using examples, and, although the illustrations used in the following articles are single indeterminate members, the method has been used in the analysis of more complex indeterminate members such as frames and trusses. The examples presented here are intended to be a very brief introduction to the subject.

175　Axially loaded tension member.　Figures 316a and 316b represent an axially loaded bar that has been reinforced by two bars of

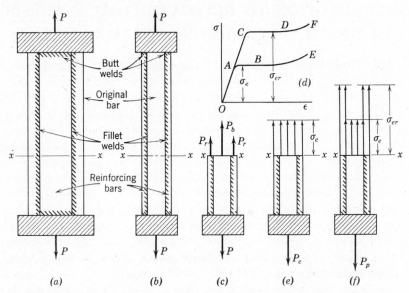

FIG. 316　Fully plastic load for statically indeterminate tensile member.

identical dimensions which are fastened on the sides of the bar by fillet and butt welds. Figure 316c shows that on any section xx of the member the axial load P is resisted by P_b and $2P_r$, which are the forces in the original bar and reinforcing bars, respectively. Since the forces in the two reinforcing bars are assumed to be equal and are arranged symmetrically, there is only one independent equation of equilibrium for use in determining the forces P_b and P_r. This equation is

$$P = P_b + 2P_r \tag{663}$$

The force system therefore is statically indeterminate.

Elastic Solution.　The additional equation needed is obtained from the fact that the longitudinal strains in all three bars are the same. Let ϵ represent the strain in the bars, and let E_b and E_r be the moduli of elasticity, respectively, and a_b and a_r the cross-sectional areas, respectively. Since $P_r = E_r \epsilon a_r$ and $P_b = E_b \epsilon a_b$, the additional equation is obtained by eliminating ϵ from these latter equations, which gives

$$P_r = P_b(E_r a_r / E_b a_b) \tag{664}$$

Furthermore, if the reinforcing bars are made of the same material as the original bar, $E_r = E_b$, and hence Eq. 664 reduces to

$$P_r = P_b(a_r / a_b) \tag{665}$$

Let the tensile stress-strain diagrams be represented by Fig. 316d in which OAB applies to the material in the bar and OCD to the material in the reinforcing bars. The yield points are σ_e and σ_{er}, respectively.
Value of P_e. From Eqs. 663 and 665 the load P is found to be

$$P = P_b(1 + 2a_r / a_b) \tag{666}$$

But P_e is the load that causes inelastic strain to be impending at some section in the member. Therefore this load occurs when $P_b = \sigma_e a_b$, that is, when the stress in the original bar is σ_e. The substitution of this value of P_b in Eq. 666 gives

$$P_e = \sigma_e a_b + 2\sigma_e a_r \tag{666a}$$

The first inelastic strains will occur in the original bar when this value of P_e is exceeded, but since the reinforcing bars have a higher yield point these bars will strain elastically until the stress σ_{er} is reached. Therefore the reinforcing bars will act as an elastic core to restrict the yielding of the original bar and thus prevent failure by general yielding until the load P has exceeded P_e and has reached the fully plastic load P_p.

Fully Plastic Solution. Let P_{bp} and P_{rp} represent the fully plastic tensile forces in the original bar and in each reinforcing bar, respectively. These values are $P_{bp} = \sigma_e a_b$ and $P_{rp} = \sigma_{er} a_r$, and it is assumed that each of these forces remains constant as each bar strains inelastically until the strain hardening effect in the material is reached as indicated by the upward slope in the curves at E and F in Fig. 316d. Therefore, from the equilibrium equation (Eq. 663) the fully plastic load is found to be

$$P_p = \sigma_e a_b + 2\sigma_{er} a_r \tag{667}$$

This fully plastic load, which is somewhat greater than P_e, is the load that will cause failure by general yielding of the reinforced member. The reason for this fact is that the elastic core provided by the reinforcing bars, which restricts the extent of yielding in the original bar at loads between P_e and P_p, is destroyed when P_p is reached.

176 Beam fixed at one end, supported at other end; load concentrated at mid-span. Figure 317a represents such a beam for which the length of the span is l and the load P. The reaction R_1 at the supported end and the shear V_2 and moment M_2 at the fixed end as shown in Fig. 317b are the unknown quantities needed for plotting the shear and moment diagrams. These quantities must be found before solving for the loads P_e or P_p. For this purpose, however, two separate sets of values of R_1, V_2, and M_2 must be found; the first set for use in finding P_e is found by Castigliano's principle or the dummy load method as described in Part IV, and the second set for use in finding P_p is determined from the fact that the load P_p occurs when the fully plastic condition (two plastic hinges in this beam) is reached.

Value of P_e. From the methods of Chapter 16 it is found that $R_1 = \frac{5}{16}P$, $V_2 = \frac{11}{16}P$, and $M_2 = \frac{3}{16}Pl$ when the load P is smaller than or equal to P_e. The shear and moment curves for this beam are shown in Fig. 317c. The maximum bending moment occurs at the fixed end, and therefore as the load P is increased the load P_e is reached when inelastic strain is about to occur in the upper and lower extreme fibers at the fixed end as shown in Fig. 317d. Let σ_e be the stress at which inelastic strain starts in these fibers. Then from the formula $\sigma_e = M_2 c/I$, in which $M_2 = \frac{3}{16}P_e l$, the value of P_e is found to be

$$P_e = \frac{16}{3}(\sigma_e I / cl) \tag{668}$$

Value of Fully Plastic Load P_p. If the load on the beam is increased to values larger than P_e, inelastic strains will occur in the section at the fixed end and will spread along the beam and also penetrate to the full depth of the beam as shown by the black area near the fixed end in Fig. 317e. At a certain load somewhat less than P_p a plastic hinge will form at the fixed end and the bending moment M_2 at the hinge will be $kM_e = k(\sigma_e I/c)$, where k is a form factor whose value depends on the shape of the cross section (see Table 23, Chapter 17). In the meantime, while the load has been increasing to values larger than P_e, it is likely that some inelastic strains have started at the section at mid-span, but, since the bending moment at this section is smaller than at the fixed end, a still greater load must be applied before another plastic hinge will develop at the mid-span. Let it be assumed that the load has been increased to a value that will produce plastic hinges at the mid-span and the fixed end. At each of these sections the bending moment is equal to $k(\sigma_e I/c)$. When both plastic hinges have developed it will be found that there can be no further increase in load because the beam will continue to deform and will probably collapse under this load which is the load P_p. The unknown quantities needed for drawing the

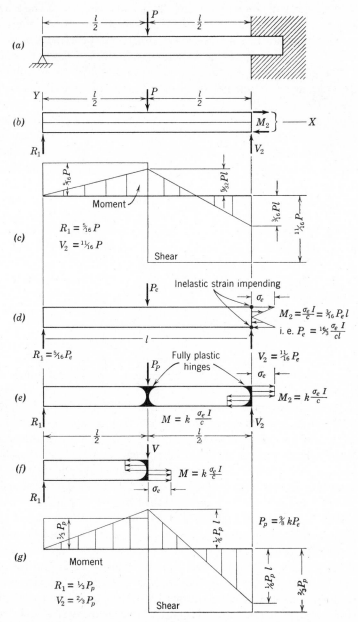

moment and shear diagrams are P_p, R_1, and V_2 (Fig. 317e). The known values of the moments at the plastic hinges at mid-span and the fixed end make it possible to solve for these unknowns by resorting to the equations of equilibrium. For this purpose the two free-body diagrams shown in Figs. 317e and 317f are used. From Fig. 317f, by taking moments about the section at mid-span, one equation of equilibrium gives

$$R_1 l/2 = k(\sigma_e I/c)$$

from which $$R_1 = 2k(\sigma_e I/cl) \qquad (669)$$

From Fig. 317e by taking moments about the fixed end, the equilibrium equation gives

$$R_1 l - P_p(l/2) + k(\sigma_e I/c) = 0 \qquad (670)$$

The substitution of R_1 from Eq. 669 into Eq. 670 gives

$$P_p = 6k(\sigma_e I/cl) \qquad (671)$$

By combining Eqs. 671 and 668 it is found that

$$P_p = \tfrac{9}{8} k P_e \qquad (672)$$

Finally, the values of R_1, V_2, and M_2 are found in terms of P_p by use of Eqs. 669 and 671, and the equilibrium equation $\Sigma V = 0$. They are $R_1 = \tfrac{1}{3}P_p$, $V_2 = \tfrac{2}{3}P_p$, and $M_2 = \tfrac{1}{6}P_p l$. The moment and shear diagrams are shown in Fig. 317g.

Significance of Fully Plastic Load. The fully plastic load P_p will produce failure of the beam by general yielding, and is therefore considered as an upper limit of the load. However, the maximum deflection of the beam caused by loads which are slightly less than P_p will be of the same order of magnitude as the deflection under the load P_e because of the existence of the elastic core in the beam at loads smaller than P_p. For many structural purposes the load P_p (or a slightly smaller load) is therefore the maximum utilizable load which the beam can resist. The working load can be found by dividing P_p by a reduction factor or factor of safety N.

It should be noted from Eq. 672 that the value of P_p is $\tfrac{9}{8}k$ times P_e. The factor k depends upon the type of cross section. The existence of the factor $\tfrac{9}{8}$ (instead of unity) arises from the fact that the beam is statically indeterminate. For example, if the beam were simply supported at each end, the value of P_p would be k times P_e. Thus, if more supports (forces and couples) act on a beam than are necessary to preserve equilibrium, that is, if the beam is made statically indeterminate, the ratio of P_p to P_e usually is raised.   This fact will be demonstrated again in the following articles.   •

177   Influence of lack of complete fixity at end of beam.   It is recognized that the completely fixed condition at the end of a beam can seldom be achieved in an actual beam and that also some settlement of the supports may occur.   These facts are sometimes taken into account in the elastic solution of the problem by assuming that the end of a beam is only partially fixed and then adjusting the coefficients of the fixed-end moments as, for example, by using $M_2 = \frac{1}{7}Pl$ instead of $M_2 = \frac{3}{16}Pl$ for the fixed-end moment in Figs. 317a, 317b, and 317c.   These adjustments grow out of the fact that, even though the fixture at the end may have strength enough to resist the bending moment, it is not usually stiff enough to prevent some change in slope at the so-called fixed end.   These end conditions will now be considered for the fully plastic condition.

Let it be assumed that the connection at the right-hand end of the beam in Fig. 317a is only partially restrained and thus some change in slope at this end occurs.   This condition causes a shift upward of the moment curve (Fig. 317c), which means that the moment at the center of the beam may be larger than at the partially restrained end.   As the loads are increased, the first plastic hinge to develop may be at the midspan rather than at the partially restrained end.   However, the final values of the fully plastic load P_p as found from Figs. 317e and 317f are not affected by the order in which the two plastic hinges develop. It is only necessary that the connection at the end be strong enough to resist the fully plastic moment.   In a similar way it can be seen that a slight amount of settlement of either support will not affect the value of P_p.

Caution.   For beams having certain types of cross section, such as very thin-walled tubular sections, the fully plastic moment may never develop because localized buckling is likely to occur at a load lower than the fully plastic load.   Beams having standard rolled sections such as I beams and channels usually must be supported laterally in order to resist the fully plastic load in bending because of several effects.   First, there is a tendency for the compression flange to buckle laterally. Secondly, if the plane of the bending loads makes a small angle, say 1° to 5°, with the principal axis, the resulting loss in resisting capacity due to unsymmetrical bending very rapidly lowers the fully plastic load.   For example, let a 36-in. 150-lb wide-flange I beam be subjected to bending loads up to the fully plastic load lying in a plane making about 4° with the principal axis of the section.   Under these conditions the fully plastic load, instead of being equal to $1.14M_e$ as it would be for the load in the principal axis, is equal to M_e, where $M_e(= \sigma_e I/c)$ is the bending moment at which inelastic strain would be impending if the plane of the load coincided with the principal axis. If the angle is greater than $4°$, the fully plastic load will be even less than M_e. Third, if the plane of the load does not pass through the shear center, the beam is subjected to a twisting moment. This twisting moment, in addition to causing an increase in the angle between the plane of loads and the principal axis and thereby increasing the unsymmetry of loading, will also produce torsional shearing stresses and certain longitudinal stresses in the beam as discussed in Art. 90. Fourth, the direct shearing stresses in the web of such beams may have some effect in developing the plastic hinge.

Problem

326. A horizontal beam has a span length l and is fixed at each end. The beam is subjected to a concentrated load P at mid-span. Let I/c represent the section modulus of the beam and σ_e the yield point of the material in the beam, and let k represent the form factor for the cross section for computing the fully plastic bending moment. Compute the values of the elastic limit load P_e and the fully plastic load P_p for the beam.   *Ans.* $P_e = 8(\sigma_e I/cl); P_p = 8k(\sigma_e I/cl)$.

178   Closed ring subjected to concentrated load. Let Fig. 318a represent such a closed ring whose mean radius is R; it is subjected to a load $2P$. It is required that the fully plastic value of the load be found.

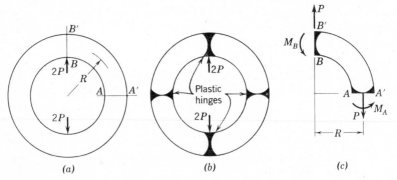

Fig. 318   Fully plastic ultimate load for closed ring.

This load is reached when four fully plastic hinges occur as shown by the black areas in Fig. 318b, which are symmetrically located at the quarter points with respect to the load. A free-body diagram of one quadrant of the ring is shown in Fig. 318c. The horizontal cross section AA' of the ring must resist a bending moment M_A and the axial force

P, whereas the vertical section BB' must resist a bending moment M_B and a shearing force P. Since the quadrant of the ring is in equilibrium the sum of the moments about a line in section BB' is zero; hence

$$M_B + M_A - PR = 0 \qquad (673)$$

Equation 673 with its three unknowns M_B, M_A, and P must be supplemented with two additional relations amongst the unknowns. These two relationships are the interaction curves between the moment M_A and the axial load P on section AA' and between the moment M_B and the direct shear P on section BB'. Such curves are given in Chapter 18 where it is shown that the curves relating bending moment and axial load may be used as an approximation of the curve relating bending moment and direct shear load. Hence in Eq. 673, since the direct axial load P and the direct shear load P are equal, the bending moment M_B may be assumed to be equal to M_A when the fully plastic hinge develops on each of these sections. Therefore by the substitution of $M_B = M_A = M$, Eq. 673 reduces to

$$2M = PR \qquad (674)$$

The final operation in solving for M and P is graphical. Equation 674 is transformed into a form for plotting in the graph of the interaction curve (see Figs. 306, 309, 310, 311, and 312 of Chapter 18) by multiplying both sides by the ratio P_e/M_e and by dividing by $2P$. When this is done, Eq. 674 becomes

$$\frac{M}{P} \cdot \frac{P_e}{M_e} = \frac{R}{2} \frac{P_e}{M_e} \qquad (675)$$

Equation 675 is represented in Figs. 306, 309, 310, 311, and 312 of Chapter 18 by a straight line passing through the origin of the coordinate axes M/M_e and P/P_e and with slope equal to $(R/2)(P_e/M_e)$. The following illustrative problems show how Eq. 675 is used.

Illustrative Problems

Problem 327. Compute the load $2P$ on the ring in Prob. 110 (in Chapter 6) which will produce fully plastic hinges on sections AA and BB (see Fig. 319a) assuming that the ring is made of mild steel whose yield point is σ_e. Compare the fully plastic load with the value of $2P$ found in Prob. 110 for impending inelastic strain in the ring.

Solution. One quadrant of the ring is taken as a free-body diagram as shown in Fig. 319b. With plastic hinges at AA and BB, we may assume $M_B = M_A = M$ and then apply Eq. 675. $P_e = (\pi d^2/4)\sigma_e = \pi\sigma_e$ and $M_e = \sigma_e I/c = \sigma_e(\pi d^3/32) =$

$(\pi/4)\sigma_e$. When these quantities are substituted in the right-hand side of Eq. 675, we have

$$\frac{M}{P}\frac{P_e}{M_e} = \frac{R}{2}\frac{\pi\sigma_e}{(\pi/4)\sigma_e} = 5$$

We refer to Fig. 309, Chap. 18, and select the line through the origin having a slope of 5 as indicated by the foregoing equation. This line intersects the fully plastic curve relating M and P at the point whose coordinates are

$$P/P_e = 0.31 \quad \text{and} \quad M/M_e = 1.55$$

Therefore the fully plastic value of P is $P = 0.31P_e = 0.31\pi\sigma_e = 0.97\sigma_e$, and $2P = 1.94\sigma_e$. From Prob. 110 the maximum fiber stress is at the inside fiber of the

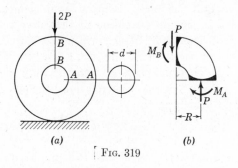

(a)   (b)

Fig. 319

ring at the point B and is $\sigma_e = 9.17P/a$, whence the value of P at which inelastic strain is impending is

$$P = \frac{\sigma_e(\pi d^2/4)}{9.17} = \frac{\pi(2)^2}{4 \times 9.17}\sigma_e = 0.34\sigma_e$$

and $2P = 0.68\sigma_e$. Thus the fully plastic load is about 285 per cent greater than the load which causes the first inelastic strain.

Problem 328. In Fig. 320a parts of two links of a chain are shown. The chain is subjected to a load $2P$. The geometrical shape of each side of a half-link $AA'BB'$ is made up of four parts. The parts $BB'CC'$, $CC'DD'$, and $DD'EE'$ are curved, with radii r_1, r_2, and r_3, respectively. The part $AA'EE'$ is straight and lies a distance h from the vertical centerline. The radius $r_1 = \frac{1}{2}d$ so that the two links are in contact over the arc of angle 2α. Such chains are usually made of mild steel which has a yield point σ_e. Compute the fully plastic value of the load $2P$ in terms of σ_e and d. It should be noted that in Fig. 320 all dimensions are stated in terms of the diameter d of the cross section of the link.

Solution. The link is in the fully plastic condition when plastic hinges develop at four sections of symmetry located at AA' and BB' (lower half of link not shown), respectively. From the symmetry of the link it is assumed that half of the load $2P$ is supported at each section AA' and that the moments M_A at these sections are equal. A free-body diagram of one-fourth of the link is shown in Fig. 320b. The pressure of the upper link on this link along the arc BC where they are in contact is assumed to be uniformly distributed. By writing the equations of equilibrium $\Sigma F_V = 0, \Sigma F_H = 0$ it is found that the resultant of the uniformly distributed pressure on the arc BC is $P \sec \frac{1}{2}\alpha$, the axial load on section BB' is $P \tan \frac{1}{2}\alpha$, and there is no shearing force on section BB'. The remaining equation of equilibrium is obtained by equating to zero the sum of the moments about the centroid of section BB', which gives

$$\Sigma M = M_B + M_A + (P \sec \tfrac{1}{2}\alpha)(d \sin \tfrac{1}{2}\alpha) - Ph = 0$$

There are three unknown quantities M_B, M_A, and P in this equation, but we may assume that M_B is equal to the fully plastic value of $k(\sigma_e I/c) = 1.7(\sigma_e I/c)$, since the

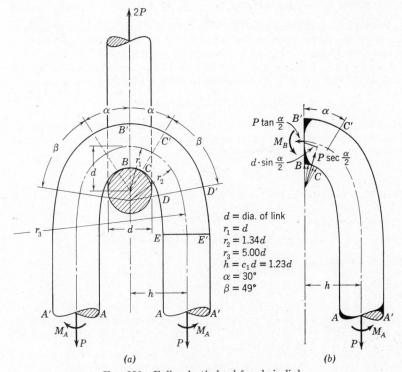

FIG. 320   Fully plastic load for chain link.

axial force $P \tan \frac{1}{2}\alpha$ on section BB' will always be relatively small when compared to P_e (see Art. 172).   The substitution of this value of M_B and of $h = c_1 d$ into the foregoing equation gives

$$1.7(\sigma_e I/c) + M_A - Pd(c_1 - \tan \tfrac{1}{2}\alpha) = 0$$

The values M_A and P remain to be found.   For this purpose we may use the interaction curve of Fig. 309 (Chapter 18) showing the relationship between M and P for the fully plastic condition.   The foregoing equation is transformed so as to contain the ratios M/M_e and P/P_e which are ordinates and abscissas, respectively, in

Fig. 309. This is done by dividing all terms of the equation by $\sigma_e I/c$, which gives the equation

$$1.7 + \frac{M_A}{\sigma_e I/c} - \frac{Pd}{\sigma_e I/c}\left(c_1 - \tan\frac{1}{2}\alpha\right) = 0$$

Now, for the denominator under M_A we replace $\sigma_e I/c$ by its equivalent M_e, and under Pd we replace $\sigma_e I/c$ by $\sigma_e \pi d^3/32$, which is obtained by inserting the section modulus I/c for the circular cross section. By making these substitutions the equation becomes

$$1.7 + \frac{M_A}{M_e} - 8\left(c_1 - \tan\frac{1}{2}\alpha\right)\frac{P}{P_e} = 0 \qquad (a)$$

in which P_e has been substituted for the quantity $(\pi d^2/4)\sigma_e$. Equation a represents a straight line in the chart of Fig. 309 (Chapter 18) and we need only to choose values of the constant c_1 and angle α in order to plot this line.

Conveyor Chain Link. For one type of chain link as shown in Fig. 320 the value of $c_1 = 1.23$ and $\alpha = 30°$. The substitution of these quantities in Eq. a gives

$$M_A/M_e - 7.68(P/P_e) + 1.7 = 0$$

The straight line nn in Fig. 309 (Chapter 18) represents this equation and the coordinates of the point of intersection of nn with the curve FB represent the desired values of M_A and P. These coordinates are

$$P/P_e = 0.41 \qquad \text{and} \qquad M_A/M_e = 1.43$$

Since $P_e = (\pi d^2/4)\sigma_e$ and $M_e = \sigma_e I/c = (\pi d^3/32)\sigma_e$, the values of P and M_A are

$$P = 0.41(\pi d^2/4)\sigma_e = 0.32d^2\sigma_e$$

and
$$M_A = 1.43(\pi d^3/32)\sigma_e = 0.14d^3\sigma_e = 0.44Pd$$

The fully plastic load is $2P$, and hence

$$2P = 0.64d^2\sigma_e$$

Effect of Reducing Angle α. Let it be assumed that in Fig. 320a the radius r_2 is used from section BB' to CC' instead of $r_1 = d$. This would reduce the value of α to approximately zero and cause the links to be in contact over a very small area. If $\alpha = 0$ and $c_1 = 1.23$, Eq. a becomes

$$(M_A/M_e) - 9.84(P/P_e) + 1.7 = 0$$

The line $n'n'$ in Fig. 309 represents this equation and gives values of $P/P_e = 0.32$ and $M/M_e = 1.53$, respectively, and the corresponding value of the fully plastic load is

$$2P = 0.50d^2\sigma_e$$

This load $2P$ is only 78 per cent of the load when $\alpha = 30°$. Therefore the arrangement of the links so as to be in contact over an angle 2α increases the fully plastic load appreciably. It should be noted, though, that the elastic deflection of the links will increase the value of α so that this angle is not zero when inelastic strains begin.

Effect of Changing Half-width h. In a manner similar to that of the foregoing discussion of the effect of reducing the angle α, it can be shown that if the half-width h of the link is decreased the fully plastic load is increased, and conversely that if the half-width h is increased the fully plastic load is decreased. It is important, there-fore, to observe that the deformation of the link in Fig. 320a caused by the load 2P is such that the half-width h is reduced. Thus the deformation of the link, whether elastic or plastic, tends to increase the resistance to the load, first, because the angle α increases and, second, because the half-width h decreases.

Comparison of Foregoing Results with Empirical Formulas. Bach has given the following formula for the safe load on a chain made of wrought iron or mild steel:

$$2P = 13,750d^2$$

This formula is based entirely on the results of tests of chain links of various diame-ters d. The result of the preceding analysis is $2P = 0.64\sigma_e d^2$ which, like Bach's formula, makes the load proportional to the square of the diameter, but also pro-portional to the yield point σ_e. For a yield point $\sigma_e = 35,000$ lb per sq in.

$$2P = 22,400d^2$$

But this is the fully plastic load. If a reduction factor $N = 1.6$ is used, this for-mula gives the same value as Bach's.

Goodenough and Moore have used an elastic analysis of the link to give the for-mula for the maximum tensile stress (see Art. 58, Fig. 111) in the link as $\sigma = 2(2P/a)$. From this formula, setting $a = \pi d^2/4$, we have $2P = 0.40\sigma d^2$. Setting $\sigma = \sigma_e = 35,000$ lb per sq in., the load is $2P = 14,000d^2$. It appears therefore that Bach's empirical formula for *safe* load gives a value of $13,750d^2$, and Goodenough and Moore's formula gives $14,000d^2$ for a load which causes impending tensile yielding. The foregoing analysis indicates that the load given by each formula has a factor of safety of 1.6 based on the load that will cause failure by general yielding. The results of the test of the link by Goodenough and Moore support this conclusion.

Useful Strength. In Art. 58 it was shown that within the elastic behavior of the material the maximum stress in a chain link is $\sigma_c = 4.2(2P/a)$ as indicated in Fig. 111. The load $(2P)_e$ that starts inelastic strain in the most stressed fiber is obtained from the foregoing equation by letting $\sigma_c = \sigma_e$, where σ_e is the yield point in compression, and setting $a = \pi d^2/4$. This gives $(2P)_e = 0.18d^2\sigma_e$. It should be noted that $2P = 0.40d^2\sigma_e$ as obtained from Bach's and Goodenough and Moore's formulas is approximately the average of the lower and upper limiting values $(2P)_e = 0.18d^2\sigma_e$ and $2P = 0.64d^2\sigma_e$ as discussed at the end of Art. 58.

Problem

329. Let the chain links in Prob. 328 be circular in shape. Then the angle α is very small and is assumed to be zero. If the mean diameter D of the link is four times the diameter d of the cross section of the link, compute the fully plastic load in terms of σ_e and d.

PART SIX

Introduction to Instability—Buckling Loads

Chapter 20

ELASTIC AND INELASTIC BUCKLING
OF COLUMNS

179 Introduction. In Art. 4 it was pointed out that the maximum load that can be applied to a member without causing it to cease to function satisfactorily in the structure or machine (and hence to fail structurally) may be limited by the elastic deflection of the member. It was also pointed out that there were at least two different types of action or behavior of a member under which elastic deflection may limit the load-carrying capacity.

One action consists of the deflection of a member which, as the loads increase, remains in stable equilibrium for all elastic deflections, as, for example, a simply supported beam. The important fact to observe in this type of action is that the deflections and stresses are proportional to the loads, and furthermore the elastic deflections are usually small enough to make second-order terms negligible in mathematical expressions for the deflections. The relations between the loads and the elastic deflections of a member under the conditions in which the deflections are proportional to the loads may be obtained by several methods, two of which are treated in Part IV.

The other structural action in which elastic deflection may limit the maximum load that can be applied to the member without causing the member to fail structurally is denoted as *elastic buckling*. Such buckling action can occur in members that have certain relative proportions. Such members are frequently called thin-walled or light-weight members and include slender columns; thin-walled cylinders under axial compression, uniform external lateral (radial) pressure, or torsion; wide-flanged I beams; thin plates under edge compression, or shear.

The significant fact or dominant characteristic of buckling, however, is the same in all cases, namely, that the elastic deflections and stresses in the member are *not* proportional to the loads as buckling takes place, even though the material acts elastically (stress is proportional to strain).

585

Elastic buckling action arises out of a condition of neutral equilibrium that develops when the applied load on the member reaches a so-called critical value. At this critical load the member is in equilibrium throughout a considerable range of small elastic deflections. But if the load is increased slightly above the critical load the deflection of the member increases abruptly (not in proportion to the load), and unless it is extremely slender the member quickly passes into a completely unstable condition, owing to inelastic action as discussed in Art. 181, leading to total collapse. Buckling, therefore, is frequently referred to as structural instability. Furthermore, in this type of failure the critical or buckling load usually (but not always, see Art. 192) represents the practical maximum or ultimate load that the member can be expected to resist even though when the member is subjected to this load the stress in the material is less than the compressive elastic limit. When elastic buckling is the cause of failure of a member, therefore, the problem is not that of determining the relationship between loads and deflection, but that of obtaining an expression for the critical or buckling load.

The first published analysis of elastic instability or buckling was made by Leonhard Euler (1707–1783), who in 1744 published a penetrating paper on the subject. The simplest illustration of elastic buckling is that of the failure of a straight, slender column subjected to a gradually applied axial load. A brief review of the elastic buckling of a slender column is given in the next article.

Caution. Attention is called to the fact that the influence on buckling of temperature, especially elevated temperature, and of time, such as in prolonged loading leading to creep, are *not* considered in the subsequent discussions.

180   Elastic buckling of ideal slender column. If the slender column is perfectly straight, the load truly axial, and the material perfectly homogeneous, the column will remain straight under any value of the load; it will not bend. If at a certain (critical) load, however, a small lateral force is applied, giving the column any small deflection, and the lateral force is then removed, the critical axial load is the load that will hold it in the slightly bent position. The critical load, however, is nearly constant for a range of small elastic deflections in which the column is in neutral equilibrium, and therefore the deflections (and hence strains and stresses) are not proportional to the applied load, although the material acts elastically. This behavior is represented by the line OAB in Fig. 321a where OA represents the critical or buckling load for the ideal slender column. The length AB represents a relatively small deflection (larger deflections indicated by BCD are considered in the next article); the value of the deflection δ in the sketch of the deflected column is greatly exaggerated.

The expression for the critical load may be found by applying to the deflected column the elastic curve equation $EI(d^2y/dx^2) = M$ for a bar subjected to bending that causes small deflections. For the column shown in Fig. 322a the bending moment M is equal to $-Py$ and hence the equation for the slightly deflected column is $EI(d^2y/dx^2) = -Py$.

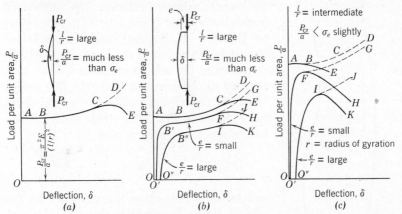

FIG. 321   Relation between load and deflection for columns.

The solution * of this equation for the critical or buckling value for P, that is, the smallest value of P that will hold the column in a slightly deflected form, gives

$$P_{cr} = \frac{\pi^2 EI}{l^2} \quad \text{or} \quad \sigma_{cr} = \frac{P_{cr}}{a} = \frac{\pi^2 E}{(l/r)^2} \qquad (676)$$

in which E is the modulus of elasticity of the material, l is the length of the pivot-ended column, I is the moment of inertia of the cross section about the centroidal axis having the least moment of inertia, r is the least radius of gyration of the cross section ($I = ar^2$), l/r is the slenderness ratio, and σ_{cr} is the uniform stress in the column when the load P_{cr} is acting on the column just before the lateral force is applied (σ_{cr} is called the buckling stress). It is important to note that the only property of the material that influences the critical or elastic buckling load is the stiffness of the material as measured by the modulus of elasticity. The influence of the relative values of the dimensions on the buckling load (or load per unit area) is indicated by the slenderness ratio l/r. Equation 676 is called Euler's formula; it is discussed further in Art. 181.

* See any textbook on strength of materials.

Higher Buckling Loads. A slender column (one having a relatively large l/r), and other members having relative dimensions such that they fail by buckling before the stress exceeds the elastic limit of the material, may have several elastic buckling or critical loads. If the column is restrained from buckling under the lowest buckling load, it may buckle at a higher value of the load, as the load is increased. For example, a pivot-ended slender column (Fig. 322a) will buckle in the form of one lobe at the load given by Eq. 676. If, however, the member is prevented from bending in the form of one lobe by restraints at the middle as shown in Fig. 322b, the load can be increased above the first critical load until the column buckles in the form of two lobes shown in Fig. 322b. This second critical load is given by the expression

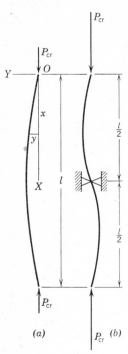

$$P'_{cr} = \frac{\pi^2 EI}{(\tfrac{1}{2}l)^2} \quad \text{or} \quad \frac{P'_{cr}}{a} = 4\,\frac{\pi^2 E}{(l/r)^2}$$

and hence is four times the value of the first critical load. In general, the critical elastic buckling load (or load per unit area) for an ideal slender column is

$$\frac{P_{cr}}{a} = K\,\frac{\pi^2 E}{(l/r)^2}$$

(a)

P_{cr} (b)

Fig. 322

in which the value K depends on the restraints to which the column is subjected.

Similarly, if lateral restraints were applied at two equally spaced points, the elastic buckling load would be increased a great deal more. However, the column would then probably fail structurally by direct yielding or by inelastic buckling rather than by elastic buckling. In other words, the critical elastic buckling load has no physical significance unless that critical value is reached before the yield strength of the material is developed.

Local Buckling. A change in the relative dimensions of a member may also bring about a radical change in the type of elastic buckling from one involving the member as a whole to one involving only a part of the member. For example, aluminum columns * having an equal-leg

---

* "Some New Experiments on Buckling of Thin-walled Construction," by F. J. Bridget, C. C. Jerome, A. B. Vosseller, *Transactions of the American Society of Mechanical Engineers*, Vol. 56, 1934, pp. 569–578.

angle section behaved in accordance with Fig. 323. When the ratio t/w for a leg of the angle section was relatively large, the column buckled as a unit in accordance with the Euler column formula (Eq. 676), but

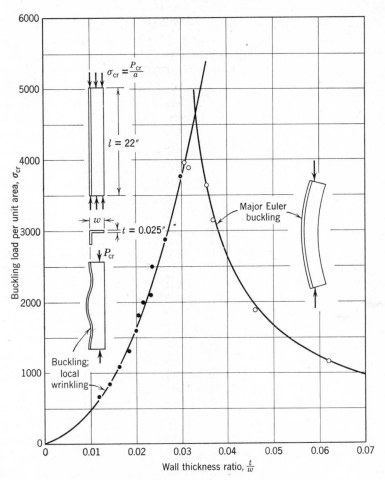

FIG. 323   Buckling loads for local buckling and Euler buckling.

when the values of t/w were relatively small, buckling of one side or leg of the angle occurred first; this action is sometimes designated as sheet buckling, crimpling, or wrinkling, and is, in general, a local action in contrast to general buckling of the whole member as a unit. Figure 324 shows the similar wrinkling of the thin flanges of a channel section or one-half of an H section. Under most conditions local buckling reduces the buckling load for the member, but under certain conditions it may be taken advantage of to redistribute the load in the member so that additional load may be applied before the strength of the member as a whole is developed (see Art. 192).

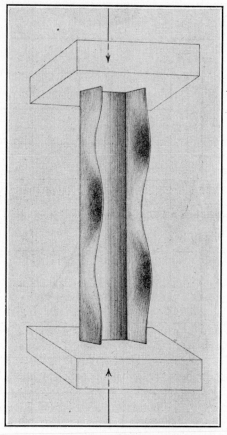

FIG. 324 Local buckling (wrinkling) of thin flanges of channel section (or half of H section; see reference 13).

181 Imperfect slender column. Deviations from the ideal conditions assumed in the foregoing article always exist in actual columns and also in other members that fail by elastic buckling. It is important, therefore, to consider the influence on the critical elastic buckling load of such imperfections, especially of slight eccentricity of loading or initial crookedness in the column. If these deviations from ideal conditions are small, the elastic deflection of the slender column starts with the first increment of load and increases slowly as the load increases until the load approaches the critical value for the ideal column, as given by Eq. 676, but by the time this load is reached the deflection of a slender column may no longer be approximated by the expression $1/R = -d^2y/dx^2$, as was done in deriving Eq. 676. Therefore, a discussion of the load-deflection relationship for large deflections of an ideal column is desirable before the effect of deviations from ideal conditions can be explained. It should be noted here, however, that many columns would be considered to have failed before such large deflections occur.

Large Deflections. Southwell * has shown that, when large deflections occur and the correct relationship between the curvature and deflection is used, the load found to keep a slender ideal elastic column in a bent position may be larger than P_{cr} as given by Eq. 676, especially if the column is very slender (l/r large) and if P_{cr}/a is much less than the elastic limit σ_e. At larger deflections the load for such columns increases as shown by the ordinates to the curve BCD in Figs. 321a and 321b. However, if at some deflection, such as at C in Figs. 321a and 321b, the elastic limit of the material is exceeded (due to excessive bending and direct compression) the maximum resisting bending moment is developed after a slight additional deflection (as will be explained later), and the load rises slightly above the load at C and then drops as indicated by the curve CE instead of continuing to rise as indicated by CD.

A real column with its imperfections is frequently considered to be equivalent to an ideal column with a small eccentricity of loading e, as shown by Fig. 321b. The curve $O'B'FG$ represents the load-deflection relationship for this column. The curve approaches the curve $OABCD$ if the material remains elastic; but if at some deflection, such as represented by F, the elastic limit is exceeded, the load rises slightly and then drops as shown by FH. Similar remarks apply to the curve $O''B''IJ$ which indicates the influence of a larger eccentricity e. It should be noted that the maximum load occurring between F and H for a small eccentricity e is very nearly equal to P_{cr} as obtained from Eq. 676 which is for small deflections of an ideal column, and hence Euler's formula gives a satisfactory value for the buckling load on very slender real columns. However, for ideal columns that are less slender, in which P_{cr}/a is only slightly less than σ_e, the actual load-deflection relationship is represented in Fig. 321c by $OABE$ instead of $OABCD$. This behavior is explained by the fact that only a small amount of lateral deflection indicated at the point B is necessary to raise the maximum stress in the column to the elastic limit.

* Southwell, R. V., *Introduction to Theory of Elasticity*, 2nd edition, Oxford University Press, England, p. 434.

The curves $O'FH$ and $O''IK$ in Fig. 321c show that in a column having an intermediate value of l/r the relative effect of eccentricity of loading is much more pronounced than in the very slender column of Figs. 321a and 321b, and hence Euler's formula may not give a satisfactory value of the buckling load for real columns with intermediate value of slenderness ratios.

Failure of Columns. Slender Columns. The question arises as to whether it is appropriate to use the term buckling or instability in describing the failure of a slender column that is loaded eccentrically. If the columns whose load-deflection relationships are represented by the curves $OABCE$, $O'B'FH$ and $O''B''IK$ in Fig. 321b are used as machine or structural parts, their failure would, in most instances, be considered to take place by excessive deflection at a load and deflection represented approximately by the points B, B' and B''. But the loads at B, B', and B'' are smaller than the loads that are required to cause a condition of instability or total collapse as indicated by the ordinates to C, F, and I, which represent the load and deflection where inelastic strain begins, for, as noted previously, the type of instability that is associated with total collapse is initiated by inelastic strains, although the total collapse doesn't occur until some (relatively small) additional load is applied. Hence, failure of the slender members (that is, the condition that limits the maximum utilizable load) is not a condition of instability in the usual meaning of the term.

Columns of Intermediate Slenderness. Such eccentrically loaded columns are represented by curves in Fig. 321c in which it is shown that after relatively small lateral deflections occur the column will reach the condition of instability associated with total collapse as is shown by the coordinates of points B, F, and I. In other words, inelastic strain occurs and is followed after some increase in load by instability and collapse at relatively small lateral deflections—not greatly different from those indicated in Fig. 321b by the points B, B', and B''.

Which Type of Failure Occurs? Although these two types of failure, namely, failure by excessive deflection before the collapse load occurs and failure by collapsing at or before excessive deflection occurs, were associated with two ranges of values of l/r, it is not easy to determine which type of failure will take place for a given value of l/r except, perhaps, when l/r is very large, as may occur in certain lightweight construction. In other words, for l/r values in the usual range used in columns for heavy machines and structures the type of failure is not easily determined. Furthermore, for curves $O'FH$ and $O''IK$ in Fig. 321c it is not known how much the load increases after inelastic strains have started, that is, how far to the left and below the points F and I do the inelastic strains begin that lead finally to collapse, for the amount of increase of load depends on the shape of the cross section, on the shape of the stress-strain diagram of the material, as discussed in Art. 183, and on the value of l/r. Thus a wholly rational method or formula is difficult to devise, and hence empirical methods are frequently used in design specifications, etc.

182 Inelastic buckling. Buckling, as has previously been stated, is not restricted solely to elastic action. For, if the value of l/r is relatively small so that the compressive stress in the column reaches the compressive elastic limit of the material before the load reaches the value of the elastic buckling load, the behavior of the column may be very similar to that of elastic buckling, namely, rather abrupt increases in deflection at a fairly well-defined load. This behavior is called inelastic or plastic buckling.

The problem of determining the buckling load for a column that does not buckle until it is strained inelastically can best be considered under two headings. First, the material in the column will be assumed to have a yield point, that is, the slope of the compressive stress-strain curve changes abruptly to zero when the elastic limit is reached; the stress-strain curve suddenly becomes horizontal and remains so until relatively large inelastic strains have developed. For such material the proportional (elastic) limit and the yield point are equal. Mild steel is assumed to exhibit this type of stress-strain curve.

A column having a relatively small l/r (less than approximately 100 for structural steel) and made of such material would buckle when the stress in the column reaches the elastic limit (and yield point) of the material; in other words, inelastic behavior is not accompanied by an increase in load, as will be found to occur under the second heading for material that does not have a yield point. The so-called flat-top stress-strain diagram means that the load on the column remains constant at the elastic limit until the inelastic compressive strains attain a value equal to the full length of the flat or horizontal portion of the curve. This, in turn, means that before such a large inelastic strain could be developed, the deviations (even though very small) from ideal conditions would permit bending to start, leading to buckling.

Under the second heading it will be assumed that the compressive stress-strain curve changes in slope gradually as the stress is increased above the elastic limit of the material; aluminum alloys, some heat-treated steel, etc., exhibit this type of behavior. Inelastic buckling loads for columns made of material having this type of stress-strain curves will be determined in the following articles.

Significance of Inelastic Buckling for Material Not Having a Yield Point. In certain compression members, especially in aircraft structures where the strength-weight ratio of a member is of great importance, columns made of material having the second type of stress-strain diagram are used of such relative dimensions that small amounts of inelastic strains occur in the member before it buckles. These inelastic strains, however are not sufficient to cause damage to the column. In fact, the maximum inelastic strain in the column as the buckling load is impending is of the same order of magnitude as that of the elastic strain at the proportional limit of the material and is usually considerably less than the strain corresponding to the yield strength based on 0.2 per cent offset. But by permitting this small amount of inelastic strain a larger design load may be justified than if only strains within the elastic range were permitted. It is important to note, however, that when the buckling load is finally reached the deflection of the column may suddenly increase, leading to collapse.

The same considerations apply to some so-called heavy structures although to a lesser degree since the strength-weight ratio is usually of less importance in heavy structures such as building frames, bridges, etc. For a further brief discussion of this topic, see the solution of Probs. 330 and 331. The influence of small inelastic strains in increasing the load-carrying capacities of members subjected to tensile loads and to bending is discussed in Part V.

183   Two solutions for inelastic buckling load for ideal column. As previously noted, the buckling load for a column is considered to be the axial load that will hold the column in a slightly deflected position, and, since an ideal column would not bend under any axial load, a small lateral force must be applied to produce the initial deflection. This procedure, however, may be carried out in either of two ways: (a) the lateral force may be assumed to be applied first and then the axial load required to hold the column in the slightly bent position is applied and the lateral force removed; or (b) the unknown buckling critical load may be assumed to be applied first and then the lateral force is applied to cause the deflection, and is then removed. For *elastic* behavior of the column the solution for the (Euler) buckling load will be the same for the two procedures, since the physical process constitutes a reversible system and hence does not depend on the strain history in arriving at a given physical state.

But, as emphasized in Chapter 13, if the physical process is nonreversible, such as occurs in inelastic behavior of material, the order of applying the forces to the column in the two procedures would lead to different values for the buckling loads. The main condition involved in the process may be emphasized by stating that, for inelastic behavior, a single-valued relationship between loads and deflections (or between stress and strain) does not exist. But, as pointed out in Chapter 13, a single-valued relationship between stress and strain will exist not only for elastic strains but also for inelastic strains provided that all strains increase as the load increases (no fiber in the member is allowed to unload).

The two solutions for the buckling load, therefore, will be for the assumptions (a) that the lateral force and the last increment of the axial load are applied simultaneously so that the strains in all the fibers at any cross section increase although they are not uniformly distributed on the section after the lateral force is applied, and (b) that an axial load equal to the buckling load is applied first and then followed by the application of a small lateral force which deflects the column; the bending in this case causes the strains in the fibers on the convex side to decrease (unload) and on the concave side to increase.

The essential difference in the two assumptions lies in the fact that under the second assumption the strains in some of the fibers on the convex side behave elastically and hence the change in stress $\Delta\sigma$ accompanying the decrease in strain $\Delta\epsilon$ is given by $\Delta\sigma = E \Delta\epsilon$, in which E is the elastic modulus of elasticity, whereas under the first assumption $\Delta\sigma = E_T \Delta\epsilon$ for each fiber, in which E_T is the tangent modulus corresponding to the inelastic stress σ ($\sigma = P/a$, in which P is the buckling load).

The buckling load found for the first assumption is called the tangent-modulus load and will be found to be given by the expression $P_T = \pi^2 E_T I/l^2$. For the second assumption the buckling load is called the double-modulus load and will be found to be given by the expression $P_D = \pi^2 E_D I/l^2$, in which E_D is called the reduced modulus or double modulus since it may be expressed in terms of E and E_T.

In the following discussion of these two solutions we need not be concerned about whether or not the assumed physical conditions would be likely to occur. The problem is to determine the extent of the difference in the buckling loads for these two assumed conditions; the significance of the values found will be considered later. Furthermore, as previously noted, neither of these solutions applies to a column made of material having a yield point, since for such material both E_T and E_D are zero and hence $P_T = P_D = 0$.

184 Tangent-modulus formula for inelastic buckling load. Load at which inelastic bending of ideal column begins. Let Fig. 325a represent the column subjected to a gradually increasing axial load P. It is assumed for convenience that the column has a rectangular cross section. It is also assumed that the slenderness ratio l/r is sufficiently small to prevent elastic buckling. The load P may therefore attain a value which causes a uniform stress σ on the cross section of the column that is greater than the elastic limit σ_e of the material.

The stress-strain diagram for the material is shown in Fig. 325d. In this diagram σ represents the uniformly distributed compressive stress on each cross section of the column and ϵ the corresponding strain; it is assumed that the value of the buckling load P_T (or buckling stress $\sigma_T = P_T/a$) and the corresponding inelastic strain are represented by a point in the neighborhood of C on the stress-strain curve and hence, as previously noted, impending inelastic buckling involves only small inelastic strains.

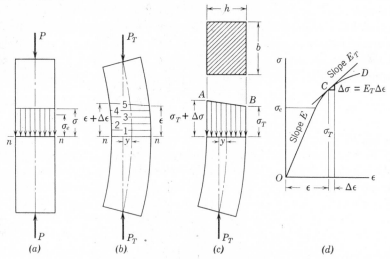

FIG. 325   Strain and stress distribution for tangent-modulus load.

The problem is to find the smallest load $P_T = a\sigma_T$ which will cause the ideal column to remain in a slightly bent position when a small lateral force is applied simultaneously with the last increment of axial load and then is removed. As increments of the axial load P are applied to the ideal column, the longitudinal strains across section nn increase but remain uniformly distributed as shown by the lines marked 1, 2, 3, and 4 in Fig. 325b. As P approaches the value P_T which we wish to determine, let a small lateral force be applied *simultaneously* with the last increment of load as P attains the value P_T. The resulting distribution of strain is as shown by the line marked 5 in Fig. 325b in which the lateral bending is greatly exaggerated.

The resulting stress distribution on section nn is shown in Fig. 325c by the sloping line AB and is obtained from Fig. 325d by taking the stresses corresponding to the strains. The assumption that line AB is straight is equivalent to the assumption that the slope of tangent lines to the stress-strain curve, such as that shown at C in Fig. 325d, is constant during the change in strain from ϵ to $\epsilon + \Delta\epsilon$. This assumption is justified because the increment $\Delta\epsilon$ is small for the small lateral bending imposed on the column. The slope of the tangent line at any point such as C is called the *tangent modulus* and is denoted by E_T; the increment of stress corresponding to $\Delta\epsilon$ is therefore $\Delta\sigma = E_T \Delta\epsilon$. The desired value P_T of the axial load P may now be found in the same manner that the Euler load for the beginning of *elastic* buckling is usually obtained. Thus, let Fig. 325c be a free-body diagram showing the forces acting on the lower half of the column. Equilibrium of the column requires that the external bending moment $P_T y$ for any cross section shall be equal and opposite to the resisting moment about the centroidal axis of the cross section of the internal forces on the section. This fact is expressed by the equation

$$P_T y = \frac{(\Delta\sigma/2)I}{h/2} \qquad (677)$$

In Eq. 677 let $\Delta\sigma$ be replaced by $E_T \Delta\epsilon$, and in turn let $\Delta\epsilon$ be replaced by the expression h/R which is obtained by relating the strain in the extreme fiber to the radius of curvature R of the column. Furthermore, for small deflections the curvature $1/R$ is given by the expression $1/R = -d^2y/dx^2$. With these substitutions, Eq. 677 becomes

$$E_T I (d^2 y/dx^2) = -P_T y \qquad (678)$$

The solution of this differential equation as given by Eq. 676 is

$$P_T = \frac{\pi^2 E_T I}{l^2} \qquad \text{or} \qquad \frac{P_T}{a} = \frac{\pi^2 E_T}{(l/r)^2} \qquad (679)$$

in which P_T may be considered to be either the smallest load that will hold the ideal column in a slightly bent form or the largest load under which the ideal column will not bend. This formula is called the tangent-modulus formula or Engesser's formula. It is generally regarded as the maximum (buckling) load that a real column having slight imperfections can safely be expected to resist, although the double-modulus load discussed in the next article indicates that the ideal column can resist a load somewhat greater than P_T without failing by inelastic buckling.

The solution of the tangent-modulus equation for a column of given material and dimensions involves a trial-and-error process for the reason that a value of E_T cannot be selected unless P_T is known. Furthermore, a stress-strain diagram for the given material must be available. The method of solution is illustrated in the following problems.

Illustrative Problems

Problem 330. A straight column having a square cross section 1 in. on a side and a length of 10 in. is loaded axially through special bearing blocks that allow free rotation when bending of the column starts. The member is made of material for which the compressive stress-strain curve is shown by OBC in Fig. 326. The tangent modulus for this stress-strain curve is shown by abscissas to the curve $DEFG$ on the upper scale. Compute the load P_T.

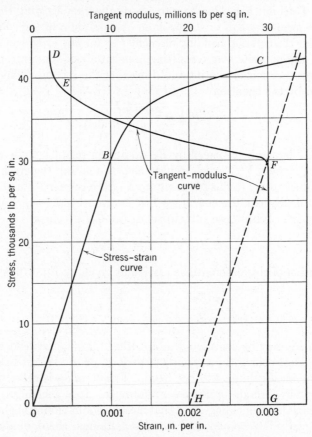

FIG. 326   Values of tangent modulus for a material not having a yield point.

Solution. The load P_T and the average stress σ in the column are the same number since the cross-sectional area is 1.0 sq in. We must by trial and error select from the curves in Fig. 326 a set of corresponding values of stress σ (or P_T) and tangent modulus E_T which will satisfy Eq. 679. As a first trial value, select $E_T = 4,000,000$ lb per sq in., which corresponds to $\sigma_T = P_T = 38,500$ lb. The right side of Eq. 679 is

$$\frac{\pi^2 \times 4,000,000 \times \frac{1}{12} \times 1 \times (1)^4}{(10)^2} = 32,900 \text{ lb}$$

Since the left side is 38,500 lb, a new trial is necessary. For the second trial assume that $E_T = 4,600,000$ lb per sq in., which from Fig. 326 corresponds to $\sigma_T = P_T = 38,000$ lb. The right side of Eq. 679 is now 37,800 lb, which is very close to the assumed value. Hence the answer is $P_T = 37,800$ lb.

Problem 331. In Prob. 330 the stress at the tangent-modulus load was found to be 37,800 lb per sq in., which, according to Fig. 326, corresponds to a strain of 0.00175 in. per in. If it is specified that the strain (or stress) in the column must not exceed the value corresponding to the yield strength of the material, based on 0.2 per cent offset, will this stress and strain at the tangent modulus load be within the required limit?

Solution. The yield strength based on 0.2 per cent offset, as shown by the line HI in Fig. 326, is 42,500 lb per sq in., which corresponds to a strain of 0.0034 in. per in. Therefore the stress and strain at the tangent-modulus load are less than values at the yield strength. It should be pointed out that the stress and strain at which the tangent-modulus load occurs in nearly all inelastic columns are smaller than the stress and strain values corresponding to the yield strength. This fact shows that, although the tangent-modulus formula is obtained on the assumption that some inelastic strain occurs, the inelastic strains which correspond to this load are smaller than the inelastic strains (the offset) that are usually assumed to be permissible without causing damage to the load-resisting behavior of the material or structure.

Problems

332. Solve Prob. 330 if the column length is $l = 12$ in. instead of $l = 10$ in.

Ans. $P_T = 37,000$ lb.

333. Assume that the dimensions of the angle section of the pivot-ended column shown in Fig. 323 are $t = 0.025$ in., $w = 0.5$ in., and $l = 22$ in. Show by use of Fig. 323 that the column fails as a unit by elastic buckling (not by local buckling). Calculate the stress in the column at the critical (buckling) load.

185 Double-modulus formula. Let the column be an ideal axially loaded member of such relative proportions that it does not start to bend (buckle) until the uniform strains on each cross section exceed the elastic (proportional) limit strain of the material.

In deriving the tangent-modulus formula (Art. 184) the lateral force required to start bending in an *ideal* column was applied simultaneously with the final increment of the axial load so that the bending was not accompanied by a reduction in the strain on any fiber (no fiber was allowed to unload). If, however, a small lateral force is applied *after* the (desired) axial load has been applied, the strains on one side of the column will be reduced by a small increment and on the other side they will be increased by a corresponding increment. Both increments of inelastic strain are assumed to be quite small; the influence of this assumption will be examined later.

Let Fig. 327a represent the column; in Fig. 327b the line DE represents the uniform distribution of the strain ϵ which corresponds to the stress

σ_D and the load $P_D = a\sigma_D$, which is the load to be determined. In Fig. 327d this stress σ_D and strain ϵ are represented by the point F. After the load P_D is applied, a small lateral load will cause the column to bend as shown (greatly exaggerated) in Fig. 327b. The load P_D is the smallest load that will hold the column in this bent position after the small lateral force is removed. The value of P_D is found in the same manner as was the load P_T in Art. 184. A free-body diagram (Fig. 327c) of the lower part of the column shows that the force P_D produces a

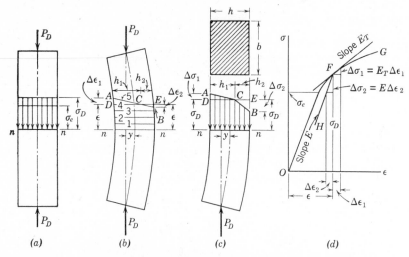

FIG. 327   Strain and stress distribution for double-modulus load.

bending moment P_Dy on any section such as nn, and this bending moment must be resisted by the forces on the section. The stresses are represented by the ordinates to the line ACB. Between C and A the stresses are greater than σ_D, but they are smaller than σ_D between C and B. The reason for this fact is shown in Fig. 327b where the strain ϵ is increased by $\Delta\epsilon_1$ on the concave side and decreased by $\Delta\epsilon_2$ on the convex side. Hence, $\epsilon + \Delta\epsilon_1$ corresponds to $\sigma_D + \Delta\sigma_1$, whereas the strain $\epsilon - \Delta\epsilon_2$ corresponds to $\sigma_D - \Delta\sigma_2$. In Fig. 327$d$ the strain $\epsilon + \Delta\epsilon_1$ corresponds to a stress just to the right of F on the curve OFG, but $\epsilon - \Delta\epsilon_2$ corresponds to a stress on the curve FH just to the left and below F.

The equilibrium of the column requires that the bending moment P_Dy shall be equal and opposite to the resisting moment. This condition is expressed as follows:

$$P_Dy = \tfrac{2}{3}h_1^2 b(\Delta\sigma_1/2) + \tfrac{2}{3}h_2^2 b(\Delta\sigma_2/2) \qquad (680)$$

In the following discussion it will be shown that Eq. 680 may be transformed into the equation $-P_D y = E_D I/R = E_D I(d^2 y/dy^2)$ for which, as previously noted, the solution is known to be $P_D = \pi^2 E_D I/l^2$; the term E_D is called the double modulus or the reduced modulus, and it is expressed in terms of E and E_T. The procedure is as follows. In addition to Eq. 680, the equation

$$P_D = \int \sigma \, da = \sigma_D a \tag{681}$$

may be obtained from the conditions of equilibrium. But the integral $\int \sigma \, da$, over section nn, of the $\sigma \, da$ forces under the line ACB (Fig. 327c) will be equal to $\sigma_D a$ only if Eq. 682 holds.

$$(\Delta \sigma_1/2) h_1 b = (\Delta \sigma_2/2) h_2 b \tag{682}$$

The equilibrium equations, 680 and 682, contain the solution of the problem, but the quantities $\Delta \sigma_1$, $\Delta \sigma_2$, h_1, and h_2 in these equations must be expressed in terms of certain given quantities, namely, the dimension h and the properties E and E_T of the material. For this purpose it is noted from Fig. 327d that if the increments of inelastic strain $\Delta \epsilon_1$ and $\Delta \epsilon_2$ are small the corresponding increments of stress may be found from the relationship

$$\Delta \sigma_1 = E_T \, \Delta \epsilon_1 \quad \text{and} \quad \Delta \sigma_2 = E \, \Delta \epsilon_2 \tag{683}$$

Equations 683 are transformed by substituting $\Delta \epsilon_1 = h_1/R$ and $\Delta \epsilon_2 = h_2/R$, where R is the radius of curvature of the slightly bent column, with the result that

$$\Delta \sigma_1 = E_T h_1/R \quad \text{and} \quad \Delta \sigma_2 = E h_2/R \tag{684}$$

Equations 682 and 684 are combined, eliminating $\Delta \sigma_1$, $\Delta \sigma_2$, and R, with the result that $h_1{}^2 E_T = h_2{}^2 E$. Furthermore, $h_1 + h_2 = h$. These two equations are solved simultaneously with the result that

$$h_1 = \frac{h \sqrt{E}}{\sqrt{E} + \sqrt{E_T}} \quad \text{and} \quad h_2 = \frac{h \sqrt{E_T}}{\sqrt{E} + \sqrt{E_T}} \tag{685}$$

Equation 680 is transformed by means of Eqs. 684 and 685 into the equation

$$P_D y = \frac{bh^3}{12R} \left[\frac{4E_T}{(1 + \sqrt{E_T/E})^2} \right] \tag{686}$$

Equation 686 is simplified by letting the quantity in the bracket be represented by E_D, which is called the double-modulus value, and by noting that $bh^3/12$ is the moment of inertia I. Thus, by making use of the expressions

$$E_D = \frac{4E_T}{(1 + \sqrt{E_T/E}\,)^2} \quad \text{and} \quad I = \frac{bh^3}{12} \tag{687}$$

Eq. 686 is written

$$P_D y = E_D I/R \tag{688}$$

It should be noted, however, that Eq. 687 applies only to a rectangular cross section. Thus the expressions for E_D and I depend on the shape of the cross section of the column. In Eq. 688 if $1/R$ is replaced by $-d^2y/dx^2$, which is a close approximation for small deflections, the equation becomes

$$E_D I \frac{d^2y}{dx^2} = -P_D y \tag{689}$$

Equation 689 is the same as Eq. 678, except that E_D replaces E_T. The solution of Eq. 689 gives

$$P_D = \frac{\pi^2 E_D I}{l^2} \quad \text{or} \quad \frac{P_D}{a} = \frac{\pi^2 E_D}{(l/r)^2} \tag{690}$$

which is the double-modulus formula. It should be noted from Eq. 687 that the double modulus E_D is always greater than the tangent modulus E_T since the value of E is larger than E_T. This means that the double-modulus load (Eq. 690) is always greater than the tangent-modulus load. The significance of this fact is discussed in the following problem and in the next article.

Illustrative Problem

Problem 334. Determine the double-modulus load for the column in Prob. 332. *Solution.* The solution is by trial and error. Let a pair of corresponding values $E_T = 3,000,000$ lb per sq in. and $\sigma = 39,500$ lb per sq in. be selected from Fig. 326. From Eq. 687 E_D is found to be 6,940,000 lb per sq in. The substitution of these values in Eq. 690 gives

$$39,500 = \frac{\pi^2 6,940,000(\frac{1}{12})}{12^2} = 39,700 \text{ lb}$$

and the right side is nearly equal to the left side so that the double-modulus load is $P_D = 39,500$ lb. The tangent-modulus load found in Prob. 332 is $P_T = 36,200$ lb. Thus, for the conditions specified, the double-modulus load is about 10 per cent larger than the tangent-modulus load. It was assumed in solving for the double-modulus load that the ideal column would not bend until the double-modulus load is reached. However, in a real column there will always be some imperfection which will cause slight bending even before the tangent-modulus load is reached and more bending before the double-modulus load is reached. Hence, the important assumption that $\Delta\epsilon_1$ and $\Delta\epsilon_2$ in Figs. 327c and 327d are small that was used in Eq. 683 in deriving Eq. 687 will not be true, and therefore the column may never be able to resist the double-modulus load, unless E_T is constant, that is, unless the curve FG in Fig. 327d is a straight line in which case Eq. 683 may be true for large values of $\Delta\epsilon_1$ and $\Delta\epsilon_2$. These facts are discussed further in the next article.

186 Significance of the two solutions for the inelastic buckling load. A comparison of the buckling loads obtained from the two solutions is shown by the curves in Fig. 328 for columns of rectangular cross

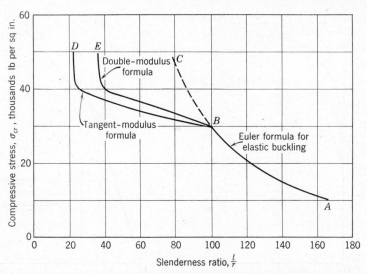

FIG. 328 Column curves for inelastic buckling according to tangent-modulus and double-modulus formulas.

section and made of material having the stress-strain diagram given in Fig. 326. From Fig. 328 it will be noted that, if the value of l/r is less than about 100, inelastic buckling occurs, and that the buckling load obtained from the double-modulus formula for a given value of l/r is somewhat greater than the tangent-modulus load for the same value of l/r.

In attempting to determine the meaning or significance of the two formulas, the question naturally arises: How closely does the behavior of a real column approach to that assumed in obtaining either one of the formulas? The answer to this question depends on two factors or conditions. These are, first, the extent of the lateral deflection or bending and the change, $\Delta\epsilon$, in strain accompanying the bending before the load as given by each formula is reached, and, second, the shape of the stress-strain curve in the neighborhood of the stress, P_T/a or P_D/a, corresponding to the buckling load as given by each formula.

As suggested in the preceding problem, a real column will not remain straight (will not wait to bend) until the load P_D is reached, as is assumed in the derivation of the double-modulus formula. In fact, even when great care is exercised in testing a real column, there is sufficient deviation from ideal conditions to cause the column to start to deflect laterally at an axial load that is even less than P_T, the tangent-modulus load. But such small lateral deflections are accompanied by increments

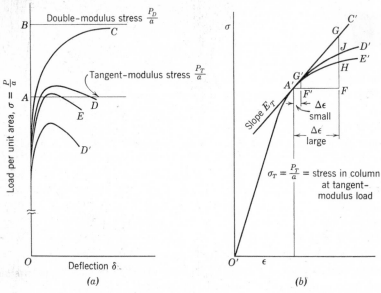

FIG. 329   Physical interpretation of tangent-modulus and double-modulus formulas.

of strain $\Delta\epsilon$ sufficiently small to nearly satisfy the conditions assumed in the derivation of the tangent-modulus formula, namely, that the stress $\Delta\sigma$ accompanying the bending strain $\Delta\epsilon$ shall be given by the expression $\Delta\sigma = E_T \Delta\epsilon$. If, however, an attempt is made to increase the load above P_T, it will be found that except for materials having a constant value of E_T a real column will not permit the load to reach the value P_D as given by the double-modulus formula; the column will buckle and collapse at a load less than P_D.

In order to explain the influence of the magnitude of $\Delta\epsilon$ and of the shape of the stress-strain curve on the buckling load, let the curve $O'A'C'$ in Fig. 329b represent the stress-strain curve of the material in a real column that bends slightly below P_T, its tangent-modulus load. Let $P_T/a = \sigma_T$ be the tangent-modulus stress and be represented by the stress OA in Fig. 329a; likewise let $\sigma_D = P_D/a$ be the double-modulus stress and be represented by OB. Since the curve $A'C'$ is a straight line and hence has the same (constant) slope E_T at any stress greater than the stress P_T/a, the correct value of $\Delta\sigma$ is given by the expression $\Delta\sigma = E_T \Delta\epsilon$ for both small and large values of $\Delta\epsilon$; for small values $\Delta\sigma = F'G' = E_T \Delta\epsilon$, and for large values $\Delta\sigma = FG = E_T \Delta\epsilon$. In a real column having such a stress-strain curve the lateral deflection may (probably will) start below the tangent-modulus load as indicated below A in Fig. 329a, but the load-deflection curve will rise to the double-modulus load as shown by the curve OC even though $\Delta\epsilon$ is relatively large, but of the same order of magnitude as ϵ.

Now let the stress-strain curve be represented by $O'A'D'$, which has the same tangent modulus E_T at A' as the previous curve, but which continues to be curved downward as indicated by $A'D'$. For such a material $\Delta\sigma$ will be approximately equal to $E_T \Delta\epsilon$ if $\Delta\epsilon$ is small; if, however, $\Delta\epsilon$ is relatively large, $\Delta\sigma = FJ$, but FJ is much less than FG which is the value of $\Delta\sigma$ as given by $E_T \Delta\epsilon$. The load-deflection relationship for a column of the material represented by the stress-strain curve $O'A'D'$ will be represented by a curve such as OD in Fig. 329a which shows that the double-modulus load is never reached because the increment of stress $\Delta\sigma$, and therefore the resisting bending moment, is not so large as assumed by stating that $\Delta\sigma = E_T \Delta\epsilon$. Similar remarks apply to the stress-strain curve $O'A'E'$ which corresponds to the curve OE in Fig. 329a. If a real column made of the material represented by $O'A'D'$ is subjected to an axial load that is kept axial by some adjustments which offset the lateral deflection as the load is increased, the load will reach the double-modulus value of B in Fig. 329a, but as soon as buckling occurs the load will suddenly drop and tend to follow the curve OD.

If deviations from ideal conditions in a real column cause bending for which $\Delta\epsilon$ is relatively large (same order of magnitude of ϵ) at loads lower than the tangent-modulus load, the same arguments as in the previous paragraph may be used to show that the maximum load on the column may not be as high as predicted by the tangent-modulus load. This fact is illustrated by the curve OD' in Fig. 329a, which represents the load-deflection curve of a column having a stress-strain curve similar to $O'A'D'$ and in which $\Delta\epsilon$ is large at loads below P_T. Note that the load on this column never reaches the tangent-modulus load.

From the foregoing considerations it should be expected that the tangent-modulus formula would predict a more reliable value for the inelastic buckling load than would the double-modulus formula; the latter formula should be looked upon as giving upper limit values that are unattainable in real columns of most materials. This conclusion is also in accord with experimental evidence, for the results of tests of columns in which great care was taken to satisfy, as nearly as possible, the conditions for an ideal column indicate that the buckling loads usually lie between the tangent-modulus and the double-modulus loads. The foregoing remarks, which apply only to columns made of material exhibiting a compressive stress-strain curve of gradual curvature above the proportional limit, may be interpreted to mean that:

The inelastic buckling load for a real column that deviates relatively little from ideal conditions is predicted satisfactorily by the tangent-modulus formula, and the double-modulus formula should be considered to give an upper limit value of the inelastic buckling load that cannot be expected to be attained in a real column.

The problem of introducing in the analysis of inelastic buckling of a column the influence of large deviations from ideal conditions is a complex and difficult one; no satisfactory solution at present is available. Owing to the unpredictable character of deviations from ideal conditions and the large influence that these conditions may have on inelastic buckling loads, reliance in obtaining buckling loads usually has been placed primarily on experience and on empirical relationships based on results of tests that simulate as closely as possible conditions met in practice. However, the need for reducing weight in certain applications and for saving material in other applications has made it highly desirable to obtain from a rational analysis the more basic nature of the action in the column which leads to inelastic buckling and to determine the limiting conditions within which such action is likely to occur. Furthermore, such an analysis can be useful also in planning tests and in interpreting experimental results.

It is fully realized that the use, in a complete structure, of members that fail by inelastic buckling introduces in design practice difficulties in interpreting the significance of a rational analysis, but this condition exists in applying rational analysis to practice in general. Or, to state this idea differently, rational analysis usually follows rather than precedes practice, but in turn it eventually influences practice.

Chapter 21

BUCKLING OF CYLINDRICAL TUBES UNDER UNIFORM EXTERNAL PRESSURE

187 The problem defined. The main features of buckling discussed in the preceding chapter are also exhibited in the failure of relatively thin-walled cylinders subjected to external lateral uniform pressure. By tube or thin-walled cylinder is meant one in which the thickness of the wall or shell is small in comparison with the outside diameter of the vessel. Such cylindrical tubes or shells are used under external

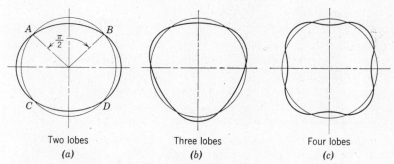

Two lobes   Three lobes   Four lobes
  (a)   (b)   (c)

FIG. 330   Effect of length and end restraint on buckling configuration of thin-walled cylinders subjected to lateral pressure.

pressure as boiler tubes, oil-well casings, vacuum tanks, large penstocks in which a partial vacuum sometimes occurs, etc. A thin-walled tube under external pressure will fail, if the pressure is gradually increased, when the external pressure reaches a limiting or critical value. The problem here considered is that of determining the least value of the uniform external pressure that will cause the thin-walled tube to buckle and collapse; this pressure is called the *critical load or collapsing pressure*.

A thin-walled tube usually buckles according to a rather definite pattern, depending on its relative dimensions and the conditions of restraint at its ends. In Fig. 330 are shown the more common forms assumed by the tubes as they collapse; the forms are described by stating the number of lobes (two, three, four, etc.). The number of lobes for a tube of given dimensions is the result largely of the restraint at the circumference or edge of the ends of the length or portion of the cylinder under consideration. If any section of the tube is maintained

FIG. 331 Views of thin-walled tubes that buckled under external pressure.

round by means of a disk or a stiffening ring, the tube is said to be simply supported at the section, and if, in addition, the section is prevented from tilting (changing slope) when the tube deflects, the tube is said to be *fixed* at the section.

The restraint at the ends of a tube of given diameter and wall thickness, however, has negligible effect on the number of lobes and on the collapsing pressure of the tube unless the length of the tube is less than a critical value. Figure 331 is a photograph of collapsed tubes (see reference 7); for each tube shown $d/t = 143$, but for the long tube $l/d = 10.7$, and for the short tube $l/d = 1.67$. The number of lobes varied from two for the long tube to six for the short tube, and the collapsing pressure was, of course, least for the two-lobe failure and greatest for the six-lobe failure. The effect of end restraint on the number of lobes and on the collapsing pressure is discussed further in Art. 190.

Buckling of Flat Plate. In the last article of this chapter will be given also a brief discussion of the problem of the buckling of a flat plate loaded in the plane of the plate.

188 Critical load for elastic buckling of long thin-walled cylinder. A thin-walled tube whose length is large in comparison to the diameter will buckle elastically in the form of two lobes when subjected to uniform external pressure. In finding the critical or collapsing pressure for the long tube, the critical pressure for elastic buckling of an isolated *ring* will first be obtained. The ring considered will consist of the portion of the tube between two transverse planes a unit distance apart. This circular ring is shown in Fig. 332. It is assumed to be perfectly circular before the application of the external pressure. Each cross section of the arc AB is subjected to direct compression just as is each section of a straight slender column under a central axial load. The critical or buckling load for a straight slender column is given by the familiar Euler's formula $P = \pi^2 EI/l^2$. If, then, the curvature of the arc AB is neglected, and Euler's equation is applied to the shell, Euler's formula becomes

$$\frac{pd}{2} = \frac{\pi^2 EI}{(\pi d/4)^2}$$

and hence
$$p = \tfrac{8}{3}E(t/d)^3 \tag{691}$$

This value, however, would be expected to be only approximate, and hence the buckling pressure for the *curved* member AB (Fig. 332) will be obtained.

The method of obtaining the collapsing pressure for the elastic buckling of the ring is to assume that the ideal circular section is deflected elastically into an oval or elliptical section which differs only slightly from a circle, and then to find the external pressure which will just hold the ring in equilibrium in this shape. This procedure corresponds to that used in finding the buckling load for an ideal slender column, as given by Euler's formula.

From inspection of Fig. 330a it is evident that there are four points of counterflexure in the ring of Fig. 332, that is, four sections at which the bending moments are zero. These are at the quarterpoints A, B, C, and D of Fig. 330a. Furthermore, the radial deflection w of the ring at each of these four points is also zero. Let a free-body diagram of one-quarter of the arc of the ring, such as AB, be drawn as shown in Fig. 332a. The external forces holding this arc of the ring in equilibrium are the circumferential forces P and the total uniform pressure of intensity p. The condition of equilibrium requires that the force P shall be equal

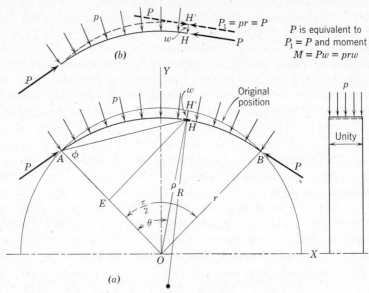

FIG. 332   Forces acting on one quadrant of cylindrical shell.

to pr, where r is the radius of the ideal thin-walled circular ring. Since the deflection of arc AB is the result mainly of bending, the elastic curve equation * is approximately

$$EI(1/R - 1/r) = -M \tag{692}$$

The minus sign on the right-hand side of Eq. 692 arises from the fact that the sign of the bending moment is positive if it produces a decrease in the curvature of the beam, and negative if it produces an increase in curvature.

* Equation 692 may be obtained from the elastic curve equation for a *straight* beam as follows: For a straight beam the elastic curve equation is $EI/R = \pm M$. In this equation $1/R$ is the change in curvature produced by the bending moment M, since the straight beam has no initial curvature. Hence if the initial curvature is $1/r$ and the radius of curvature is changed at a given section to $1/R$ by the moment M, the change in curvature produced by M is $1/R - 1/r$. Therefore $EI(1/R - 1/r) = -M$.

Equation 692 is now transformed by substituting for R the expression * for the radius of curvature R in polar coordinates (ρ, θ):

$$R = \frac{[\rho^2 + (d\rho/d\theta)^2]^{3/2}}{\rho^2 - (\rho d^2\rho/d\theta^2) + 2(d\rho/d\theta)^2} = \frac{\rho^2}{\rho - (d^2\rho/d\theta^2)} \qquad (693)$$

in which the squares of the term $d\rho/d\theta$ are neglected in obtaining the last expression. Since $\rho = r - w$ (see Fig. 332), Eq. 693 may be written

$$R = \frac{(r - w)^2}{r - w - (d^2/d\theta^2)(r - w)} = \frac{r^2 - 2rw}{r - w + (d^2w/d\theta^2)} \qquad (694)$$

in which the term w^2 is neglected in obtaining the last expression since it is relatively small.

If the value of R from Eq. 694 is substituted † in Eq. 692, the elastic curve equation becomes

$$(d^2w/d\theta^2) + w = -Mr^2/EI \qquad (695)$$

In the above equations it is assumed that each section of the ring deflects only in the radial direction; for the small deflection involved, this assumption is justified.

For the solution of Eq. 695 it is necessary to express M in terms of the variable w. The value of M at any section H in Fig. 332 is equal to the algebraic sum of the moments of all the forces acting to the left of section H. Hence the moment per unit length of the tube is

$$M = P(AE) - p(AH)\tfrac{1}{2}(AH) = -p[\tfrac{1}{2}(AH)^2 - (AO)(AE)] \qquad (696)$$

in which $P = pr = p \cdot AO$. But in the triangle AOH, the law of cosines gives

$$(OH)^2 = (AO)^2 + (AH)^2 - 2(AO) \cdot (AH) \cos \phi \qquad (697)$$

$$= (AO)^2 + (AH)^2 - 2(AO) \cdot (AE)$$

Hence from Eq. 697

$$\tfrac{1}{2}(AH)^2 - (AO)(AE) = \tfrac{1}{2}[(OH)^2 - (AO)^2]$$

* See any textbook on calculus.

† From Eq. 694 $\dfrac{1}{R} = \dfrac{r - w + (d^2w/d\theta^2)}{r^2 - 2rw}$

Then $\dfrac{1}{R} - \dfrac{1}{r} = \dfrac{r - w + (d^2w/d\theta^2)}{r^2 - 2rw} - \dfrac{1}{r} = \dfrac{(d^2w/d\theta^2) + w}{r^2 - 2rw}$

If the term $2rw$ in the denominator in the above expression is considered to be negligibly small compared to r^2, Eq. 695 results from substitution of this expression in Eq. 692.

But $(OH)^2 = (r - w)^2 = r^2 - 2rw + w^2 = r^2 - 2rw$, if the term w^2 is neglected. Therefore

$$\tfrac{1}{2}(AH)^2 - (AO)(AE) = \tfrac{1}{2}(r^2 - 2rw - r^2) = -rw$$

Placing this value in the parentheses of Eq. 696 we find *

$$M = prw \qquad (698)$$

The value of M from Eq. 698 is now substituted in Eq. 695, which then becomes

$$d^2w/d\theta^2 + w[1 + (pr^3/EI)] = 0 \qquad (699)$$

Let $1 + (pr^3/EI) = k^2$. Then Eq. 699 may be written

$$(d^2w/d\theta^2) + k^2w = 0 \qquad (700)$$

A solution of this differential equation is

$$w = C_1 \sin k\theta + C_2 \cos k\theta \qquad (701)$$

The conditions for determining the constants C_1 and C_2 are as follows: at $\theta = 0$, $w = 0$; and at $\theta = \pi/2$, $w = 0$. Applying the first condition we find that, in Eq. 701, C_2 must be zero. Applying the second condition we have

$$0 = C_1 \sin k(\pi/2) \qquad (702)$$

But C_1 cannot be zero, since this value would cause Eq. 701 to reduce to $w = 0$ for all values of θ. Hence

$$\sin k(\pi/2) = 0 \qquad (703)$$

The smallest value for the angle $k(\pi/2)$ in Eq. 703, other than zero, is $k(\pi/2) = \pi$, and hence $k = 2$. But $k^2 = 1 + (pr^3/EI)$, and $I = \tfrac{1}{12}t^3$. Therefore

$$p_{cr} = \frac{3EI}{r^3} = \frac{E}{4}\left(\frac{t}{r}\right)^3 = 2E\left(\frac{t}{d}\right)^3 \qquad (704)$$

The value of p_{cr} given in Eq. 704 is the uniform collapsing (critical) pressure (force per unit area) for the ring section shown in Fig. 332, where t is the thickness of the ring section and d is the outside diameter of the ring. The factor 2 in Eq. 704 is to be compared with 2.67 in Eq. 691 in which the arc AB was assumed to act as a straight column.

---

* This value for M could be obtained directly from Fig. 332b if it is assumed that a small deflection of the ring has a negligible effect on the action lines and directions of the forces acting on the ring, for the force $P = pr$ at H after the deflection w occurs is equivalent to the force $P_1 = P = pr$ at H' and a moment $M = prw$. That is, P may be resolved into the force $P_1 = P$ and the moment $M = prw$.

A Long Tube. In the isolated ring considered in the foregoing analysis, a curvature in the longitudinal plane of the tube accompanies the change in curvature in the transverse plane. In a wide, shallow beam (such as the ring) this curvature is appreciable, and if it is prevented, as it would be if the ring were a part of a tube of considerable length, the transverse bending moment in the shell accompanying the elastic deflection w as given by Eq. 698 is modified somewhat as follows: In a rectangular flat plate supported along all four edges, the bending moment M_x in one transverse plane as found in the theory of flat plates is

$$M_x = \frac{EI_x}{1 - \mu^2} \left(\frac{\partial^2 w}{\partial x^2} + \mu \frac{\partial^2 w}{\partial z^2} \right) \tag{705}$$

in which $\partial^2 w / \partial x^2$ and $\partial^2 w / \partial z^2$ are the curvatures of the plate at any point in the two rectangular transverse planes, and μ is Poisson's ratio. In the case of the long tube, $\partial^2 w / \partial z^2 = 0$, and hence

$$M_x = \frac{EI_x}{1 - \mu^2} \frac{\partial^2 w}{\partial x^2} = \frac{EI_x}{(1 - \mu^2)R} \tag{706}$$

The bending moment in the ring, in accordance with the ordinary theory of flexure for bending in one plane only, is equal to EI_x/R. Thus E in the expression for the moment, and also in the expression for the collapsing pressure for the ring, is replaced by $E/(1 - \mu^2)$ to obtain the collapsing pressure for the *long* tube. Therefore

$$p_{cr} = \frac{2E}{1 - \mu^2} \left(\frac{t}{d} \right)^3 \tag{707}$$

or, since $p = 2\sigma t/d$, Eq. 707 becomes

$$\sigma_{cr} = \frac{E}{1 - \mu^2} \left(\frac{t}{d} \right)^2 \tag{707a}$$

In Eq. 707 p_{cr} is the critical or collapsing uniform external pressure (force per unit area) for a *long* tube, in which bending of the tube walls can occur only in the transverse plane. In Eq. 707a σ_{cr} is the uniform circumferential stress in the tube wall corresponding to the collapsing external pressure p_{cr}, just before the tube buckles.

Illustrative Problem

Problem 335. A long, thin-walled cylindrical tube, such as an oil-well casing, has an outside diameter of 8 in. and a wall thickness of ¼ in. It is subjected to a uniform external pressure. The tube is made of steel having a yield point of 50,000 lb per sq in. Will the tube fail by elastic buckling, and, if so, what is the critical or buckling pressure? For steel assume that $E = 30 \times 10^6$ lb per sq in. and $\mu = \frac{1}{4}$. *Solution.* The critical pressure for elastic buckling is

$$p_{cr} = \frac{2E}{1 - \mu^2} \left(\frac{t}{d}\right)^3 = \frac{2 \times 30 \times 10^6}{1 - (\frac{1}{4})^2} \frac{1}{(32)^3} = 1950 \text{ lb/in.}^2$$

The circumferential compressive stress in the wall of the tube when the tube is subjected to this pressure is

$$\sigma_{cr} = \frac{p_{cr}d}{2t} = \frac{1950 \times 8}{2 \times \frac{1}{4}} = 31,200 \text{ lb/in.}^2$$

Since this value of σ_{cr} is less than the yield point of the material, the tube will fail by elastic buckling at a pressure of 1950 lb per sq in.

Problems

336. A long cylindrical tube made of ductile steel has an outside diameter of 4 in. and a wall thickness of $\frac{1}{8}$ in. It fails by elastic buckling when subjected to uniform external pressure. What is the least value the yield point of the material can have?

337. A long cylindrical thin-walled tube has an outside diameter of 3 in. The tube fails by elastic buckling at a pressure of 6000 lb per sq in. The tube is made of aluminum for which $E = 10 \times 10^6$ and $\mu = \frac{1}{3}$. Calculate the wall thickness of the tube.

338. A steel cylindrical tube in a boiler has an outside diameter of 2 in. It is subjected to an external pressure of 200 lb per sq in. The compressive yield point of the material is 45,000 lb per sq in. What maximum wall thickness must the tube have to resist failure by elastic buckling? What circumferential compressive stress will exist in the wall of the tube when the tube is subjected to the critical pressure?

339. A long cylindrical ventilating pipe is 15 in. in diameter and is made of steel $\frac{1}{20}$ in. thick (18 U. S. Standard gage). The pipe is subjected externally to atmospheric pressure (14.7 lb per sq in.). A suction fan is placed at the exhaust end of the pipe which causes the internal pressure in the pipe to be less than atmospheric pressure. Calculate the internal pressure at which elastic buckling would be expected to occur.

189 Empirical formulas. An extensive series of experiments to determine the collapsing pressure of lap-welded steel tubes 3 in. to 10 in. in diameter was made in 1906 for the National Tube Company by R. T. Stewart. A similar series of experiments was made on seamless cold-drawn steel and brass tubes and also on lap-welded steel tubes by A. P. Carman and M. L. Carr in 1917. The diameter of these tubes ranged from $1\frac{1}{2}$ in. to $3\frac{1}{2}$ in.

These experimental investigations were consistent and showed that the collapsing pressure of long thin-walled cylindrical tubes, having values of t/d not greater than about 0.03 and subjected to external uniform pressure p (in pounds per square inch) is approximately

$$p_{cr} = 50,000,000(t/d)^3 = \tfrac{5}{3}E(t/d)^3 \qquad \text{for steel tubes}$$

in which $E = 30,000,000$ lb per sq in. for steel, and

$$p_{cr} = 25,000,000(t/d)^3 = 2E(t/d)^3 \qquad \text{for brass tubes}$$

in which $E = 12,500,000$ lb per sq in. for brass.

For tubes having a value of t/d between 0.03 and 0.07, Carman and Carr found that the following equations fit the test results satisfactorily, in which p_{cr} is the collapsing pressure expressed in pounds per square inch.

For seamless cold-drawn steel tubes: $p_{cr} = 95,520(t/d) - 2090$.
For lap-welded steel tubes: $p_{cr} = 83,270(t/d) - 1025$.
For brass tubes: $p_{cr} = 93,360(t/d) - 2474$.

190 Effect of end restraints on elastic buckling of tube. *Edges of Shell at Ends Simply Supported.* In a thin-walled tube the ends may be restrained from collapsing by plugs or disks that are fitted in the ends (as is usual in the testing of tubes) without influencing the collapsing pressure of the tube, provided that the tube is relatively long. A relatively long tube will collapse at the central portion of the tube in the form of two lobes which is the form associated with the minimum critical pressure for the tube having given dimensions (t/d) and made of material having given properties. If, however, the tube is sufficiently short relative to the diameter, the restraint of the ends will prevent the tube from collapsing in two lobes, and hence the external pressure may be increased above the minimum critical pressure before elastic buckling occurs. The second critical pressure corresponds to collapse or buckling in the form of three lobes; similarly the third critical pressure corresponds to four lobes, etc. (see Fig. 331). It is here assumed that the tube in all cases collapses by elastic buckling.

The effect of the number of lobes N on the critical pressure for elastic buckling of a tube is illustrated in Fig. 333; only the useful portion of the curve corresponding to any value of N is shown in Fig. 333. The equation for the critical pressure for elastic buckling of the tube expressed in terms of the number of lobes which in turn involves the type of end restraint is rather long and complicated, but it may be written in the form

$$p = KE(t/d)^3 \tag{708}$$

in which p is the uniform external pressure at which a thin-walled cylinder will collapse in N number of lobes. The value of K, corresponding to a given value of l/r (or of l/d) and a given number of lobes, may be found from Fig. 333, provided that the ends of the tubes are simply supported (prevented from collapsing but free from an edge moment). For example, Fig. 333 shows that a tube for which $l/r = 4$ and $d/t = 50$ will collapse in three lobes, if the tube fails by elastic buckling, and that

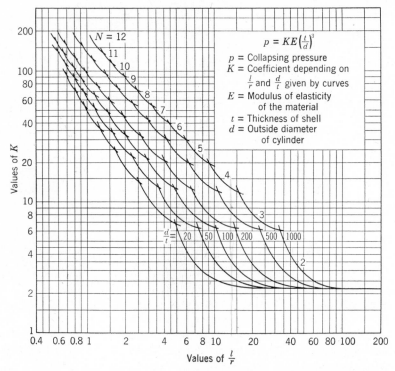

$$p = KE\left(\frac{t}{d}\right)^3$$

p = Collapsing pressure
K = Coefficient depending on
     $\frac{l}{r}$ and $\frac{d}{t}$ given by curves
E = Modulus of elasticity
     of the material
t = Thickness of shell
d = Outside diameter
     of cylinder

Fig. 333 Buckling coefficients for round, thin-walled cylinders with pressures on sides only; edges simply supported and $\mu = 0.30$ (see reference 7).

the value of K for use in Eq. 708 is approximately 11.0. On the other hand, if the tube had a value $l/r = 10$, the elastic collapse of the tube would occur in the form of two lobes, and the value for K in Eq. 708 would be approximately 3.6.

It will be observed that, if the tube is relatively long so that it collapses in the form of two lobes, Eq. 708 reduces to Eq. 707, that is, $K = 2/(1 - \mu^2)$.

Edges of Shell at Ends Fixed. If the ends of the thin-walled cylinder are not only maintained round (simply supported) but also prevented

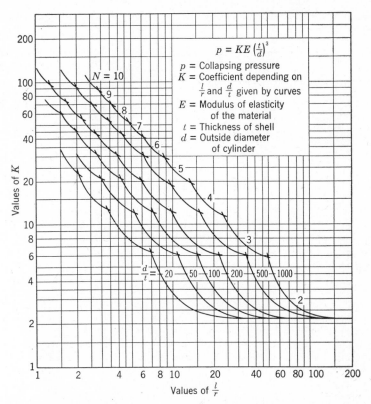

FIG. 334   Buckling coefficients for round, thin-walled cylinders with pressures on sides only; edges fixed and $\mu = 0.30$ (see reference 7).

from tipping by a restraining edge moment, the values of K for use in Eq. 708 are as given in Fig. 334.

Illustrative Problem

Problem 340.   A thin-walled cylindrical tube has an outside diameter of 10 in. and a wall thickness of $\frac{1}{10}$ in.   The tube is 40 in. long, and the ends are maintained round by circular disks or plugs (the edges of the ends of the tube are simply supported but not fixed).   The tube is made of steel having a yield point of 50,000 lb per sq in.   Assume for steel that $E = 30 \times 10^6$ and $\mu = 0.30$.   Will the tube fail by elastic buckling, and, if so, what is the critical or collapsing pressure?

Solution. $\dfrac{l}{r} = \dfrac{40}{5} = 8 \qquad \dfrac{d}{t} = \dfrac{10}{\frac{1}{10}} = 100$

Figure 333 shows that, for these values, if the tube buckles elastically it will buckle in the form of three lobes, and that the value of K is 7. Therefore, the elastic buckling pressure is

$$p_{cr} = KE(t/d)^3$$

$$= 7 \times 30 \times 10^6 (\tfrac{1}{100})^3 = 210 \text{ lb/in.}^2$$

This pressure would cause a circumferential stress

$$\sigma_{cr} = \frac{pd}{2t} = \frac{210 \times 10}{2 \times \tfrac{1}{10}} = 10,500 \text{ lb/in.}^2$$

Since the value of σ_{cr} is less than the yield point of the material, the tube will fail by elastic buckling at the external pressure of 210 lb per sq in.

Problems

341. A steel cylindrical tank 24 ft long has an outside diameter of 8 ft. A wall thickness of $\frac{1}{4}$ in. is required to resist internal pressure. Occasionally a partial vacuum occurs in the tank. The tank is subjected externally to atmospheric pressure. Is there danger that the tank may fail by elastic buckling? If so, find the minimum internal pressure that can exist without buckling. For steel use $E = 30 \times 10^6$, $\mu = 0.30$. Assume the yield point of the material to be 40,000 lb per sq in., and also assume that the ends of the shell of the tank are fixed.

342. A riveted steel water pipe is laid and held on the bottom of a river in which the water is approximately 20 ft deep; the river is $\frac{1}{4}$ mile wide. A break in this pipe line may develop some distance from the stream crossing, causing a rapid withdrawing of the conveyed water which in turn causes the pressure in the pipe to decrease somewhat (2 lb per sq in., say) below atmospheric pressure. If the pipe is 4 ft in diameter and is made of steel plate $\frac{1}{4}$ in. thick, will the pipe probably collapse? If so, estimate the spacing for stiffening rings to prevent collapse, assuming a stiffening ring to cause the section of the pipe at the ring to be simply supported. (The ring maintains a circular section for the pipe but does not introduce a longitudinal bending moment at the ring section.)

343. A cylindrical gasoline tank 20 ft long and 8 ft in diameter failed by collapsing when the pressure in the tank was gradually decreased below atmospheric pressure. The external pressure was that of the atmosphere (14.7 lb per sq in.), and the thickness of the shell was 0.20 in. The tank was made of steel having a yield point of 40,000 lb per sq in. The tank was empty when it failed. Calculate the internal pressure at which the buckling would be expected to occur. Assume, first, that the ends of the shell of the tank were simply supported, and, second, that they were fixed.

191. Inelastic buckling of tube.

If the wall thickness of a long thin-walled tube of given diameter is assumed to increase, that is, if t/d is assumed to increase, the critical elastic buckling pressure p_{cr}, as given by Eq. 707, increases much faster than t/d increases. Thus a value of p may be reached that causes a maximum circumferential stress in the wall of the tube equal to the yield point of the material before the critical pressure for elastic buckling is reached. The maximum external pressure that can be applied to the tube may still be limited by action that is predominately buckling of the tube, but the action is designated as *inelastic buckling*, similar to inelastic buckling of columns discussed in the preceding chapter. The critical pressure for inelastic buckling is less than that at which elastic buckling would occur for the given value of t/d if the material remained elastic, mainly because the stiffness of the material decreases rapidly as inelastic deformation develops.

Inelastic buckling may occur also in a relatively short tube even if the tube has a relatively thin wall; the end restraint of the short tube may prevent elastic buckling by increasing the number of lobes in the mode of buckling until the pressure becomes so large that the elastic limit stress of the material is attained before the critical pressure for elastic buckling is reached.

No wholly satisfactory analytical method is available for determining the collapsing pressure for inelastic buckling of a tube. One method is to replace E in Eqs. 707 and 708 by the tangent modulus E_T, as was done for inelastic buckling of columns in the preceding chapter. The collapsing pressure then becomes

$$p_{cr} = KE_T(t/d)^3 \tag{709}$$

It should be noted that, if a material has a yield point, the value of E_T is zero at this stress, and hence E_T and p_{cr} in Eq. 709 become equal to zero. This fact is interpreted to mean that it is impossible to have a critical external pressure p that will cause a stress $\sigma = pd/2t$ greater than the yield point, no matter what the value of t/d may be. It will be observed also that Eq. 709 must be solved by trial and error, since E_T is a function of σ_{cr} and hence of $p_{cr}(p = 2\sigma t/d)$, as was done in the solution of Prob. 330.

For materials like aluminum alloys, brass, stainless steel, and some heat-treated steels, which do not have yield points but instead exhibit a gradual increase of plastic strain with increase of stress, the tangent modulus may be obtained directly from the stress-strain curves as illustrated in Fig. 326. Many such graphs can be found in the literature (see, for example, pp. 1048 and 1049 of Vol. 46, *Proceedings of the American Society for Testing Materials*).

The conditions that must be satisfied to result in failure of a *long* tube by inelastic buckling may be obtained from Eq. 707a. Thus

$$\sigma_{cr} = \frac{E_T}{1 - \mu^2}\left(\frac{t}{d}\right)^2 \tag{710}$$

where σ_{cr} is the circumferential stress in the tube wall when the tube is subjected to the critical or buckling pressure p_{cr}. If the value of σ_{cr} corresponding to the critical *elastic* buckling load is less than the proportional limit, the tube will fail by elastic buckling, that is, E_T is then the elastic modulus E. But, if σ_{cr} is above the proportional limit, the value of E_T will be less than E and a pair of values of E_T and σ_{cr} which satisfy Eq. 710 must be found from a curve such as in Fig. 326. As noted previously, this is done by a trial-and-error process. The value of μ in Eq. 710, however, is greater for plastic deformation than for elastic strain; for steel, $\mu = 0.30$, approximately, for elastic strain, and $\mu = 0.50$ for inelastic strain. An average value of $\mu = 0.40$ for steel is suggested for use in Eq. 710, since strains in the tube wall when inelastic buckling (bending) occurs will be partly elastic and partly inelastic.

Illustrative Problem

Problem 344. A long cylindrical tube has an outside diameter of 10 in. and is made of a steel whose stress-strain diagram is shown in Fig. 326. The tube is required to withstand an external pressure of $p = 3000$ lb per sq in. Compute the thickness t of the cylinder wall so that it will take twice the given pressure to buckle the tube.

Solution. We use Eq. 710, but since neither t nor σ_{cr} are known we make the substitution for $t = pd/2\sigma_{cr}$. Thus Eq. 710 is

$$\sigma_{cr} = \frac{E_T}{1 - \mu^2}\left(\frac{t}{d}\right)^2 = \frac{E_T}{1 - \mu^2}\left(\frac{p}{2\sigma_{cr}}\right)^2$$

Let $p = 2 \times 3000 = 6000$ lb per sq in. and $\mu = 0.4$, since it is expected that the buckling will be inelastic. Then

$$\sigma_{cr} = \frac{E_T}{0.84}\left(\frac{6000}{2\sigma_{cr}}\right)^2$$

From Fig. 326 by trial and error it is found that the corresponding values $E_T = 5,000,000$ lb per sq in. and $\sigma = \sigma_{cr} = 37,500$ lb per sq in. will satisfy this equation. Therefore

$$t = \frac{pd}{2\sigma_{cr}} = \frac{6000 \times 10}{2 \times 37,500} = 0.8 \text{ in.}$$

Problem

345. A long cylindrical tube has an outside diameter of 8 in. and a wall thickness of $\frac{1}{2}$ in. and is made of the steel whose stress-strain diagram is shown in Fig. 326. Compute the critical or buckling pressure if the tube is subjected to a uniform external pressure.

192 Buckling of flat plates. There are many types of members and structures in addition to those discussed in the foregoing articles that may fail by buckling. Some examples are: A thin-walled cylinder subjected to either axial or torsional loads; a thin-walled cylinder subjected to bending loads; a plate girder or any other wide-flanged thin-walled beam; and a flat plate subjected to compressive loads that lie in the plane of the plate. In many of these examples the typical buckling may be a local wrinkling or bulging of the thin wall or thin plate.

In some applications this wrinkling quickly leads to failure, and hence it is highly desirable to prevent the wrinkling by means of stiffeners, etc., whereas in other applications this wrinkling (initial buckling) permits the member to redistribute the load throughout the member so that it does not fail as a whole until a larger load is applied. Thus (initial) buckling is not always equivalent to structural failure, and hence wrinkling may permit the member to take advantage of its post-buckling strength. This condition is of special importance in lightweight (airplane) design in which the strength-weight ratio is a controlling factor, although the same idea is used in the design of some thick-walled (heavy) structures by the so-called theory of limit design.

The post-buckling strength of a thin plate may be explained as follows. Figure 335a represents a thin rectangular plate loaded uniformly in the plane of the plate along two edges; the other two edges are simply supported, that is, they can rotate but cannot deflect in a direction perpendicular to the plane of the plate. When the uniform compressive load (and corresponding uniform stress σ) reaches a certain value, a wavelike series of bulges (two in this case) will begin to appear along the vertical centerline of the plate; the number of such bulges will depend on the relative dimensions of the plate and the type of support at the edges of the plate, in much the same manner in which the number of bulges or lobes in the thin-walled cylinder (Fig. 331) was affected by its relative dimensions.

The deflection of the bulges will be alternately positive and negative as shown in Fig. 335. The value of σ_{cr} at which these bulges appear is given by the typical equation for buckling (see Eq. 707a for tube), namely,

$$\sigma_{cr} = \frac{P_{cr}}{a} = K \frac{\pi^2 E}{12(1 - \mu^2)} \left(\frac{t}{b}\right)^2 \tag{711}$$

in which t and b are the thickness and width, respectively, of the plate. K depends on the edge conditions of the plate; values for K have been obtained by mathematical analysis and are usually given in the form of curves similar to those shown in Figs. 333 and 334 for tubes. If all edges are simply supported as in Fig. 335 and if $h/b \geqq 1.3$, the value of K is constant and is 4.0. (See reference 13.) If the two loaded edges are simply supported, one unloaded edge is simply supported and one unloaded edge is free, as is approximately the case for the flange of the channel in Fig. 324 in which the web provides the simple support for one unloaded edge, the value of K is nearly constant and equals 0.5 when $h/b \geqq 4$.

But, as previously noted, the load P_{cr} or stress σ_{cr} at which this wrinkling occurs is not the maximum load or stress that can be resisted by the plate without collapsing. As the load is increased above the

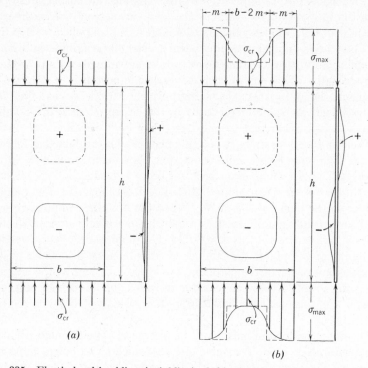

FIG. 335   Elastic local buckling (wrinkling) of thin flat plate subjected to uniform pressure on two parallel edges and simply supported on all four edges.

value P_{cr}, the stress close to the simply supported edges increases, as shown in Fig. 335b. The stress σ_{cr} in the mid-section, where the bulges form, remains approximately constant as the deflections of the bulges continue to increase; this action is shown in Fig. 335b. Thus the load associated with buckling failure of the plate will depend upon how much deflection of the bulges may be permitted to develop. However, the maximum load (see reference 13) that the plate will resist is usually assumed to be reached when the maximum stress in the neighborhood of the two simply supported edges reaches the yield strength of the material. See Prob. 346 for the method of computing the maximum load on the plate.

Use of Stiffeners on Thin Sections. As previously noted, in many applications stiffeners are used to strengthen thin sections against the possibility of failure by buckling. Such stiffeners were considered in Art. 190 for thin-walled tubes subjected to external pressure. When stiffeners such as angles and Z bars are fastened on flat plates, that part of the plate nearest to the stiffener is most efficient in carrying the compressive load; the plate wrinkles at regions most remote from the stiffeners, and thus the wrinkled portion carries a lesser share of the load. The maximum buckling loads of such stiffened plates are usually found by considering that a certain so-called effective width of the plate on each side of the stiffener acts with the stiffener, and then computing the buckling load for the member consisting of the stiffener and this effective width of plate. A detailed treatment of these problems is beyond the scope of this discussion; furthermore, special methods are used in their solution to which the reader is referred * for further study.

Illustrative Problems

Problem 346. A flat aluminum alloy plate 10 in. wide, 30 in. long, and 0.10 in. thick has all edges simply supported. Compressive loads in the plane of the plate are applied to the 10-in. sides. Compute (a) the compressive load at which buckling (first appearance of bulges) will occur, (b) the compressive load at which the maximum stress at the unloaded edges of the plate reaches a value of $\sigma_{max} = 30,000$ lb per sq in. which is the yield strength of the material.

Solution. (a) We use Eq. 711 in which $K = 4.0$, $\mu = 0.3$, $E = 10,000,000$ lb per sq in., $t = 0.10$ in., and $b = 10$ in. Thus

$$\sigma_{cr} = \frac{P_{cr}}{10 \times 0.10} = 4.0 \frac{\pi^2 \times 10,000,000}{12(1 - 0.3^2)} \left(\frac{0.10}{10}\right)^2 = 3630 \text{ lb/in.}^2$$

and
$$P_{cr} = 3630 \times 1.0 = 3630 \text{ lb}$$

(b) It is assumed that as the load is increased the stress σ_{cr} (Fig. 335a) remains equal to 3630 lb per sq in. over a central width of the plate equal to $b - 2m$ (see Fig. 335b); the increase in the load is due to the fact that the two widths m near the unloaded edges are able to resist additional stress. The actual distribution of stress is indicated by the curve (Fig. 335b), but in calculating the ultimate load the assumption is usually made that the stress is distributed according to the dotted lines, that is, that the stress σ_{cr} acts over the central width $b - 2m$, and the stress σ_{max} acts (uniformly) over the two widths m. Thus the ultimate load is given by the equation

$$P_{ult} = \sigma_{cr}(b - 2m)t + 2\sigma_{max}mt$$

In this equation all quantities are known except m. Von Kármán and Marguerre

* See, for example, *Airplane Structural Analysis and Design*, by E. E. Sechler and L. G. Dunn, John Wiley & Sons, 1942, and *Theory of Elastic Stability*, by S. Timoshenko, McGraw-Hill Book Co., 1936.

have suggested several empirical formulas, based on the results of tests of aluminum alloy plates for determining m. One of these is

$$m = 0.5b \sqrt[3]{\sigma_{cr}/\sigma_{max}}$$

Hence $m = 0.5 \times 10 \sqrt[3]{3630/30,000} = 2.46$ in.

Therefore $P_{ult} = 3630(10 - 4.92)0.10 + 2 \times 30,000 \times 2.46 \times 0.10 = 16,600$ lb

The ultimate load on the plate is, therefore, about four and one-half times the load at which the first wrinkling or bulging occurs.

Problem 347. A rectangular plate of aluminum alloy of dimensions 30 in. by 10 in. by 0.064 in. is bent to form a channel (see Fig. 324); the web is 5 in. wide, and each flange is 2.5 in. wide. The channel is loaded axially by a compressive force that is parallel to the 30-in. dimension. (a) Compute the buckling load if the assumption is made that the column will act as an Euler column, that is, local buckling will not occur. (b) Determine the load on the assumption that localized buckling will occur, as shown in Fig. 324, before the Euler load is reached.

Solution. (a) *Euler Load.* From Eq. 676

$$P_{cr} = \frac{\pi^2 EI}{l^2} = \frac{\pi^2 \times 10,000,000 \times 0.40}{(30)^2} = 4400 \text{ lb}$$

(b) *Local Buckling Load.* A flange will be the first part of the column to fail by local buckling because one edge is free. The problem is solved by considering a single flange as a flat plate loaded on two edges (the 2.5 in. edges) simply supported on one of the other two (30-in.) edges (along the junction of web with flange) and free on the fourth side. The critical stress is given by Eq. 711 in which $K = 0.5$ since $h/b = 30/2.5 = 12 > 4$. Also $E = 10,000,000$ lb per sq in., $\mu = 0.3$, $t = 0.064$ in., $b = 2.5$ in. Therefore

$$\sigma_{cr} = 0.5 \frac{\pi^2 \times 10,000,000}{12(1 - 0.3^2)} \left(\frac{0.064}{2.5} \right)^2 = 2970 \text{ lb/in.}^2$$

In calculating the load P_{cr} it is assumed that the stress $\sigma_{cr} = 2970$ lb per sq in. is distributed uniformly in the whole cross section when local buckling of the flange starts. Thus

$$P_{cr} = \sigma_{cr}a = 2970 \times 0.64 = 1900 \text{ lb}$$

This load is smaller than the Euler load found in (a), and therefore the column may be expected to fail by localized buckling as illustrated by Fig. 324.

Selected References

1. Engesser, F. R., "Ueber die Bestimmung der Knickfestigkeit Gegliederter Stabe," *Zeitschrift des österreichischen Ingenieur- und Architekten-Vereines,* 1913, pp. 769–772.
2. Holmquist, J. L., and A. Nadai, "A Theoretical and Experimental Approach to the Problems of Collapse of Deep-Well Casing," *Drilling and Producing Practice,* American Petroleum Institute, 1940, p. 392.
3. Osgood, W. R., "Column Curves and Stress-Strain Diagrams," *Research Paper 492, Bureau of Standards Journal of Research,* Vol. 9, October 1932. Examines

several of the more common empirical formulas to determine the necessary slope of the stress-strain diagram in order that these formulas may be comparable with the Considére-Engesser theory.

4. Osgood, W. R., "The Double-Modulus Theory of Column Action," *Civil Engineering*, March 1935, p. 173.
5. Ramberg, W., A. E. McPherson, and S. Levy, "Experimental Study of Deformation and Effective Width in Axially Loaded Sheet Stringer Panels," *Technical Note* 684, National Advisory Committee for Aeronautics, January 1939.
6. Southwell, R. V., "The Strength of Struts," *Engineering (London)*, Vol. 94, Aug. 23, 1912, p. 249. The double-modulus theory of columns.
7. Sturm, R. G., "A Study of the Collapsing Pressure of Thin-Walled Cylinders," *Bulletin* 329, Engineering Experiment Station, University of Illinois, 1941.
8. Von Kármán, Theo., "Mitteilungen über Forschungsarbeiten," *Verein deutscher Ingenieure*, Heft 81, Berlin, Julius Springer, 1910. The double-modulus theory of strength of columns.
9. Tuckerman, L. B., "Aircraft: Materials and Testing," *Proceedings of the American Society for Testing Materials*, Vol. 35, 1935, Pt. II, pp. 3–46.
10. Westergaard, H. M., "Buckling of Elastic Structures," *Transactions of the American Society of Civil Engineers*, Vol. 85, 1922, pp. 576–654.
11. Shanley, F. R., "Applied Column Theory," *Transactions of the American Society of Civil Engineers*, Vol. 115, 1950, pp. 698–727.
12. Hoff, N. J., S. V. Nardo, and B. Erickson, "An Experimental Investigation of the Process of Buckling of Columns," *Proceedings of the Society for Experimental Analysis*, Vol. IX, No. 1, 1951, p. 201.
13. Stowell, E. Z., G. J. Heimerl, C. Libove, and E. E. Lundquist, "Buckling Stresses for Flat Plates and Sections," *Proceedings of the American Society of Civil Engineers*, Vol. 77, Sep. No. 77, July 1951.

Appendix I

A BRIEF INTRODUCTION TO THE MATHEMATICAL THEORY OF ELASTICITY

193 Introduction. In Art. 8 (Chapter 1) is given a method· or procedure for determining stresses in members subjected to loads. This procedure was called the method of mechanics of materials or the method of ordinary mechanics. The results of a more detailed method usually designated as the mathematical theory of elasticity are made use of in parts of several of the preceding chapters, and hence a very brief discussion of the theory as applied to conditions frequently designated as a two-dimensional problem, that is, a problem involving either a plane state of stress or a plane state of strain is given in this appendix. (See Chapter 3 for definitions of plane state of stress and plane state of strain.) Both methods make use of a relation between stress and strain which is usually considered to be associated with elastic material, and hence both methods give stresses accompanied by elastic (and therefore small) strains. The method of ordinary mechanics makes use of an assumed strain distribution in the body obtained from observing (or assuming) the primary or major strains in the body as a whole under the given loading, but usually these primary strains are assumed to occur in one direction only, and the relation between these strains and the stresses in the same direction are assumed to be given by Hooke's law, namely $\sigma = E\epsilon$; the effect of strains in the other directions in the body are neglected.

In the method of the theory of elasticity no simplifying assumption is made concerning the strains, and hence in this method it becomes necessary to take into account the complete distribution of the strains in the body and to assume a more general statement of Hooke's law in expressing the relation between stresses and strains. The values of stresses calculated by both methods are only approximately equal to the stresses in an actual physical body mainly because the material in the physical body deviates from the ideal material assumed in the two

627

methods. In this respect both methods are approximate, but they are, nevertheless, of great value in many engineering problems in determining the nature and order of magnitude of the stresses in actual physical bodies subjected to loads.

194 Elementary theory of elasticity. The procedure in the theory of elasticity is not such that the derivation of the formulas for the stresses expressed in terms of loads may be obtained directly. It is instead a procedure in which all the fundamental conditions which the stresses and strains must meet are formulated, and then the expressions for the stresses are made to satisfy these conditions. These conditions involve the equilibrium of every element (small part) of the body including the surface elements where the external forces (loads) act, and also the correct distribution of the strains throughout the body. The first of these fundamental conditions which will be considered is the equilibrium of any element of the body.

Equations of Equilibrium for an Element. A small rectangular element A in a body such as that shown in Fig. 336a is isolated so that the forces

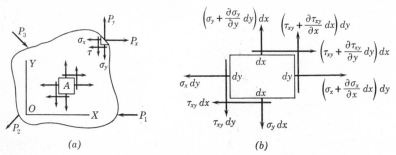

(a)   (b)

FIG. 336   Forces acting on differential element of body.

acting on its faces may be made external to the element as indicated in Fig. 336b. The dimensions of the element are dx and dy in the plane of the paper and unity perpendicular to the plane of the paper, and the positive directions of the forces acting on the element are as shown in Fig. 336. In general the stresses vary throughout the body, and at any point the change in the stress in the x direction over the length dx is expressed as $(\partial\sigma_x/\partial x)dx$, where $\partial\sigma_x/\partial x$ is the rate of change of the stress in the x direction (assumed to be constant over the length dx). The changes in the stresses σ_y and τ_{xy} are expressed in a similar manner. The forces acting on the isolated element are shown in Fig. 336b. By applying the equations of equilibrium to the forces acting on this element (neglecting the weight of the element), the following equations are found.

$$\Sigma F_x = 0 \qquad \partial\sigma_x/\partial x + \partial\tau_{xy}/\partial y = 0 \qquad (712)$$

$$\Sigma F_y = 0 \qquad \partial\sigma_y/\partial y + \partial\tau_{xy}/\partial x = 0 \qquad (713)$$

These equations are called the *differential equations of equilibrium;* they must be satisfied by the forces acting on every element (at every point) in the body. It should be noted that these equilibrium equations do not constitute a relationship between the stresses and the external loads but involve only the rates of change in the stresses at any point in the body. Thus, in order that the relationship between the stresses and the external loads may be established, the expressions for the stresses σ_x, σ_y, and τ_{xy} must not only satisfy Eqs. 712 and 713 but must also give the values of the normal and shearing stresses which exist at the boundaries of the body.

Distribution of the Strains in the Body. The next condition to be met in finding the desired expressions for the stresses σ_x, σ_y, and τ_{xy} at any point in the body is to consider their relationship with the strains ϵ_x, ϵ_y, and γ_{xy} at the point. These relationships are usually given by the equations developed in Chapter 3 and referred to as Hooke's law for two dimensional stresses, namely,

$$\epsilon_x = \frac{1}{E}(\sigma_x - \mu\sigma_y) \qquad \epsilon_y = \frac{1}{E}(\sigma_y - \mu\sigma_x)$$

$$\gamma_{xy} = \frac{1}{G}\tau_{xy} = \frac{2(1+\mu)}{E}\tau_{xy} \qquad (714)$$

However, no immediate use can be made of these relationships between stress and strain for finding the expressions for σ_x, σ_y, and τ_{xy}, because no assumption concerning the distribution of the strains in the body is permitted. In other words, the strains ϵ_x, ϵ_y, and γ_{xy} have a geometric relationship to each other so that no assumption can be made concerning the distribution of one of these strains which does not take into account its relationship to the other two strains. The significance or meaning of this geometric relationship among the strains may be interpreted as follows. Let an elastic body such as rubber plate (in which the strains are large enough to be observed) be composed of many elements, such as $ABCD$, represented by the heavy lines in Fig. 337a. The strains of the elements under the action of a load P must be such that the strained elements will fit together exactly to make up the body and thus preserve the continuity of the body in its deformed state as indicated by the dotted lines in Fig. 337a. This geometric relationship among the strains must be established since it is a condition that the distribution of the strains must satisfy.

One method of obtaining this relationship among the strains is to express the strains ϵ_x, ϵ_y, and γ_{xy} at a point in terms of the rates of displacement of the point. For example, consider the strain of the element

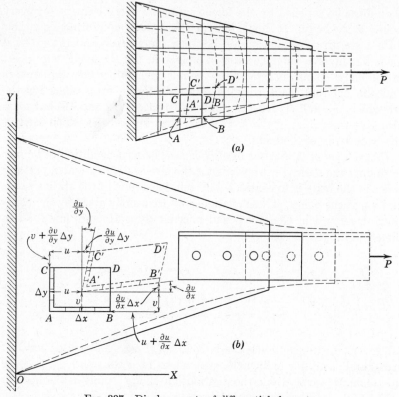

FIG. 337   Displacements of differential element.

$ABCD$ in the plate shown in Fig. 337b in which the strains are greatly exaggerated. A point such as A is displaced by amounts u and v in the x and y directions, respectively, to a point A'. The points B and C are displaced to B' and C', respectively, in such a way that the fibers Δx and Δy are not only changed in length but are also changed in direction, the difference in amount of rotation of Δx and Δy giving rise to shearing strains at A. For example, the point B is displaced in the x direction by the amount $u + (\partial u/\partial x)\ \Delta x$, where $\partial u/\partial x$ is the rate at which the displacement u is taking place in the x direction along the length Δx (assumed to be constant over the length Δx). Hence, the x component of the elongation of the fiber Δx is equal to $(\partial u/\partial x)\,\Delta x$ and therefore, by definition, the strain ϵ_x in the x direction is

$$\epsilon_x = \frac{(\partial u/\partial x)\,\Delta x}{\Delta x} = \frac{\partial u}{\partial x}$$

Similarly, the strain in the y direction is

$$\epsilon_y = \frac{(\partial v/\partial y)\,\Delta y}{\Delta y} = \frac{\partial v}{\partial y}$$

By definition the shearing strain γ_{xy} at the point A is equal to the decrease in the right angle BAC of the elemental block. The change in this angle is equal to the difference between the angle $B'A'C'$ and a right angle; this difference is equal to the sum of two small angles, namely, the angle that $A'B'$ makes with the horizontal and the angle that $A'C'$ makes with the vertical. Each of these angles may be expressed by the tangent of the angle, since the angle is small, as follows: The displacement of A in the y direction is v, and the displacement of B in the y direction is $v + (\partial v/\partial x)\,\Delta x$, where $\partial v/\partial x$ is the rate at which the displacement v is taking place along the length Δx (assumed to be constant over the length Δx). Hence, the tangent of one of the angles (the slope of $A'B'$) is equal to $\dfrac{(\partial v/\partial x)\,\Delta x}{\Delta x + (\partial u/\partial x)\,\Delta x}$ which for small strains reduces to $\partial v/\partial x$.

In a similar manner it can be shown that the slope of $A'C'$ with the vertical is equal to $\partial u/\partial y$. The shearing strain γ_{xy} at any point A therefore is

$$\gamma_{xy} = \partial u/\partial y + \partial v/\partial x$$

The strains at any point in a body are therefore given in terms of the displacements of the point by the following expressions:

$$\epsilon_x = \partial u/\partial x \tag{715}$$

$$\epsilon_y = \partial v/\partial y \tag{716}$$

$$\gamma_{xy} = \partial u/\partial y + \partial v/\partial x \tag{717}$$

The above expressions for the strains at a point indicate that there is a definite relationship among the three strains at a point, since all three strains are expressed in terms of the two displacements u and v. This relationship is a necessary condition determined by the geometry of the strains, but the relationship can be obtained by purely mathematical manipulation as follows. Equation 715 is differentiated twice with respect to y (partial differentiation); Eq. 716 is differentiated twice with respect to x; and Eq. 717 is differentiated once with respect to x and once with respect to y. The sum of the derivatives of Eqs. 715 and 716 is found to be identical to the derivative of Eq. 717. Therefore,

$$\frac{\partial^2 \epsilon_x}{\partial y^2} + \frac{\partial^2 \epsilon_y}{\partial x^2} = \frac{\partial^2 \gamma_{xy}}{\partial x \, \partial y} \tag{718}$$

When the strains satisfy Eq. 718, they are said to be compatible with each other and Eq. 718 is called the *equation of compatibility*. In nearly all cases the fact that the strains are compatible with each other indicates that the continuity of the body will be preserved by these strains, and hence in the subsequent discussion the equations of compatibility may be thought of as equations of continuity.*

The equation of compatibility may be stated in terms of the stresses if in Eq. 718 the strains ϵ_x, ϵ_y, and γ_{xy} are expressed in terms of the stresses by use of Eqs. 714. Differentiating each of Eqs. 714 as required for substituting the expressions in Eq. 718, we have

$$\frac{\partial^2 \sigma_x}{\partial y^2} - \mu \frac{\partial^2 \sigma_y}{\partial y^2} + \frac{\partial^2 \sigma_y}{\partial x^2} - \mu \frac{\partial^2 \sigma_x}{\partial x^2} = 2(1 + \mu) \frac{\partial^2 \tau_{xy}}{\partial x \, \partial y} \tag{719}$$

Equation 719 may be interpreted as follows. If σ_x, σ_y, and τ_{xy} satisfy Eq. 719, the strains which accompany these stresses will be compatible with one another and the continuity of the body will be insured (except in some special cases as already noted).

Stresses at Any Point. It has been shown that the differential equations of equilibrium (Eqs. 712 and 713) insure a distribution of the stresses σ_x, σ_y, and τ_{xy} in a body which will preserve the equilibrium of every element of the body, but the fact that these equations are satisfied does not necessarily mean that the stresses σ_x, σ_y, and τ_{xy} are the actual stresses in the body due to a given set of loads; the distribution of the stresses σ_x, σ_y, and τ_{xy} must also give the actual normal and shearing stresses which exist at the boundary of the body. Furthermore it was shown that Eq. 719 insures that the stresses are accompanied by the proper strain distribution in the body. The problem, then, is to obtain equations that express the stresses σ_x, σ_y, and τ_{xy} in terms of the external loads and the dimensions of the body and that satisfy Eqs. 712, 713, and 719. This problem is primarily a problem in mathematics rather than in mechanics. There are several possible methods of attacking the

---

* In certain problems where the equations of compatibility are satisfied, it may be necessary to check the displacements in order to determine whether or not continuity is satisfied.

problem. One method frequently used is to find a function ϕ in x and y, called a stress function, which will satisfy all the above equations and from which the formulas for the stresses may be found. This method is discussed in the following paragraph.

Stress Function. G. B. Airy showed that there always exists an expression in x and y, say $\phi(x, y)$, from which the stresses σ_x, σ_y, and τ_{xy} at any point (x, y) in a body can be determined as follows:

$$\sigma_x = \partial^2\phi/\partial y^2 \qquad \sigma_y = \partial^2\phi/\partial x^2 \qquad \tau_{xy} = -\partial^2\phi/\partial x\,\partial y \qquad (720)$$

(The stress due to the weight of the body is neglected in these equations.) However, the fact that such an expression for ϕ exists for given problems does not mean that ϕ can be found. The expression ϕ is called a stress function and has been established only for members of relatively simple shapes loaded in particular ways.

It can be shown, by substituting the derivatives of σ_x, σ_y, and τ_{xy} from Eqs. 720 into Eqs. 712 and 713, that the stresses as given by Eqs. 720 will always satisfy the differential equations of equilibrium. But as already pointed out, the stresses σ_x, σ_y, and τ_{xy} must also satisfy Eq. 719 in order to maintain the necessary relationship among the strains in the body. If the expressions for the stresses σ_x, σ_y, and τ_{xy} given in Eqs. 720 are differentiated as required in Eq. 719 and these derivatives are substituted in Eq. 719, the following equation is obtained:

$$\frac{\partial^4\phi}{\partial x^4} + 2\frac{\partial^4\phi}{\partial x^2\,\partial y^2} + \frac{\partial^4\phi}{\partial y^4} = 0 \qquad (721)$$

Equation 721 is interpreted as follows. If a stress function ϕ in x and y can be found which satisfies this equation, the stresses are given by Eqs. 720, provided that Eqs. 720 also gives the values of the normal and shearing stresses which exist at the boundaries of the body. It is often quite easy to find a stress function ϕ that satisfies Eq. 721, but it is difficult to find such a function that will also give the stresses at the boundary of a given body subjected to a given loading. Ordinarily such a procedure is not attempted but rather the opposite procedure is taken, namely, an expression for ϕ which satisfies Eq. 721 is discovered and is then investigated to determine what problem it solves.

Use of Equations of Theory of Elasticity. One of the uses of the above equations is to check a set of formulas for the stresses σ_x, σ_y, and τ_{xy} in order to determine whether or not the conditions set forth by the theory of elasticity are met. The following problem will serve to illustrate this use.

Illustrative Problem

Problem 348. A straight beam has a uniform cross section of width unity and depth $2c$. The beam is subjected to a uniformly distributed load w per unit length over its entire span length l, as indicated in Fig. 338. The following formulas for

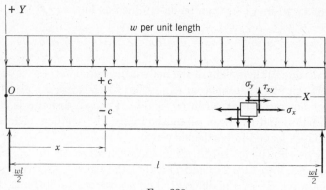

FIG. 338

the stresses in this beam were obtained from Airy's stress function for the beam (see any text on theory of elasticity).

$$\sigma_x = -\left(\frac{wlx}{2} - \frac{wx^2}{2}\right)\frac{3y}{2c^3} - \frac{wy}{10c}\left(5\frac{y^2}{c^2} - 3\right)$$

$$\sigma_y = -w\left(\frac{1}{2} + \frac{3}{4}\frac{y}{c} - \frac{1}{4}\frac{y^3}{c^3}\right)$$

$$\tau_{xy} = -\frac{3}{4c^3}\left(\frac{wl}{2} - wx\right)(c^2 - y^2)$$

Determine whether the stresses given by these expressions satisfy Eqs. 712, 713, and 719 and also whether these expressions give the stresses existing along the upper and lower boundaries of the beam, and determine what kind of support the beam must have at its ends if these formulas give the stresses at the end section of the beam. Note that these expressions for the stresses have dimensions of pounds per inch because the width of the beam has been taken as unity.

Solution. Differential Equations of Equilibrium. The partial derivatives of the stresses needed for substitution in Eqs. 712 and 713 are as follows:

$$\frac{\partial \sigma_x}{\partial x} = -\frac{3y}{2c^3}\left(\frac{wl}{2} - wx\right) \qquad \frac{\partial \tau_{xy}}{\partial y} = +\frac{3y}{2c^3}\left(\frac{wl}{2} - wx\right)$$

$$\frac{\partial \sigma_y}{\partial y} = -\frac{3w}{4c^3}(c^2 - y^2) \qquad \frac{\partial \tau_{xy}}{\partial x} = +\frac{3w}{4c^3}(c^2 - y^2)$$

Thus Eq. 712 is shown to be satisfied as follows:

$$\frac{\partial \sigma_x}{\partial x} + \frac{\partial \tau_{xy}}{\partial y} = -\frac{3y}{2c^3}\left(\frac{wl}{2} - wx\right) + \frac{3y}{2c^3}\left(\frac{wl}{2} - wx\right) = 0$$

Likewise, Eq. 713 is shown to be satisfied as follows:

$$\frac{\partial \sigma_y}{\partial y} + \frac{\partial \tau_{xy}}{\partial x} = -\frac{3w}{4c^3}(c^2 - y^2) + \frac{3w}{4c^3}(c^2 - y^2) = 0$$

Since these two equations are satisfied, it is certain that the formulas for σ_x, σ_y, and τ_{xy} constitute distributions of the stress that satisfy the conditions of equilibrium, but they may not necessarily give the stresses that exist at the boundaries of the beam.

Stresses at the Boundaries of the Beam. It is known that $\sigma_y = -w$ at the upper boundary of the beam (the negative sign indicates compressive stress) and that $\sigma_y = 0$ at the lower boundary of the beam. Also $\tau_{xy} = 0$ at both upper and lower boundaries of the beam. If the values $y = +c$ and $y = -c$ are substituted in the above formulas for σ_y and τ_{xy}, it will be seen that these formulas do give the known values of these stresses at the top and at the bottom of the beam except near the concentrated forces at the supports.

According to the formulas given in the statement of the problem, the stresses at the right end section of the beam are

$$\sigma_x = -\frac{wy}{10c}\left(5\frac{y^2}{c^2} - 3\right) \quad \text{and} \quad \tau_{xy} = +\frac{3wl}{8c^3}(c^2 - y^2)$$

It can be shown by evaluating the integrals $\int_{-c}^{+c} \sigma_x\, da$ and $\int_{-c}^{+c} \sigma_x y\, da$ that the stress σ which the theory gives for any point at the end of the beam will not give a resultant thrust or a resultant moment on the end of the beam, and furthermore from the integral $\int_{-c}^{+c} \tau_{xy}\, da$ it is seen that the shearing stress given by the theory for any point on the end section of the beam results in the vertical shear $wl/2$ at the end of the beam. In other words the supports at the end of the beam must be made up of forces distributed in accordance with the stresses at the ends of the beam as given by the above formulas, the resultant due to these stresses being a vertical force equal to $wl/2$.

The conclusion drawn from the above facts is that, if the beam is simply supported in the customary way, that is, by concentrated reactions, the formulas from the theory of elasticity as set forth in this problem do not give the stresses in the beam in the section at a support; but it is known from St. Venant's principle that these formulas do give the correct stresses in the beam at all sections except those at the supports or within a small distance from the supports.

Equation of Compatibility. The requirement for the compatibility of the strains with one another is stated in terms of the stresses by Eq. 719. The partial derivatives of the stresses needed for substitution in Eq. 719 are as follows:

$$\frac{\partial^2 \sigma_x}{\partial x^2} = +\frac{3wy}{2c^3} \qquad \frac{\partial^2 \sigma_x}{\partial y^2} = -\frac{3wy}{c^3} \qquad \frac{\partial^2 \tau_{xy}}{\partial x\, \partial y} = -\frac{3wy}{2c^3}$$

$$\frac{\partial^2 \sigma_y}{\partial x^2} = 0 \qquad \frac{\partial^2 \sigma_y}{\partial y^2} = +\frac{3wy}{2c^3}$$

Thus, Eq. 719 is shown to be satisfied as follows:

$$-\frac{3wy}{c^3} - \mu\,\frac{3wy}{2c^3} + 0 - \mu\,\frac{3wy}{2c^3} = -2(1+\mu)\,\frac{3wy}{2c^3}$$

or $$-(1+\mu)\,\frac{3wy}{c^3} = -(1+\mu)\,\frac{3wy}{c^3}$$

The fact that Eq. 719 is satisfied by the stresses σ_x, σ_y, and τ_{xy} means that the strains which accompany these stresses are related to each other in such a way that the continuity of the beam is insured.

Comparison of Stresses with Those Obtained by Ordinary Mechanics. A comparison is here made for the longitudinal normal stresses only; that is, the stress $\sigma_x = -My/I$ from the ordinary theory is compared with the stress σ_x from the theory of elasticity as stated in this problem. If it is noted that the bending moment is $M = (wlx/2) - (wx^2/2)$ and the moment of inertia is $I = \frac{2}{3}c^3$, the stress σ_x from the theory of elas-

ticity is $\sigma_x = -\dfrac{My}{I} - \dfrac{wy}{10c}\left(5\dfrac{y^2}{c^2} - 3\right)\cdot$ It thus appears that the term $\dfrac{wy}{10c}\left(5\dfrac{y^2}{c^2} - 3\right)$

constitutes the difference between the longitudinal normal stresses as obtained by the two methods. At the mid-point of the beam where the maximum moment $M_{\max} = \frac{1}{8}wl^2$ occurs, the maximum value of σ_x, as given by ordinary mechanics, is $\sigma_x = Mc/I = \frac{3}{16}wl^2/c^2$, and the above stated difference between this stress and that given by the theory of elasticity is $w/5$. Hence the ratio of difference $w/5$ and the stress $\sigma_x = \frac{3}{16}wl^2/c^2$ as obtained by ordinary mechanics is

$$\frac{\sigma_{\text{difference}}}{\sigma_{\text{ordinary mech.}}} = \frac{w/5}{\frac{3}{16}wl^2/c^2} = \frac{16}{15}\frac{c^2}{l^2} = \frac{4}{15}\left(\frac{d}{l}\right)^2$$

where $d = 2c$ is the depth of the beam. Thus, for example, if the length of the beam is 10 times its depth, the above ratio is $\frac{4}{1500}$ or about $\frac{1}{4}$ of one per cent. Hence it can be observed that for most beams of ordinary proportions subjected to uniformly distributed load the difference between the stresses as obtained by the formula of ordinary mechanics and by the formula of the theory of elasticity is negligible.

195   Essential difference between method of ordinary mechanics and theory of elasticity.

Both methods satisfy the conditions of equilibrium. In the theory of elasticity, the deformations of each element of the body must be such that elastic continuity of the (assumed ideal) material is preserved (except in particular cases when discontinuities, such as tension cracks in reinforced concrete, are permitted according to some arbitrary rule). Most of the complications and difficulties in determining stresses by the theory of elasticity arise out of satisfying this condition of continuity of elastic deformation. In the method of ordinary mechanics, on the other hand, assumptions are made concerning the distributions of the primary strains in the body as a whole so that the main difficulties mentioned above are avoided; the assumptions concerning primary strains in the body, however, are not made arbitrarily but usually are based on measured strains in the members or of models of the members, etc.

Both methods assume that the member is made of (ideal) homogeneous, isotropic material for which there is a definite relation between stress and strain as expressed by Hooke's law, but in the theory of elasticity it is not permissible to make any modifying and simplifying assumptions regarding the strains. In the method of ordinary mechanics the conditions of statics are always satisfied but sometimes the conditions of continuity are not satisfied. Continuity will be maintained by local plastic deformation (yielding), but this does not satisfy the mathematical or elastic continuity required in the theory of elasticity. The failure to satisfy mathematical continuity, however, usually is not serious, for even if the results in some small part of the body are seriously affected the influence of such local action does not extend very far from the local region.

The theory of elasticity is often said to give the exact solution for stresses, whereas the method of ordinary mechanics gives an approximate solution. This statement is correct in relation to the stresses that would occur in the assumed ideal elastic material. But, as pointed out in Art. 193, both methods give only approximately the values of the stresses at any point in an actual physical body. Furthermore, it is important to observe that neither method gives any information as to the significance of stresses in causing failure of the member. But if observation and experiments on a member subjected to loads indicate that a shearing or tensile stress is associated with the failure of the member, both methods may give valuable information for use in design.

One other fact should be emphasized. Since the theory of elasticity gives an exact solution (on the basis of the assumptions made), it is often inferred that the method of ordinary mechanics as applied to actual physical bodies gives values of stresses that are always in error in determining the useful strength of a member whereas the theory of elasticity gives the correct values. If, however, a member is made of material that can yield slightly without affecting appreciably the function of the member in resisting the loads, the useful strength of the member may be indicated by the method of ordinary mechanics more closely than by the theory of elasticity. Both methods are of great value, however, and each method supplements the other.

Appendix II

THE ELASTIC-MEMBRANE (SOAP-FILM) ANALOGY FOR TORSION

196 Purpose of the discussion. In Appendix I the basic ideas and equations involved in the application of the theory of elasticity for determining the stresses in two-dimensional stress problems were discussed. The procedure by the theory of elasticity in solving for the torsional stresses in a prismatic bar involves the development of similar differential equations of equilibrium and the equations of compatibility of strains for triaxial (spatial) states of stress. These equations are obtained by the same general method as was used in obtaining Eqs. 712, 713, and 719 of Appendix I; their development is omitted here, however, since it is not the purpose of this appendix to give a wide range of applications of the theory of elasticity. However, inasmuch as the results of the application of the theory of elasticity to the torsion of a bar, as given by St. Venant, are used in Chapter 9, and furthermore, since the soap-film analogy which is given emphasis in Chapter 9 is based on the results obtained from the theory of elasticity, it seems desirable to discuss briefly St. Venant's method of solving for the stresses in a bar subjected to torsion, without showing how St. Venant developed the method.

197 Torsion stress function. In 1853 St. Venant in his classical memoir on the torsion of prisms showed that, if a bar whose transverse section is not circular is twisted by applying moments at its ends, a plane transverse section *does not* remain a plane section after twisting but becomes a warped surface, and that the shearing stress on any cross section does not vary directly with the distance from the center of the section as is the case for a bar having a constant circular cross section.

The solution of the "torsion problem" may be accomplished by means of a stress function that satisfies the conditions specified in the following paragraphs, for it will be recalled from the discussion in Appendix I that a stress function simply furnishes a means of solving the differential equations of equilibrium and of the equations of compatability. In order to solve these equations for the stresses in a prismatic bar subjected to twisting moments at its ends, a stress function ϕ satisfying the following conditions may be used.

(1) ϕ must be a function of x and y, where x and y are coordinates of any point in the cross sectioh with respect to axes lying in a transverse plane cross section of the bar; furthermore ϕ must have a constant value at every point on the boundary line of the transverse plane cross section. For convenience this constant value at the boundary line is chosen as $\phi = 0$.

(2) The stress function ϕ of x and y must satisfy the equation

$$\partial^2\phi/\partial x^2 + \partial^2\phi/\partial y^2 = -2G\theta \tag{722}$$

where G is the shearing modulus of elasticity and θ is the angle of twist per unit of length of the bar.

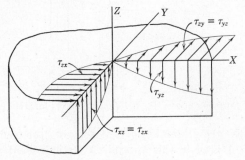

FIG. 339   Distribution of shearing stresses in bar of non-circular cross section.

For a function ϕ in x and y which satisfies the foregoing conditions it has been shown that:

(a) The shearing stresses τ_{zx} and τ_{zy} (see Fig. 339) at any point in the bar are given by the derivatives of ϕ.

$$\tau_{zx} = \partial\phi/\partial y \qquad \tau_{zy} = -\partial\phi/\partial x \tag{723}$$

(b) The volume underneath the surface representing the stress function (see Fig. 340) is proportional to the twisting moment T. This interpretation comes from the fact that in the analysis the equation

$$T = 2\iint \phi\, dx\, dy \tag{724}$$

is obtained in which $\phi\, dx\, dy$ is the element of volume underneath the surface representing the stress function as shown in Fig. 340.

The following important geometrical interpretation of these stresses may be made. In Fig. 340 the values of the function ϕ in x and y are plotted perpendicular to the xy plane at every point (x, y). Thus the upper ends of the ordinates representing the function ϕ in x, and y will lie in a dome-shaped surface which is stretched over the transverse cross section as shown in Fig. 340. The ordinates, ϕ, to the surface at all points (x, y) along the boundary line of the cross section are zero, since this condition is specified under (1) above. (It is this bubble-like surface

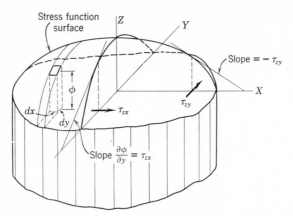

FIG. 340   Surface representing St. Venant's stress function for torsion.

representing the stress function ϕ that suggests the soap-film analogy which is proved later in this appendix.) It is evident therefore from Fig. 340 that the stress $\tau_{zx} = \partial\phi/\partial y$ at any point is represented by the slope of the surface directly above the point in the direction of y, and similarly the shearing stress τ_{zy} is represented by the negative of the slope of the surface in the x direction.

Use of the torsion stress function as described above will now be made in the illustrative problems which follow.

Illustrative Problems

Problem 349. A shaft consisting of a prismatic bar having a constant circular transverse cross section is subjected to a twisting moment T. Find the shearing stresses in the shaft, in terms of T and the dimensions of the cross section of the shaft.

Solution. In order to solve the problem a stress function ϕ in x and y will be found that satisfies conditions 1 and 2. In problems involving torsion the equation of the boundary curve of the cross section of the bar affords a means of establishing the stress function ϕ, since if ϕ is set equal to the equation of the boundary then $\phi = 0$ at every point on the boundary and the first of the two conditions is satisfied. For the circular bar the equation of the boundary of the cross section is $x^2 +$

$y^2 = r^2$, or $x^2 + y^2 - r^2 = 0$. A reasonable guess at the stress function, therefore, is $\phi = C(x^2 + y^2 - r^2)$, where C is a constant, since this function satisfies condition 1, namely, that $\phi = 0$ at every point on the boundary of the cross section. Furthermore, by substitution of this expression for ϕ into Eq. 722 and solving for the constant C the stress function can be made to satisfy the second condition. The proposed function is differentiated partially twice with respect to x and twice with respect to y, and the derivatives are substituted into Eq. 722, giving the equation

$$2C + 2C = -2G\theta$$

and hence

$$C = -\tfrac{1}{2}G\theta$$

Therefore

$$\phi = -\tfrac{1}{2}G\theta(x^2 + y^2 - r^2) \tag{725}$$

satisfies the conditions required of the torsion stress function. The stresses can be obtained immediately by differentiating ϕ, but in order to express the stresses in

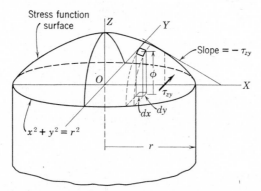

Fig. 341 Surface representing stress function for bar having circular cross section.

terms of the twisting moment and the dimensions of the shaft the term $G\theta$ can be eliminated from Eq. 725 by making use of the condition (Eq. 724) that twice the volume under the surface representing the stress function (see Fig. 341) is equal to the twisting moment. Thus

$$T = 2\iint \phi \, dx \, dy \tag{726}$$

If the expression for ϕ from Eq. 725 is substituted in this integral, we have

$$T = 2\iint -\tfrac{1}{2}G\theta(x^2 + y^2 - r^2) \, dx \, dy \tag{727}$$

$$= -G\theta\left\{ \iint x^2 \, dx \, dy + \iint y^2 \, dx \, dy - r^2 \iint dx \, dy \right\}$$

$$T = -G\theta(I_y + I_x - \pi r^4)$$

Since $J = I_x + I_y = \pi r^4/2$, we have

$$T = -G\theta(J - 2J) = G\theta J$$

and finally

$$G\theta = T/J \quad \text{or} \quad \theta = T/JG \tag{728}$$

Therefore

$$\phi = -\frac{1}{2}\frac{T}{J}(x^2 + y^2 - r^2) \tag{729}$$

The values of ϕ are shown plotted perpendicular to the xy plane in Fig. 341, giving a surface which represents the stress function. The stresses are now obtained by Eq. 723 (i.e., by obtaining the slopes to the surface representing the stress function).

$$\tau_{zx} = \frac{\partial \phi}{\partial y} = -\frac{Ty}{J} \qquad \text{if } y = r, \ \tau_{zx} = -\frac{Tr}{J} \tag{730}$$

$$\tau_{zy} = -\frac{\partial \phi}{\partial x} = \frac{Tx}{J} \qquad \text{if } x = r, \ \tau_{zy} = \frac{Tr}{J} \tag{731}$$

Thus, the stresses obtained by the torsion stress function method are the same as those found by the method of ordinary mechanics for a bar having a circular cross section.

Problem 350. A shaft consisting of a prismatic bar having an elliptical cross section with a major axis of $2h$ and minor axis of $2b$ is subjected to a twisting moment T. Find the shearing stresses in the shaft in the fibers at the ends of the major and minor axes of the cross section.

Solution. The equation of the boundary of the cross section is $(x^2/h^2) + (y^2/b^2) = 1$. Hence a reasonable trial value of the stress function is

$$\phi = C \left(\frac{x^2}{h^2} + \frac{y^2}{b^2} - 1 \right) \tag{732}$$

where C is a constant. This function ϕ is zero at every point along the boundary of the ellipse, and hence it satisfies the first condition for the torsion stress function. If this function ϕ, Eq. 732, is differentiated and the derivatives substituted into the equation $(\partial^2 \phi / \partial x^2) + (\partial^2 \phi / \partial y^2) = -2G\theta$, we have

$$\frac{2C}{h^2} + \frac{2C}{b^2} = -2G\theta \qquad \text{or} \qquad C = -\frac{h^2 b^2}{h^2 + b^2} G\theta \tag{733}$$

This value of the constant C is substituted in the expression for ϕ, thereby giving the expression

$$\phi = -\frac{h^2 b^2}{h^2 + b^2} G\theta \left(\frac{x^2}{h^2} + \frac{y^2}{b^2} - 1 \right) \tag{734}$$

which is a stress function that satisfies both conditions required by the torsion stress function. The constant $G\theta$ can be expressed in terms of the twisting moment T and the dimensions of the shaft by means of the equation involving the volume V underneath the stress function surface, namely,

$$T = 2V = 2 \iint \phi \, dx \, dy \tag{735}$$

If the expression for ϕ from Eq. 734 is substituted in this integral, we have

$$T = 2 \iint -\frac{h^2 b^2}{h^2 + b^2} G\theta \left(\frac{x^2}{h^2} + \frac{y^2}{b^2} - 1 \right) dx \, dy \tag{736}$$

$$= -\frac{2h^2 b^2}{h^2 + b^2} G\theta \left(\frac{1}{h^2} \iint x^2 \, dx \, dy + \frac{1}{b^2} \iint y^2 \, dx \, dy - \iint dx \, dy \right)$$

$$= -\frac{2h^2 b^2}{h^2 + b^2} G\theta \left(\frac{I_y}{h^2} + \frac{I_x}{b^2} - a \right)$$

But since for the ellipse $I_x = \pi h b^3/4$, $I_y = \pi b h^3/4$, $a = \pi h b$, we have

$$T = -\frac{2h^2b^2}{h^2+b^2} G\theta \left(-\frac{1}{2}\pi h b \right) \tag{737}$$

Hence
$$G\theta = \frac{(h^2+b^2)}{\pi h^3 b^3} T \quad \text{or} \quad \theta = \frac{h^2+b^2}{\pi h^3 b^3} \frac{T}{G} \tag{738}$$

Therefore by substituting the value of $G\theta$ from Eq. 738 in Eq. 734 the stress function is

$$\phi = -\frac{T}{\pi h b} \left(\frac{x^2}{h^2} + \frac{y^2}{b^2} - 1 \right) \tag{739}$$

The stresses are now obtained by the use of Eq. 723.

$$\tau_{zx} = \partial\phi/\partial y = -2Ty/\pi h b^3 \quad \text{for } y = b, \ \tau_{zx} = -2T/\pi h b^2 \tag{740}$$

$$\tau_{zy} = -\partial\phi/\partial x = +2Tx/\pi h^3 b \quad \text{for } x = h, \ \tau_{zy} = +2T/\pi h^2 b \tag{741}$$

From these results it will be observed that the shearing stress $\tau_{zx} = -2T/\pi h b^2$ at the end of the minor axis (nearest to the axis of twist) is larger numerically than the shearing stress $\tau_{zy} = 2T/\pi h^2 b$ at the end of the major axis (farthest from the twisting axis), since $h > b$ and hence $h^2 b > h b^2$. This fact shows that the stress has its maximum value on the circumference nearest to the axis of the shaft instead of farthest from the center of the shaft as occurs in a shaft having a circular cross section.

198 The elastic-membrane (soap-film) analogy for solid sections. It was shown in the preceding article that the torsional stress function used for determining the stresses in a prismatic bar subjected to a twisting moment can be represented as a surface over a transverse cross section of the bar. It was pointed out that the slope of this surface at any point in any direction x represents the magnitude of the shearing stress in the y direction at a point directly below on the transverse cross section. Furthermore, it was observed that the volume included between the surface representing the stress function and the transverse cross section over which the surface lies is equal to one-half the twisting moment applied to the bar. With these facts as a background, the soap-film analogy is presented in the following paragraphs.

Prandtl showed that, if an elastic membrane, such as a soap film, is stretched over an opening which has the same shape as the cross section of the bar and is subjected to a small difference of pressure on its two sides, the differential equation of this deflected (bubble-like) soap film has the same form as the differential equation (see Eq. 722) of the stress function. From this fact it follows that the soap film offers a means of actually constructing the stress function surface for any kind of a solid cross section. This analogy will now be proved. (The analogy does not apply directly to hollow bars as will be shown in the next article.)

Proof of the Soap-film Analogy. Consider a soap film to be stretched over an opening such as shown in Fig. 342a and deflected by small amounts z by a pressure p as shown in Fig. 342b. The proof of the analogy is obtained by writing one of the equations of equilibrium for the forces which act on an element of the soap film of dimensions dx and dy, namely, $\Sigma F_z = 0$. A free-body diagram of such an element is shown in Figs. 342a and 342b. The tensile force S per unit length in the soap film is assumed to be the same at all points and in all directions. It is also assumed that the total tensile force acting on the

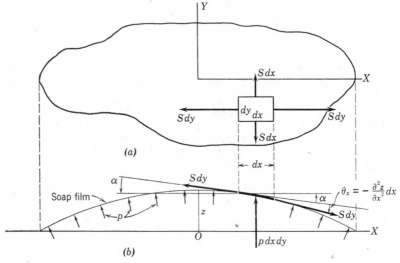

FIG. 342   Forces acting on differential element of elastic membrane (soap film).

element along the dy edges is $S\,dy$ and the total tensile force acting along the dx edges is $S\,dx$. These assumptions are valid for small deflections of the soap film.

Consider first the vertical components of the forces $S\,dy$ in Fig. 342b. The $S\,dy$ force at the left edge of the element acts tangent to the surface and makes the angle α with the X axis. The $S\,dy$ force at the right edge acts tangent to the surface and makes the angle $(\alpha + \theta_x)$ with the X axis, where $\theta_x = -(\partial^2 z/\partial x^2)dx$; $\partial^2 z/\partial x^2$ is the rate of change in slope, along the dx dimension of the element and is considered to remain constant over the length dx. The sum of the vertical components of these two $S\,dy$ forces is therefore

$$S\,dy \sin \alpha - S\,dy \sin (\alpha + \theta_x) = S\,dy\,\alpha - S\,dy\,(\alpha + \theta_x)$$

$$= -S\,dy\,\theta_x = S\,\frac{\partial^2 z}{\partial x^2}\,dx\,dy$$

since the angles α and $(\alpha + \theta_x)$ are small.

In a similar manner it can be shown that the sum of the vertical components of the two $S\,dx$ forces acting on the element is $S(\partial^2 z/\partial y^2)\,dx\,dy$.

The only other vertical component which acts on the element is that due to the pressure p, and this component may be taken approximately as $p\,dx\,dy$.

The above vertical components of the forces acting on the element are now substituted in the equilibrium equation.

$$\Sigma F_z = +S\frac{\partial^2 z}{\partial x^2}\,dx\,dy + S\frac{\partial^2 z}{\partial y^2}\,dx\,dy + p\,dx\,dy = 0 \qquad (742)$$

If Eq. 742 is divided by $S\,dx\,dy$, we obtain the equation

$$\partial^2 z/\partial x^2 + \partial^2 z/\partial y^2 = -p/S \qquad (743)$$

Equation 743 is the differential equation of the soap film and has the same form as the differential equation of the torsion stress function as given by Eq. 722. Table 25 shows a list of the properties of the soap-film surface and the stress function surface that are analogous.

TABLE 25

PROPERTIES SHOWING THE ANALOGY BETWEEN THE SOAP-FILM SURFACE AND THE SURFACE REPRESENTING THE TORSION STRESS FUNCTION

Properties of Soap Film and Stress Function Which Are Analogous	Torsion Stress Function	Soap Film
Differential equations of the surfaces	$\dfrac{\partial^2 \phi}{\partial x^2} + \dfrac{\partial^2 \phi}{\partial y^2} = -2G\theta$	$\dfrac{\partial^2 z}{\partial x^2} + \dfrac{\partial^2 z}{\partial y^2} = -\dfrac{p}{S}$
Values of function at boundary of section	$\phi = 0$ along boundary of section.	$z = 0$ along boundary of opening.
Slopes of surfaces in x and y directions	Slope in x direction = $+\partial\phi/\partial x$ = −stress in y direction. Slope in y direction = $\partial\phi/\partial y$ = stress in x direction.	Slope in x direction = $+\partial z/\partial x$ is proportional to stress in y direction; slope in y direction = $\partial z/\partial y$ is proportional to stress in x direction.
The volumes under the surfaces	The volume under the stress function surface is $$\iint \phi\,dx\,dy = T/2$$ where T is the twisting moment in the bar.	The volume under the soap film is $\iint z\,dx\,dy$ and is proportional to one-half the twisting moment.

The foregoing discussion forms the basis for the use of the soap-film analogy as employed in Chapter 9 in determining the torsional resistance of bars having solid cross section.

199 Torsional resistance of hollow thin-walled tubes. In Art. 197 of this appendix a rather brief discussion was given of the analysis of the torsional resistance of a prismatic bar of solid cross section. The analysis of the resistance of a hollow prismatic bar requires further consideration.

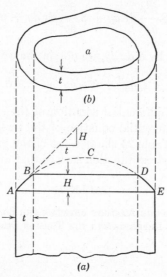

FIG. 343   Membrane (soap-film) analogy for torsion of hollow cylinder.

Let Fig. 343a represent a hollow bar whose cross section is shown in Fig. 343b. According to the analysis for solid bars, if the bar in Fig. 343 had a solid cross section a stress function would have to be found which satisfies the two equations

$$\partial^2\phi/\partial x^2 + \partial^2\phi/\partial y^2 = -2G\theta \tag{744}$$

and $\phi = 0$ along the outside boundary of the cross section   (745)

In Fig. 343a let the arc $ABCDE$ be a cross section of the surface representing the function ϕ for the hollow bar. Since the bar is hollow, the surface BCD extending over the hollow portion can have no physical significance since the stresses here are zero, i.e., do not exist. Hence, the surface BCD must be replaced by a surface which has a slope of zero everywhere over the hollow portion; such a surface is represented by the plane BD whose distance above the cross section is H. The surface representing the stress function ϕ is, therefore, $ABDE$. The same use can now be made of the stress function represented by the surface $ABDE$ in solving the problem of the torsional resistance of a hollow bar as was made of the function ϕ in Art. 197 for the solid bar. These uses are as follows.

(a) The twisting moment T to which the hollow bar is subjected is equal to twice the volume underneath the surface $ABDE$, and is, therefore, approximately, given by the equation

$$T = 2aH \tag{746}$$

where a is approximately the inside area of the hollow section (or, area within mean perimeter) and H is the height of the plane BD above the cross section, *provided that the hollow bar has a relatively thin wall.*

(b) The slope of the surface at any point is equal to the stress in the bar in a direction perpendicular to the direction in which the slope is taken. Hence, if the wall of the hollow bar is relatively thin, the slope at any point along the arcs AB or DE may be taken without serious error as H/t, where t is the wall thickness of the section. The maximum shearing stress in the hollow bar at any point is, therefore,

$$\tau = H/t \tag{747}$$

where the distance H may be obtained from Eq. 746.

(c) Since there is in the hollow bar an inside boundary in addition to the outside boundary, a condition must be added so that the boundary condition on the inside is satisfied. This condition is that

$$\int \tau \, dl = 2G\theta a \tag{748}$$

in which the integration extends around the inside boundary; τ is the stress tangent to the inside boundary, dl is an element of length of the inside boundary, θ is the angle of twist per unit of length, and a is the area of the hollow portion. The proof that Eq. 748 is the inside boundary condition that must be satisfied is not within the scope of this appendix. Since $\tau = H/t$, Eq. 748 is rewritten

$$(H/2a)\int (dl/t) = G\theta \tag{749}$$

If the wall thickness t is constant, Eq. 749 can be written

$$(H/2a)(l/t) = G\theta \tag{750}$$

where l represents the circumference of the inside boundary of the thin-walled section.

The preceding method of determining the torsional resistance of hollow thin-walled tubes is employed in Chapter 9 where several illustrative problems are given.

Soap-film Analogy for Hollow Bars. From the foregoing analysis for the torsional shearing stresses in a hollow bar, it can be shown that the soap-film analogy can be made to apply to bars having hollow cross sections provided that the opening representing the cross section has the central portion or inside boundary of the opening raised a distance H above the outside boundary of the opening, somewhat as the plane BD in Fig. 343 is raised a distance H above the cross section. It is very inconvenient to use the soap-film analogy as an experimental method of determining stresses in a hollow bar due to the difficulties in maintaining the flat plate representing the inner boundary at the proper distance above the outside boundary of the opening over which the soap film is stretched.

Appendix III

PROPERTIES OF AN AREA

§ 1 Product of Inertia and Principal Moments of Inertia.

200 Introduction. In the problems considered in this book there are certain properties of areas that are needed, such as the location of the centroid; the first moment of the area and the second moment or moment of inertia of the area with respect to an axis either perpendicular to the area or lying in the plane of the area; the product of inertia of the area with respect to a set of perpendicular axes lying in the area; and the value of the property Z for use in Winkler-Bach's formula for the stresses in curved beams (Art. 48).

The first three properties, namely, centroids, first moments, and moments of inertia of areas, are discussed in books on elementary mechanics and therefore will not be considered in this appendix. However, the product of inertia of an area is not discussed in many elementary texts, and hence it will be considered in the following articles. One important use of product of inertia is in determining moments of inertia of an area about unsymmetrical axes, and hence these two properties of an area are closely related.

Product of Inertia Defined. If the moments of inertia of an area a with respect to any two rectangular axes are known, the moment of inertia with respect to any other axis through the point of intersection of the two axes may frequently be obtained most easily in terms of the moments of inertia of the area with respect to the two rectangular axes and an expression of the form $\int xy\, da$, in which da is an element of the given area and x and y are the coordinates of the element with respect to the two rectangular axes. This expression is called the *product of inertia* of the area with respect to the axes and is denoted by I_{xy}. Hence the product of inertia of an area with respect to any two rectangular

649

axes may be defined as the sum of the products obtained by multiplying each element of area by the product of the two coordinates of the element with respect to the two rectangular axes. That is,

$$I_{xy} = \int xy \, da \tag{751}$$

The product of inertia of an area, like the moment of inertia of an area, is of four dimensions in length and is, therefore, expressed as inches (or feet, etc.) to the fourth power (in.^{4}, ft.^{4}, etc.). Unlike moment of inertia, however, the product of inertia of an area is not always positive, but may be negative or may be zero, since either x or y may be negative and hence their product may be negative, and the sum of the products may be equal to zero.

Axes of Symmetry. The product of inertia of an area with respect to two rectangular axes is zero if either one of the axes is an axis of symmetry. This follows from the fact that, for each product $xy \, da$ for an element on one side of the axis of symmetry, there is an equal product of opposite sign for the corresponding element on the other side of the axis, and hence the expression $\int xy \, da$ equals zero.

Illustrative Problems

Problem 351. Find the product of inertia of the area of the triangle, shown in Fig. 344, with respect to the X and Y axes.

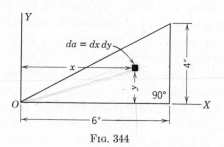

Fig. 344

Solution.

$$I_{xy} = \int xy \, da = \int_0^6 \int_0^{\frac{2}{3}x} xy \, dx \, dy$$

$$= \frac{2}{9} \int_0^6 x^3 \, dx = 72 \text{ in.}^4$$

Problem 352. Find the product of inertia of the area of the quadrant of a circular area (Fig. 345) with respect to the X and Y axes, in terms of its radius r.

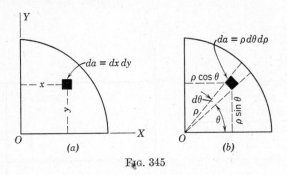

F$\mathbf{I}$G. 345

First Method. Let the elementary area be selected as shown in Fig. 345a and expressed in terms of rectangular coordinates; then

$$I_{xy} = \int_0^r \int_0^{\sqrt{r^2-x^2}} xy \, dx \, dy = \int_0^r x \left[\frac{y^2}{2} \right]_0^{\sqrt{r^2-x^2}} dx$$

$$= \int_0^r x \cdot \frac{r^2 - x^2}{2} \, dx = \frac{1}{2} \int_0^r (r^2 x - x^3) \, dx$$

$$= \frac{1}{2} \left[\frac{r^2 x^2}{2} - \frac{x^4}{4} \right]_0^r = \frac{1}{8} r^4$$

Second Method. Let the elementary area be selected as shown in Fig. 345b and be expressed in terms of polar coordinates; then

$$I_{xy} = \int xy \, da = \int_0^r \int_0^{\pi/2} \rho \cos \theta \cdot \rho \sin \theta \cdot \rho \, d\rho \, d\theta$$

$$= \int_0^r \int_0^{\pi/2} \rho^3 \, d\rho \cdot \frac{1}{2} \sin 2\theta \, d\theta$$

$$= \frac{1}{2} \frac{r^4}{4} \int_0^{\pi/2} \sin 2\theta \, d\theta = \frac{r^4}{8} \left[- \cos 2\theta \cdot \frac{1}{2} \right]_0^{\pi/2}$$

$$= - \frac{r^4}{16} (-2) = \frac{1}{8} r^4$$

Problems

353. Find the product of inertia of the area of a rectangle having a base b and an altitude h, with respect to two adjacent sides.   *Ans.* $I_{xy} = \pm \frac{1}{4} b^2 h^2$.

354. Find the product of inertia of a right-angle triangle (Fig. 346) with respect to the X and Y axes shown, the X axis being a centroidal axis.

Ans. $I_{xy} = -\frac{1}{72}b^2h^2 = -32$ in.^{4}

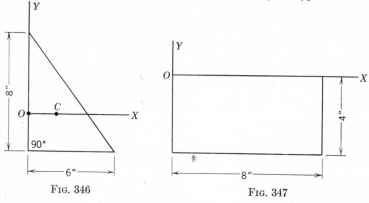

FIG. 346   FIG. 347

355. Find the product of inertia of the rectangular area with respect to the X and Y axes as shown in Fig. 347.

356. Find the product of inertia, with respect to the coordinate axes, of the area bounded by the parabola $y^2 = hx$, the line $x = b$, and the X axis.

Ans. $I_{xy} = \frac{1}{6}hb^3$.

201   Parallel axis theorem for products of inertia.

When the product of inertia of an area is known for any pair of rectangular axes passing through the centroid of the area, the product of inertia of the area with respect to any parallel set of axes may be determined without integrating. Thus, in Fig. 348, $X'X'$ and $Y'Y'$ are axes through the

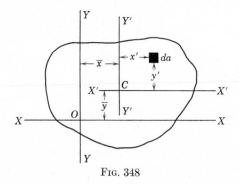

FIG. 348

centroid C of the area; XX and YY are parallel axes passing through the point O. The coordinates of C with respect to XX and YY are denoted by $\bar{x}$ and $\bar{y}$. If the product of inertia of the area with respect to XX and YY be denoted by I_{xy} and the product of inertia with respect to $X'X'$ and $Y'Y'$ be denoted by $\bar{I}_{xy}$, then, by definition,

$$I_{xy} = \int (x' + \bar{x})(y' + \bar{y}) \, da$$

$$= \int x'y' \, da + \overline{xy} \int da + \bar{y} \int x' \, da + \bar{x} \int y' \, da$$

Since each of the last two integrals is the first moment of the area with respect to a centroidal axis, each integral is equal to zero. The equation then becomes,

$$I_{xy} = \bar{I}_{xy} + a\overline{xy} \qquad (752)$$

That is, the product of inertia of any area with respect to any pair of rectangular axes in its plane is equal to the product of inertia of the area with respect to a pair of parallel centroidal axes plus the product of the area and the coordinates of the centroid of the area with respect to the given pair of axes.

Illustrative Problem

Problem 357. Find the product of inertia of the area shown in Fig. 349 with respect to the X and Y axes.

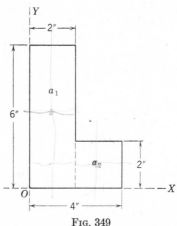

FIG. 349

Solution. The area may be divided into rectangles a_1 and a_2 as shown. Using Eq. 752 we have, for the area a_1,

$$I_{xy} = 0 + 12 \times 1 \times 3 = 36 \text{ in.}^4$$

and for area a_2,

$$I_{xy} = 0 + 4 \times 3 \times 1 = 12 \text{ in.}^4$$

Hence, for the entire area,

$$I_{xy} = 36 + 12 = 48 \text{ in.}^4$$

Problems

358. Find the product of inertia of the area shown in Fig. 350 with respect to the X and Y axes.　　　　　　　　　　　　　　　　*Ans.* $I_{xy} = 561$ in.[4]

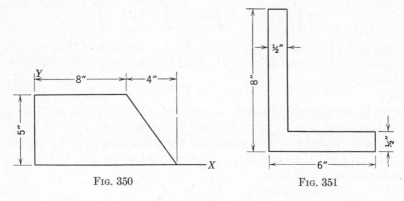

FIG. 350　　　　　　　　　　　　　　FIG. 351

359. Locate the centroid of the angle section shown in Fig. 351, and determine the product of inertia with respect to centroidal axes parallel to the two legs of the angle.

202　Relation between moments of inertia and products of inertia. Let I_x, I_y, I_{xy} denote the moments of inertia and the product of inertia of the area in Fig. 352 with respect to the axes OX and OY. Let it be required to find the moments of inertia, I'_x and I'_y, and the product of inertia, I'_{xy}, with respect to the axes OX' and OY' which are

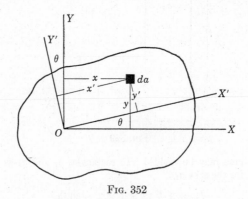

FIG. 352

inclined an angle θ with the axes OX and OY. The moment of inertia of the area in Fig. 352 with respect to the axis OX' is expressed by the equation

$$I'_x = \int y'^2 \, da = \int (y \cos \theta - x \sin \theta)^2 \, da$$

$$= \cos^2 \theta \int y^2 \, da + \sin^2 \theta \int x^2 \, da - 2 \sin \theta \cos \theta \int xy \, da$$

$$= I_x \cos^2 \theta + I_y \sin^2 \theta - 2I_{xy} \sin \theta \cos \theta \tag{753}$$

In a similar manner Eq. 754 may be derived.

$$I'_y = I_x \sin^2 \theta + I_y \cos^2 \theta + 2I_{xy} \sin \theta \cos \theta \tag{754}$$

Likewise

$$I'_{xy} = \int x'y' \, da = \int (x \cos \theta + y \sin \theta)(y \cos \theta - x \sin \theta) \, da$$

$$= (\cos^2 \theta - \sin^2 \theta) \int xy \, da + (\cos \theta \sin \theta) \int (y^2 - x^2) \, da$$

$$= I_{xy} \cos 2\theta + \tfrac{1}{2}(I_x - I_y) \sin 2\theta \tag{755}$$

Thus from Eqs. 753, 754, and 755, the moments of inertia and product of inertia of an area with respect to any set of rectangular axes may be found, without integrating, in terms of the moments of inertia and product of inertia with respect to a given set of rectangular axes passing through the same origin.

By adding Eqs. 753 and 754, the following important equation is found:

$$I'_x + I'_y = I_x + I_y \tag{756}$$

That is, the sum of the moments of inertia of an area with respect to all pairs of rectangular axes having a common point of intersection is constant. It should be noted also that each side of Eq. 756 is equal to the polar moment of inertia of the area with respect to an axis intersecting the area at the common point.

Axes for Which the Product of Inertia Is Zero. It may be shown that through any point in an area one set of rectangular axes may be drawn for which the product of inertia is zero. Thus, in Eq. 755, if I'_{xy} is made equal to zero, we obtain the equation

$$\tan 2\theta = - \frac{I_{xy}}{\tfrac{1}{2}(I_x - I_y)} \tag{757}$$

and hence, when θ (Fig. 352) has a value given by this equation, the product of inertia with respect to the OX' and OY' axes is zero; in the next article it will be shown that the axes for which the product of inertia is zero are principal axes.

203 Principal axes. In the analysis of many engineering problems the moment of inertia of an area must be found with respect to a certain axis called a principal axis. A principal axis of inertia of an area, for a given point in the area, is an axis about which the moment of inertia of the area is either greater or less than for any other axis passing through the given point. It can be proved that through any point in an area two rectangular axes can be drawn for which the moments of inertia of the area are greater and less, respectively, than for any other axes through the point. There are then two principal axes of inertia of an area for any point in the area. Further, it can be shown that axes for which the product of inertia is zero are principal axes. And since the product of inertia of an area is zero for axes of symmetry, it follows that axes of symmetry are principal axes. The above statements may be demonstrated as follows.

The direction of the principal axes may be determined from Eq. 753, which may be written in the form

$$I'_x = I_x \frac{1 + \cos 2\theta}{2} + I_y \frac{1 - \cos 2\theta}{2} - I_{xy} \sin 2\theta$$

$$= \frac{I_x + I_y}{2} + \frac{I_x - I_y}{2} \cos 2\theta - I_{xy} \sin 2\theta \qquad (758)$$

The value of θ which will make I'_x have a maximum or a minimum value may be found by equating to zero the first derivative of I'_x with respect to θ. Thus,

$$dI'_x/d\theta = \sin 2\theta (I_y - I_x) - 2I_{xy} \cos 2\theta = 0$$

Hence,

$$\tan 2\theta = 2I_{xy}/(I_y - I_x) \qquad (759)$$

which is the same as Eq. 757. From this equation two values of 2θ are obtained which differ by 180°, the corresponding values of θ differing by 90°. For one value of θ the value of I'_x will be a maximum, and for the other, a minimum. If $I_{xy} = 0$ (which will always be the case if either the X or Y axis is an axis of symmetry), the value of θ is zero, and hence axes of symmetry are principal axes.

Illustrative Problem

Problem 360. Find the moments of inertia of the angle section, shown in Fig. 353, with respect to principal axes passing through the centroid.

Solution. The steps in the solution will be made as follows:

(a) The centroid of the area will be located, that is, $\bar{x}$ and $\bar{y}$ will be found.

(b) The moments of inertia and the product of inertia ($\bar{I}_x$, $\bar{I}_y$, and $\bar{I}_{xy}$) with respect to the centroidal X and Y axis will then be found by the methods discussed in Art. 200.

(c) The directions of the principal axes will then be found by the equations of Art. 203.

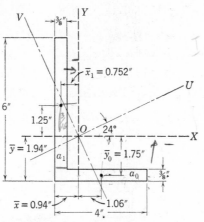

FIG. 353

(d) The moment of inertia with respect to each of the principal axes, U and V, will then be found by means of Eqs. 753 and 754 of Art. 202.

$$\bar{x} = \frac{4 \times \frac{3}{8} \times 2 + 5\frac{5}{8} \times \frac{3}{8} \times \frac{3}{16}}{4 \times \frac{3}{8} + 5\frac{5}{8} \times \frac{3}{8}} = \frac{3.396}{3.61} = 0.94 \text{ in.}$$

$$\bar{y} = \frac{4 \times \frac{3}{8} \times \frac{3}{16} + 5\frac{5}{8} \times \frac{3}{8} \times 3\frac{3}{16}}{4 \times \frac{3}{8} + 5\frac{5}{8} \times \frac{3}{8}} = \frac{7.01}{3.61} = 1.94 \text{ in.}$$

$$\bar{I}_x = \tfrac{1}{12} \times \tfrac{3}{8} \times (5\tfrac{5}{8})^3 + 5\tfrac{5}{8} \times \tfrac{3}{8} \times (1\tfrac{1}{4})^2 + \tfrac{1}{12} \times 4 \times (\tfrac{3}{8})^3 + 4 \times \tfrac{3}{8} \times (1\tfrac{3}{4})^2$$

$$= 5.57 + 3.30 + 0.02 + 4.59 = 13.48 \text{ in.}^4$$

$$\bar{I}_y = \tfrac{1}{12} \times 5\tfrac{5}{8} \times (\tfrac{3}{8})^3 + 5\tfrac{5}{8} \times \tfrac{3}{8} \times (\tfrac{3}{4})^2 + \tfrac{1}{12} \times \tfrac{3}{8} \times 4^3 + 4 \times \tfrac{3}{8} \times (1\tfrac{1}{16})^2$$

$$= 0.02 + 1.19 + 2.00 + 1.69 = 4.90 \text{ in.}^4$$

The value of $\bar{I}_{xy}$ may be found by means of the formula in Art. 201. Thus,

$$\bar{I}_{xy} = \bar{I}_{0xy} + a_0\bar{x}_0\bar{y}_0 + \bar{I}_{1xy} + a_1\bar{x}_1\bar{y}_1$$

$$= 4 \times \tfrac{3}{8} \times 1.06 \times (-1.75) + 5.62 \times \tfrac{3}{8} \times 1.25 \times (-0.752) = -4.76 \text{ in.}^4$$

The directions of the principal axes are found from the formula of Art. 203. Thus,

$$\tan 2\theta = \frac{2 \times (-4.76)}{4.90 - 13.48} = 1.11$$

$$2\theta = 48° \text{ or } 228° \qquad \theta = 24° \text{ or } 114°$$

From the formula of Art. 202, the moment of inertia with respect to the axis making an angle of 24° with OX (denoted by U) is

$$I_u = 13.48 \cos^2 24° + 4.90 \sin^2 24° - 2(-4.76) \sin 24° \cos 24°$$

$$= 11.23 + 0.81 + 3.53 = 15.59 \text{ in.}^4$$

Using $\theta = 114°$ and denoting the corresponding axis by V, we have,

$$I_v = 13.48 \cos^2 114° + 4.90 \sin^2 114° - 2(-4.76) \sin 114° \cos 114°$$

$$= 2.23 + 4.08 - 3.53 = 2.78 \text{ in.}^4$$

Problems

361. In the Z section shown in Fig. 354, $\bar{I}_x = 25.32$ in.^{4} and $\bar{I}_y = 9.11$ in.^{4} Find the principal moments of inertia for axes through the centroid.

Ans. $I_u = 3.10$ in.^{4}; $I_v = 31.3$ in.^{4}

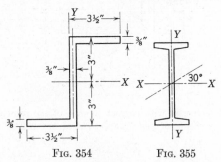

FIG. 354   FIG. 355

362. Show that the moment of inertia of the area of a square is constant for all axes in the plane of the area which pass through the center.

363. Figure 355 represents the cross section of a standard 10-in. 25-lb I beam. $\bar{I}_x = 122.1$ in.^{4}, $\bar{I}_y = 6.89$ in.^{4}, and $a = 7.37$ in.^{2} Find the moment of inertia and the radius of gyration of the section with respect to a line making an angle of 30° with the x-axis.

204 Graphical Solution for Moments of Inertia. Let the moments of inertia I_x and I_y and the product of inertia I_{xy} of an area with respect to a given set of rectangular axes, OX and OY, in the area be known (Fig. 352); and let it be required to find the moments of inertia I'_x and I'_y and the product of inertia I'_{xy}, with respect to another set of rectangular axes OX' and OY' passing through the same point in the area, in terms of the known values I_x, I_y, I_{xy}, and the angle θ between the axes OX and OX'.

Equations 753, 754, and 755 give the algebraic expressions for I'_x, I'_y, and I'_{xy}, and it will now be shown that the equations may be solved graphically; two graphical solutions are given.

Muller-Breslau Construction. In Fig. 356, let OA be laid off to represent I_y and OB to represent I_x (it is assumed that $I_x > I_y$); also let

BC be laid off equal to I_y. At A let a perpendicular AD be erected equal to I_{xy}; if I_{xy} is positive, AD is laid off upwards; if negative, it is laid off downwards. At B also erect a perpendicular BD_1, equal but opposite to AD. With DD_1 as a diameter, draw a circle. Through D draw a line parallel to the axis OX' cutting the circle at the point E.

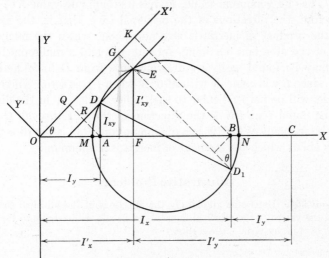

Fig. 356   Muller-Breslau construction.

From E drop a perpendicular on the axis OX intersecting the axis at F. Then

$$OF = I'_x, \quad FC = I'_y \quad \text{and} \quad FE = I'_{xy}$$

Proof.

$$OF = OG \cos \theta + EG \sin \theta$$

and

$$FE = OG \sin \theta - EG \cos \theta$$

but

$$OG = OK - KG = OK - DR$$
$$= I_x \cos \theta - I_{xy} \sin \theta$$

and

$$EG = AQ - AR$$
$$= I_y \sin \theta - I_{xy} \cos \theta$$

hence

$$OF = I_x \cos^2 \theta + I_y \sin^2 \theta - I_{xy} \sin 2\theta$$

and

$$FE = \tfrac{1}{2}(I_x - I_y) \sin 2\theta + I_{xy} \cos 2\theta$$

Hence (see Eqs. 753 and 755)

$$OF = I'_x \quad \text{and} \quad FE = I'_{xy}$$

Now from Eq. 754 $I'_x + I'_y = I_x + I_y$

hence $FC = I'_y$

Principal Axes and Principal Moments of Inertia. From the graphical construction in Fig. 356, it will be noted that OM is the minimum value of I'_x and ON is the maximum value, and that in each case the line EF vanishes and hence I'_{xy} becomes zero. Further, when I'_x has its minimum value, I'_y has its maximum value MC (which is equal to ON); and when I'_x has its maximum value, I'_y has its minimum value NC.

Therefore, the directions of the principal axes, that is, the axes for which the product of inertia is zero and about which the moment of inertia of the area is a maximum for one axis and a minimum for the other, may be found easily by drawing lines from D to M and from D to N, since E will coincide with M or N when I'_{xy} is zero. These lines, of course, will be perpendicular to each other. Also, from the diagram it will be noted that DN is the direction of the axis through O about which the moment of inertia is a maximum and DM is the direction of the axis about which the moment of inertia is a minimum.

Illustrative Problem

Problem 364. Determine graphically the directions of the principal centroidal axes and the values of the principal moments of inertia with respect to these axes of a 6-in. by 4-in. by ⅜-in. angle section.

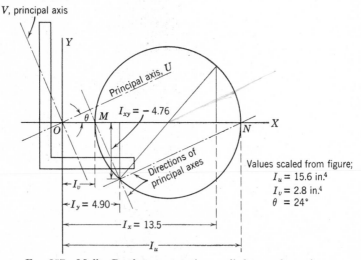

Fig. 357   Muller-Breslau construction applied to angle section.

Solution. From Prob. 360 we have

$$\bar{I}_x = 13.5 \text{ in.}^4 \qquad \bar{I}_y = 4.90 \text{ in.}^4 \qquad \bar{I}_{xy} = -4.76 \text{ in.}^4$$

Figure 357 shows the constructions from which the following values are obtained:

$$I_u = 15.6 \text{ in.}^4 \qquad I_v = 2.8 \text{ in.}^4 \qquad \theta = 24°$$

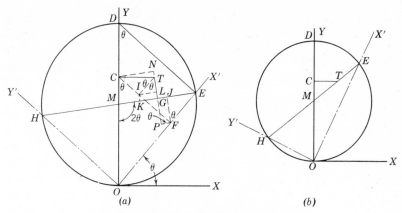

FIG. 358   Mohr-Land construction.

Mohr-Land Construction. This construction is sometimes called the Dyadic circle. Figure 358a is constructed as follows:

(a) On OY lay off $OC = I_x$ and $CD = I_y$; $I_x > I_y$.

(b) Lay off $CT = I_{xy}$ parallel to OX(+ to right, − to left).

(c) On OD as a diameter draw a circle; M is the center.

(d) Draw OX' making the given angle θ with OX, cutting the circle at E.

(e) Draw the diameter EH and draw TG perpendicular to EH.

Then $TG = I'_{xy}$ $EG = I'_x$ $HG = I'_y$

Proof. Draw CF and $DE \perp OE$; $TI \perp CF$; FJ and $IK \perp HE$; IL, CN, and $FP \perp$ to TG.

Then $\angle CFP = \angle ODE = \angle OCF = \angle ITC = \angle ITL = \angle JFE = \theta$

$$\angle OCN = \angle OME = 2\theta \text{ and } \angle CTN = 180° - 2\theta$$

$$GE = JK + JE - GK$$

$$JK = FI \sin \angle CFJ = FI \cos \angle CFP = (CF - IC) \cos \theta$$

$$= (I_x \cos \theta - I_{xy} \sin \theta) \cos \theta$$

$$JE = FE \sin \angle JFE = I_y \sin^2 \theta$$

$$GK = IL = CT \cos \theta \sin \theta = I_{xy} \sin \theta \cos \theta$$

Therefore $GE = I_x \cos^2 \theta + I_y \sin^2 \theta - 2I_{xy} \sin \theta \cos \theta = I'_x$

Also $\qquad GH = HE - GE = OD - GE = I_x + I_y - I'_x = I'_y$
(see Eq. 756)

$$TG = NP - NT - PG$$

$$NP = CF \sin \angle FCN = I_x \cos \theta \sin \theta$$

$$NT = CT \cos \angle CTN = CT \cos (180° - 2\theta) = -CT \cos 2\theta$$

$$= -I_{xy} \cos 2\theta$$

$$PG = FJ = FE \cos \angle JFE = I_y \cos \theta \sin \theta$$

$$TG = \tfrac{1}{2} I_x \sin 2\theta + I_{xy} \cos 2\theta - \tfrac{1}{2} I_y \sin 2\theta$$

$$= \tfrac{1}{2}(I_x - I_y) \sin 2\theta + I_{xy} \cos 2\theta = I'_{xy}$$

Principal Axes and Principal Moments of Inertia. Draw a diameter *HE* through *T* (Fig. 358*b*), thus making $I'_{xy} = 0$ (see Art. 203). Then, *OE* and *OH* are the principal axes, and *TE* and *TH* are principal moments of inertia.

Problems

365. Solve Prob. 361 graphically.
366. Solve Prob. 363 graphically.

§ 2   Values of Z for Use in Curved-Beam Formula

205   Values of Z found by integration.   By definition we have (see Art. 48).

$$Z = -\frac{1}{a} \int \frac{y}{R + y} \, da \qquad (760)$$

For sections of simple form, such as rectangular and circular sections, the value of Z may easily be found by direct integration. The value of Z for trapezoidal sections, I sections, etc., may also be found by direct integration, but the expressions are rather clumsy to use; it is often convenient therefore, and sometimes necessary, to obtain a value of Z by a graphical method or by a numerical integration method; these methods are explained in the following articles.

By writing the dimensional equation for Z it becomes evident that Z is an abstract number, and hence its value will be the same regardless of the unit of length used for expressing the value of y, R, and a, provided, of course, that the same unit of length is used for each of these three quantities.

Rectangular Area. Let Fig. 359 represent a normal section of a curved beam having a rectangular section of width b and depth $2c$,

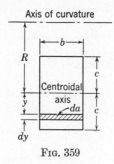

Axis of curvature

Centroidal axis

Fig. 359

the distance from the centroidal axis of the section to the axis of curvature being R. Then

$$Z = -\frac{1}{2bc} \int_{-c}^{+c} \frac{y}{R + y} b\, dy = -\frac{1}{2c} \int_{-c}^{+c} \frac{y}{R + y} dy \qquad (761)$$

First Method. If $\dfrac{1}{R + y} = (R + y)^{-1} = \dfrac{1}{R}\left(1 + \dfrac{y}{R}\right)^{-1}$ is expanded

in a converging series by the binomial theorem, we have

$$Z = -\frac{1}{2c} \int_{-c}^{+c} \left(\frac{y}{R} - \frac{y^2}{R^2} + \frac{y^3}{R^3} - \frac{y^4}{R^4} + \cdots\right) dy \qquad (762)$$

By integrating and substituting limits, the following expression is found:

$$Z = \frac{1}{3}\left(\frac{c}{R}\right)^2 + \frac{1}{5}\left(\frac{c}{R}\right)^4 + \frac{1}{7}\left(\frac{c}{R}\right)^6 + \cdots \qquad (763)$$

Second Method. Equation 761 may be integrated directly; thus

$$Z = -\frac{1}{2c} \int_{-c}^{+c} \left(1 - \frac{R}{R + y}\right) dy$$

$$Z = -\frac{1}{2c}\left[y - R\log_e (R + y)\right]_{-c}^{c}$$

Hence

$$Z = -1 + \frac{R}{2c}\log_e \left(\frac{R + c}{R - c}\right) \qquad (764)$$

Circular Area. *First Method.* Let c denote the radius of the circular area; then, as indicated in Fig. 360,

$$da = 2c \cos \theta \, dy \qquad y = c \sin \theta$$

Hence

$$dy = c \cos \theta \, d\theta$$

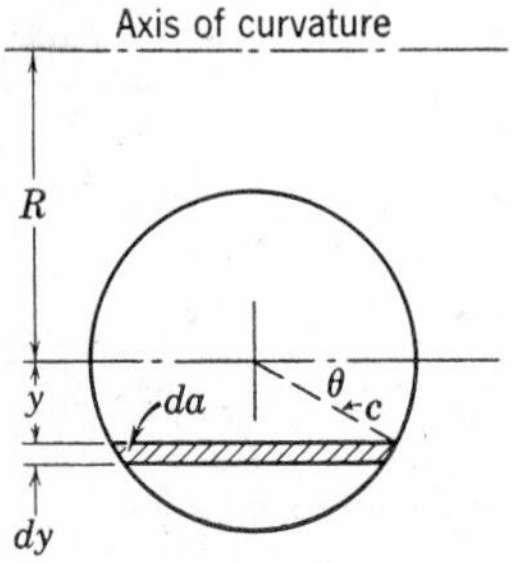

Axis of curvature

FIG. 360

Therefore

$$Z = -\frac{1}{a} \int \frac{y}{R + y} \, da$$

$$= -\frac{1}{\pi c^2} \int_{-\pi/2}^{+\pi/2} \frac{c \sin \theta}{R + c \sin \theta} 2c^2 \cos^2 \theta \, d\theta$$

$$= -\frac{2c}{\pi} \int_{-\pi/2}^{+\pi/2} \frac{\cos^2 \theta \sin \theta \, d\theta}{R + c \sin \theta} \qquad (765)$$

If $\dfrac{1}{R + c \sin \theta}$ is expanded in a converging series and if each term then under the integral is integrated separately, the final result is

$$Z = \frac{1}{4}\left(\frac{c}{R}\right)^2 + \frac{1}{8}\left(\frac{c}{R}\right)^4 + \frac{5}{64}\left(\frac{c}{R}\right)^6 + \frac{7}{128}\left(\frac{c}{R}\right)^8 + \frac{21}{512}\left(\frac{c}{R}\right)^{10} + \cdots \quad (766)$$

Second Method. Equation 765 may also be integrated as follows:

$$Z = -\frac{2c}{\pi} \int_{-\pi/2}^{\pi/2} \frac{\cos^2 \theta \sin \theta \, d\theta}{R + c \sin \theta}$$

$$= -\frac{2}{\pi} \int_{-\pi/2}^{\pi/2} \frac{\sin \theta - \sin^3 \theta}{\sin \theta + m} \, d\theta \qquad \text{where } m = \frac{R}{c}$$

$$= \frac{2}{\pi} \int_{-\pi/2}^{\pi/2} \left[\sin^2 \theta - m \sin \theta + (m^2 - 1) - \frac{m(m^2 - 1)}{\sin \theta + m} \right] d\theta$$

$$= \frac{2}{\pi}\left[\frac{\pi}{2} + (m^2 - 1)\pi \right] - 2m\sqrt{m^2 - 1} = 2m^2 - 2m\sqrt{m^2 - 1} - 1$$

$$= -1 + 2\left(\frac{R}{c}\right)^2 - 2\left(\frac{R}{c}\right)\sqrt{\left(\frac{R}{c}\right)^2 - 1} \qquad (767)$$

By similar methods Wilson and Quereau found the expressions for other section areas as given in Table 26.

TABLE 26

ANALYTICAL EXPRESSIONS FOR Z

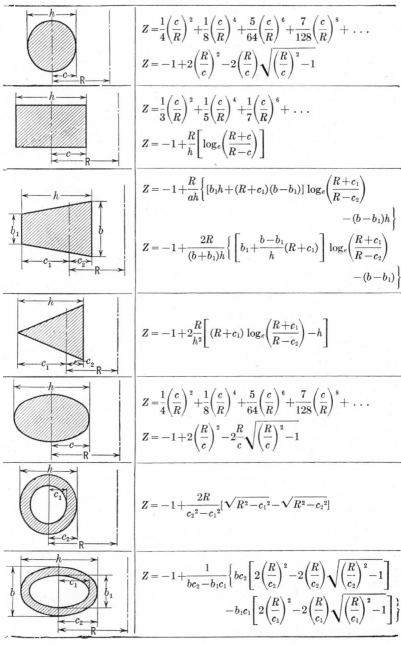

$$Z = \frac{1}{4}\left(\frac{c}{R}\right)^2 + \frac{1}{8}\left(\frac{c}{R}\right)^4 + \frac{5}{64}\left(\frac{c}{R}\right)^6 + \frac{7}{128}\left(\frac{c}{R}\right)^8 + \ldots$$

$$Z = -1 + 2\left(\frac{R}{c}\right)^2 - 2\left(\frac{R}{c}\right)\sqrt{\left(\frac{R}{c}\right)^2 - 1}$$

$$Z = \frac{1}{3}\left(\frac{c}{R}\right)^2 + \frac{1}{5}\left(\frac{c}{R}\right)^4 + \frac{1}{7}\left(\frac{c}{R}\right)^6 + \ldots$$

$$Z = -1 + \frac{R}{h}\left[\log_e\left(\frac{R+c}{R-c}\right)\right]$$

$$Z = -1 + \frac{R}{ah}\left\{[b_1 h + (R+c_1)(b-b_1)]\log_e\left(\frac{R+c_1}{R-c_2}\right)\right.$$
$$\left. - (b-b_1)h\right\}$$

$$Z = -1 + \frac{2R}{(b+b_1)h}\left\{\left[b_1 + \frac{b-b_1}{h}(R+c_1)\right]\log_e\left(\frac{R+c_1}{R-c_2}\right)\right.$$
$$\left. - (b-b_1)\right\}$$

$$Z = -1 + 2\frac{R}{h^2}\left[(R+c_1)\log_e\left(\frac{R+c_1}{R-c_2}\right) - h\right]$$

$$Z = \frac{1}{4}\left(\frac{c}{R}\right)^2 + \frac{1}{8}\left(\frac{c}{R}\right)^4 + \frac{5}{64}\left(\frac{c}{R}\right)^6 + \frac{7}{128}\left(\frac{c}{R}\right)^8 + \ldots$$

$$Z = -1 + 2\left(\frac{R}{c}\right)^2 - 2\frac{R}{c}\sqrt{\left(\frac{R}{c}\right)^2 - 1}$$

$$Z = -1 + \frac{2R}{c_2{}^2 - c_1{}^2}[\sqrt{R^2 - c_1{}^2} - \sqrt{R^2 - c_2{}^2}]$$

$$Z = -1 + \frac{1}{bc_2 - b_1 c_1}\left\{bc_2\left[2\left(\frac{R}{c_2}\right)^2 - 2\left(\frac{R}{c_2}\right)\sqrt{\left(\frac{R}{c_2}\right)^2 - 1}\right]\right.$$
$$\left. - b_1 c_1\left[2\left(\frac{R}{c_1}\right)^2 - 2\left(\frac{R}{c_1}\right)\sqrt{\left(\frac{R}{c_1}\right)^2 - 1}\right]\right\}$$

TABLE 26 (*Continued*)

ANALYTICAL EXPRESSIONS FOR Z

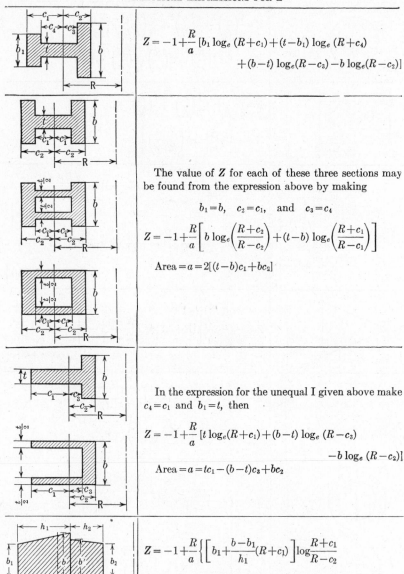

$$Z = -1 + \frac{R}{a}\,[b_1 \log_e (R+c_1) + (t-b_1) \log_e (R+c_4)$$
$$+ (b-t)\log_e(R-c_3) - b\log_e(R-c_2)]$$

The value of Z for each of these three sections may be found from the expression above by making

$$b_1 = b, \quad c_2 = c_1, \quad \text{and} \quad c_3 = c_4$$

$$Z = -1 + \frac{R}{a}\left[b \log_e\left(\frac{R+c_2}{R-c_2}\right) + (t-b)\log_e\left(\frac{R+c_1}{R-c_1}\right)\right]$$

$$\text{Area} = a = 2[(t-b)c_1 + bc_2]$$

In the expression for the unequal I given above make $c_4 = c_1$ and $b_1 = t$, then

$$Z = -1 + \frac{R}{a}\,[t \log_e(R+c_1) + (b-t)\log_e (R-c_3)$$
$$-b\log_e (R-c_2)]$$

$$\text{Area} = a = tc_1 - (b-t)c_3 + bc_2$$

$$Z = -1 + \frac{R}{a}\left\{\left[b_1 + \frac{b-b_1}{h_1}(R+c_1)\right]\log\frac{R+c_1}{R-c_2}\right.$$

$$\left. + \left[b_2 - \frac{b'-b_2}{h_2}(R-c_3)\right]\log\frac{R-c_2}{R-c_3} + (b'-b_2) - (b-b_1)\right\}$$

206 Graphical method for determining Z. *Line Polygon Method.**
In Fig. 361 the boundary of the cross-sectional area is the heavy-line
curve $ACEK$, etc. Divide the area in several strips of equal width (six
such strips are shown; usually about ten strips should be used for ac-
curate results). Let $\overline{AB}$, $\overline{CD}$, $\overline{EF}$, etc., be the heights of the mean ordinates of the strips, the mean ordinate of any strip being assumed propor-
tional to the area of the strip.

The centroidal axis will first be found, by the string polygon method.
Draw the line (vector) polygon $A'B'C'D'$, etc., the total length of which
represents the area of the section. Select a pole J and draw the rays
$A'J$, $B'J$, etc. Draw the strings a', b', c', d', etc., corresponding to the
rays, in the usual way, and locate the point, P, of intersection of the first
and last strings; the line $G'G''$ through P and parallel to the median lines
$\overline{AB}$, $\overline{CD}$, etc., is the centroidal axis, and G is the centroid of the area.

Now, to obtain a value of Z, draw a line RS parallel to OG and at a
distance of unity from OG, according to the same scale used in drawing
the section. From the intersections, V_1, V_2, etc., of RS with the median
lines, draw lines V_1O, V_2O, etc., to the center of curvature O. These
lines in turn locate points H_1, H_2, etc., where they intersect the centroidal axis $G'G''$. At the ends of the vectors $A'B'$, $B'C'$, etc., in the
vector polygon, erect perpendiculars such as $B'B''$, $C'C''$, etc., the
length of which are unity to the same scale used in drawing the vector
polygon. From the ends B'', C'', etc., of these lines lay off lengths
$B''B'''$, etc., equal to GH_1, GH_2, etc., respectively. Through each of
the points B''', C''', etc., draw lines (q_1, q_2, etc.) parallel to the vector
(line) polygon. The value of Z is found by dividing the sum of the
lengths of q_1, q_2, q_3, etc., by the area a of the section (represented by
the sum of the lengths q'_1, q'_2, q'_3, $\cdots$) and subtracting unity from the
quotient. That is,

$$Z = \frac{\Sigma q}{a} - 1 = \frac{\Sigma q}{\Sigma q'} - 1 \tag{768}$$

Proof. By definition

$$Z = -\frac{1}{a}\int \frac{y\,da}{y+R}$$

This may be written

$$Z = -\frac{1}{a}\int\left(1 - \frac{R}{y+R}\right)da = -\frac{1}{a}\int da + \frac{1}{a}\int \frac{R}{y+R}\,da$$

$$= -1 + \frac{1}{a}\int \frac{R}{y+R}\,da \tag{769}$$

---

* Devised by A. E. Hershey.

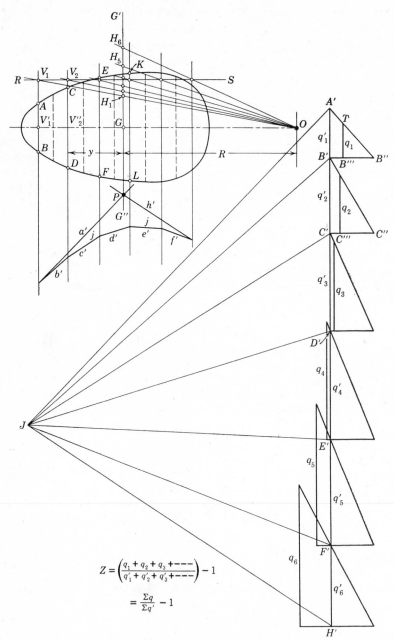

$$Z = \left(\frac{q_1 + q_2 + q_3 + ----}{q'_1 + q'_2 + q'_3 + ----}\right) - 1$$

$$= \frac{\Sigma q}{\Sigma q'} - 1$$

Fig. 361   Line polygon construction.

Each strip is an elementary area da and is at the distance y from the centroidal axis. That is, $GV'_1 = y$. Also $OG = R$. Then, in triangles OV'_1V_1 and OGH_1, we have

$$GH_1/OG = V'_1V_1/OV'_1$$

Hence

$$GH_1 = \frac{R}{y + R}$$

since $V'_1V_1 = 1$ and $OV'_1 = OG + GV'_1 = y + R$

Now $A'B' = 2AV'_1$, which represents the area da of the first strip. Further,

$$B'B'' = 1 \quad \text{and} \quad B''B''' = GH_1 = \frac{R}{y + R}$$

Thus

$$B'''T/B'''B'' = A'B'/B'B''$$

which becomes

$$q_1 = \frac{R}{y + R}\, da$$

Hence

$$q_1 + q_2 + \text{etc.} = \Sigma q = \int \frac{R}{y + R}\, da$$

Also,

$$a = q'_1 + q'_2 + \text{etc.} = \Sigma q'$$

Therefore,

$$Z = (\Sigma q/\Sigma q') - 1$$

207   Numerical integration method for determining Z.   In this method suggested by A. M. Wahl, more accurate results are obtained by determining Z from the equation

$$Z = \frac{1}{aR} \int \frac{y^2\, da}{R + y} \tag{770}$$

than by using Eq. 760; the reason is that the integral in Eq. 770 consists of a series of positive terms whereas the integral in Eq. 760, which is used for the mathematical integration, is a series of terms which are positive for $+y$ and negative for $-y$. This condition means that the computation of Z involves the difference between two quantities that differ by a very small amount. Hence, a small error in one of the quantities makes a large error in the difference between them. The method described here (Eq. 770) avoids this difficulty and furthermore can be carried out with slide-rule calculations with good results.

Let Fig. 362a represent the cross-sectional area a of a curved beam which is symmetrical to the line AB. As in the graphical method we divide the area into an even number n of strips of equal thickness Δ as shown by Fig. 362b, in which only the upper half of the area is used.

Thus b_0, b_1, $\cdots$, b_n are the half-widths of the area at the edge of each strip. Let y_0, y_1, $\cdots$, y_n be the distances from the centroid to the corresponding half width b_0, b_1, $\cdots$, b_n. By the application of Simpson's

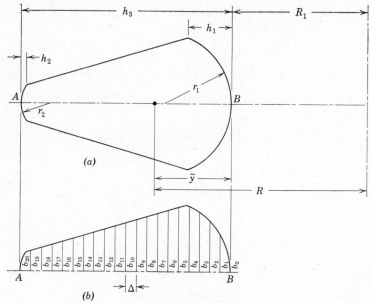

FIG. 362   Numerical integration method.

rule for numerical integration we get the following equation for the cross-sectional area:

$$a = \tfrac{4}{3}\Delta[\tfrac{1}{2}b_0 + (b_2 + b_4 + b_6 + \cdots + b_{n-2})$$
$$+ 2(b_1 + b_3 + b_5 + \cdots + b_{n-1}) + \tfrac{1}{2}b_n] \quad (771)$$

In a similar manner we obtain Eq. 772 for computing the location of the centroid of the area.

$$a\bar{y} = \tfrac{4}{3}\Delta[\tfrac{1}{2}b_0 0 + (2b_2\Delta + 4b_4\Delta + \cdots + \{n-2\}b_{n-2}\Delta)$$
$$+ 2(b_1\Delta + 3b_3\Delta + 5b_5\Delta + \cdots + \{n-1\}b_{n-1}\Delta) + \tfrac{1}{2}b_n n\Delta] \quad (772)$$

Finally, the value of Z is found from the equation, based on Simpson's rule, as follows:

$$Z = \frac{4\Delta}{3aR}\left[\frac{1}{2}\frac{y_0^2 b_0}{R + y_0} + \left(\frac{y_2^2 b_2}{R + y_2} + \frac{y_4^2 b_4}{R + y_4} + \cdots + \frac{y_{n-2}^2 b_{n-2}}{R + y_{n-2}}\right)\right.$$
$$\left. + 2\left(\frac{y_1^2 b_1}{R + y_1} + \frac{y_3^2 b_3}{R + y_3} + \cdots + \frac{y_{n-1}^2 b_{n-1}}{R + y_{n-1}}\right) + \frac{1}{2}\frac{y_n^2 b_n}{R + y_n}\right] \quad (773)$$

In Eq. 773 the value of y takes a negative sign when y is measured toward the center of curvature from the centroid and is positive when away from the center of curvature. The use of these equations is illustrated in the following problem.

Illustrative Problem

Problem 367. The area in Fig. 362 has the following dimensions: $h_1 = 0.980$ in., $h_2 = 0.113$ in., $h_3 = 4.62$ in., $r_1 = 1.52$ in., $r_2 = 0.726$ in., $R_1 = 3$ in. Find the area a, the location of the centroid, and the value of Z by making use of Eqs. 771, 772, and 773.

Solution. Let the half area be divided into 20 strips as shown in Fig. 362b, each strip having a thickness $\Delta = 0.231$ in. The values of b_0, b_1, b_2, etc., are scaled from an accurate sketch of Fig. 362, and these values are recorded in the accompanying table. Columns 2 through 8 in the table have been computed by slide rule for the terms in Eqs. 771, 772, and 773, respectively.

TABLE OF VALUES IN EQS. 771, 772 AND 773 FOR SOLVING PROB. 367

(1)	(2)	(3)	(4)	(5)	(6)	(7)	(8)
n	Values of b	Values of Terms in Eq. 771	Values of Terms in Eq. 772	Values of y	Values of y^2	Values of $R + y$	Values of Terms in Eq. 773
0	0	0	0	−1.990	3.950	3.000	0
1	0.81	1.62	1.62Δ	−1.759	3.090	3.231	1.550
2	1.10	1.10	2.20Δ	−1.528	2.330	3.462	0.740
3	1.27	2.54	7.62Δ	−1.297	1.680	3.693	1.154
4	1.40	1.40	5.60Δ	−1.066	1.135	3.924	0.405
5	1.37	2.74	13.70Δ	−0.835	0.695	4.155	0.456
6	1.31	1.31	7.86Δ	−0.604	0.364	4.386	0.110
7	1.24	2.48	17.36Δ	−0.373	0.139	4.617	0.074
8	1.17	1.17	9.36Δ	−0.142	0.020	4.848	0.004
9	1.10	2.20	19.80Δ	+0.089	0.008	5.079	0.004
10	1.04	1.04	10.40Δ	+0.320	0.102	5.310	0.021
11	0.97	1.94	21.34Δ	+0.551	0.304	5.541	0.108
12	0.90	0.90	10.80Δ	+0.782	0.610	5.772	0.095
13	0.84	1.68	21.84Δ	+1.013	1.030	6.003	0.290
14	0.77	0.77	10.78Δ	+1.244	1.545	6.234	0.191
15	0.70	1.40	21.00Δ	+1.475	2.170	6.465	0.470
16	0.63	0.63	10.08Δ	+1.706	2.900	6.696	0.274
17	0.57	1.14	19.38Δ	+1.937	3.750	6.927	0.618
18	0.50	0.50	9.00Δ	+2.168	4.690	7.158	0.327
19	0.43	0.86	16.34Δ	+2.399	5.750	7.389	0.668
20	0	0	0	+2.630	6.900	7.620	0
		27.42	236.08Δ				7.559

The area is found from Eq. 771 as follows.

$$a = \tfrac{4}{3}\Delta \text{ (sum of column 3 in table)} = \tfrac{4}{3}0.231 \times 27.42 = 8.46 \text{ sq in.}$$

The centroidal distance $\bar{y}$ is found from Eq. 772 as follows.

$$a\bar{y} = \tfrac{4}{3}\Delta \text{ (sum of column 4 in table)} = \tfrac{4}{3}(0.231)^2 \times 236.08$$

$$\bar{y} = 1.986 \text{ in.}$$

and
$$R = R_1 + \bar{y} = 4.986 \text{ in.}$$

The value of Z is found from Eq. 773 as follows.

$$Z = \frac{4\Delta}{3aR} \text{ (sum of column 8 in table)} = 0.0552$$

This is the curved beam of Prob. 94. The student should solve this problem by making use of the quantities a, $\bar{y}$, and Z as computed here and make a comparison of the results obtained with the answers to Prob. 94.

INDEX